design techniques for electronics engineers

ELECTRONICS BOOK SERIES

Also published by *Electronics*
• **Microprocessors**
• **Large scale integration**
• **Data communications**
• **Applying microprocessors**
• **Circuits for electronics engineers**

Library of Congress Catalog Card No. 77-8323

 McGraw-Hill Publications Co.
1221 Avenue of the Americas
New York, New York 10020

design techniques for electronics engineers

Electronics

Magazine

Book Series

table of contents

Preface

As every electronics engineer knows, there's more to designing a circuit or a system than just coming up with a circuit diagram and plugging in components of the right value. Engineering a product that works entails a whole raft of associated techniques—making measurements, interpreting data, making calculations, choosing materials, controlling environment, laying out and packaging the right components, and interconnecting them swiftly and without error. All of these steps take time and money—the two traditional enemies of engineers trying to make a contractual deadline or answer a marketing department's cry for help.

This book is intended to help electronics engineers save time and money in accomplishing the many adjunct tasks that comprise design. It is a compilation of articles from Engineer's Notebook, a regular and highly popular feature in *Electronics* magazine. There are 48 chapters containing 293 articles with a wealth of valuable tips that can shorten design time, increase engineering productivity, and free engineers from routine tasks for more creative work. It takes a how-to approach that is generously illustrated with charts, diagrams, calculator programs, tables and nomograms.

Representing the accumulated experience of hundreds of design engineers, this volume is an invaluable resource that can be called upon again and again.

Ribbon cable makes coils for printed-circuit boards

by Jim Edrington and F.E. Hinkle Jr.
Applied Research Laboratories, University of Texas at Austin

A microhenry inductor loop made from flexible ribbon cable is easy to mount on printed-circuit boards, and its inductance value is easy to control. This loop is a cross between the familiar wire-coil inductor and a printed-circuit inductor. Since the ribbon-cable loop is three-dimensional, a larger amount of inductance is possible for a given area than a printed-circuit coil can provide. Moreover, the ribbon inductor is much easier to manufacture and control than the usual wire-coil inductor.

Figure 1 illustrates the technique of bending the flexible cable into a semicircle and soldering the ends into a pc board so that the conductors interconnect to form a multiturn coil with a "D" cross section.

The inductance of a "D" cross-section coil may be calculated from the formula for a circular coil, with the effective radius of the "D" coil substituted for the actual radius of a circle. For a single-layer n-turn circular coil with radius a and length l, the inductance in microhenries is

$$L = n^2 a^2 / (9a + 10l)$$

where a and l are in inches.

For a "D" coil with the dimensions shown in Fig. 2, the effective circumference, C, is the length of the ribbon cable, B, plus the pc-board spacing, S. The effective radius can be calculated from

$$r_{eff} = C/2\pi = (B+S)/2\pi$$

Thus, the inductance in microhenries of the coil made with ribbon cable is

$$L = n^2 [(B+S)/2\pi]^2 / [9(B+S)/2\pi + 10l]$$

where all dimensions are in inches.

The measured and calculated inductances of an actual "D" coil are plotted versus the length (l) of the coil in Fig. 3. The coil for this test was made of a 2-inch length of Ansley Flexstrip with a pc-board spacing of 1.75 in. With 10 conductive strips per inch, the Flexstrip forms a coil with 10 turns per inch. The calculated values of inductance proved to be close to the measured values over a range of coil lengths from 0.5 to 3.0 in. (n = 5 to n = 30).

Since flexible cable of this type can be purchased in precut sizes, the manufacture of highly repeatable inductors can be simplified. An impedance transformer can be made by adding a second coil inside the first. A

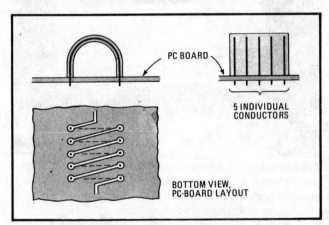

1. Loops good. Flexible ribbon cable is mounted on printed-circuit board, with individual conductors cross-connected in series, to form an inductance coil. One loop can be nested inside another to form a transformer, and individual turns of the loop can be tapped. These coils have the amounts of inductance needed for rf tuning.

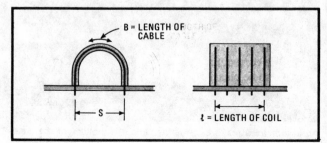

2. Sizing it up. Definitions of dimensions used in text are illustrated. A given ribbon has a fixed number of conductors per inch of ribbon width (coil length), so n and l are equivalent quantities.

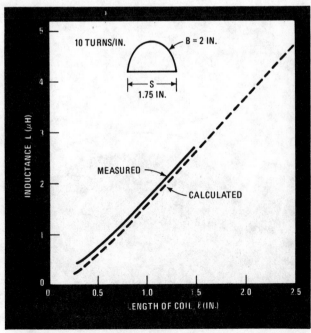

3. Microhenries. Inductance of ribbon-cable inductor is shown as a function of coil length, l. Since ribbon has 10 conductors per inch of width (coil length), abscissa represents 0 to 25 turns.

multiple tapped inductor is easily formed by bringing out any of the turns on the printed-circuit board. Since every turn is terminated on the board, other electrical components may be wired with the coil. For example, capacitors may be paralleled with the coil to form tuned rf circuits. □

Etching your own pc boards quickly and accurately

by Herman Levin and G. Thomas Oppenheimer
Colorado State University, Fort Collins, Colo.

Putting together an efficient etching tank for laboratory or prototype production of printed circuits is relatively simple. There's no need to buy a commercial kit for a tank that will require constant stirring and either takes at least half an hour to etch one board or, if large enough to work faster and ensure no undercutting, becomes very costly.

This froth etcher is designed for fast turnaround of both single- and double-sided boards on which fine resolution is also important. It produces uniformly etched pc boards in about four minutes with very little undercutting. As a bonus, the process automatically aerates the etchant, greatly extending its life.

Constructing the etcher is quite simple. All that you need is a heat-resistant glass dish with cover, a tungsten-carbide hacksaw blade for notching the dish cover, some two-part epoxy adhesive, a holder for the boards being processed, three ceramic aquarium aerators, some rubber air tubes for holders, and a thermometer. You cement the aerators to the bottom of the glass dish, and a quick-change pc-board holder to the cover. Then you cement the thermometer and tube holders to the side of the dish and notch the cover to provide egress for them. Mix up a batch of ferric chloride in a concentration of 1¼ pounds of FeCl to every quart of water at a temperature between 100°F and 110°F, and you're ready to start etching.

To etch, you simply:

■ Place the etcher on a hot plate and fill it with etchant to a level that just reaches the bottom of the copper-clad pc board.

■ Heat the etchant to its lower operating temperature

The continuous air flow through the aerators creates a surface froth that scrubs the board with constantly agitated etchant. The sliding clamp holder which is attached to the cover dish permits rapid insertion or reversal of the printed-circuit board.

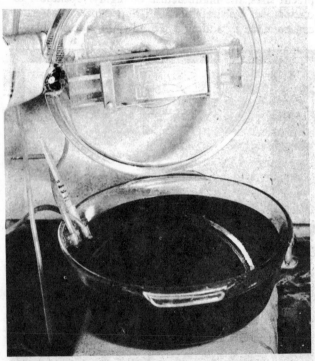

Observing the etching process is easily done by lifting the heat-resistant glass etcher cover to which the printed-circuit board is attached. Before the cover is removed, the air supply must be turned off to prevent any spattering of the etchant.

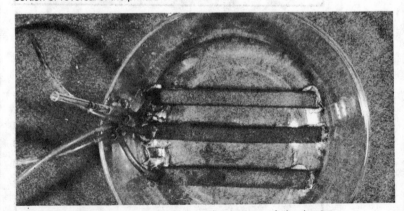

Aquarium aerators are cemented into the bottom of the heat-resistant dish, along with sections of plastic tubing to support the rubber tubing and thermometer. The tubes are connected by T-fittings to a single tube connected to the main air supply.

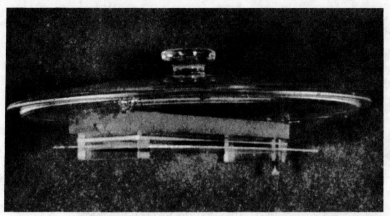

Plexiglass holder clamps grip the edge of the pc board, assuring uniform etch of the entire surface. One clamp is threaded and fitted with a nylon screw to accommodate boards of various sizes. A rubber band around the clamps provides tension.

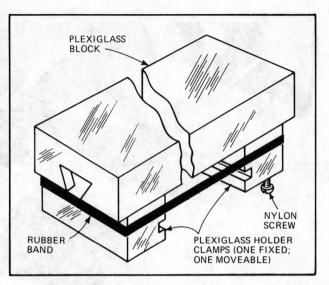

PLEXIGLASS BLOCK

NYLON SCREW

RUBBER BAND

PLEXIGLASS HOLDER CLAMPS (ONE FIXED; ONE MOVEABLE)

(100°F) and turn the hot plate off.

■ Place the board to be etched in the holder, cover the dish, and turn the air supply on, adjusting it to create a continuing vigorous froth over the total surface of the etchant.

■ After a few minutes—anything from three and a half to eight minutes, depending on the freshness of solution—inspect the board, if you want to, by raising the cover (the air supply must be turned off first to prevent splattering of the etchant).

This system is also easily adapted to etching outsized boards that don't fit the glass dish. For these, you replace the glass dish with a covered polystryene box, of a type sold for household storage. You then place the etchant container in very hot water, so as to heat the etchant before pouring it into the etcher. The etchant, of course, could be used at room temperature at some sacrifice in speed. □

Soluble masks protect pc boards from solder

by H. G. Peters and K. Romano
IBM Corp., Owego, N.Y.

Two kinds of water-soluble solder masks can, when applied to a circuit board before wave-soldering, keep solder out of plated-through holes. These holes must be kept open to permit dry components—thermally sensitive electrical devices—to be hand-soldered to the circuit board after the wave-soldering operation. Most previously known solder-mask or resist materials must be removed with solvent cleaning, which is expensive, or they leave questionable residues that impede hand-soldering. (Although a fluffy white residue appears when one of the two new materials is applied in excess, if allowed to dry for several days, it is easily brushed or blown off.)

Water-soluble masks are also useful for protecting large tab areas or other large areas of copper that are not to be soldered. Masking prevents solder from bridging between circuit lines on a printed-circuit board, even when hand-soldering or non-wet components are not involved. And, when parts of a board are to be coated with something, water-soluble masks can protect the areas that are not to be coated when the coating itself is not water-soluble; otherwise its application would wash off the mask material.

However, water-soluble masks do not work well on tin-lead plated parts, especially when large areas have to be masked, because the alloy reflows and lifts the mask from the circuit board.

The two new materials are based on sodium silicate and gum arabic, or acacia, both in water solution and both with small quantities of other materials added. The materials have different characteristics and react differently in any production process. However, both meet the primary objective—to prevent solder from wetting the masked areas, whether soldered as soon as the mask has dried, or days or weeks later. And neither material hampers any subsequent production process, nor permits solder reflow, which could cause bridging between masked circuit lines.

Like most other water-soluble masking materials, the new ones meet current regulations of the U.S. Occupational Safety and Health Administration and state agencies; they are, in fact, pollution-free. Even if large quantities of mask materials were accidentally spilled, no pollution limits would be exceeded because all of the ingredients have extremely high tolerance levels in waste water. They are also relatively nontoxic; continued exposure of production workers to either of the two

even millions of megohms—is caused by minute traces of the mask material, too small to affect soldering, but nevertheless sufficient to establish a tiny current path.

The constituents of both materials, which can be purchased from any chemical supply house at a low price, are easily mixed in a laboratory. The total costs will depend on production levels, mask-preparation time, and operator technique.

Water-soluble masks can be applied by any of several methods, such as by brushing, spraying, dipping, or screening. All application methods are relatively simple. However, when the gum-arabic mask is silk-screened, long fine strings or webs of material sometimes form when the screen is lifted off the substrate. As these webs break and fall to the substrate, they mask areas that should not be masked. This webbing apparently occurs only with samples of gum that have *not* been stored for a long time in a warehouse; natural aging of the gum eliminates the webbing.

Mask-maker. Brushing and screening are two of several methods by which new water-soluble masking materials can be applied to printed-circuit boards. The materials keep solder away from selected areas as the board moves through a wave-solder machine.

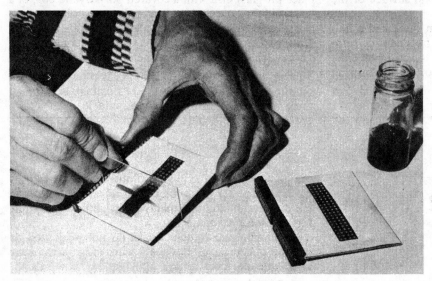

Accelerated aging—heating at 75°C for one week—gives the same effect by driving off interstitial or bound water from the gum molecules. If a gum of any age is aged further by heating, a mask material made from it leaves no web. Webbing is also eliminated immediately by adding a small amount of potassium chloride to gum of any age; the chloride eliminates the forces that cause webbing. Because chloride addition is minimal, negligible residues are left after mask removal.

materials has no serious or long-lasting effects.

A good solder mask must be pliable to permit normal handling after masking, and it must adhere to the substrate throughout any subsequent processing steps. In previous evaluations of gum arabic as a masking material, it has adhered poorly after extended shelf life. However, the new formulation contains a humectant—a substance such as ethylene glycol—that promotes moisture retention, so that there is no loss of adhesion from physical abuse, from successive mechanical handling processes after masking, or from extended exposure to temperatures as high as 150°F.

The new water-soluble masks can be left on the surface for several months at ambient or elevated temperatures without corroding, as some materials do. Furthermore, they actually improve the insulation-resistance, which on a series of test boards averaged an order of magnitude higher than on boards made with the IBM standard mask. The lower resistance encountered with the standard mask—still well up in the thousands or

The mask material must not dry while being applied, but, once on the substrate, the film must dry quickly to prevent flow of material into non-masked areas. Gum arabic in water solution satisfies these requirements, but sodium silicate, if dried too fast, leaves a residue after soldering and cleaning. Adding a humectant to the mask formulation makes it dry to a non-flowing tacky film in three to five minutes and dry completely within 10 minutes.

Water-soluble masks can be used effectively on plated-through holes as large as 0.25 inch in diameter, small and large surface areas, and even large tinned surfaces, although the tin should be precleaned to increase adhesion. The masks can be adapted to nearly any production process by varying the chemical constituents of the material.

Versatile breadboard checks out designs quickly

by M.J. Salvati
Sony Corp. of America, Long Island City, N.Y.

At a cost of only around $25, a breadboard system can be put together that is both versatile and convenient to use. Nearly any type of component, including integrated circuits and discrete semiconductors, can be interconnected rapidly with ordinary hookup wire. And since the parts are not soldered and need no special adaptors, they remain undamaged and can be used again. The breadboard, of course, can be tailored to suit specific needs or outfitted with an adjustable power supply and different connectors for added flexibility.

The heart of the breadboard is its socket, which is manufactured by El Instruments, Inc. of Derby, Conn. (A similar socket, which is known as Superstrip, is available from AP Instruments in Painesville, Ohio.) Although relatively expensive—approximately $17 when ordered singly—the socket is well worth the investment.

It has 64 rows of plug-in contacts along its length. Each row contains two groups of contacts, one on either side of the socket's midpoint. There are five tie points for each contact group. Component leads, input and output wires, and test probes can be simply inserted into the desired tie point.

Dual in-line packages snap right into the socket be-

1. Basic breadboard. Oscilloscope sweep circuit (on right) can be rapidly laid out and tested with easy-to-use breadboard. Because components are plugged in, they can be used again. A circuit can be breadboarded almost as quickly as it can be drawn.

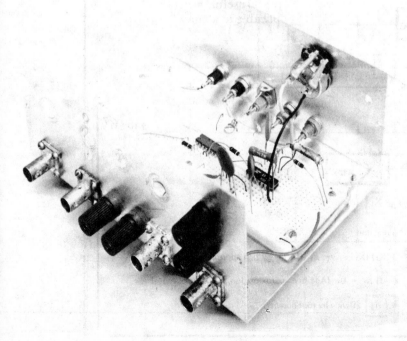

cause the contact spacing is the same as the pin spacing of the standard DIPs. Along its lengthwise edges, the socket has groups of parallel-connected contacts that serve as power and ground buses. Hookup wire and component leads can range from AWG #22 to #26.

A basic version of the breadboard is depicted in Fig. 1, with a design for an oscilloscope sweep circuit already laid out. The socket is mounted in a minibox on a 3/32-inch-thick Lucite sheet. This increases the separation between the socket's contacts and the minibox so that the breadboard's capacitance to ground is reduced.

Since the minibox is made of two U-shaped pieces of aluminum that fit together as a closed box, it completely shields the circuit being checked and makes it easy to mount potentiometers, coils, and other components that are too large to be plugged directly into the socket. Connections to these components are made with 3-inch lengths of #22 wire having miniature alligator clips attached at one end.

Five binding posts on the back panel are provided for power input, and several sets of suitable input and output signal connectors are located on the front panel. Short lengths (2 to 3 inches) of #22 wire are soldered to the connectors for carrying the signal to and from the socket. With this arrangement, even many lead changes or jiggling will not upset the breadboarded circuit.

For the ultimate in breadboarding convenience, two miniboxes can be fastened together, and the lower minibox used to house one or more regulated power supplies, as shown in Fig. 2. This deluxe version, which costs about $75 to build, offers two sockets, a choice of supply voltage, and a meter for reading out the level of the supply voltage. It is built with a pair of miniboxes measuring 8 by 6 by 3½ inches and outfitted front and back with BNC connectors.

The breadboard has fixed positive and negative 5-volt supplies, as well as variable positive and negative supplies that can be adjusted from 9 to 18 v. (The schematic for these supplies is also shown in Fig. 2.) The terminals for the regulated voltages are located between the two sockets, and the meter can be switched between the two variable supplies. A slide switch at the bottom of the front panel allows the supplies to be set before they are applied to the breadboarded circuit.

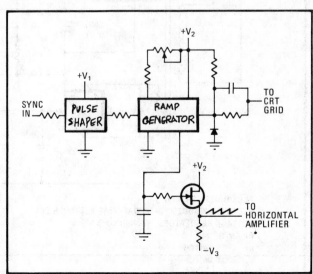

Fairchild's 7800-series voltage regulators are recommended for this application because they are compact, easy to use, and can handle almost all the power requirements needed by this type of breadboard. Moreover, the internal overload protection of the regulators is excellent for breadboard purposes.

Naturally, the number and nature of the regulated voltages should satisfy the user's most frequent requirements. Similarly, the type of input and output connectors, the size and location of the panel holes, and the number of sockets depend on specific needs. □

2. Super breadboard. A choice of regulated supply voltages gives the breadboard additional flexibility. Here the supply circuit shown is housed in the bottom minibox. The supply provides fixed ±5-volt outputs and variable (from ±9 to ±18 v) outputs with a meter readout.

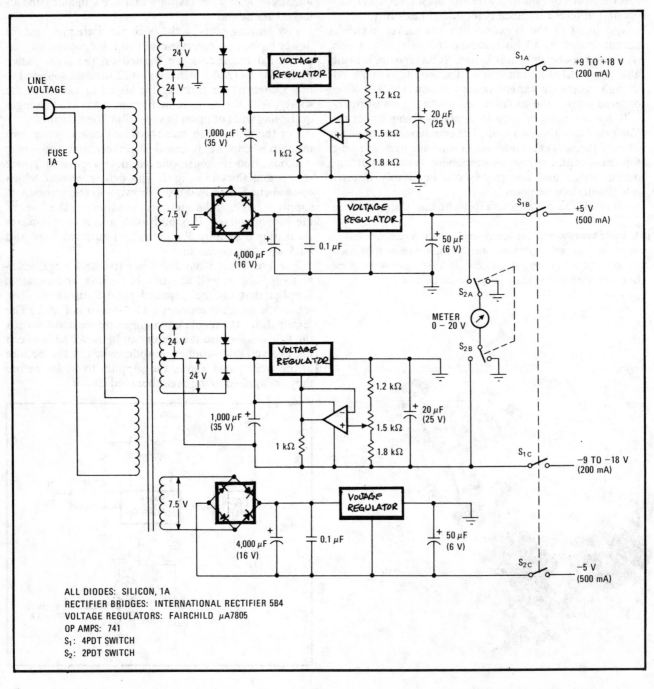

ALL DIODES: SILICON, 1A
RECTIFIER BRIDGES: INTERNATIONAL RECTIFIER 5B4
VOLTAGE REGULATORS: FAIRCHILD μA7805
OP AMPS: 741
S_1: 4PDT SWITCH
S_2: 2PDT SWITCH

Laminated bus strips ease pc-board layout

by Ray Jodoin
Rogers Corp., Chandler, Ariz.

Laminated pc-board bus bars can increase the effective ground-plane area of any two-sided printed-circuit-board layout and reduce layout time for the circuit. Two basic types of these bus bars are vertical bus strips (one, two, or three layers) that mount between rows of integrated circuits, and under-the-DIP strips (two or three layers) that mount underneath every IC in a row. Both of these types (shown in the figures) are sold commercially in standard lengths.

In the layout of a two-sided circuit board, one side is normally dedicated to the ground plane, and the other side is used for logic interconnections and voltage distribution. The use of a ground plane with any high-speed system is desirable for several reasons. Because the ground plane provides a low-inductance path for supply currents, it helps minimize noise on the power supply lines. Also, since this configuration of the pc board minimizes the signal-line impedance, coupling that re-

sults in cross talk is decreased. Moreover, a ground plane allows signal lines to have a constant characteristic impedance so that termination techniques can be used to eliminate ringing.

With today's complex integrated circuits, however, it is difficult to accommodate both signals and voltage lines within the confines of a single layer; therefore, the ground plane is sometimes broken up, and short signal lines, crossovers, and voltage bus are put on the ground-plane side of the board. As much as 40% of the ground-plane side of the board can be used for signal lines, but isolation of large areas of the ground plane must be avoided to prevent "current crowding" and inductive problems.

To further conserve space on the board, power can be distributed by the laminated bus bars. By this technique a large area of board is freed for line layout, and routing of lines becomes less complex.

Of course, a ground plane is easily maintained by using multilayer pc boards, although this approach is inevitably more costly and slower to implement than a system that utilizes a two-sided board. But the use of bus bars offers several other advantages over the multilayer approach:

■ Vertical bus strips act as board stiffeners, often eliminating the need for separate mechanical stiffeners.
■ Under-the-DIP bus strips offer a large thermal mass

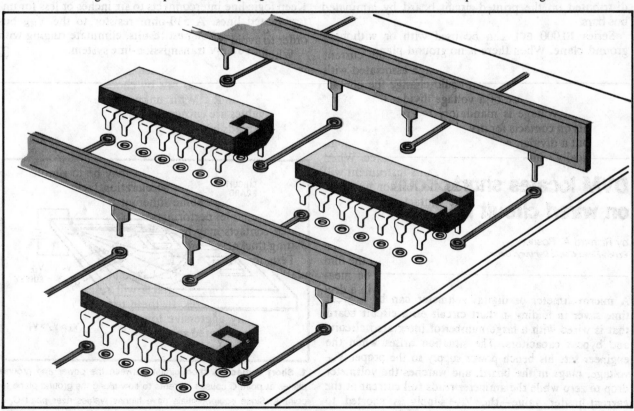

1. Off-boarding the bus. Laminated insulated bus bars save space and simplify layout on printed-circuit boards. Vertical bus strips shown here mount between rows of integrated circuits and have extra advantage of serving as board stiffeners.

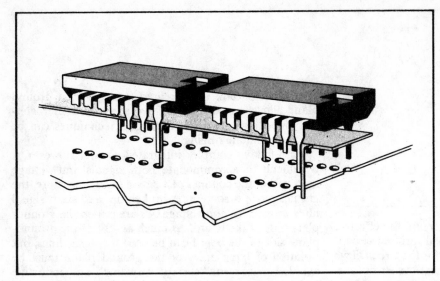

2. Under-the-DIPs. Laminated bus-bar strips that mount directly under the IC also provide large thermal mass for heat-sinking. These off-the-board buses, like those shown in Fig. 1, are available in a variety of sizes, shapes, and numbers of layers. They are of greatest importance in compact high-speed circuits such as those using ECL ICs.

and act as heat sinks for the integrated circuits.

■ Distributed capacitance of up to 1,800 picofarads per square inch of bus-conductor area is attainable, thereby reducing significantly the number of bypass capacitors required for filtering out high-frequency noise.

Today's high data rates and fast switching characteristics make these advantages even more important when emitter-coupled-logic ICs are used. Two-sided boards are definitely compatible with ECL systems if proper design rules are followed. An ECL system performs best in a terminated-transmission-line environment. This requires the use of a –2.0-volt termination supply (V_{TT}) in addition to the –5.2-v V_{EE} supply. Both voltages can be distributed on the printed-circuit board by laminated bus bars.

Series 10,000 ECL can be used with or without a ground plane. When there is no ground plane, the V_{CC}

bus line must be a minimum of 0.1 inch wide per row of packages and should be pinned out to several connector pins if an edge connector is used. V_{EE} should be bused to pin 8 of each device (pin 12 of a 24-pin package). Each device should be bypassed between V_{CC} and V_{EE} with a low-inductance 0.01-microfarad capacitor. To minimize ringing, logic-line interconnects should not be longer than 6 inches.

When a ground plane is used, it should be pinned to every seventh connector of the edge connector (if any). V_{EE} should be bused to pin 8 of each device (pin 12 of a 24-pin package). A low-inductance 0.01-μF bypass capacitor should be provided for every two to six devices. Keep logic line interconnects to six inches or less for unterminated lines. A 510-ohm resistor to the V_{EE} bus should be used. For best results, eliminate ringing with a terminated –2-v transmission-line system. □

DVM locates short circuit on wired circuit board

by Richard A. Rosner
Perkin-Elmer Corp., Danbury, Conn.

A microvoltmeter or digital voltmeter can be a great time saver in finding a short circuit on a circuit board that is wired with a large number of integrated circuits and bypass capacitors. The situation arises when the engineer sets his bench power supply to the proper V_{CC} voltage, plugs in the board, and watches the voltmeter drop to zero while the ammeter reads full current at the current-limiter value—the V_{CC} supply is shorted to ground.

If visual inspection does not reveal the short and none

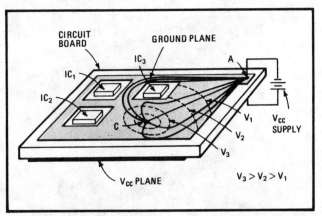

1. Short subject. A short circuit between the power and ground planes at point C causes currents to flow along the ground plane to point A. Since equipotentials have highest values near point C, a probe that measures voltages on the ground plane relative to point A indicates the location of the short.

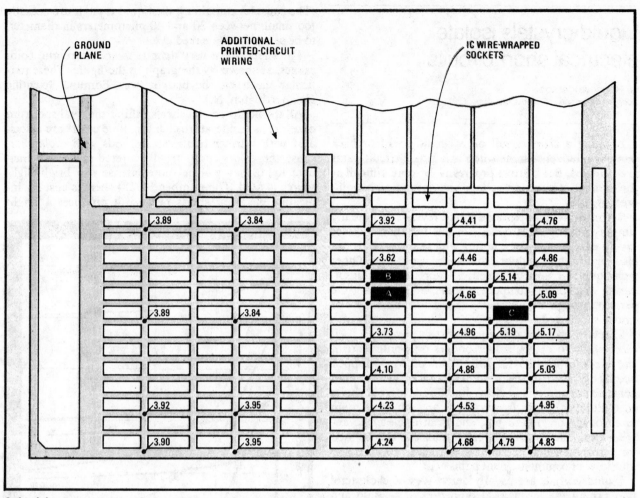

2. Look here. On this circuit card, signals are carried by 600 wrapped wires above the ground-plane side of the board. A short circuit from an IC pin to the ground plane at point C was located by measuring ground-plane voltages (shown in millivolts) relative to the negative supply connection at point A. The positive side of the supply is connected to the power plane below point B.

of the ICs feels hot to the touch, measurement of the potential between the power-supply ground connection and other points on the ground plane will indicate the location of the short-circuit point in a few minutes.

This technique is effective because a potential difference of several millivolts can exist from one end of the ground plane to the other as current flows through it. If current enters the ground plane at the location of the short circuit and leaves at the power-supply return, as shown in Fig. 1, the voltage difference is greatest between these two points.

Figure 2 shows the voltages measured at several points on part of a shorted board. The short turned out to have been caused by a 0.5-millimeter ball of solder splatter that was held in place (and out of view) by a bundle of wires. □

Liquid crystals isolate electrical short circuits

by Roger Anderson
Honeywell Information Systems, San Liego, Calif.

Isolating a short circuit on a circuit board or back panel is relatively simple when only single-circuit paths are involved. But it grows progressively more difficult as the number of common voltage and ground paths is increased.

Surprisingly, encapsulated liquid crystals can greatly simplify finding short circuits in this situation. Besides saving money and parts, testing with liquid crystals can also significantly reduce trouble-shooting time. Other techniques for isolating electrical shorts call for unsoldering or clipping component leads, or increasing the current through the unit being tested until a hot spot or smoke is detected.

Sheets of encapsulated liquid crystals have been used successfully to detect: solder bridges on printed-circuit and wire-wrapped boards; wire shorts on wire-wrapped boards and back panels; internal shorts of such components as capacitors and delay lines; and internal shorts on multilayer boards from a pin to an etch, from a pin to a voltage or ground bus, and from one etch to another etch. Encapsulated liquid crystals can also be used for detecting shorts in cables or harnesses, or wherever multiple- or common-circuit paths exist.

Liquid crystals are usually derivatives of cholesterol that exhibit the mechanical properties of a liquid and certain optical properties of a solid. They have a rather unusual characteristic—the capacity to reflect different wavelengths of light with variations in temperature so that they visibly change color. Liquid crystals have a reproducible color range within specified temperature limits.

Since the colors are derived from scattered incident light, they are most visible when observed against a dark background, like black ink. The black ink can absorb any light transmitted through the liquid crystals and allows the selectively (determined by temperature) reflected light to be viewed.

Encapsulated liquid crystals can be supplied as Mylar sheets, and the colors can be seen through the Mylar.

(The capsules containing the liquid crystals are actually too small, between 20 and 40 micrometers in diameter, to be seen with the naked eye.)

The sheets have very definite temperature and color ranges, as shown by the graph in the figure. These particular sheets can be bought from Edmund Scientific Co., Barrington, N.J.

All the liquid-crystal sheets exhibit the total spectrum of colors as temperature changes. Blue colors are associated with warmer temperatures, reds with cooler. Because the colors result from scattered (reflected) incident light, they will be more intense if a bright light source is used. The number 500274 sheet is best for indicating electrical shorts because it produces a bright

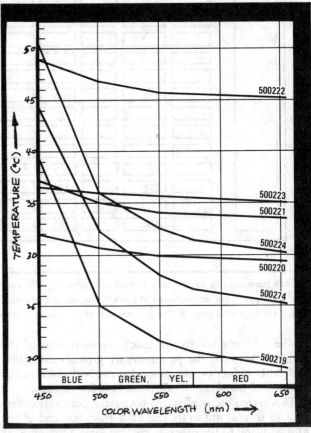

Sample lot. Every sheet of encapsulated liquid crystals has its own color response over a given temperature range. The sheets shown here are sold by Edmund Scientific. The one numbered 500274 is a good choice for isolating electrical short circuits.

Making shorts colorful. In left photo, a bright blue spot of the liquid-crystal sheet pinpoints a shorted capacitor on a wire-wrapped circuit board. In the right-hand picture, a shorted wire traces its own path as a blue streak of color across the liquid crystals.

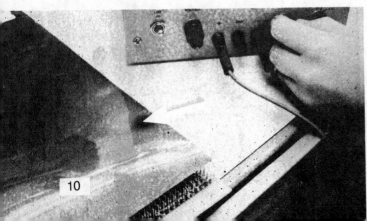
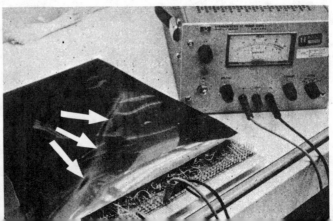

blue spot that shows up well against a dark brown background at the start.

The liquid-crystal sheet must be placed directly on the circuit under test. The closer the liquid crystals are to the faulty part, the more readily the short will be detected. To locate faults in hard-to-reach places, the sheet can be cut into narrow strips that are laid directly on the suspect components.

By carefully controlling the amount of current applied to the circuit, it's possible to locate the short without damaging wires or good components. The current flow is concentrated through the shorted device and/or path, and the liquid-crystal sheet changes color precisely at the location of the short because of the heat the short generates, as shown by the left photograph.

As little as 12 milliwatts of dissipated power at a shorted junction will cause a color change in the sheet. The greater the current that can be safely applied, the easier it will be to find the short because of the increased heat generated. Even a shorted wire on a back panel is generally easy to identify, since its position is traced in color across the entire sheet, as the other photograph indicates. Special care should be taken not to exceed the rated current capacities of the wires. □

Current tests ensure IC-package orientation

by Sylvan E. Shulman
Hughes Aircraft Co., Fullerton, Calif.

The symmetry of integrated-circuit packages makes it all too easy to orient them incorrectly in fixtures of automated testing systems or on circuit boards. Even though dual in-line packages may accidentally be rotated 180° from their correct mounting positions and flat-packs may be rotated or flipped over, they may fit into a jig or board. Such misalignments cost time and money to trouble-shoot and rework, but faulty orientation of most transistor-transistor-logic circuits can be detected routinely by a nondestructive automated measurement.

These measurements are important because, at incoming inspection, the IC packages are loaded into a chute that feeds them to an automatic tester. If the package emerges in the wrong position, voltages applied to the wrong terminals cause wrong results and may damage the IC.

To realize the importance of testing a stuffed board, it's only necessary to remember that the possibility of an insertion error on a board rises exponentially with the number of ICs. If a board contains 40 ICs and the insertion error per IC is 1%, then the yield of good boards is $(99\%)^{40}$, or 66.8%. Therefore 33.2% of the boards contain an incorrectly inserted IC.

The technique for measuring IC orientation is based on the current paths furnished by the input clamp diode in more than 95% of all TTL circuits or the substrate diode between every transistor collector and ground. These diodes are shown as D_1 and D_2 in the typical TTL gate of Fig. 1. They can carry currents of not more than 100 milliamperes.

In Fig. 1, the integrated-circuit gate is not connected to any power supplies except a constant-current source. If the current source drives a 1-milliampere current through the IC from the ground terminal to an input terminal such as terminal 1, the voltage drop across those terminals is about 0.7 volt. This ground-to-input current flows through clamp diode D_1 and is shown as I_1 in Fig. 1. Similarly, if 1 milliampere is driven through the IC from the ground terminal to an output port, the voltage across the terminals is about the same. This current flows through the substrate diode D_2 and is I_2 in Fig. 1.

By contrast, if the constant-current source is connected to drive 1 milliampere from the V_{CC} terminal to the input, that current, I_3, flows through a silicon-diffused re-

	TERMINAL VOLTAGES FOR ORIENTATION-TEST CURRENTS		
Current	Terminals	Level (mA)	Terminal voltage (V)
I_1	Ground to input	1	0.7 ± 30%
I_2	Ground to output	1	0.7 ± 30%
I_3	V_{CC} to input	1	1.4 ± 20%
I_4	V_{CC} to output	1	1.4 ± 20%

1. Current situation. Current flow from supply terminal to input or output terminal of a typical TTL gate produces a voltage that is different from the voltage that is produced when current flows from ground to input or output, and this difference can be used to check IC orientation. The forward voltage drop across a base-to-emitter junction is about 0.7 volt; across a diode, it is about 0.55 V; and across a diffused resistor, it depends on current. One milliampere through the 4-kΩ resistor produces 0.7 V, but through the 1.6-kΩ resistor, 1 mA produces only 0.1 V.

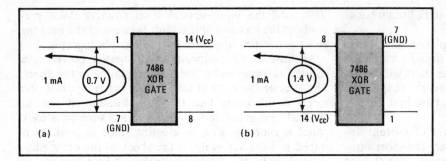

2. Single IC. Test set sends 1-mA current through left-corner terminals and monitors resulting voltage. If IC is positioned correctly, as at (a), terminal voltage is in range 0.49–0.91 V. If IC is incorrectly positioned, as at (b), the range is 1.12–1.68 V, so test station ejects unit without applying possibly damaging test voltages.

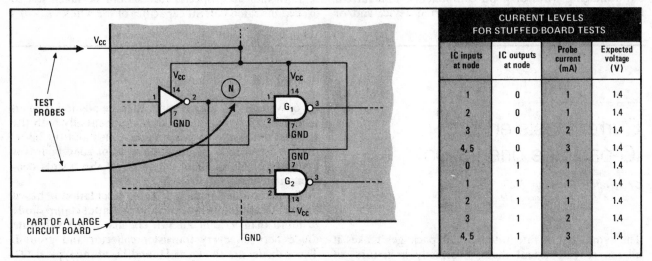

IC inputs at node	IC outputs at node	Probe current (mA)	Expected voltage (V)
1	0	1	1.4
2	0	1	1.4
3	0	2	1.4
4, 5	0	3	1.4
0	1	1	1.4
1	1	1	1.4
2	1	1	1.4
3	1	2	1.4
4, 5	1	3	1.4

CURRENT LEVELS FOR STUFFED-BOARD TESTS

3. Stuffed board. To check orientation of IC mounted on circuit board, probes connect current source to V_{CC} terminal of board and to any node on the board. Voltage across probes is 1.4 V (±20%) if all packages are mounted properly. A lower voltage indicates that some IC is turned around or upside down—here, gate G_2 has its ground pin where its V_{CC} pin should be, so voltage at probes is only 0.7 V. Table shows current-source levels that should be used in testing orientation of standard TTL integrated circuits; high-power TTL requires more current.

sistor as well as a base-to-emitter junction. Although the diffused resistor is labeled as 4 kilohms in the circuit diagram, its resistance is strongly dependent on the current level. At 1 mA, the drop across the resistor is about 0.7 V; this value is added to the 0.7-V drop through the base-emitter junction to make the voltage between the V_{CC} and input terminals about 1.4 V.

Likewise, if the current I_4 from the V_{CC} terminal to an output terminal is 1 mA, the voltage across the terminals is again about 1.4 V. In this case, the drop across the diffused resistor is on the order of 0.1 V. The base-emitter drop and diode drop add up to 1.3 V. (All of these voltage values are experimental results.)

For incoming inspection of ICs, when a unit slides out of the loading chute into an automated test fixture, the orientation of the package can be checked as shown in Fig. 2. The 1-mA current source is connected between the lower left terminal and the upper left terminal of the package, and the voltage across these terminals is measured. If the package is positioned properly, the current flow is from ground to input, and the voltage is 0.7 V. The test station can then power up the chip and measure performance characteristics.

If the IC has been loaded 180° out of position, the current flows from the power-supply terminal to an output, and the voltage is 1.4 V. When this too-high voltage is sensed, the tester ejects the IC into a bin for reloading.

A similar sort of test can ensure correct orientation of all the ICs mounted on a circuit board. The test fixture for this stuffed-board test must be a bed-of-nails arrangement that makes contact with every circuit node on the board. No power is applied to the board except a current source that drives current from the common V_{CC} terminal to one or another node. The amount of current that the source must supply depends on how many inputs and/or outputs are connected to that node, as listed in the table of Fig. 3. The tabulated values are for conventional TTL ICs; high-power TTL requires larger currents. Correct orientations produce 1.4 V across the current-source terminals; if a package is misoriented so that current flows into its ground pin, the voltage is only 0.7 V.

Figure 3 shows a portion of a circuit board that contains a number of ICs, with the current source connected between V_{CC} and node N. This node connects one output and two inputs, so the test current is 1 mA in accordance with the table, and the voltage drop from the V_{CC} terminal to node N should be 1.4 V. However, gate 2 has been mounted incorrectly, with its ground pin and supply pins reversed. In this position, current flows from ground to the node, the voltage is only 0.7 V, and the go/no-go tester rejects the board.

Although the discussion here has been limited to TTL devices, the testing technique is also applicable to metal-oxide-semiconductor devices. □

Make your own small switches for pc boards

by Ralph Wilbur
West Engineering Co., Santa Monica, Calif.

Testing and troubleshooting both breadboard and production circuit boards can often be simplified by permanently installing good-quality switches on the boards at strategic locations. Such switches, inexpensive and simple to make, take up little room on the boards. To build them, you'll need only a few standard terminals and a piece of spring wire.

A single-pole double-throw switch is constructed on prepunched or drilled circuit board by using five standard hollow gold-plated staked terminals and a section of spring wire. Four of the terminals are arranged in a square (say, 0.042-inch centers) and staked to a board. A piece of spring wire is then bent into an appropriate loop (see Fig. 1). A fifth terminal is trimmed to the base, as shown in Fig. 2, and sleeved over the short end of the spring wire. The long end of the wire is then inserted into one of the staked terminals and soldered into place. This becomes the shorting slug.

The result of all this is a movable shorting slug spring-loaded against two other adjacent terminal bases. Twisting or pushing the wire loop causes the shorting slug to snap into the detent formed by the other adjacent terminal base (Fig. 3). Connections can be made from either side of the board to wire or etched connectors. □

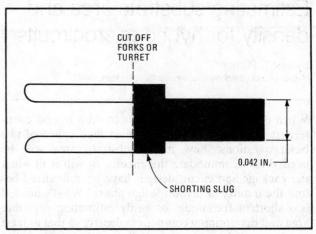

2. Shorting slug. Any type of hollow terminal will do, since only the bottom is used; gold plating stands up quite well.

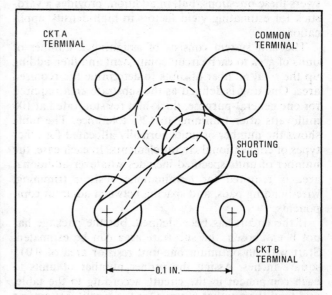

1. Shaping up. The shape of the spring wire is less important than the terminal-spacing and board-thickness dimensions.

3. Small switch. Pushing the spring-loaded wire loop moves the shorting slug from one set of terminals to the other set.

Estimating substrate area and density for hybrid microcircuits

by Lyle F. Pittroff
Helipot Division, Beckman Instruments Inc., Fullerton, Calif.

When converting discrete circuits to their hybrid counterparts, the engineer usually must face either of two basic questions: how much substrate area will be needed to accommodate the circuits, or will it fit when the package and circuit designs have been finalized before the inquiry or layout-design phase? What's needed is a shortcut technique for easily estimating substrate area and determining component density so that at least you know you're in the right ball park. A technique that Beckman Instruments calls the unit system not only answers these questions, but, in addition, provides a yardstick for estimating yield factors in high-density applications.

The unit system consists of assigning a number of units of area to each circuit component and then adding up the total number of units to determine the required area. One unit is defined as the substrate area required for one general-purpose, thick-film resistor, rated at 100 milliwatts after trimming to ±2% tolerance. The table shows the number of units normally allocated for other types of conventional circuit elements. In each case, the number of units specified includes whatever additional area is required for terminations, resistor trimming, wire-bonding pads, and spacing between adjacent components.

If the circuit has been defined, but the package has not been chosen, the substrate area can be estimated. Start with an optimum one-unit resistor area of 0.015 square inches. Assign the proper number of units to each component in the circuit, according to the table, and total the number of units for the circuit. Determine the substrate area required as follows:

$$A_s = (0.015 \text{ in.}^2) \, U_T$$

where A_s is the required substrate area, and U_T is the total number of units. A potential package choice, based on available substrate area, can then be made from the many different styles available.

When the circuit and package designs are both firm, the component density in square inches per unit can be estimated. Add up the total number of units for the circuit, according to the table. Determine the available substrate area in the package size you intend to use. Calculate the component density as follows:

$$D = A_s/U_T$$

A component density of 0.015 in.^{2}/unit is considered a moderate density level if the supplier of your final package has the freedom to make pin assignments. Us-

ing more specialized fine-line screening techniques, densities to 0.006 in.^{2}/unit have been achieved. Note that component density is appraised in area per unit, instead of units per area. Area per unit is more directly correlated to layout dimensioning.

Some components require special consideration because of their large size or an unusually large number of leads. Since the unit system is strictly a shortcut method, a considerable amount of good judgment and common sense must be applied. The following general guidelines should be considered:

- It may be easier to deduct the area required for large capacitor chips before applying the unit system.
- High component densities are easier to achieve in smaller packages because of proximity to pins.
- Some circuits naturally flow from input to output without complex feedback interconnections.
- Packaging efficiency is usually greater in larger hybrid packages, but yield and testing help set the limit. □

TYPICAL UNIT SYSTEM COMPONENT AREAS

Component type	Units per component
RESISTORS (CERMET, THICK FILM)	
General purpose (up to 100 mW)	1.0 units
Precision, ratio tracking	
aspect ratio ≤ 4:1, ≤ ±1%	2.0 units
CAPACITORS	
Screened (cermet)	270 pF/unit
Chip capacitors 0.1″ x 0.1″	2.0 units
DIODES, PASSIVATED CHIP	
Signal/switching	0.5 units
Zener/reference	0.5 units
Schottky/hot carrier	0.5 units
TRANSISTORS, PASSIVATED CHIP	
Bipolar small signal	0.5 units
Bipolar low/medium power	1.0 units
JFET	0.5 units
INTEGRATED CIRCUITS, PASSIVATED	
Linear (741, 710, 107, etc.)	2.0 units
Digital (935, 946, 7400, etc.)	4.0 units
MOS arrays (3101, etc.)	0.5 units/lead
MSI devices (74145, etc.)	0.5 units/lead

For metric-system applications, the unit system can be used as shown, except that the one-unit resistor area becomes 9,677 square millimeters.

Hand-soldering DIP circuits can save testing dollars

by William Mansfield and Herbert Perkins
Datatron Inc., Santa Ana, Calif.

Nowadays, integrated circuits are frequently mounted on printed-circuit boards by dropping their leads through plated-through holes and then flow-soldering. Although this method may yield the shortest assembly time, it is not necessarily the least expensive because the costs of product inspection and production testing can run high. Also, isolating faults on defective devices is extremely difficult, and removing installed devices risks the possibility of damage to both part and board.

Surprisingly, a return to hand-soldering leads on only one side of the board can mean substantial savings in nonrecurring engineering costs, as well as the costs of inspection and production testing. Since most ICs are supplied in dual-in-line packages, device leads can simply be bent away from the DIP body by 90°, so that the resulting flattened package can be easily attached to the board, as shown in the figure.

Abandoning plated-through holes, moreover, releases the opposite side of the board for other circuit functions. All the real estate on the bottom becomes available for circuit paths, permitting increased density of both wiring and components. This additional real estate also enhances reliability because wider line spacing can be employed to reduce the likelihood of solder bridging.

The cost penalty of hand-soldering a board containing 50 ICs—an increase in assembly time of approximately 15 minutes—can be offset by a saving of about $1.75 a board that results from fewer plated-through holes. And because layouts are more flexible, charges for engineering time can be cut by as much as 30%.

All IC leads are easily accessible for probing so that production testing and debugging is simpler. And any single IC lead can be unsoldered and lifted for fault isolation. With plated-through holes, removing an IC from the board risks debarrelled holes and raised wiring. Since repair is often unsuccessful, and the entire board must be scrapped, losses can run as high as $500 to $1,000 for a single ruined board. The savings from avoiding a scrapped board offset the cost penalty for hand-soldering some 100 boards.

Furthermore, plated-through holes are the historically weak link in the soldering operation, since they can introduce contaminants or open up during thermal cycling. Hand-soldering avoids these difficulties, in addition to providing a secure mechanical connection that can withstand the stress of exposure to shock, vibration, and direct pull. □

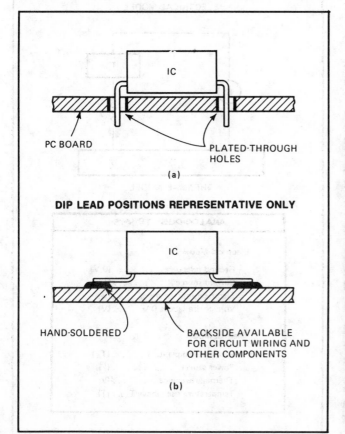

Hand-soldering has advantages. Plated-through holes (a) require space on both sides of printed-circuit board and make fault isolation difficult. By bending IC leads and hand-soldering (as in b), back of board becomes free for other circuit wiring, and single lead is easily unsoldered for testing. (Photo shows some mounted devices.) Cost penalty of hand-soldering is offset by savings in other operations.

15

Evaluating power dissipation in microcircuit design

by Lyle F. Pittroff
Microcircuit Operations, Helipot Div., Beckman Instruments, Fullerton, Calif.

Converting a circuit from the discrete-component concept into a single miniaturized microcircuit is analogous to the design and development of a larger system. Although specific design problems must be handled on an individual basis, several key areas must be considered early in the game.

This Engineer's notebook covers package-temperature rise, component ratings, and component compatibility; a later notebook will focus on a shortcut technique for estimating the substrate area required for any given circuit. This latter article will also discuss component density and hopefully answer the question, "Will it fit?" when circuit designs have been finalized.

Microcircuits shrink the package size, but package power remains the same, and the power density can be increased significantly. An estimate of the temperature rise in a new microcircuit design can be a critical step in the package-selection process. Two specific areas must be evaluated:

- Substrate/package temperature rise above the ambient or heat-sink maximum operating temperature.
- Individual component/junction temperature rise above the substrate/package temperature.

A simple review of the thermal model for the package and those components dissipating significant power will quickly reveal whether or not the design is in the right ball park for most hybrid-circuit configurations. With the fundamental thermal model shown in the first figure, a steady-state Ohm's law network analogy can be used to evaluate component temperature rise.

For the initial approximation, transistors and diodes dissipating less than 100 milliwatts, resistors, and most ICs are assumed to be operating at the case temperature. It is also assumed that all of the heat generated by internal circuit elements is being conducted away by the case (there is no radiant energy).

Conventional thermal model designations for a hybrid microcircuit are outlined in the second figure. The package temperature rise is a function of the total power dissipation (P_T) of all internal circuit elements:

$$T_R = T_C - T_A = P_T \Theta_{CA}$$

where T_R is the temperature rise between two specified points, T_C is the case temperature, T_A is ambient temperature, and Θ_{CA} is the thermal resistance from the case to ambient without a heat sink.

As a rule of thumb, the thermal resistance, Θ_{CA}, of a package in free air (no forced cooling and minimum pin conduction) causes a temperature rise of about 35°C per watt of power dissipation per square inch of package area (35°C/w/in.^{2}). For example, the temperature of a circuit dissipating 1 w would rise approximately 35°C above ambient in a 1-inch-square package or 70°C above ambient in half that package area. This general rule is conservative and should prove a safe first approximation for most pc-board applications.

The individual component temperature rise above the substrate temperature is a function of the component's power dissipation and thermal resistance. Although significant temperature rises are usually limited to the larger devices, some typical values of chip thermal resistance for smaller semiconductors are given.

The maximum allowable junction temperature (T_J) for silicon devices depends on the application, and in

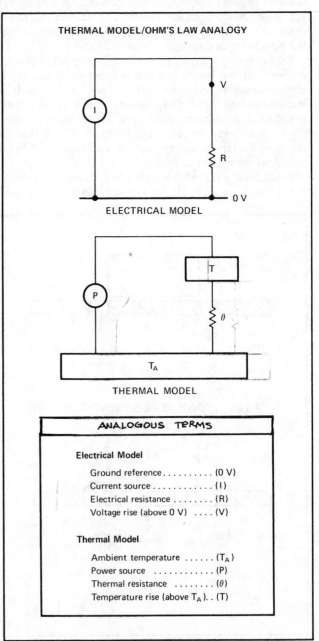

THERMAL MODEL/OHM'S LAW ANALOGY

ELECTRICAL MODEL

THERMAL MODEL

ANALOGOUS TERMS

Electrical Model

Ground reference . . . . (0 V)
Current source . . . . (I)
Electrical resistance . . . . (R)
Voltage rise (above 0 V) . . . . (V)

Thermal Model

Ambient temperature . . . . . . (T_A)
Power source . . . . (P)
Thermal resistance . . . . (θ)
Temperature rise (above T_A). . (T)

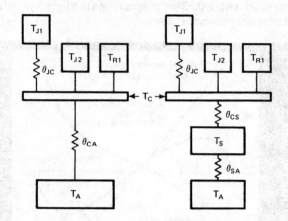

CONVENTIONAL THERMAL MODELS FOR HYBRID MICROCIRCUITS

MODEL PARAMETERS

T_A = Ambient temperature
T_S = Heat sink temperature
T_C = Case temperature
T_{J1} = Q_1 junction temperature (power device)
T_{J2} = Q_2 junction temperature (small signal device)
T_{R1} = Resistor R_1 temperature
θ_{JC} = Thermal resistance from power die junction to case
θ_{CA} = Thermal resistance from case to ambient (no heat sink)
θ_{CS} = Thermal resistance from case to heat sink
θ_{SA} = Thermal resistance from heat sink to ambient
T_R = Temperature rise between two specified points

TYPICAL SEMICONDUCTOR CHIP THERMAL RESISTANCE		
Category	Typical Device Types	Typical θ_{JC}
Small signal	2N2484, 2N2605	150°C/W
Low power	2N2219, 2N2905	60°C/W
Medium power	2N3724, 2N4030, 2N2194	44°C/W

some cases, it is limited by system specifications. The seat-of-the-pants rule is to never allow a junction to exceed 200°C in general utility applications. High-reliability applications often further limit T_J to 150°C or 175°C.

Component compatibility is yet another design consideration that must not be overlooked in building hybrid microcircuits. Realistically, it is sometimes more economical or better design practice to leave certain devices in discrete form outside of the microcircuit package. Large capacitors, for instance, as well as large power transistors and diodes, large inductive devices, and special parts head the list of discretes requiring individual attention.

To judge component compatibility, usually both performance and packaging objectives must be surveyed in the context of the over-all system. Each application imposes its own unique combination of economical, electrical, mechanical, and environmental circumstances.

Even conductors and crossovers are sometimes subject to the considerations of component compatibility. Fine-line screening techniques permit very narrow line widths to be realized, but Ohm's law still prevails and halving the line width doubles the line resistance between two points. Consequently, the layout of high-current paths and low-impedance lines may require special attention. □

3. Selecting circuit components

Mixed dielectrics improve capacitor stability

by George Breindel
Ross Laboratories Inc., Seattle, Wash.

Temperature characteristics of circuits like integrators, RC-dependent timers, free-running oscillators, and many others depend directly on the temperature stability of capacitors. It's well known that the capacitance of either polycarbonate or polystyrene capacitors over a range from –55°C to +125°C often varies more than system specifications can tolerate. But improved stability can be achieved if a polycarbonate is used in parallel with a polystyrene.

The figure shows that a typical polycarbonate capacitor has a positive temperature coefficient and a typical polystyrene capacitor has a negative coefficient of about the same magnitude. If a 1-microfarad capacitor is needed in a long-term integrator, then a 0.47-μF polystyrene in parallel with a 0.47-μF polycarbonate provides greatly improved temperature stability.

A further gain in stability can sometimes be realized by carefully matching the capacitor values to the respective temperature curves. For example, if a particular polystyrene capacitor has twice the stability of a particular polycarbonate, a 0.68-μF polystyrene can be used in parallel with a 0.33-μF polycarbonate to get 1 μF with a flatter temperature curve. □

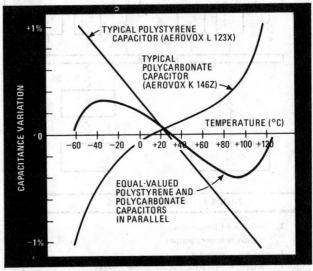

Temperature compensation. Because a polycarbonate capacitor's temperature coefficient is positive and a polystyrene capacitor's is negative, the two in parallel do better than either one alone at providing temperature stability in capacitance-dependent circuits such as RC tuners, oscillators, and integrators.

Designing with preferred component values cuts costs

by Nathan O. Sokal
Design Automation Inc., Lexington, Mass.

Designing with a minimum number of component values—so-called "preferred" values—can reduce materials and administrative costs for both manufacturing and engineering functions. The practice is no longer as common as it used to be, but it deserves to be revived now in updated form.

The accompanying tables suggest an order of preference to be followed in selecting values of resistance, inductance, capacitance, zener-diode voltage, field-effect diode current, and the like. Such components are available in sets of values that result from rounding to two (or three) digits the values obtained from $10^{n/24}$ (or $10^{n/96}$), where n ranges from zero to 23 (or 95) for each decade.

Tables 1 and 2 show the values in each of these series arranged into four columns to indicate the preferred order of component selection. Column one contains the first value and every eighth succeeding value. Column two contains values that are half way between two values in column one. Column three contains values that are half way between values in columns one and two, and column four contains all the rest. The order of pref-

TABLE 1: TWO-DIGIT SERIES (24 VALUES PER DECADE)

20% SERIES		10% SERIES	5% SERIES
First Preference	Second Preference	Third Preference	Fourth Preference
1.0			
			1.1
		1.2	
			1.3
	1.5		1.6
		1.8	
			2.0
2.2			2.4
		2.7	
			3.0
	3.3		3.6
		3.9	
			4.3
4.7			5.1
		5.6	
			6.2
	6.8		7.5
		8.2	
			9.1

TABLE 2: THREE-DIGIT SERIES (96 VALUES PER DECADE)			
2% SERIES			**1% SERIES**
First Preference	Second Preference	Third Preference	Fourth Preference
1.00			
			1.02
		1.05	
			1.07
	1.10		
			1.13
		1.15	
			1.18
1.21			
			1.24
		1.27	
			1.30
	1.33		
			1.37
		1.40	
			1.43
1.47			
			1.50
		1.54	
			1.58
	1.62		
			1.65
		1.69	
			1.74
1.78			
			1.82
		1.87	
			1.91
	1.96		
			2.00
		2.05	
			2.10
2.15			
			2.21
		2.26	
			2.32
	2.37		
			2.43
		2.49	
			2.55
2.61			
			2.67
		2.74	
			2.80
	2.87		
			2.94
		3.01	
			3.09
3.16			
			3.24
		3.32	
			3.40
	3.48		
			3.57
		3.65	
			3.74
3.83			
			3.92
		4.02	
			4.12
	4.22		
			4.32
		4.42	
			4.53
4.64			
			4.75
		4.87	
			4.99
	5.11		
			5.23
		5.36	
			5.49
5.62			
			5.76
		5.90	
			6.04
	6.19		
			6.34
		6.49	
			6.65
6.81			
			6.98
		7.15	
			7.32
	7.50		
			7.68
		7.87	
			8.06
8.25			
			8.45
		8.66	
			8.87
	9.09		
			9.31
		9.53	
			9.76

erence in Table 1 may be familiar to engineers with long memories, but extension of preferred values to include the three-digit series is an update of this concept.

No restriction is placed on the values available to the designer; if a certain value must be used, it can be used. However, when a particular application requires a resistor that can have any value in the range between 100 and 1,000 ohms, for example, a 470-ohm, 20% resistor should be used rather than one rated at 510 ohms with 5% tolerance.

All of the values in Table 1 are available with 5% tolerance. The 5% series are available only with 5% tolerance; the 10% series are available with either 5% or 10% tolerance, and the 20% series are available with 5%, 10%, or 20% tolerance. Similarly, all of the values in Table 2 are available with 1% tolerance. The preferred tolerance (and temperature coefficient spread when a choice exists) is the loosest available one that does the job reliably. The purchasing or manufacturing department can always substitute a smaller tolerance or temperature coefficient if that is advantageous for purchasing or stocking reasons.

Using preferred values results in equipment designs that require a smaller variety of components, and since larger quantities of each component are used, they can be purchased at lower prices. Common use of the preferred values in different projects and equipments also reduces overhead costs in placing and tracing orders for fewer kinds of items, in receiving and inspecting fewer kinds of items, and in stocking and kitting fewer kinds of items for use in manufacturing. Field-service costs are reduced, too, because fewer different items are needed to be distributed, stocked, reordered, and accounted for in field locations.

The standard range of values for components is generally the same in specifications for industry as for the military. As an example, Table 3 shows the standard ranges for carbon-composition resistors. Components selected from the standard range are readily available from more sources and at lower cost than are nonstandard components. □

TABLE 3: STANDARD RANGE OF VALUES FOR CARBON COMPOSITION RESISTORS, MIL-R-39008			
Power rating (watts)	Type	Minimum Resistance (ohms)	Maximum Resistance (megohms)
1/8	RCR05	2.7	22
1/4	RCR07	2.7	22
1/2	RCR20	2.7	22
1	RCR32	2.7	22
2	RCR42	10	22

Comparing the power of C-MOS with TTL

by Colin Crook
Motorola Semiconductor Products Inc., Phoenix, Ariz.

The low power dissipation of complementary-MOS circuitry is legendary by now. You've been told, time and time again, that it is lower—considerably lower—than equivalent TTL designs. How much lower is somewhat astonishing—as large as an order of magnitude or more.

Here is a set of tables that clearly demonstrates the vast difference in power requirements between C-MOS and TTL. This difference results in a significant saving in overhead for system-support needs, like power supplies and cooling equipment. The tables make a systems-level power comparison between C-MOS and TTL by examining a representative logic system—an industrial controller and sequencer.

This typical system consists of 500 IC packages: there are 200 quad NAND gates, 150 dual flip-flops, and 150 4-bit arithmetic logic units. Table 1 gives the device type numbers used for the C-MOS and TTL systems.

At medium frequencies, the dynamic power of C-MOS is significant compared to its dc power, so that certain loading and frequency conditions will be assumed. For this example, every output node of a gate package is loaded by 50 picofarads, every output node of a flip-flop package by 30 pF, and every output node (eight in all) of an arithmetic-logic-unit package by 15 pF. A reasonable assumption for the operating frequency is that

TABLE 1
LOGIC SYSTEM

Device	Number of packages	C-MOS type	TTL type
Quad NAND gate	200	MC14011CP	MC7400P
Dual flip-flop	150	MC14027CP	MC7473P
Arithmetic logic unit	150	MC14581CL	MC74181P

TABLE 2
DC POWER AT 5 VOLTS: C-MOS vs TTL

Device	Per-package power	System power	Total C-MOS system dc power		
				Typ	Max
Gate	C-MOS: Typ = 25 nW, Max = 75 µW	C-MOS: X 200 Typ = 5 µW, Max = 15 mW	Gates = 5 µW		15 mW
			Flip-flops = 7.5 µW		105 mW
	TTL: Typ = 40 mW, Max = 110 mW	TTL: X 200 Typ = 8 W, Max = 22 W	ALUs = 37.5 µW		525 mW
			TOTAL = 50 µW		645 mW
			Current at 5 V = 10 µA		129 mA
Flip-flop	C-MOS: Typ = 50 nW, Max = 700 µW	C-MOS: X 150 Typ = 7.5 µW, Max = 105 mW	Total TTL system dc power		
	TTL: Typ = 80 mW, Max = 200 mW	TTL: X 150 Typ = 12 W, Max = 30 W		Typ	Max
			Gates = 8 W		22 W
ALU	C-MOS: Typ = 250 nW, Max = 3.5 mW	C-MOS: X 150 Typ = 37.5 µW, Max = 525 mW	Flip-flops = 12 W		30 W
			ALUs = 70.5 W		112.5 W
	TTL: Typ = 470 mW, Max = 750 mW	TTL: X 150 Typ = 70.5 W, Max = 112.5 W	TOTAL = 90.5 W		164.5 W
			Current at 5 V = 18.1 A		32.9 A

TABLE 3
C-MOS DYNAMIC POWER AT 5 VOLTS

Device	Per-package power	System power	Total system power	
Gate	At 200 kHz = 1.2 mW, At 1 MHz = 6.0 mW	Average = 3.6 mW, 200 X 3.6 mW = 720 mW	Gates	= 720 mW
Flip-flop	At 200 kHz = 0.6 mW, At 1 MHz = 3.0 mW	Average = 1.8 mW, 150 X 1.8 mW = 270 mW	Flip-flops	= 270 mW
			ALUs	= 180 mW
ALU	At 200 kHz = 0.4 mW, At 1 MHz = 2.0 mW	Average = 1.2 mW, 150 X 1.2 mW = 180 mW	TOTAL	= 1.170 W

half of all the nodes switch at 1 megahertz, and the other half switch at 200 kilohertz.

Because of its enhanced noise immunity at higher supply voltages, C-MOS is often operated at 10 volts. For this reason, we will compare the dc, as well as dynamic, power consumption of C-MOS at both 5- and 10-V supply voltages to the dc power of TTL at 5 V.

At operating frequencies of 1 MHz or less, the dynamic power of TTL is negligible compared to its dc power. In fact, TTL dynamic power does not become relevant until the operating frequency exceeds 10 MHz. Therefore, there is no real need to compute TTL's dynamic power separately.

Table 2 shows the dc power requirements of C-MOS and TTL when the system supply voltage is 5 V. As you can see, the entire C-MOS system consumes only 50 microwatts typically and 645 milliwatts maximum. In con-

trast, the same system built with TTL devices requires 90.5 watts typically and 164.5 W maximum.

In Table 3, the dynamic power of a 5-V C-MOS system is computed. Here, the total system power consumption is found to be 1.17w. Table 4 gives the total dc power for a 10-V C-MOS system; it is 190 μW typically and 2.58 W maximum. The total dynamic power for this same 10-V C-MOS system is evaluated in Table 5; it is 5.04 W average.

Table 6 summarizes the results of all the preceding tables. Roughly speaking, TTL consumes about 100 times more power than C-MOS, even when worst-case dynamic operating conditions are taken into consideration for the C-MOS system. □

TABLE 4
C-MOS DC POWER AT 10 VOLTS

Device	Per-package power	System power	Total system power		
		X 200		Typ	Max
Gate	Typ = 50 nW Max = 300 μW	Typ = 10 μW Max = 60 mW	Gates = 10 μW		60 mW
Flip-flop	Typ = 200 μW Max = 2.8 mW	X 150 Typ = 30 μW Max = 420 mW	Flip-flops = 30 μW		420 mW
			ALUs = 150 μW		2,100 mW
ALU	Typ = 1.0 μW Max = 14 mW	X 150 Typ = 150 μW Max = 2,100 mW	TOTAL = 190 μW		2.58 W
			Current at 10 V = 19 μA		258 mA

TABLE 5
C-MOS DYNAMIC POWER AT 10 VOLTS

Device	Per-package power	System power	Total system power	
Gate	At 200 kHz = 4.8 mW At 1MHz = 24 mW	Average = 14.4 mW 200 X 14.4 mW = 2,880 mW	Gates = 2,800 mW	
Flip-flop	At 200 kHz = 3.0 mW At 1 MHz = 15 mW	Average = 9.0 mW 150 X 9.0 mW = 1,350 mW	Flip-flops = 1,350 mW	
			ALUs = 810 mW	
ALU	At 200 kHz = 1.8 mW At 1 MHz = 9.0 mW	Average = 5.4 mW 150 X 5.4 mW = 810 mW	TOTAL = 5.04 W	

TABLE 6
TOTAL SYSTEM POWER: C-MOS vs TTL

Logic	Dc		Ac	Totals
	Typ	Max		
TTL	90.5 W 18.1 A at 5V	164.5 W 32.9 A at 5 V	Assume small compared with dc power	Max = 164.5 W Typ = 90.5 W Power supply average = 25.5 A at 5 V
5-volt C-MOS	50 μW 10 μA at 5 V	645 mW 129 mA at 5 V	1.170 W	Max = 1.82 W Typ = 1.17 W
10-volt C-MOS	190 μW 19 μA at 10 V	2.58 W 258 mA at 10 V	5.04 W	Max = 7.62 W Typ = 5.04 W

Examining worst-case fan-out of standard C-MOS buffers

by Rob Walker
Fairchild Semiconductor, Mountain View, Calif.

Complementary-MOS buffers are normally used when an interface is needed between C-MOS and TTL circuitry. There are two more or less standard types of buffers that are generally employed—the inverting type 4049 device and the noninverting type 4050 device. Both are available from a variety of semiconductor manufacturers.

A cursory analysis of the data sheet for these buffers will lead many designers to believe that the maximum TTL fan-out of the buffers is less than two under worst-case conditions. Naturally, a buffer fan-out of only one increases component count and system cost. But if the tracking effects between TTL and C-MOS devices are taken into account, the true worst-case fan-out can be regarded as two TTL loads.

Table 1 shows the usual worst-case specifications given for the 4049 and 4050 buffers for a low-level output voltage. The available output current decreases with rising temperature, but increases for a higher supply voltage. Since one standard TTL load is normally assumed to be 1.6 milliamperes, the natural conclusion is that the type 4049 or type 4050 C-MOS buffer can't possibly drive two TTL loads under worst-case conditions.

However, a closer look at the true worst-case operating conditions shows this conclusion to be inaccurate—the worst-case fan-out of a C-MOS buffer can safely be taken as equal to two when the following factors are taken into consideration:

■ Commercial-grade TTL is only specified to $+75°C$, permitting the maximum C-MOS temperature to be regarded as $+75°C$.

■ The maximum low-level output voltage of 0.4 V for TTL is rather arbitrary. For example, Schottky TTL and low-power Schottky TTL, which are both certainly TTL-compatible, have a low-level output voltage that is less than or equal to 0.5 V.

■ Commercial TTL is specified over a V_{CC} supply range of 4.75 to 5.25 V. It is only reasonable to assume the C-MOS buffers will be using the same supply.

■ The maximum 1.6-mA low-level input current required by a TTL device is specified at a drive voltage of only 0.4 V and a supply voltage of 5.25 V. This required input current drops when the drive voltage is increased to 0.5 V and/or the supply voltage is reduced.

Table 2 is a summary of these true worst-case conditions—for a low-level output of 0.5 V, the C-MOS buffer fan-out is two, which represents a potential 50% components savings. What's more, if low-power Schottky-TTL devices are used instead of standard TTL devices, the C-MOS buffer fan-out jumps to more than nine. □

TABLE 1			
SPECIFIED WORST-CASE CONDITIONS			
TEMPERATURE	$-40°C$	$+25°C$	$+85°C$
$V_{OL} = 0.4$ V, $V_{DD} = 4.5$ V	$I_{OL} = 3.1$ mA	$I_{OL} = 2.6$ mA	$I_{OL} = 2.1$ mA
$V_{OL} = 0.4$ V, $V_{DD} = 5$ V	$I_{OL} = 3.6$ mA	$I_{OL} = 3$ mA	$I_{OL} = 2.5$ mA
V_{OL} = Low-level output drive voltage $\quad I_{OL}$ = Low-level output drive current $\quad V_{DD}$ = Supply voltage			

TABLE 2				
PRACTICAL WORST-CASE LIMITS				
PARAMETER ($T_A = 0 - 75°C$)	$V_{CC} = V_{DD} = 4.75$ V		$V_{CC} = V_{DD} = 5.25$ V	
	$V_{OL} = 0.4$ V	$V_{OL} = 0.5$ V	$V_{OL} = 0.4$ V	$V_{OL} = 0.5$ V
I_{IL} (TTL)	1.402 mA	1.363 mA	1.6 mA	1.56 mA
I_{OL} (C-MOS)	2.39 mA	2.94 mA	2.85 mA	3.41 mA
FANOUT	1.70 mA	2.16 mA	1.74 mA	2.18 mA

V_{OL} = Low-level output drive voltage
I_{OL} = Low-level output drive current
I_{IL} = Low-level input current
V_{CC} = TTL supply voltage
V_{DD} = C-MOS supply voltage
Fanout = I_{OL} / I_{IL}
T_A = Absolute temperature

Drift-matched IC op amps can save money

by Larry Choice
Burr-Brown Research Corp., Tucson, Ariz.

Using the right drift-matched IC operational amplifiers can drastically cut the cost of any multiple op amp circuit that requires low-offset voltage drift. Several individual low-drift IC op amps are presently available with guaranteed nulled-offset drifts as low as 0.6 microvolt

per degree centigrade over varying temperature ranges. They cost $16.30 to $50.75 in quantities of 100. Also available are drift-matched IC op amp pairs which can provide performance equal to two unmatched units each with a drift of ±0.5 μV/°C, yet are about half the cost of two of the least expensive unmatched low-drift units. Moreover, they need no external offset nulling to achieve low drift.

Just as transistors can be drift-matched, amplifiers can be matched for minimum "differential" (between two devices) offset voltage (Δv_{os}) and minimum "differential" drift. Unfortunately, today's dual IC op amps, unlike dual transistors, do not in general have good matching for offset voltage and drift; the best match is

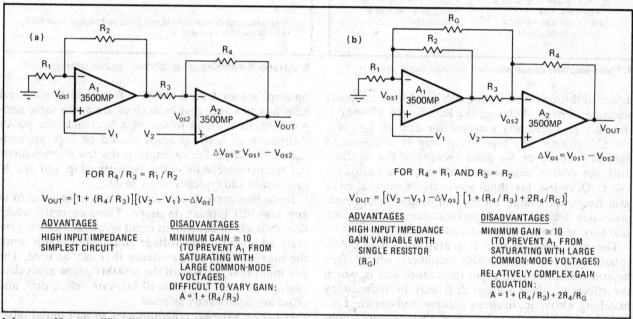

(a)

$$\Delta V_{os} = V_{os1} - V_{os2}$$

FOR $R_4/R_3 = R_1/R_2$

$$V_{OUT} = [1 + (R_4/R_3)][(V_2 - V_1) - \Delta V_{os}]$$

<u>ADVANTAGES</u>

HIGH INPUT IMPEDANCE
SIMPLEST CIRCUIT

<u>DISADVANTAGES</u>

MINIMUM GAIN ≅ 10
(TO PREVENT A₁ FROM SATURATING WITH LARGE COMMON-MODE VOLTAGES)
DIFFICULT TO VARY GAIN:
A = 1 + (R₄/R₃)

(b)

$$\Delta V_{os} = V_{os1} - V_{os2}$$

FOR $R_4 = R_1$ AND $R_3 = R_2$

$$V_{OUT} = [(V_2 - V_1) - \Delta V_{os}][1 + (R_4/R_3) + 2R_4/R_G]$$

<u>ADVANTAGES</u>

HIGH INPUT IMPEDANCE
GAIN VARIABLE WITH SINGLE RESISTOR (R_G)

<u>DISADVANTAGES</u>

MINIMUM GAIN ≅ 10
(TO PREVENT A₁ FROM SATURATING WITH LARGE COMMON-MODE VOLTAGES)
RELATIVELY COMPLEX GAIN EQUATION:
A = 1 + (R₄/R₃) + 2R₄/R_G

1. Improved two-amplifier differential circuit needs only one resistor, R_G to vary gain, but resistor values must be matched.

COMPARING LOW DRIFT IC OP AMPS								
Unit	Unit price 100−249	Max. initial offset voltage in μV @ 25°C	Max. average drift μV/°C — No trim	Offset nulled	Min. slew rate with unity gain compensation V/μsec	Temp. range	No. of external components for unity gain compensation	Max. input bias current nA @ 25°C
Burr-Brown								
3500E	$20	500	1.0		1.0	−25°C to +85°C	0	±50
3500MP	$16.70 per pair	200*	1.0*		1.0	−25°C to +85°C	0	±50
Precision Monolithics,Inc.								
SSS725AJ	$50.75	100	0.8	0.6	0.008 typ	−55°C to +125°C	4	70
SSS725EJ	$16.30	500	2.0 typ	0.6	0.008 typ	0°C to +70°C	4	80
Analog Devices								
504L	$20.40	500		1.0	0.12 typ	0°C to +70°C	1	±80
508L	$30.00	500		1.0	0.12 typ	0°C to +70°C	1	±20

* Maximum differential between the two units in the pair.

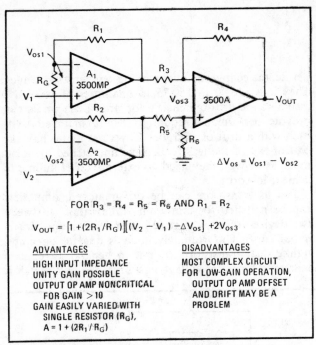

$$FOR\ R_3 = R_4 = R_5 = R_6\ AND\ R_1 = R_2$$

$$V_{OUT} = \left[1 + (2R_1/R_G)\right]\left[(V_2 - V_1) - \Delta V_{os}\right] + 2V_{os3}$$

ADVANTAGES
HIGH INPUT IMPEDANCE
UNITY GAIN POSSIBLE
OUTPUT OP AMP NONCRITICAL
FOR GAIN > 10
GAIN EASILY VARIED WITH
SINGLE RESISTOR (R_G),
$A = 1 + (2R_1/R_G)$

DISADVANTAGES
MOST COMPLEX CIRCUIT
FOR LOW-GAIN OPERATION,
OUTPUT OP AMP OFFSET
AND DRIFT MAY BE A
PROBLEM

2. Three-amplifier circuit improves common-mode rejection.

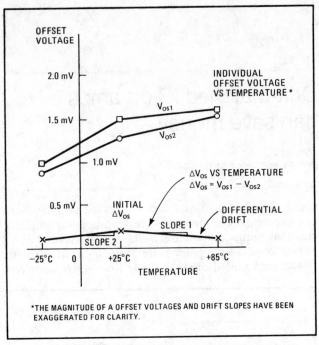

*THE MAGNITUDE OF A OFFSET VOLTAGES AND DRIFT SLOPES HAVE BEEN EXAGGERATED FOR CLARITY.

3. Offset drift matching of the 3500MP reduces differential drift.

achieved through drift testing combined with computer selection of pairs. Although the Burr-Brown 3500MP is the only one presently matched for drift as low as 1 μV/°C, certainly any type of op amp is amenable to matching. However, for good linearity of the matched drift, the drift of each unit should be no more than 5 μV/°C. Of course, low input bias currents, internal unity gain frequency compensation, and output short-circuit protection are additional performance criteria which also may be important in matched applications.

The most common use of op amp pairs is in differential input (instrumentation) amplifiers, which often require extremely high input impedance and in which the effects of offset voltage drift may be reduced by matching. Other applications needing drift-matched ICs include multiple-pole active filters, dual-reference voltage sources, voltage-to-current amplifiers, and matched dual-channel amplifiers or filters.

To assure optimum drift performance, certain precautions are necessary: because two separate matched op amps are used, the 3500MP is furnished with a metal heat sink to assure that both chips are at the same temperature. In addition to use of a heat sink, the power dissipation of both op amps should be kept approximately the same. For example, just a few degrees internal temperature differential between chip and the IC case would add typically 10 μv to ΔV_{os}.

Input bias currents are always a matter of concern in any low-drift bipolar op amps. These currents, which flow through an equivalent input source resistance, generate additional offset voltage and drift, and this limits the maximum input impedance that can be used. The low input bias currents of the 3500MP allow equivalent source resistance of up to 10 kilohms before drift and offset are significantly affected.

Using an external potentiometer to null initial offset voltage can add offset voltage drift. When a matched pair of op amps is employed, it is advisable to adjust $\Delta V_{os} = 0$ to minimize offset adjustment effects on drift, and not $V_{os1} = 0 = V_{os2}$. □

How to really look at low-drift IC op amps

by Stan Harris
Analog Devices, Inc., Norwood, Mass.

There's more to high accuracy in an integrated-circuit operational amplifier than low drift with temperature. Total output error accumulates from a number of sources, all of which should be considered when choosing an op amp. An error budget analysis that accounts for worst-case error voltages attributable to gain, offset voltage and bias currents, CMRR, as well as other parameters, will give a much more significant measure of accuracy than simply comparing microvolts/°C specifications.

To make the analysis, first assume a circuit configuration—either the actual circuit or some arbitrary circuit. Then list the specifications that are meaningful for accurate circuit operation, noting the minimum or maximum value of each parameter over the required tem-

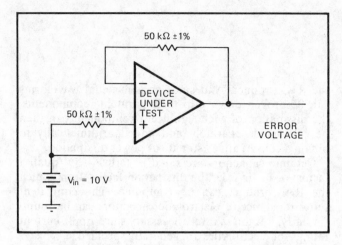

50 kΩ ±1%

DEVICE
UNDER
TEST

ERROR
VOLTAGE

50 kΩ ±1%

V_{in} = 10 V

perature range. Such min and max values are usually available from the spec sheets, but if they are not, then either use experience to assign the value from the given typical value, or get in touch with the op amp makers to ascertain a proper value. It may take some spec sheet interpretation to be reasonably sure that all the parameters of concern are specified in the same way by the various manufacturers (e.g., warmed-up versus initial values, CMRR at what V_{in}?).

Now go down the list and compute the value of each input error by considering how the specifications contribute to error in the operating configuration. If, for example, an amplifier is intended for accurate dc operation, the following specs are important and should be considered: gain, input bias and offset currents, offset voltage, input offset voltage drift, common-mode and power supply rejection ratios—and their changes (or values) over the temperature range. In the non-inverting circuit shown, the source resistance, R_S, is assumed to

be 50 kilohms, R_S mismatch is 2%, input is 10 volts, and power supply variation is assumed to be ±5%.

Several IC op amps, each of which provides excellent performance in one or more of the characteristics that comprise the error budget analysis, are compared. The error parameters of six different op amp types are detailed for two temperature ranges.

Choosing op amp A from those listed, the errors are defined and calculated as follows:

■ Gain: with a minimum gain of 10^6, 10 μV are required across the amplifier inputs to generate a 10-v output voltage. This 10 μV is the gain-error voltage.

■ Bias current: a 1% resistor tolerance gives a total resistor mismatch of 1 kilohm. This results in a 10-μV input voltage error, due to the 10-nanoampere maximum I_b spec.

■ Offset current: the offset current of 1 nA through the 50-kilohm source resistance gives a 50-μV error voltage.

■ Offset voltage: most high-accuracy op amps can be easily offset-voltage-nulled (one op amp used in the analysis could not be), thus effectively eliminating this parameter as an error source.

■ Offset-voltage drift: the maximum spec sheet number multiplied by the appropriate temperature range produces this error voltage. (In general, a linear interpolation will not introduce significant variations from reality—but it might.)

■ CMRR: given a 10-v common-mode signal, the 110-decibel minimum spec results in 32 μV of common-mode error voltage.

■ PSRR: with a ±5% power-supply tolerance, a worst-case change of 1.5 v, multiplied by a maximum PSRR of 10 μV/v, gives an error voltage of 15 μV. □

OP AMP ERROR BUDGET ANALYSIS										
Error parameter (min or max)	T_A = +25°C to +45°C					T_A = 0°C to +70°C				
	A	B	C	D	E	A	B	C	D	E
Gain	(1×10⁶) 10 μV	(8×10⁴) 125 μV	(1×10⁶) 10 μV	(10×10⁴) 100 μV	(5×10⁴) 200 μV	(50×10⁴) 20 μV	(est. 6×10⁴) 167 μV	(80×10⁴) 12.5 μV	(est. 7×10⁴) 143 μV	(2.5×10⁴) 400 μV
Bias current (I_b)	(10 nA) 10 μV	(2 nA) 2 μV	(80 nA) 80 μV	(50 nA) 50 μV	(75 nA) 75 μV	(15 nA) 15 μV	(est. 2.5 nA) 2.5 μV	(100 nA) 100 μV	(est. 75 nA) 75 μV	(120 nA) 120 μV
Offset current (I_{os})	(1 nA) 50 μV	(0.2 nA) 10 μV	(5 nA) 250 μV	(30 nA) 1500 μV	(10 nA) 500 μV	(1.6 nA) 80 μV	(est. 0.3 nA) 15 μV	(7 nA) 350 μV	(est. 45 nA) 2250 μV	(15 n A) 750 μV
Offset voltage (V_{os})	(trim to 0) 0	(500 μV) 500 μV	(trim to 0) 0	(trim to 0) 0	(trim to 0) 0	(trim to 0) 0	(est. 730 μV) 730 μV	(trim to 0) 0	(trim to 0) 0	(trim to 0) 0
Offset voltage drift ($\Delta V_{os}/\Delta_T$)	(0.5 μV/°C) 10 μV	(5.0 μV/°C) 100 μV	(0.6 μV/°C) 12 μV	(1.0 μV/°C) 20 μV	(15 μV/°C) 300 μV	(0.5 μV/°C) 35 μV	(5.0 μV/°C) 350 μV	(0.6 μV/°C) 42 μV	(1.0 μV/°C) 70 μV	(15 μV/°C) 1050 μV
CMRR	(110 dB) 32 μV	(96 dB) 160 μV	(120 dB) 10 μV	(est. 96 dB) 160 μV	(90 dB) 320 μV	(100 dB) 100 μV	(96 dB) 160 μV	(115 dB) 18 μV	(est. 90 dB) 320 μV	(90 dB) 320 μV
PSRR	(10 μV/V) 15 μV	(16 μV/V) 24 μV	(5 μV/V) 7.5 μV	(est. 50 μV/V) 75 μV	(15 μV/V) 22.5 μV	(15 μV/V) 22.5 μV	(16 μV/V) 24 μV	(7 μV/V) 10.5 μV	(est. 60 μV/V) 90 μV	(15 μV/V) 22.5 μV
Noise	Difficult to estimate because of non-uniform specifications. Range approximately from 2 μV to 10 μV, not a significant % of the total.									
Total	127 μV	921 μV	369.5 μV	1905 μV	1417.5 μV	272.5 μV	1448.5 μV	533 μV	2948 μV	2662.5 μV
Price (100-lot)	$20.00	$14.95	$16.30	$20.00	$2.25					

25

Ac power considerations in capacitor selection

by John Kropp
Mepco/Electra, Inc., a North American Philips Co., Morristown, N.J.

There are as many different ways of calculating power dissipation in a capacitor as there are ways to use a capacitor. The dissipation due to an impressed ac voltage is often overlooked or considered negligible, resulting in capacitor degradation, excessive heating, and early failure. The ac voltage capability of a capacitor is quite different from its dc rating and is a function of its construction. Fortunately, dissipation due to dc leakage adds to dissipation due to ac components, permitting them to be calculated separately and superimposed.

Film capacitors are rated in terms of a frequency-dependent equivalent series RC product, which is labeled the R_SC product. And since nonsinusoidal waveforms can be broken down into their harmonic components, the dissipation of each significant component can then be calculated separately and added arithmetically to obtain a conservative estimate of power dissipation.

Ceramic capacitors are rated in terms of Q (quality factor) or its inverse, the dissipation factor, from which the R_SC product can be computed. The equivalent series resistance of electrolytic capacitors can be found similarly, but this is rarely necessary since ripple current ratings for electrolytics are generally specified.

The limitation on power dissipation is, of course, the maximum temperature the capacitor can tolerate. This is, in turn, a function of the internal structure and case size, which determines the surface area available for dissipating the power. The approximate relationship (assuming free-air convection around the entire surface) between surface area and temperature rise above ambient is:

$$T_{rise} = 133(P/A)°C$$

where P is the dissipation expressed in watts, and A is

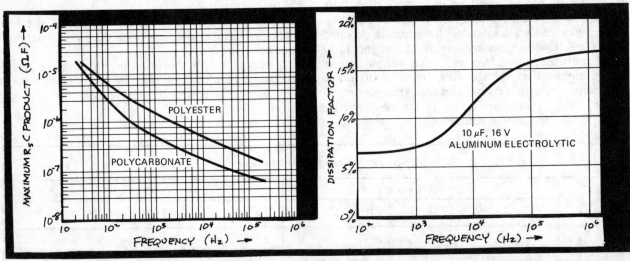

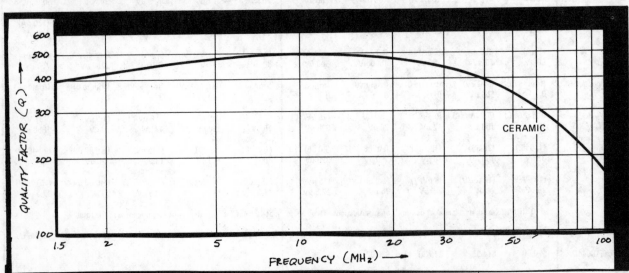

the surface area of the case expressed in square inches.

The typical frequency curves show how the maximum $R_S C$ product varies with frequency for polycarbonate and polyester film capacitors, how Q varies with frequency for ceramic capacitors, and how dissipation factor varies with frequency for electrolytic capacitors. For film capacitors, the temperature curves illustrate how the maximum permissible power dissipation is related to ambient temperature for various capacitor sizes. The table associated with each temperature graph gives approximate capacitor dimensions. The Group A plots are representative of Mepco/Electra series C280A/C280M units, Group B plots represent series C280M units, and Group C plots represent series C281 units.

A sample power computation will show how to use the graphs. Suppose a polycarbonate capacitor of 0.33 microfarad must handle an impressed voltage (V_{ac}) of 180 volts at a frequency (ω) of 1 kilohertz in an ambient temperature of 50°C. Since the power dissipated is:

$$P = I^2 R_S$$

and:

$$I = V_{ac} \omega C$$

then:

$$P = R_S V_{ac}^2 \omega^2 C^2$$

or:

$$P = (R_S C) V_{ac}^2 \omega^2 C$$

The film capacitor frequency curves indicate that the $R_S C$ product is $5 \times 10^{-7}\ \Omega F$. Substituting for this product and for the capacitor's operating conditions in the last equation yields:

$$P = (5 \times 10^{-7})(0.33 \times 10^{-6})(2\pi \times 1{,}000)(180)^2$$
$$P = 0.214\ w$$

If the Group A capacitors are chosen, those with curve numbers of 8 to 12 can be used at 50°C, and the minimum size capacitor is 0.374 by 0.8666 by 0.571 inch.

When curves for maximum power dissipation versus ambient temperature are not given for a capacitor, the

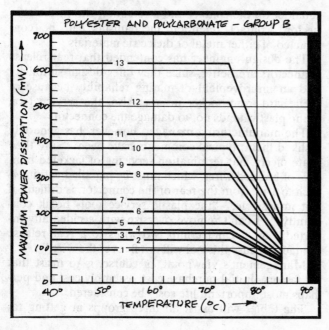

GROUP A - DIMENSIONS			
Curve	Thickness (in.)	Width (in.)	Height (in.)
1	0.157	0.492	0.354
2	0.197	0.492	0.394
3	0.236	0.492	0.433
4	0.236	0.689	0.433
5	0.276	0.689	0.472
6	0.256	0.886	0.453
7	0.295	0.886	0.492
8	0.374	0.886	0.571
9	0.374	1.18	0.571
10	0.394	1.18	0.709
11	0.472	1.18	0.787
12	0.492	1.18	0.807

GROUP B - DIMENSIONS			
Curve	Thickness (in.)	Width (in.)	Height (in.)
1	0.177	0.512	0.394
2	0.197	0.512	0.433
3	0.236	0.512	0.473
4	0.197	0.689	0.433
5	0.236	0.689	0.453
6	0.276	0.689	0.512
7	0.335	0.689	0.571
8	0.256	1.024	0.611
9	0.295	1.024	0.650
10	0.335	1.024	0.709
11	0.374	1.024	0.749
12	0.433	1.182	0.768
13	0.531	1.182	0.867

power dissipation must be limited to a value that will not cause the capacitor's internal temperature to rise above its maximum rated value. Some conservative estimates for this maximum internal hot-spot temperature are: 100°C for ceramic plate capacitors, polycarbonate capacitors, polyester foil capacitors, and metalized polyester capacitors, 125°C for solid electrolytic capacitors, and 90°C for conventional aluminum electrolytics.

Other factors can also limit the level of the applied ac voltage. For example, in film capacitors, the maximum ac voltage rating at line frequency must be respected at all frequencies since it is determined by dielectric strength, not power dissipation. Similarly, some capacitors are rated for voltage steepness, a rating that must be respected, regardless of waveform or dissipation. (Voltage transients in the order of 20 to 50 volts/microsecond can cause dielectric breakdown in metalized film capacitors.) Finally, if a capacitor current rating is given, it must also be observed, no matter what the result of other calculations. □

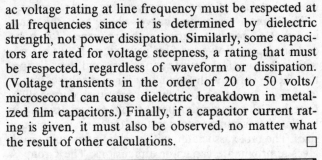

Curve	Thickness (in.)	Length (in.)	Height (in.)
1	0.185	0.571	0.342
2	0.216	0.571	0.370
3	0.256	0.571	0.409
4	0.256	0.709	0.409
5	0.299	0.709	0.453
6	0.299	0.925	0.453
7	0.342	0.925	0.504
8	0.409	0.925	0.567
9	0.409	1.220	0.575
10	0.488	1.220	0.768
11	0.591	1.220	0.866

Summing up the front-release rear-release connector debate

by Terry Leen and John Cameron
Amphenol Connector division, Bunker Ramo Corp., Broadview, Ill.

Historically, the relative merits of front-release and rear-release connectors have been controversial, both among connector manufacturers and within users' plants. Fortunately, the comparative advantages of each system are now becoming clear, and the choice between the two can be made objectively.

In the front-release connectors, the contacts are released from the front and then removed from the back, generally with metal tools. In the rear-release version, the tool is generally plastic, and is applied from the back of the connector—the wire-bundle side.

In both systems, contacts are retained by means of a shoulder on the contact and a retention clip in the connector. Contact retention mechanisms can be constructed of either metal or dielectric materials.

The design engineer has contended that rear-release connectors are better, since they offer design simplicity and an improvement of mating reliability because of their hard-front socket inserts. Also, the service tool, being plastic, tends not to damage the connector.

The manufacturing manager, however, has generally disliked them; typical comments have been: "Sure they mate nicely, but termination servicing of jacketed bundles of braided wires, which must be pigtailed within ¼-inch to 1-in. from the rear of the connector, is difficult if not impossible;" "the plastic service tools break constantly;" "I can't remove oversize wire accidentally inserted;" or "I can't crimp two wires to a rear release contact because the tool will not fit over the wire."

Management's viewpoint, of course, is to insist that all factors—initial purchase cost, assembly cost and perhaps most important, life cost—be considered.

The tables will assist all three groups in getting to-

TABLE 1: FRONT-AND REAR-RELEASE CONNECTORS COMPARED

FRONT-RELEASE

ADVANTAGES

Contact identification easier

Low life cost of metal tools

Larger wire diameters possible

Wire shielding may be close to grommet sealing surface, also is easily serviceable

No auxiliary tools needed for broken wired contacts

DISADVANTAGES

Male pins may bend during removal

High initial cost of metal tools

Closed-entry hard-front insert design adds parts, complexity

Contacts not serviceable in mated connector

Not adaptable to CTJS, Mil-T-81714

Moderate to high connector life cost

REAR-RELEASE

Male pins won't bend on removal

Low initial cost of plastic tools, ready availability for servicing

Closed-entry hard-front insert design less complex

Contacts serviceable in mated connector

Adaptable to CTJS, Mil-T-81714

Low to moderate connector life cost

Visual contact identification difficult

High life cost of plastic tools

Wire diameters restricted

Wire shielding not very close to grommet sealing service, as tools need clearance

Auxiliary tools needed for broken wired contacts

Broken tips of plastic tools may lodge inside contact pockets, preventing contact insertion or removal

TABLE 2: LIFE COST OF PLASTIC VS. METAL TOOLS

Description	Plastic	Metal
Initial cost (insertion and removal set)	0.55¢	$30
Average tool life (insertions and removals)	100	100,000
Cost / insertion and removal	0.0055¢	0.0003¢

TABLE 3: LIFE COST OF TYPICAL CONNECTORS VS. MATERIAL

Material	Reliable life @ 200°C (hours)	Material cost / lb	Cost / lb / hr
DAP	45	$0.75	$0.0167
GFE	1,500	$1.75	$0.00117
Astrel 360	70,000	$25	$0.00036
Silicone	7,500	$3	$0.0004

Note: All connectors are of similar size and employ front and rear plastic and metal retention systems.

TABLE 4: LIFE COST OF CONNECTORS

Connector design	Reliable life @ 200°C (hours)	Connector cost (mated pair)	Cost/pair/hr	Failure mode
Front release Polymer retention MIL-C-81511	7,500	$55	$0.00734	Rubber
Front release Metal retention MIL-C-26500	1,500	$50	$0.0334	Plastic
Rear release Polymer retention MIL-C-83723	7,500	$30	$0.004	Rubber
Rear release Metal retention MIL-C-83723	1,500	$30	$0.02	Plastic

gether on the decision. Table 1 summarizes the basic points of comparison. More specific application life-cost considerations must be based on the connector materials and the type of insertion-removal tool.

Insertion-removal tools, normally used with removable-crimp contacts, can be either metal or plastic. Life costs of typical tools are compared in Table 2.

Connector life is determined, not by the type of retention system, but by the connector materials. These are basically metal, rubber, and plastic. The latter two rubber or plastic determine the "reliable life" of a connector operating at 200°C. (The reliable life of a plastic ma-

terial is defined as the time required for it to lose 8% of its original weight; the plastic thus loses its strength, and a contact would be pushed out. The reliable life of silicone rubber is defined as the time required for it to lose 50% of its original elongation; the rubber thus loses its ability to seal).

Table 3 summarizes the life cost of materials used in connectors. Table 4 summarizes the life cost of typical connectors of similar size employing front or rear, plastic or metal retention systems. □

A guide to hybrid-circuit component compatibility

by Lyle F. Pittroff
Helipot Division, Beckman Instruments, Fullerton, Calif.

Hybrid microcircuitry offers the potential of accommodating a wide variety of component types and values, but no process can completely avoid restrictions. Realistically, it is sometimes more economical or better design practice to leave certain devices in discrete form outside of the microcircuit package. Heading the list of discrete components that require special consideration are large capacitors, large power transistors and diodes, specially selected or sorted devices, and large inductive parts. Each application imposes a unique combination of economical, electrical, mechanical, and environmental circumstances. Although evaluation of the complete system is always essential, a convenient starting point is a review of the individual components.

Even though conductor patterns and crossovers may not appear subject to consideration for component compatibility, some applications require analyses of their effects on the circuits. Fine-line screening techniques permit very narrow line widths, but Ohm's law prevails—halving the line width doubles the line resistance between two points. Consequently, paths of high current and lines of low impedance may require special layout consideration, and these should be brought to the attention of the manufacturer. High-conductivity materials with line resistivity of less than 0.01 ohm per square are used for these applications.

Screen-printed crossovers may affect the microcircuit design because the bottom conductor forms a small capacitor of typically less than 2 picofarads. Insulating glass between the two conductors has a dielectric constant of approximately 8, and the actual capacitance value depends on the total area of the crossover design. In most applications, crossover location and design can be controlled so that crossover capacitance does not interfere with circuit performance. However, circuits that are sensitive to capacitive coupling between lines should be noted accordingly. In addition to controlling crossover design, critical circuit areas can be guarded by the optimum arrangement of conductor patterns.

Resistors and resistor networks often provide the "value-added" opportunity for the microcircuit manufacturer specializing in thick-film materials and processing. This is analogous to the manufacturer of monolithic ICs who specializes in combining unique semiconductor geometries into a single component. The basic capabilities of thick-film resistors are shown in Table 1.

Evaluating resistors.

The value of the thick-film resistor is determined by the film resistivity specified in ohms per square. Film thickness is not considered a variable during layout design and manufacture. Key parameters are based upon uniformly screen-printing the film to a specified thick-

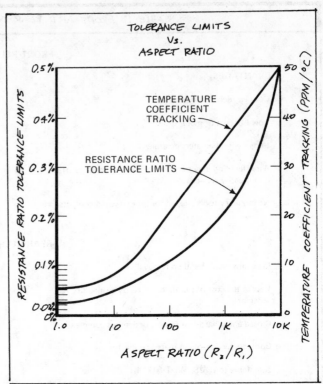

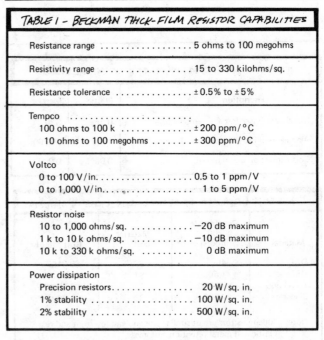

TABLE 1 – BECKMAN THICK-FILM RESISTOR CAPABILITIES

Resistance range	5 ohms to 100 megohms
Resistivity range	15 to 330 kilohms/sq.
Resistance tolerance	±0.5% to ±5%
Tempco	
100 ohms to 100 k	±200 ppm/°C
10 ohms to 100 megohms	±300 ppm/°C
Voltco	
0 to 100 V/in.	0.5 to 1 ppm/V
0 to 1,000 V/in.	1 to 5 ppm/V
Resistor noise	
10 to 1,000 ohms/sq.	−20 dB maximum
1 k to 10 k ohms/sq.	−10 dB maximum
10 k to 330 k ohms/sq.	0 dB maximum
Power dissipation	
Precision resistors	20 W/sq. in.
1% stability	100 W/sq. in.
2% stability	500 W/sq. in.

ness and sheet resistivity. For example, a film material having a resistivity of 1,000 ohms per square may be used to make a 3,300-ohm resistor and a 500-ohm resistor by using length-to-width ratios of 3.3 to 1.0 and 0.5 to 1.0, respectively.

Resistors made of the same film material can provide close temperature tracking and initial ratio adjustment. Practical limits of production tolerance on initial ratio and tracking depend significantly on the aspect ratio between resistors. Although other factors, such as absolute value, resistor proximity to each other, and substrate-area restrictions, affect the tolerance limits, the basic relationship between aspect ratio and tolerance limits

TABLE 2 - BECKMAN CERMET CAPACITOR CAPABILITIES

Capacitance material	12,500 pF/sq. in.
	35,000 pF/sq. in.
	80,000 pF/sq. in.
Capacitance tolerance	
10 pF to 30 pF	±1 pF
30 pF to 2,500 pF	±3%
Capacitance temperature characteristic	(−55°C to +125°C)
12,500 pF/sq. in. material	+ 1.5%
35,000 pF/sq. in. material	+10%, −30%
80,000 pF/sq. in. material	+ 2%, −15%
Power factor	2% maximum
Temperature range	−65°C to +150°C
Insulation resistance	10^9 ohms minimum
Maximum working voltage	50 volts

are shown in Fig. 1.

Generally speaking, the ratio and tracking tolerances shown in the figure are achievable with discrete components only by specifying tighter temperature coefficients and tolerances. Also, choice of resistor values, power ratings, and tolerances for microcircuit applications should be based on circuit requirements instead of the numerical values normally associated with discrete devices. Thick-film resistor tolerances tighter than 0.5% are considered difficult to achieve, and packaging restrictions may further limit initial tolerance.

Capacitor considerations

The most significant consideration for capacitors is physical size, and this is directly related to economics. Screen-printed capacitors consist of screen-printed top and bottom plates and a screen-printed dielectric material. Their characteristics are described in Table 2. The capacitor layout and material considerations allow significant flexibility. The substrate area and packaging constraints normally set the upper value limit. Chip capacitors are available in many shapes and sizes, and size is related to the product of the capacitance and voltage rating. Capacitor values to 0.1 μF and voltage ratings to 200 v are usually compatible with economic considerations and packaging constraints. Commonly used chip capacitors utilize NPO and K1200 dielectric. Note that NPO and K1200 chips differ considerably in capacitance per unit volume. For example, a 2,200-pF NPO chip and a 0.047-pF K1200 chip have about the same dimensions. Tantalum chips allow significantly higher capacitance values but also are larger and cost more.

Hybrid microcircuitry encourages great design flexibility in that nearly any combination of smaller-signal active devices, bipolar, logic or linear ICs, and MOS ICs can be combined on the same hybrid substrate. Virtually all passivated semiconductor dice are process-compatible with standard die-mount and wire-bonding techniques. The significant differences between a packaged semiconductor device and the chip version are the criteria for testing and selection.

A key consideration in the conversion to a hybrid design is to determine what parameters the manufacturer will be able to buy in chip form on a production basis. Semiconductor dice are available at a reasonable cost when purchased to dc wafer-probed parameters. Custom-probe testing specifications will have a definite effect on cost and lead time, although this approach is commonly used where breakdown voltage, leakage current, or offset voltage is critical to circuit performance.

The hybrid manufacturer's task, beginning at the inquiry stage, is to evaluate the economies of either specially testing or lot-qualifying semiconductor devices. In some cases, it is far more economical to sample an incoming lot of devices for temperature or ac parameters than to take the yield on the finished hybrids, which have all of the manufacturing cost inputs expended.

Although every rule has an exception, these guidelines should be considered early in the design phase:

- Diode reverse-voltage ratings below 200 v are available in chip form.
- Operational-amplifier offset voltage drift of ±10 v/°C can be guaranteed without special testing.
- Temperature-compensated zeners better than ±50 ppm/°C may have to remain outwide the package.
- Average power dissipation in a single transistor greater than 1 W may require special consideration.

Passivated semiconductor dice are available from most semiconductor manufacturers in a variety of forms. Dice are most commonly shipped after they have been probe-tested, dotted, scribed, and broken from the original wafers. Depending on the type of chip, the individual chips may be shipped in waffle carriers or in vials of 5,000 or more. Most hybrid manufacturers usually stock numerous chip devices in substantial quantities. □

Bistable action of 555 varies with manufacturer

by Robert W. Bockstahler
General Dynamics Corp., Pomona, Calif.

The 555 integrated circuit, which has myriad uses as a timer and oscillator, can also function as a bistable flip-flop in such applications as TTL-compatible drivers for displays or latch elements for burglar alarms. This flip-flop operates from many different supply voltages, uses little power, and requires no external components other than bypass capacitors in noisy environments.

Pin 2 (the trigger pin of the 555) is an active-low SET function. Pin 4 (the reset of the 555) serves as an active-low RESET, and pin 6 (threshold) as an active-high RESET. Both the RESETs can be used, or just one, with the other connected in its inactive state. The table shows how the output responds to various input signals.

It is important to know the detailed characteristics of the particular 555 used as a bistable element because the circuitry differs from manufacturer to manufacturer, and certain functions, therefore, interact differently. The table points out, for example, that the threshold overrides the trigger on the LM555H, but the trigger overrides the threshold on the NE555V. □

| INPUTS | | | OUTPUT | |
PIN 4 (RESET) (ACTIVE-LOW)	PIN 6 (THRESHOLD) (ACTIVE-HIGH)	PIN 2 (TRIGGER) (ACTIVE-LOW)	NATIONAL LM555H	SIGNETICS NE555V
⊔	0	1	RESETS (⌐_)	RESETS (⌐_)
⊔	1	1	0	0
⊔	0	0	⊔	⊔
⊔	1	0	0	⊔
1	⊓	1	RESETS	RESETS
1	⊓	0	⊔	1
0	⊓	1	0	0
0	⊓	0	0	0
1	0	⊔	SETS (_⌐)	SETS (_⌐)
1	1	⊔	0	⊓
0	0	⊔	0	0
0	1	⊔	0	0

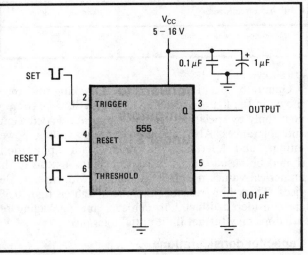

Bistable operation. A 555 timer can be used as a set/reset flip-flop, with pin 2 as the active-low SET input. Pin 4 can be used as active-low RESET input, with pin 6 inactive (i.e., low), or pin 6 can be used as active-high RESET input, with pin 4 inactive (high); in the latter case, an LM555H performs somewhat differently from an NE555V. Flip-flop operation with both pin 4 and pin 6 as control inputs is also possible; for example, pin 4 might be the RESET and pin 6 a power-on CLEAR.

4. Adjusting component values

Accurately trimming closed resistor loops

by R. M. Stitt
Burr-Brown Research Corp., Tucson, Ariz.

Adjusting or tuning circuits could often be considerably simplified if resistors that are connected in a closed loop could be measured and trimmed to the desired value. This is particularly true for thick-film-resistor layouts, which could be significantly improved if the right adjustments could be made.

A circuit that allows measurement and trimming of closed resistor loops is shown in the figure. (The closed resistor loop formed by resistors R_1, R_2, and R_3 is highlighted.) The circuit provides a metered readout, as well as two light-emitting diodes for visual indication of both positive and negative deviations from the desired resistance value.

With the connections shown, resistor R_2 is the segment of the loop to be measured. Resistor R_2 is placed in the negative-feedback loop of amplifier A_2, and all of the external nodes of this amplifier are grounded. Therefore, whatever current in injected into A_2's inverting input must flow through resistor R_2 and must appear at A_2's output as a negative voltage that is equal to the input current times the resistor value. If the input current is –1 milliampere, then A_2's output voltage will be equivalent to the value of resistor R_2 in kilohms.

Resistor R_3 simply acts as the load resistance of amplifier A_2. On the other hand, resistor R_1 acts as a summing resistor that is tied to ground, but it makes no contribution to A_2's output voltage. Since there is no voltage drop across this resistor, no current flows through it.

The network consisting of amplifier A_1, zener diode D_Z, and resistors R_4, R_5, and R_6 forms a voltage reference for amplifier A_2. To assure optimum performance, the zener regulates its own operating current. Amplifier A_3 is connected as a summing amplifier with a milliammeter in its feedback loop, and amplifier A_4 performs as a comparator (with hysteresis so that the LEDs are both dark when a null is reached).

When resistor R_2 is equal to the desired resistance value, that of the standard resistor (R_{STD}), the output voltage of amplifier A_2 will equal $-V_{REF}$, and no current will flow through the meter. Because the meter is connected inside a full-wave bridge, it will indicate both positive and negative deviations from the null point as positive deflections. And since a regulated current flows in the feedback loop of amplifier A_3, any voltage drops across the bridge diodes will not affect the meter's reading.

Amplifier A_4, the comparator, drives the LEDs so that they indicate whether the deviation from the null is positive or negative. Its output current (10 milliamperes) is adequate to drive the LEDs directly. The LEDs clamp each other, preventing their rather low reverse breakdown voltage ratings from being exceeded.

There are a few restrictions to keep in mind about the circuit. Amplifier A_2, for instance, must be capable of driving the load formed by the closed loop, and its input impedance must be high enough for measuring the value of resistor R_2 accurately. For a more sensitive null indication, the values of summing resistors R_7 and R_8

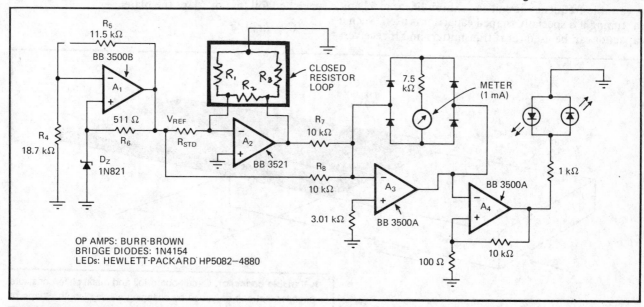

Trimming circuit. Individual resistors in closed resistor loop (R_1, R_2, and R_3) can be trimmed to desired value (R_{STD}). The resistor to be trimmed (R_2 in this case) is placed in the negative-feedback loop of amplifier A_2. When $R_2 = R_{STD}$, the milliammeter indicates a null, and both light-emitting diodes are dark. The LEDs show whether R_2's resistance deviation is positive or negative with respect to the null.

can be made smaller. But since the output-current ratings of amplifiers A_1 and A_2 must be observed, a more sensitive meter is required if the circuit's sensitivity is to be increased significantly.

Furthermore, the output-current rating of amplifier A_1 must be considered when resistor R_{STD} is chosen. If low-value resistors are to be trimmed, the magnitude of V_{REF} must be reduced to avoid overloading amplifier A_1. An inverting amplifier with a gain of less than unity could be inserted at the output of A_1. □

Pc board forms custom variable capacitor

by Robert L. Taylor
I & F Electronics, Nashville, Tenn.

A variable-frequency circuit can exhibit linear mechanical tuning if a specially shaped capacitor is used. Such a capacitor can be used for rf transmitters and rf receivers that have linear slide dials, for position transducers that have direct read-out on a frequency counter, and for many other applications.

One of the simplest capacitor configurations is a metal plate sliding under a printed-circuit board that has been etched to give the desired variation of capacitance (C) with overlap distance (x), as shown in Fig. 1. The capacitance depends upon the dielectric constant and thickness of the board and upon the area of unetched foil that overlaps the plate:

$$C = k\varepsilon_o A/d$$

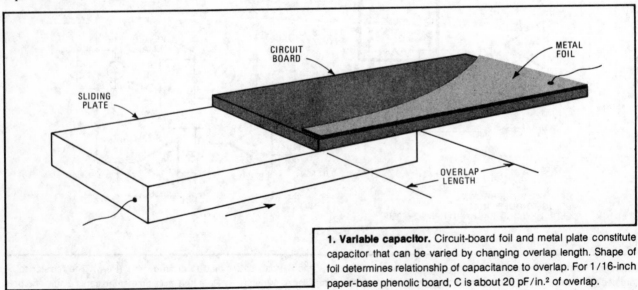

1. Variable capacitor. Circuit-board foil and metal plate constitute capacitor that can be varied by changing overlap length. Shape of foil determines relationship of capacitance to overlap. For 1/16-inch paper-base phenolic board, C is about 20 pF/in.² of overlap.

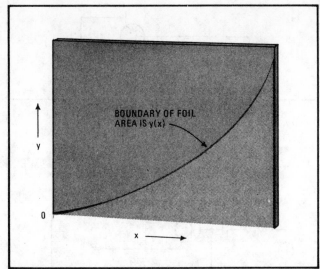

2. Etched board. Foil can have any pattern, to provide any increasing function of capacitance with overlap distance (x). For convenience in analysis, foil shown here covers area from y = 0 to y = y(x). Therefore overlap area is integral of y(x).

where k is the dielectric constant, ε_o is 8.85×10^{-12}, A is the overlap area, and d is the board thickness (all quantities expressed in MKS units). For a typical 1/16-inch paper-base phenolic board, C is about 20 picofarads per square inch.

The overlap area, A, is a function of the shape of the foil pattern on the board (Fig. 2)

$$A = \int y(x)\,dx$$

and therefore the capacitance is related to the pattern by

$$C(x) = (k\varepsilon_o/d)\int_0^x y(\xi)\,d\xi$$

If the foil area is to be shaped so that the resonant frequency of an LC tank circuit changes linearly with the overlap length, as represented graphically in Fig. 3, then

$$f = \tfrac{1}{2}\pi(LC)^{1/2} = -mx + b$$
$$= -(f_{max} - f_{min})x/s + f_{max}$$

or

$$C = M/(H - x/s)^2$$

where

s = the maximum overlap length, corresponding to resonant frequency f_{min} in Fig. 3
L = the inductance in the tank circuit,
$H = 1/(1 - f_{min}/f_{max})$
$M = 1/[4\pi^2 L(f_{max} - f_{min})^2]$

To obtain the oscillation frequency f_{max} when the overlap is zero, a fixed capacitor must be placed in parallel with the variable one. The value of this capacitance is M/H^2, and therefore the variable capacitance must be reduced by this amount. That is,

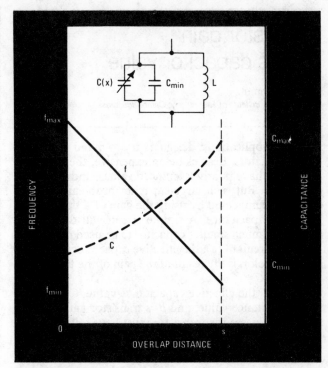

3. Linear tuning. To make resonant frequency of LC tank circuit change linearly with overlap, foil needs shape defined in text.

$$C(x) = M/(H - x/s)^2 - M/H^2$$

The foil shape that produces this capacitance relation is found from

$$C(x) = (k\varepsilon_o/d)\int_0^x y(\xi)\,d\xi$$

or

$$y(x) = (d/k\varepsilon_o)\,C'(x)$$

where C'(x) is the derivative of C with respect to x. Thus the desired foil pattern is

$$y(x) = 2Md/k\varepsilon_o s(H - x/s)^3$$

As an example, suppose the resonant frequency of a 1-microhenry tank circuit is to vary linearly from 40 to 20 MHz when the overlap changes from zero to 5 inches. In this case
f_{max} = 40 MHz
f_{min} = 20 MHz
L = 10^{-6} H
s = 5 in.
These values yield
M = 63 pF
H = 2
$C(x) = 63/(2 - x/5)^2 - 15.8$ pF
$y(x) = 1.3/(2 - x/5)^3$ in.
where x is expressed in inches, and 1/16-in. paper-base phenolic circuit board is used.

Other foil shapes can be devised to provide other capacitance-variation relationships. The function y(x) is found from the derivative of C(x). Properly constructed, these capacitors have excellent mechanical stability and fair temperature stability. □

Transistor gain boosts capacitor value

by L. E. Schmutz
Massachusetts Institute of Technology, Cambridge, Mass.

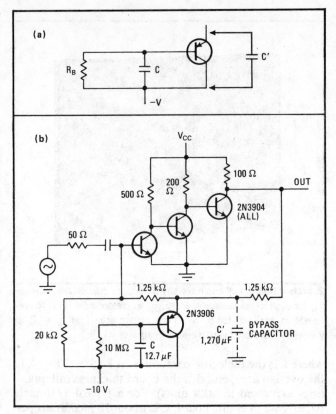

Capacitance multiplier. A large effective capacitance (C') can be obtained from a small capacitor (C) by using transistor gain to multiply the actual capacitance value, as shown in (a). The technique is especially convenient in reducing the size of the bypass capacitor in a cascaded emitter-coupled amplifier (b). Here, the capacitance needed is decreased by a factor of 100—from 1,270 to 12.7 µF.

In many applications, designers try to avoid specifying large capacitors. Besides being expensive, they are usually leaky, have poorly toleranced values, and are physically large. But such large-capacitor problems as these can be circumvented by using the gain of a transistor to multiply capacitance. A simple circuit will do the job, allowing a much smaller capacitor to be used instead.

In the circuit of (a), the effective capacitance, which is shown in color, is the result of the gain of the transistor:

$$C' = \beta C$$

where C' is the effective capacitance value, C is the actual capacitance value, and β is transistor gain. The resistor that biases the transistor must have a large value, since its actual resistance is divided by the gain of the transistor.

$$R_B' = R_B/\beta$$

where R_B' is the effective resistance value, and R_B is the actual resistance value. (The effective resistance caused by capacitor leakage is also decreased by transistor gain.)

This capacitance-multiplier circuit is particularly useful in reducing the size of the bypass capacitor in a feedback-stabilized cascaded amplifier, like the one drawn in (b). Cascaded emitter-coupled amplifiers are widely used in applications requiring high ac gain and good frequency response. However, they normally require elaborate biasing schemes to compensate for the lack of gain uniformity between discrete transistors.

Sometimes, a direct-coupled cascade is employed so that dc feedback can be used to stabilize the bias for the transistors. Capacitor C' then bypasses the ac component to ground, maintaining the amplifier's large signal gain. But, with this approach, the resistance seen by capacitor C' is reduced by the gain of the amplifier, making it necessary for C' to be very large to achieve ordinary low-frequency break points.

If the low-end half-power point of circuit (b) will be 10 hertz, the value of capacitor C' climbs to a whopping 1,270 microfarads. But when the simple capacitance multiplier of (a) is used instead, the value of the bypass capacitor (C) can be cut down to 12.7 µF, a 100-fold reduction. □

5. Displaying LED versatility

A fail-safe font of seven-segment digits

by Brian Astle
Optel Corp., Princeton, N.J.

The trouble with most popular seven-segment display fonts is that a failure in a single segment may transform one digit into another. For example, if one segment sticks at "off," a 7 could be interpreted as a 1, or if it sticks at "on," a 0 could appear as an 8. Here is an idea for a font, which, although it has not been widely tested and would require some operator training, is fail-safe and can even be extended to mathematical symbols.

In the odd-parity font, shown in Fig. 1c, each digit contains an odd number of segments and so has odd parity. Thus if one segment either goes off or comes on, the error will be immediately recognized (the common font has both odd and even parity).

In this new font, the formats for digits 0, 1, and 4 require learning. The symbol for zero was made to resemble an imperfectly closed script zero. This is not likely to be confused with any other numeral, and offers an alternative to the slashed zero now used to distinguish zero from the letter O. The symbol representing one was chosen as the full symbol 1, with the upper left and lower right strokes deleted. Note that the symbol has full height and width, an aesthetic advantage not enjoyed by the common font one. The symbol representing four was derived from the common font symbol by deleting segment B.

The concept also can be extended to mathematical symbols. There are 64 odd-parity seven-segment symbols, 22 of which are shown in Fig. 2. The decimal-point symbol was chosen to be readily distinguishable from the minus symbol and to be similar to the European notation. The symbol for a power is similar to the vertical arrow symbol, and also suggests the conventional positional notation.

The symbol for multiplication, which is needed to represent floating-point numbers, was chosen arbitrarily. Bases other than 10 are indicated by symbols that precede the base numbers. The symbols for 10 and 11 provide the extra two symbols needed for counting in base 12. The symbol for 10 also is useful in representing floating-point decimal numbers.

Complex numbers require the symbols representing

	FONT	SEGMENTS USED	FONT	SEGMENTS USED
	0	A B C D E F	0	A B C D E
	1	B C	1	B C D
	2	A B D E G	2	A B D E G
	3	A B C D G	3	A B C D G
	4	B C F G	4	C F G
	5	A C D F G	5	A C D F G
	6	A C D E F G	6	C D E F G
	7	A B C	7	A B C
	8	A B C D E F G	8	A B C D E F G
	9	A B C D F G	9	A B C F G

(a) (b) (c)

1. Failure in one segment of seven-segment display (a) could produce misinterpreted digits with the font presently used (b). Proposed odd-parity font (c), though it requires relearning, displays meaningless character when one segment fails.

addition, subtraction, and the square root of –1. It is sometimes desirable to represent complex numbers in $r\theta$ coordinates, and a symbol for the complex plane angle is reserved to denote the use of these coordinates. When this symbol appears between two numbers, the first number represents the distance from the origin. The second number represents the angle in degrees, unless it is followed by the symbol for radians.

To complete the set of commonly used symbols, those for divide and for equal have been included, although they are not strictly necessary for number representation. Certain important numbers such as π and ε are worthy of representation and are also included.

The author has compiled an additional list of symbols for some of the more common functions, which he will make available to those who are interested. □

SYMBOL	CONVENTIONAL REPRESENTATION	ODD-PARITY, SEVEN-SEGMENT REPRESENTATION	
MINUS	–	—	G
DECIMAL POINT	. or ,	∣	C
EXPONENTIAL	Positional	⌈	A E F
TIMES	X	⊔	C D E
BASES OTHER THAN 10	Positional	L	D E F
TEN	10	⊡	A C D E G
ELEVEN	11	'I	B C F
PLUS	+	⊣	B C G
SQUARE ROOT OF –1	$\sqrt{-1}$ or j	⊐	A C D
COMPLEX PLANE ANGLE	$\angle$	⊓	A B F
DEGREES	°	⊐	A B G
RADIANS	rad	⊢	E F G
LESS THAN	<	⊏	D E G
LESS THAN OR EQUALS	⩽	⊑	D F G
GREATER THAN	>	⊐	C D G
GREATER THAN OR EQUALS	⩾	⊒	B D G
PLUS OR MINUS	±	⊡	A B D F G
APPROXIMATELY	~	d	B C D E G
DIVIDE	/ or ÷	⌐	B E G
EQUALS	=	≡	A D G
Pi	π	⊓	A B C E F
BASE OF NATURAL LOGARITHMS	e	E	A D E F G

2. Mathematical symbols can be represented in odd-parity, seven-segment font for use in more complex displays.

LEDs watch for overvoltages

by Don DeKold
Santa Fe Community College, Gainesville, Fla.

A pair of light-emitting diodes, along with a pair of zener diodes, can serve as a simple visual voltage monitor. For instance, if the two LED/zener combinations are placed at the output of an operational amplifier, they will indicate when the magnitude of the op amp's voltage exceeds a certain maximum, and whether this overvoltage is positive or negative.

For the circuit shown, LED-1 lights if the op amp's

Voltage monitor. Light-emitting diodes glow when op amp output voltage exceeds a maximum level, 15.5 volts dc in this case. For a positive overvoltage, LED-1 lights; for a negative overvoltage, LED-2 lights. Both LEDs light for an ac output of more than 31 V pk-pk.

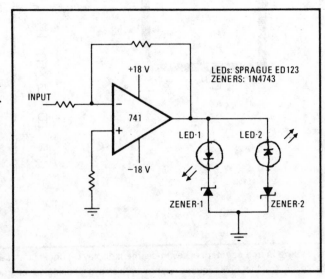

LEDs: SPRAGUE ED123
ZENERS: 1N4743

output is greater than +15.5 volts dc; about 13.9 V is dropped across zener-1 and about 1.65 V across forward-biased LED-1. In this case, LED-2 is back-biased, and no current flows through it or through zener-2. LED-2 lights for an op amp output of −15.5 V dc, while LED-1 is back-biased and remains dark.

The internal short-circuit current limiting of the op amp prevents the current flow through either forward-biased LED from exceeding 18 to 20 milliamperes. This current level allows the LEDs to glow brightly enough for you to see them easily in a well-lit room.

For an ac output signal, both LEDs will light on alternate half cycles when the signal level is more than 31 V peak-to-peak. If the signal frequency is fast enough, each LED will appear to be lighted continuously. When a pair of well-matched zener diodes is used, this feature lets you detect the op amp's output offset voltage without a voltmeter. By noting which LED lights first when the level of the amplified signal is increased, you can deduce the presence of an offset voltage as well as its polarity.

The diode loading across the op amp's output also serves to limit voltage to the maximum 15.5-V level, but it does not affect signal voltages that are less than this amplitude. □

Different-color LEDs can switch each other

by F. Gerard Albers
University of Dayton, Dayton, Ohio

The inequality of threshold voltages of light-emitting diodes of differing colors can be used to minimize the circuitry needed for a display, especially if the application is not a critical one. The voltage drop across a LED that is conducting, therefore, can control another LED of a different color.

In the two-color display of (a), the green LED will light when the switch is open. But when the switch is closed, the red LED lights, producing a voltage drop of approximately 1.5 V, which is slightly below the threshold of the green LED. This lamp, then, goes out.

The concept can be expanded to multiple-unit displays, as in (b). The red LED, which is controlled by gate G_1, will disable the yellow and green LEDs when it is illuminated. If the red LED is not conducting, the display depends on the output of gate G_2.

When G_2's output is low, the yellow LED will conduct, producing approximately a 2.0-V drop at the resistor node. The green LED remains disabled because its threshold is now approximately 2.1 V because of diode D_1. When G_2's output is high, the yellow LED turns off and the green LED turns on.

The luminous intensity of such a display is quite acceptable, even in a well-lit room. And the difference in luminous intensity between the three LEDs is negligible. The 500-ohm resistor limits gate current and establishes the proper voltage drops for the LEDs □

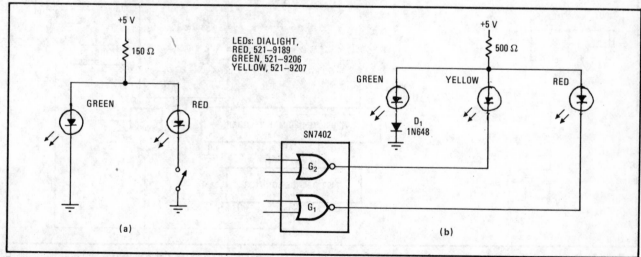

Paring display circuitry to a minimum. The different threshold voltages of LEDs of differing colors can be used to select the colors in a display. For the two-color display of (a), only the green LED conducts when the switch is open, and only the red LED conducts when the switch is closed. Similarly, a three-color display (b) can be obtained by employing two switches (gates G_1 and G_2) and a diode (D_1).

LEDs replace CRT in solid-state scope

by Forrest M. Mims, III
Albuquerque, N. M.

Thanks to the availability of low-cost light-emitting diodes, an all-solid-state oscilloscope can now be assembled. Figure 1 is the circuit diagram for a prototype that replaces the conventional CRT with a 10-by-10 array of GaAsP red LEDs. Although resolution of the 100-element screen is poor, pulses, square waves, triangle waves, and ramps are easily identifiable.

Input signals to the scope are ac- or dc-coupled to a 536 FET-input operational amplifier. The op amp is connected directly to 10 vertical columns of LEDs in series. The LEDs in each column are paired with individual resistors connected in series to form a voltage divider. The result is that each column of LEDs is a voltage sensor with a bar-graph-style readout.

The 10 LED columns are sequentially scanned by a sweep circuit composed of a 555 clock, a 7490 decade counter, and a 7441 one-of-10 decoder. A single NAND gate provides an optional automatic trigger feature for synchronizing the sweep with incoming waveforms from the op amp.

A pocket-sized version of the scope, measuring 4 by 6 by 13 centimeters, has front-panel controls that include vertical voltage sensitivity, horizontal time sweep, trigger, ac-dc, and power. The voltage sensitivity is adjustable from 0.01 volt per division to 1.0 V/division, where each LED is a division. The sweep is adjustable from 20 microseconds/division to 1.0 second/division. The amplifier and sweep circuits consume a maximum of 54 milliwatts, and the display consumes a maximum of 308 mW when all of the LEDs are on.

Figure 2 is a photograph of the scope's LED screen. The prototype scope shows only half of a bipolar waveform, and the input connections must be reversed to view the other half. □

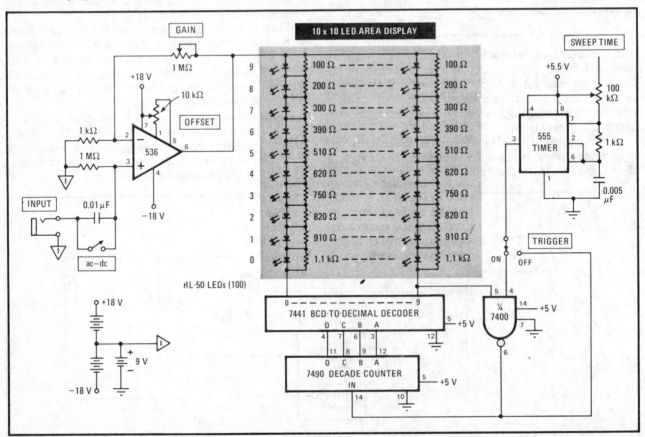

1. Solid-state scope. Waveforms are displayed on 10-by-10 array of LEDs in this scope. Incoming signal is amplified and applied to all 10 columns of LEDs, and decoder completes circuit through each column in sequence to provide scanning. Display shows only the positive half of an ac waveform. The pattern is like a bar graph in that all lights below top of waveform are lighted; thus in a ramp, the bottom two LEDs might be lit in the first column, the bottom three LEDs in the second column, the bottom four in the next column, and so forth.

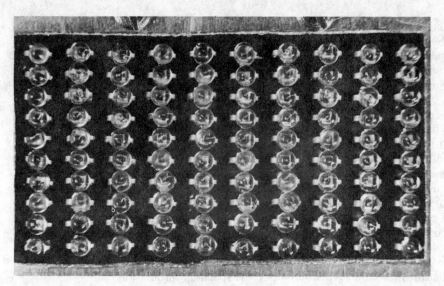

2. LED array. Light-emitting diodes are mounted on perforated board painted black to provide good contrast. Holes in board are 0.1 inch apart, so 10-by-10 array occupies area of approximately 1 by 2 in. Resistors for voltage divider are mounted right behind the LEDs, allowing compact packaging. A second board of similar size, stacked behind the LED board, holds the amplifier and scanning circuitry. Entire scope, including batteries, is about the size of a pocket calculator. Author built prototype for less than $40.

Large hexadecimal display is legible from afar

by A. J. Bryant
Manelco Electronics Ltd., Winnipeg, Manitoba

Better visibility and a wider range of alphanumeric characters result when the seven segments standard in light-emitting-diode displays are made up of two LEDs each and multiplexed with six other LEDs. The arrangement of 20 discrete LEDs described here provides 1.5-inch numerals and letters that can be read from 30 feet away with clear distinction between such "twins" as 0 and D.

The display can be particularly useful in microprocessor applications in process and machine controllers, where hexadecimal numbers representing steps or parameters must be clearly visible from distances of 10 feet or more. Commercial displays do not meet this need. The numbers 0–9 plus the letters A–F represent

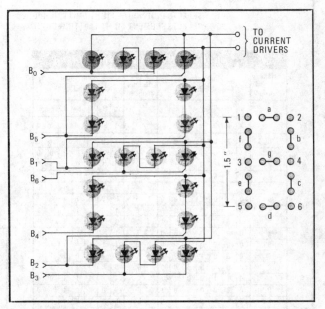

1. Really big show. Twenty light-emitting diodes arranged in a ⅞-by-1½-inch array display any symbol in the hexadecimal number system. This display can be read at distances as great as 30 feet.

41

the quantities 0–15 in hexadecimal notation.

Figure 1 shows the 20 LEDs in a 4-by-7 array. There are seven segments made up of two diodes in series and six individual diodes; the two-diode segments are labeled a, b, . . . g, as in any seven-segment display, and the six individual diodes are labeled 1, 2, . . . 6. The 13 different current paths that these segments and individual diodes provide are controlled by the outputs of a read-only memory and an on/off multiplexing voltage. So only two current drivers are required.

When a character is displayed, the multiplexing voltage causes the appropriate segments and then the appropriate individual diodes to light, but they go on and off so quickly that they appear to be on continuously.

Figure 2 shows the display-circuit arrangement and the program of the ROM. If the symbol B is to be displayed, then all of the segment LEDs and individual diodes 1, 3, and 5 must light. The program shows that for the letter B, all of the segments are 0s (low voltage). When the on/off multiplexing signal is 0, the inverter puts high voltage on the segments and they all light.

When the multiplexing signal is a 1, high voltage is applied to all of the individual diodes. The cathodes of 1, 3, and 5 have been grounded by the ROM, so those diodes light up; but the cathodes of 2, 4, and 6 are held high, so they do not light.

For representation of the hex B, the binary ROM inputs to A_3, A_2, A_1, and A_0 are 1011, and A_4 is 0 for the segments and 1 for the individual diodes. Thus the memory chip is programed so that input 01011 produces outputs 0000000 on B_6 . . . B_0, and input 11011 produces 1111000. Note that output B_7 is not used.

To provide a more even distribution of light in the multiplex mode, different current drivers can be used for the segment line and for the line to the individual diodes, or the duty cycle of the on/off signal can be changed. Most available ROMs can sink the current required by the LEDs, but a buffer may be required, depending upon the specific combination. □

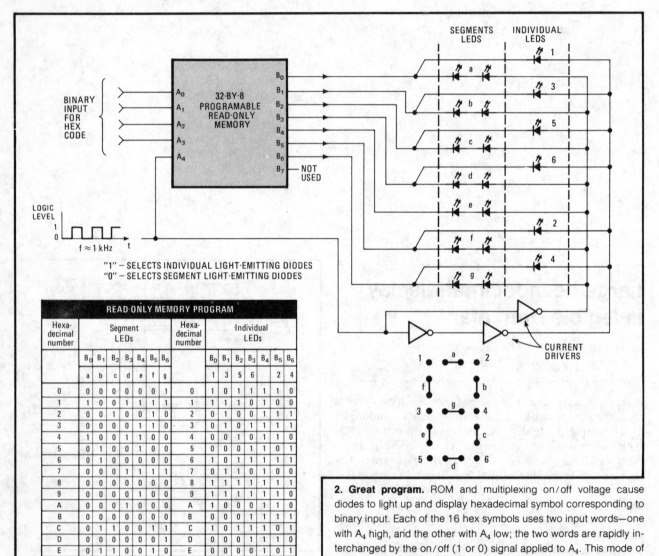

"1" – SELECTS INDIVIDUAL LIGHT-EMITTING DIODES
"0" – SELECTS SEGMENT LIGHT-EMITTING DIODES

READ-ONLY MEMORY PROGRAM															
Hexa-decimal number	Segment LEDs							Hexa-decimal number	Individual LEDs						
	B_0	B_1	B_2	B_3	B_4	B_5	B_6		B_0	B_1	B_2	B_3	B_4	B_5	B_6
	a	b	c	d	e	f	g		1	3	5	6		2	4
0	0	0	0	0	0	0	1	0	1	0	1	1	1	1	0
1	1	0	0	1	1	1	1	1	1	1	1	0	1	0	0
2	0	0	1	0	0	1	0	2	0	1	0	0	1	1	1
3	0	0	0	0	1	1	0	3	0	1	1	1	1	1	1
4	1	0	0	1	1	0	0	4	0	0	1	0	1	1	0
5	0	1	0	0	1	0	0	5	0	0	0	1	1	0	1
6	0	1	0	0	0	0	0	6	1	0	1	1	1	1	1
7	0	0	0	1	1	1	1	7	0	1	1	0	1	0	0
8	0	0	0	0	0	0	0	8	1	1	1	1	1	1	1
9	0	0	0	0	1	0	0	9	1	1	1	1	1	1	0
A	0	0	0	1	0	0	0	A	1	0	0	0	1	1	0
B	0	0	0	0	0	0	0	B	0	0	0	1	1	1	1
C	0	1	1	0	0	1	1	C	1	0	1	1	1	0	1
D	0	0	0	0	0	1	0	D	0	0	1	1	1	1	1
E	0	1	1	0	0	1	0	E	0	0	0	0	1	0	1
F	0	1	1	1	0	1	0	F	0	0	0	1	1	0	1

2. Great program. ROM and multiplexing on/off voltage cause diodes to light up and display hexadecimal symbol corresponding to binary input. Each of the 16 hex symbols uses two input words—one with A_4 high, and the other with A_4 low; the two words are rapidly interchanged by the on/off (1 or 0) signal applied to A_4. This mode of operation uses the full capability of the 32-word ROM. Any compatible ROM, driver, and LED can be used; with TTL, for example, a Signetics 8223 PROM and 5-volt signals do the job.

Built-in LED display decoder simplifies digital-clock logic

by James Blackburn
University of Western Ontario, London, Ont., Canada

Many solid-state readouts are supplied with their own built-in decoders, which can simplify the logic needed to produce a blanked display. For example, the Hewlett-Packard Co. type 5082-7300 numeric light-emitting-diode indicator accepts four-line (1, 2, 4, 8) binary-coded-decimal logic inputs. An input of 1000 generates a "1" display, while the complement of this signal (0111) results in a blank display. Therefore, the Q and $\bar{Q}$ outputs of a flip-flop can cause H-P's LED display to show either a 1 or blank.

This property is particularly useful in simplifying the logic required for a digital clock to make the transition from 12:59 to 1:00. Obviously, 13:00 must be inhibited in favor of a reset to 1:00. Since modulo-10 counters have integral reset-to-zero functions, the least-significant digit of the hours display must be reset to 1 indirectly. Additionally, the hours' most-significant digit must be blanked, causing the clock display to be 1:00.

Because of the display's built-in decoder, the desired reset-to-1 operation can be accomplished with only five dual-input NAND gates and one J-K flip-flop. The flip-flop drives the most-significant digit of the hours display.

When the time is 12:59, the flip-flop is in the 1 state, and the decade counter's A and B outputs are high while its BD_i, C, and D terminals are low. At the end of the next minute, a negative transition occurs at the counter's A_i input. Its A output then goes low and is inverted by gate G_1, causing input BD_i to go high so that the display reading should be 13:00.

Both inputs to gate G_2 are now high, producing a low at its output, which is inverted by gate G_3. The two inputs to gate G_4 then go high, causing the flip-flop to reset to the 0 state and the decade counter to reset to zero. This generates a blank at the most-significant digit of the hours display, and, because of the inversion at gate G_1, all is generated at the least-significant hours digit. The clock display now shows 1:00 as the time.

The transition from 13:00 to 1:00 occurs so quickly that the clock display indicates only a transition from 12:59 to 1:00. ⌐

Digital clock display. Because of its built-in decoder, Hewlett-Packard's solid-state readout reduces the logic required to blank a clock's display when making the transition from 12:59 to 1:00. The complement of the signal that blanks the readout produces a 1.

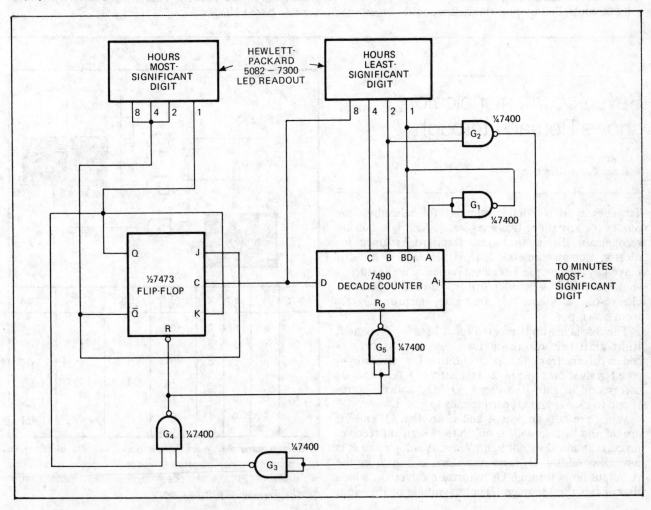

Driving LEDs directly from C-MOS logic outputs

by C.D. Patterson
Gandalf Data Communications Ltd., Ottawa, Ont., Canada

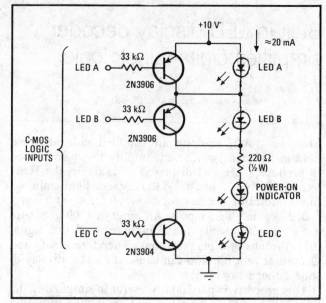

If a complementary-MOS logic system requires a number of light-emitting diodes in its display, the power dissipated in the display may be far more than that for all the rest of the circuitry.

To get a nice bright display, each LED should receive more than 15 milliamperes of current. If the requirement is for, say, four LEDs, then something like 60 mA must be provided by the supply. In addition, each LED must be driven from a high-current C-MOS inverter, such as a 14019 device wired as a current sink.

One way to cut down on current consumption is to connect all the LEDs in series in a 20-mA current chain, as shown in the figure. Each LED can then be controlled by shorting it out with a transistor.

A pnp transistor will allow a LED to turn on for positive C-MOS levels, while an npn transistor will allow a LED to turn on for negative C-MOS levels. Also, since the transistor can be operated with less than 0.3 mA of base current, normal C-MOS logic outputs can provide sufficient current for driving the LEDs.

LEDs controlled by pnp transistors should be inserted

Current-saving design. Inserting a bipolar transistor between a C-MOS logic output and a LED indicator permits the C-MOS logic device to control the LED. The current supplied by the C-MOS logic-level output is sufficient to turn on the transistor, which, in turn, causes the LED to go out. A pnp transistor is used for positive logic signals, and an npn transistor for negative logic signals.

at the top of the chain, and those controlled by npn transistors at the bottom. This avoids excessive reverse emitter-base voltages. □

Seven-segment indicator shows Roman I through V

by Yehia Hussein
Television Studios, Cairo, Egypt

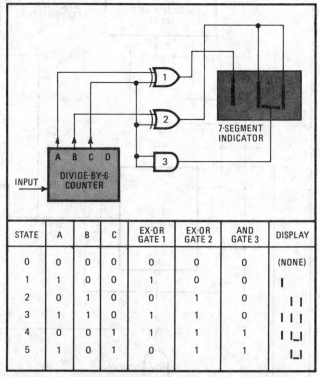

To get away from ordinary numerals for indicating time modes (or any other five-level state), here is a quickly recognizable display that uses a standard 7-segment indicator. Roman numerals I, II, III, IV, and V are displayed by turning the 7-segment indicator on its side, as shown in Fig. 1. A decoder/driver, consisting of two exclusive-OR gates and one AND gate, operates directly from BCD inputs.

The display is implemented for a MAN-4 7-segment light-emitting diode, driven by transistor decoder/drivers from the BCD output of a divide-by-6 counter, as shown in Fig. 2. Transistors Q_1, Q_2, and Q_6 correspond to gate 1 in Fig. 1; Q_4, Q_5, and Q_7 correspond to gate 2; and Q_3 corresponds to gate 3.

When the BCD outputs A and C are low, Q_1 and Q_2 are off and therefore Q_6 is off, so the I segment receives no current and does not light. When A is high and C is low, Q_2 is off, but Q_1 is on; therefore, current from the A output flows through Q_1 to turn on driver Q_6, which illuminates the I segment. The magnitude of the input

STATE	A	B	C	EX-OR GATE 1	EX-OR GATE 2	AND GATE 3	DISPLAY
0	0	0	0	0	0	0	(NONE)
1	1	0	0	1	0	0	I
2	0	1	0	0	1	0	I I
3	1	1	0	1	1	0	I I I
4	0	0	1	1	1	1	I ⌐
5	1	0	1	0	1	1	⌐

1. Roman numerals. Seven-segment display element, turned on its side, provides Roman numerals I through V. Indicator is driven by two exclusive-OR gates and one AND gate, which operate directly from BCD outputs of a digital counter.

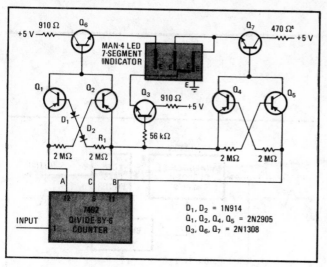

2. Circuit. Implementation of Roman-numeral indicator uses three transistors for each exclusive-OR gate and a single transistor for the AND gate. BCD data comes from divide-by-six IC. Display element is a 7-segment LED device. This novel display mode is useful for any system or situation with up to five levels or periods, such as gear positions, soccer quarters, elevator stops, and the like.

current to the driver is determined by resistor R_1. If C is high and A is low, Q_2 conducts, and again the l segment glows. When both A and C are high, Q_1 and Q_2 are both off; diodes D_1 and D_2 ensure the performance of this exclusive-OR, even when the A and C highs are unequal because of current being drawn from C to the other transistors.

The exclusive-OR gate of Q_4, Q_5, and Q_7 operates in a similar manner to illuminate the l l segments, but diodes are not needed because B and C are never high simultaneously (see truth table in Fig. 1).

The AND gate, transistor Q_3, is a direct-drive circuit that lights up the horizontal bar to convert l l to l_l, which approximates Roman numeral V. □

Light-emitting diode doubles as sensor

by Thomas T. Yen
Statham Instruments Inc., Oxnard, Calif.

A seldom recognized property of many light-emitting diodes is that, in addition to emitting light when forward-biased, they can also detect light when reverse-biased. This emitter/sensor property in a single device leads to several potential applications.

One of the more intriguing possibilities is an automatic brightness control for a LED display panel. By momentarily reverse-biasing one of the LED elements (a decimal point, for example), the emitter-come-sensor could be made to detect the ambient-light intensity, and then the intensity level of the display could be adjusted accordingly.

In another application, the emitter/sensor could serve as a simple transceiver, to be placed at points on a digital communications bus. A data link capable of two-way communications can be constructed simply by using fiber optics and a single device at each end.

Such applications require a switching circuit similar to the one shown. When the input is high, Q_1 conducts, and a forward bias current flows through D_1, which emits photons. The photocurrent is given by:

$$I \simeq \frac{V_z}{R_1} - \frac{V_1 - V_2}{R_2}$$

When the input is low, Q_1 turns off, D_1 becomes a sensor with a reverse bias of $V_1 - V_2$, and the light current through R_2 develops a voltage at the output.

Initial tests show that both infrared (gallium arsenide) and red (gallium arsenide phosphide) LEDs respond to light from a small incandescent source. Once a diode is selected, it should be tested further to determine the exact switching speed and sensitivity characteristics. Several LEDs have been tested, including the Hewlett-Packard Co. 5082-4107 (GaAs) and 5082-4440 (GaAsP) and Daimetric's DLD-32 and DLD-33, both red-LED GaAsP types. □

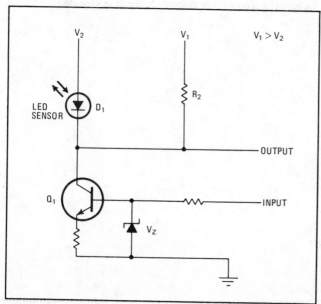

LED Switch. A few components can be added to enable the conventional LED to double as a photodetector.

6. Novel delay lines

Bucket-brigade shift register generates constant phase delay

by F.E. Hinkle
University of Texas, Applied Research Laboratories, Austin, Texas

A digitally programable constant-phase-delay network makes an interesting application for a bucket-brigade analog shift register. The circuit generates a phase delay, in degrees, that is independent of the frequency of the signal to be phase-shifted.

The analog shift register works in conjunction with a phase-locked loop so that the input frequency forms the time delay needed for a constant phase delay. The register delays the input by:

$$\tau = M/2f_v$$

where M is the number of register-delay elements or bits, and f_v is the frequency of the bit shift (biphase clock).

Since the frequency for shifting the analog bits is a function of the input frequency, the delay time will also be a function of input frequency. A phase-locked loop is used as a frequency multiplier, with a divide-by-N network in its feedback path. During lock, the frequency of the phase-locked loop will be an integral multiple of the input signal being applied to the shift register:

$$f_v = Nf_{in}$$

where N is the divide-by integer in the phase-locked loop, and f_{in} is the input frequency. When the frequency of the phase-locked loop is applied to the shift register as the bit-shift frequency, the new time delay of the register is:

$$\tau = M/2Nf_{in}$$

The delay time-to-angle conversion for the input sine wave can be defined as:

$$delay\ angle = (\tau/T_{in}) \times 360° = (\tau f_{in}) \times 360°$$

where T_{in} is the period of the input waveform. Substituting for τ in this equation yields:

$$delay\ angle = (M/2N) \times 360°$$

The delay angle of the input waveform, therefore, is independent of that waveform's frequency. By using a programable divide-by-N circuit, the amount of the delay angle can be adjusted in the desired increments. For this circuit, when M = N = 185, the delay angle is 180° for all frequencies within the range of the phase-locked loop. The circuit's major limitation is the lock-on range of the phase-locked loop. □

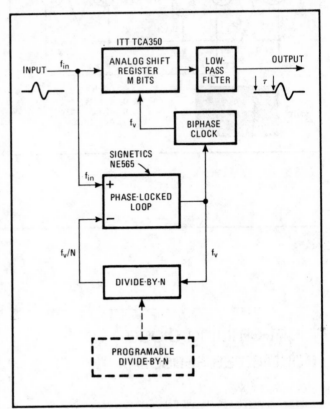

Controlled phase shift. Bucket-brigade analog shift register and a phase-locked loop provide a constant phase delay that is independent of the input frequency. The phase-locked loop determines the bit-shift frequency of the register, and a divide-by-N circuit sets the frequency of the phase-locked loop. The delay can be made variable by adding a programable divide-by-N circuit as indicated.

C-MOS decade divider clocks bucket-brigade delay line

by F.E. Hinkle
The Applied Research Laboratories, University of Texas, Austin, Texas

The bucket-brigade analog shift register is a charge-transfer device that can delay an input signal by a fixed or variable time. A TCA350 MOS bucket-brigade shift register, which has 185 stages, delays the signal by a time $t = 185/2f_c$, where f_c is the clock frequency. The clock frequency must be considerably higher than the signal frequency f_s for sampling and filtering reasons (f_c must be filtered from f_s at the output), so the maximum signal delay is about $10/f_s$. A TCA350 was used to delay 1-kilohertz tone bursts, as illustrated in Fig. 1, for measurements of distortion and insertion loss.

The TCA350 requires two clock-pulse trains of −18 volts; both are at frequency f_c, but they are separated in phase by 180°. [The function of the biphase clock in the charge transfer process is described in *Electronics*, June 21, 1971, p. 58.] A drain supply of −24 v and an input bias voltage of −8 v are also required. Figure 2 shows the circuit for the shift-register delay line, complete with clock generator and output filter.

In this circuit, an externally generated train of positive pulses at frequency f_p is applied to the 2N4403 transistor switch/level-converter, which produces negative pulses suitable for driving the biphase clock generator. The generator, a divide-by-four circuit that uses an MC14017AL C-MOS divider, is biased at −18 v and therefore can drive the TCA350 directly. It generates two non-overlapping pulses at $f_c = f_p/4$, separated by 180°. An MC14009AL C-MOS hex buffer inverts the clock pulses.

The output from the delay line consists of the delayed input signal superimposed on a clock-generated waveform. The output wave that is generated by the clocking pulses has an rms value of 3 V, and its frequency spectrum is integral multiples of f_c. A filter is needed to reject the clock frequency and its multiples; the more rejection the filter provides at f_c, the better the wideband signal-to-noise ratio is.

Of course, if f_c is so high that the following system cannot detect it, the filter requirements are not as stringent. For the four-section RC filter shown in Fig. 2, the clock-frequency energy is down about 50 decibels from

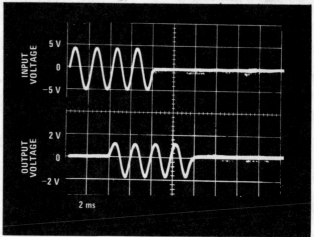

1. Delay. Dual-trace scope photo shows 2-millisecond delay of 1-kHz tone burst in bucket-brigade delay line. Output has been filtered to remove clock-frequency components. Delay is inversely proportional to clock frequency; here f_c = 46.25 kHz.

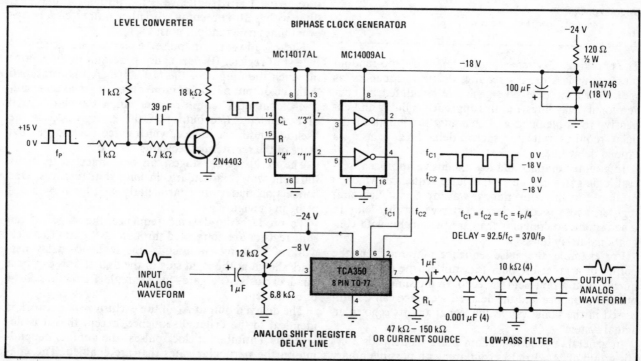

2. Circuit. The TCA350 analog shift register is an MOS charge-transfer device that requires two clock inputs. Clocks of required amplitude and phase relationship are generated by C-MOS divider plus inverters from a conventional input pulse train. Low-pass filter removes clock frequencies from output waveform. Note dc bias at input of delay line. Cascaded shift registers can delay signals for tens of milliseconds.

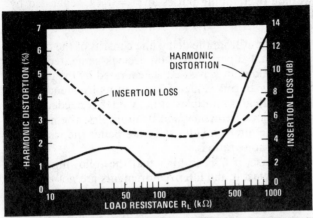

3. Load carefully. Harmonic distortion and insertion loss in circuit depend upon value of load resistor R_L, as shown. Data assumes that $f_s = 1$ kHz, $f_c = 46.25$ kHz, and input signal $= 0.77$ V rms.

the maximum allowable output signal within the low-pass filter passband. If a more elaborate filter such as a multipole active filter is used, the clock energy may be reduced even further.

The cutoff sharpness of the low-pass filter determines the maximum amount of delay realizable because a sharp cutoff allows a lower f_c. With the four-section RC filter shown, the maximum delay before signal degradation is about 2 milliseconds. The minimum delay is about 180 μs. The longest practical delay is about 18 ms. With such a long delay, however, the signal is less than

500 hertz. Since the delay changes with clock frequency, the worst-case f_c must be determined when calculating the s/n ratio of the delay line.

The usable dynamic range of the shift register also depends upon the filter response and acceptable s/n ratio. The dynamic range of the shift register is greater than 70 dB when a sharp-cutoff filter is used to remove the clock frequency. The analog shift register tracked within 1 dB as the input signal level changed from 3 V to less than 300 μV. The tracking error was measured in a filter bandwidth of 200 Hz, centered at 2 kilohertz. For input voltages above 3 V rms, the harmonic distortion exceeds 4%. For input amplitude levels of less than 0.5 V rms, the distortion is less than 0.5%. At higher input levels, clipping of signal peaks causes a distortion that is a nonlinear function of the input level.

The output stage of the TCA350 is a source follower that must be terminated in either a load resistor R_L or a constant-current load of about 0.5 milliampere. The relationship between harmonic distortion and load resistance is shown in Fig. 3; note that there is an optimum value for R_L. The distortion curve reflects a 0.2% distortion in the input signal plus the nonlinearity of the bucket brigade. If a current source is used in place of the load resistor, the current should be adjusted for minimum distortion.

Figure 3 also indicates that the attenuation of the input signal varies between 4 and 11 dB as the size of the load resistor is changed. □

Logic approach to time delay uses only integrated circuits

by John J. Carroll
U.S. Naval Avionics Facility, Indianapolis, Ind.

The checking of systems that use linear pseudo-random pulse sequences usually requires delayed sequences, as well. Often the delayed signals are simulated by conventional delay lines, but this approach is bulky and expensive to implement, and changing the length of the delay requires switching several delay lines or using a tapped delay line.

In a more compact and less expensive approach, several logic gates can delay the pulse sequence, which is produced in the conventional way by a modified shift register, and a second shift register varies the delay in much smaller increments than are practicable with conventional delay lines.

For example, the pulse sequence may represent the output of a radar or sonar transmitter; the delayed sequence would represent the echo. In the simulation, the original sequence and the delayed sequence can be processed in the same way as the signal and its echo in an actual system.

In general, a pseudo-random pulse sequence is a cyclic group of $2^n - 1$ pulses containing all possible binary combinations of n pulses except the all-0s combination. The cyclic characteristic of the sequence is the distinction between a pseudo-random and a truly random one.

Nevertheless, the sequence can almost arbitrarily approach true randomness. For example, if n = 20, the sequence contains more than a million pulses without repetition. When these are produced at a clock rate of 1 megahertz, the cycling rate is less than 1 hertz. Therefore, if the 1-MHz sequence is fed through a high-pass filter with a 10-kHz cutoff, the filter output closely approximates true random noise.

The pseudo-random pulse sequences are generated by a shift register (the sequence generator in the figure) in which the output of the last stage (A_5) is combined with the output of one or more other stages in an exclusive-OR circuit. The shift register can be Fairchild's 9300 or equivalent. The output of the exclusive-OR is the pseudo-random sequence, which is fed back to the first stage of the register for recycling.

The exclusive-OR stages can be connected in many different ways, particularly in long shift registers. One connection that works particularly well for n = 5 appears in the figure.

To produce the delayed sequence, the stages of the shift register are connected through AND gates to a network of exclusive-OR circuits—the sequence delay network shown at the right side of the figure. This can be a quad exclusive-OR gate—for example Fairchild's 9014 or equivalent.

The delayed output A_k of the exclusive-OR network is identical to the original sequence, except that it is delayed by a number of clock pulses—the number depending on the particular gates that are enabled. The enabling of these gates is done by the delay control, as described later. (The circuit delay through the shift register and exclusive-OR network is assumed to be negligible relative to the intervals between clock pulses, and therefore, to the minimum delay resolution.)

At any given time, the output of stage A_1 of the shift register equals the output of the sequence generator delayed by one pulse period. Likewise, the outputs of other stages of the shift register represent the sequence generator output, delayed by two, three, or more clock pulses (depending on the number of stages). Any of these delays can be made available at the A_k delayed output by enabling the corresponding gate between the shift register and the sequence delay network. The circuit shown provides for delays of as many as five clock-pulse periods.

The output A_k can also produce zero delay by enabling gates B_3 and B_5, which produce A_0 through the exclusive-OR network from the same stages that produced the original undelayed signal.

Delays of from five to 31 clock pulses for the circuit shown (or, in general, up to $2^n - 1$) are available by enabling other combinations of the gates. Thus, just as A_0 is the exclusive-OR of A_3 and A_5, A_1 is the exclusive-OR of A_4 and a hypothetical A_6, A_2 is the exclusive-OR of A_5 and A_7, and so on.

These relationships can be inverted, thanks to the peculiar mathematical properties of the exclusive-OR function, to express the longer delays in terms of the outputs of two or more real stages. Thus, A_6, or the sequence delayed by six clock times, is the exclusive-OR of A_1 and A_4, A_7 is the exclusive-OR of A_2 and A_5, and so on. For the higher-numbered subscripts, several substitutions may be required, yielding, for example, the fact that A_{12} is the combined exclusive-OR, or odd parity, of A_1, A_2, A_3, and A_4.

The delay control that enables the AND gates consists of the same number of shift register stages that are used for the sequence generator. Any delay from 1 to $2^n - 1$ clock times can be generated by pulsing this control shift register the corresponding number of times. With this arrangement, several different delay configurations are possible.

For example, swept delay can begin at some initial value, gradually increase to a maximum, and then reset to its initial delay. This is easy to implement by using the delay control shift register, simply by clocking it at the appropriate sweep rate.

A more complex generator can be loaded in parallel with a binary number from an external source that sets the delay to some arbitrary level without stepping through a number of intervening values. When the shift register is long, producing a long pseudo-random sequence, this parallel-loading capability can save a lot of time and trouble.

□

Network of exclusive-ORs (right) produces delayed pulse sequence; length of delay is set by delay control, similar to sequence generator.

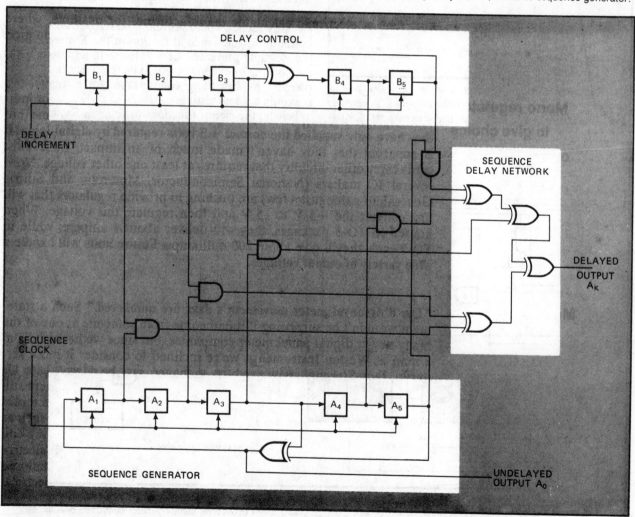

Back-and-forth scanner overcomes slewing-rate limits

by James A. Blackburn
Wilfrid Laurier University, Waterloo, Ont., Canada

An incremental plotter or line printer that can store entire lines in a buffer memory can be made to print the lines alternately forwards—from left to right—and backwards—from right to left. This refinement will significantly increase its speed because it will no longer need the carriage return function with its all-too-finite slewing rate. In fact, only the minimum character-to-character print rate will then be affected by the mechanical inertia of the print-head assembly (or, in the case of

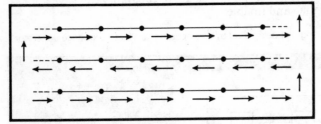

1. Zig-zag scan. Two-dimensional scan in minimum time is achieved by reversing scan direction on alternate rows, as indicated here. Initial address (0,0) is at lower left, and scan halts at (15,15).

an all-electronic display system, by the finite settling time of the amplifiers).

The technique is applicable to all two-dimensional scanning that must be performed incrementally. However, it is particularly efficient when each horizontal line contains many points, because in such cases the dead time during carriage return is proportionately large.

The circuit described here generates the required address sequences. It was designed as part of a rapid-film-scanning densitometer. The X and Y addresses can be sent via digital-to-analog converters to a servo system for incrementally moving the film holder past a photodetector. Alternatively, the vertical and horizontal count pulses may be used directly to drive stepping motors. If an appropriate clock frequency is chosen, the film may be scanned in the minimum time compatible with motor torque, sample stage inertia, and step size. A digitized replica of the image on the film may then be obtained by logging the densitometer output at each selected address.

The circuit shown in Fig. 2 performs an alternating-direction scan with TTL integrated circuits exclusively and is thus capable of high-speed performance. The clock frequency would normally be selected so that it is optimum for incremental motion in the X direction. In the example presented here a 16-by-16-address grid is employed. Other choices would be relatively easy to implement by cascading counters and/or changing the max-min address testing.

Briefly, the circuit functions as follows. Switch SW is

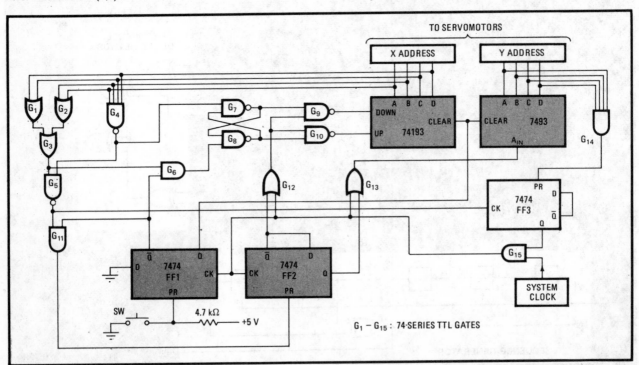

2. Scan-control logic. Logic circuit for alternating-direction incremental scanner uses 74-series TTL gates, flip-flops, and counters. Flip-flops are triggered by rising pulse edges, and counters by falling edges. Count pulses could drive stepping-motor controllers directly.

depressed. This sets all counters to zero, presets the three D-type positive-edge-triggered flip-flops (7474), and initializes the R-S flip-flop composed of gates G_7 and G_8. Note that the output of G_{14} is low; therefore clock pulses are passed freely through G_{15}. The first rising edge on the clock stream to occur after SW is released triggers flip-flop FF_1, thus enabling the X and Y counters and G_6. Gate G_{11} is now irreversibly enabled so that the end-of-line test performed by gates G_1–G_4 directly controls the PRESET function of FF_2.

As can be seen in the timing diagram (Fig. 3), the output of G_{11} rises for a half cycle because G_5 is initially high. However, the clock pulse has preceded this event by an interval equal to the propagation delay of FF_1. Therefore FF_2 does not toggle, and its Q output remains at logic 1.

Subsequent negative clock edges are passed through G_{12} and G_{10}, causing the X address to increment steadily. The timing diagram indicates the sequence of events as the end of the first line is reached. A final negative clock edge causes a count of 15 to be achieved. The output of G_4 immediately goes low, toggling G_7/G_8. As a result G_9 is enabled and G_{10} disabled, while the outputs of G_5 and G_{11} rise, enabling FF_2. A half cycle later, the rising clock-edge toggles FF_2, enabling G_{13} and disabling G_{12}. The next falling edge increments the Y address without affecting the X counter. Following this a positive edge again toggles FF_2, this time closing G_{13} but opening G_{12}. The X address now will decrement steadily until a zero count is reached, when a similar logical sequence will route a clock pulse to Y and prepare G_7/G_8 for upcounting. (Note that FF_2 can be toggled by the clock pulses only when the output of G_5 is high—that is, when either a minimum or maximum X address is obtained.)

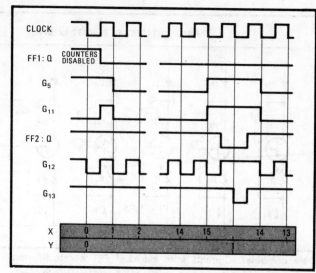

3. Pulse sequences. Timing diagram shows output states of selected gates and flip-flops in circuit that produces back-and-forth scanning, and the X and Y addresses that control servomotors.

When the fifteenth Y increment occurs, G_{14} goes high and enables FF_3. From the timing diagram it can be seen that G_5 will already be high at this moment. FF_3 does not change state until the next rising edge is applied to its clock input, at the completion of the last horizontal scan. A final falling clock edge causes G_5 to go high, toggling FF_3 and disabling G_{15} so that no further clock pulses reach the rest of the circuit. The X and Y addresses are thus frozen at this terminal count.

Once SW is released, the entire scan proceeds automatically and halts at the final address. Logging an entire image therefore requires no attention from the operator. □

Chart recorder plots total of loads in several circuits

by L.W. Herring
LWHA, Dallas, Texas

Occasionally it is desirable to record the load requirements of an electrical distribution system or the total usage of a number of communications channels during some period of time. In determining ac distribution loads, a recording wattmeter can log the data, but plotting the total power consumption for several pieces of equipment fed from separate power mains or the traffic through a number of communications channels is more

difficult. Still, if supervisory signals like pilot-light voltages are used to generate current in field-effect transistors, it is easy to develop a signal that can be plotted with any available chart recorder.

As shown in the figure, the currents from FETs used as constant-current sources are summed in a fixed resistor to obtain a voltage signal that indicates total usage rate. To provide equal weighting for each input, the current sources can be equal, or they can be set to various values to provide a scaling effect on the output voltage. Since the FETs are used as current sources, the input signals can be any convenient ac or dc voltages between 5 and 25 volts. The input signals are fed to the FETs through diodes that rectify ac and also protect against negative dc.

As an example, it might be desirable to plot the daily demand curve for five heat-treating furnaces. Two of

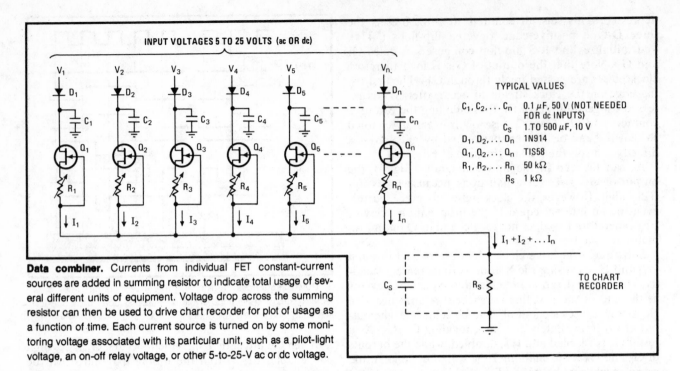

INPUT VOLTAGES 5 TO 25 VOLTS (ac OR dc)

TYPICAL VALUES

$C_1, C_2, \ldots C_n$	0.1 μF, 50 V (NOT NEEDED FOR dc INPUTS)
C_S	1 TO 500 μF, 10 V
$D_1, D_2, \ldots D_n$	1N914
$Q_1, Q_2, \ldots Q_n$	TIS58
$R_1, R_2, \ldots R_n$	50 kΩ
R_S	1 kΩ

TO CHART RECORDER

Data combiner. Currents from individual FET constant-current sources are added in summing resistor to indicate total usage of several different units of equipment. Voltage drop across the summing resistor can then be used to drive chart recorder for plot of usage as a function of time. Each current source is turned on by some monitoring voltage associated with its particular unit, such as a pilot-light voltage, an on-off relay voltage, or other 5-to-25-V ac or dc voltage.

the furnaces are 100-kilowatt/three-phase units, one is 50-kw/single-phase, and the remaining two are 25-kw/single-phase. All of the furnaces have 24-v dc indicator lamps that light on a control console when the furnaces are operating. The lamp voltages can excite FET constant-current sources that are proportional to the power ratings of their respective furnaces. The sum of these currents, passing through a common fixed resistor, produces a voltage that indicates the total power to the furnaces. This voltage drives the pen on the chart recorder.

The first FET, Q_1, is connected to the 24-v pilot light voltage for the first 25-kw furnace. Resistor R_1 is adjusted so that Q_1 delivers 100 microamperes to resistor R_S. The second 25-kw furnace pilot voltage is connected to FET Q_2, and R_2 is also adjusted for 100 μA into R_S. A resulting voltage of 0.1 v is produced across summing resistor R_S when either one of the 25-kw furnaces is on, and 0.2 v is produced when both are on.

The 50-kw pilot lead excites FET Q_3, which is set by means of R_3 to deliver 200 μA to R_S. Operation of the 50-kw furnace produces twice the voltage drop across R_S that either 25-kw unit does. Finally, the two 100-kw furnaces are connected to FETs Q_4 and Q_5, each adjusted to source 400 μA.

Each 25 kw of furnace load is represented by a constant current of 100 μA, which produces 0.1 v across summing resistor R_S. If the total current is 700 μA, the voltage is 0.7 v, indicating a 175-kw load, and this load can be recorded on any voltage-sensitive chart recorder.

This technique can also be used to plot the number of telephone lines in use at any time in an office or plant to determine whether or not a business is making effective use of its telephone service. In this example, the 10-v ac voltages that light line-button lamps are the input signals. The ac voltages are rectified by diodes D_1, D_2, and so forth before reaching the FETs. Each current source is adjusted for 100 μA so that whenever a line is in use, the voltage across the 1-kilohm summing resistor R_S increases by 0.1 v.

Any general-purpose depletion-mode junction FET with I_{DSS} of 1 to 15 milliamperes can be used for the FETs; the TIS58 has yielded excellent results. Dissipation and voltages are not critical if the input levels are kept under 30 v. A 1-kilohm value of R_S was used for convenience, but its resistance can be scaled along with the current sources to provide any desired output voltages. The maximum output voltage should not exceed 50% of the lowest input voltage. For example, if the inputs are 5, 5, 12, and 24 v, respectively, the maximum output voltage should not exceed 2.5 v. The standard input voltage for many chart recorders is 1 v, so that level is a desirable maximum output from this circuit.

Since the input voltages do not have to all be alike, 24-v dc relay levels, 5-v TTL levels, and 12-v ac signals can all be used as inputs in the same circuit. The input capacitors C_1–C_8 are required only for ac inputs, but diodes D_1–D_8 should be used with both ac and dc inputs to protect the FETs. On plots requiring long time periods with inputs that change rapidly, a capacitor C_S may be connected across summing resistor R_S to smooth the graph. □

Addressable cursor enhances linear bar-graph display

by Robert C. Moore
Johns Hopkins University, Applied Physics Laboratory, Laurel, Md.

A handful of medium-scale integrated circuits can add an addressable cursor feature to a neon dual linear bar-graph display. The bar-graph display is a digitally addressed Burroughs Self-Scan tube which normally displays two linear bars. The length of each bar is directly proportional to a voltage or a digital number. The modification described here, however, makes the entire length of both bars glow dimly, and the input voltages or digital numbers produce bright cursor lines across the bars. With cursor operation, the entire bar is always visible, and the cursor divides the bar into two fractions so that it is easy to see at a glance the position of the cursor relative to full scale. In many display applications, this cursor display is preferable to a bar graph that does not have a full-scale reference. Anything that indicates fractional displacement (such as a ship's rudder indicator or a gage that shows the level of the liquid in a container) is indicated more clearly by a cursor display than by a bar graph.

Each bar is a neon lamp with one large anode and 201 cathode segments. The first cathode, called a "reset" cathode, is used to initiate the neon glow at one end of the bar. Cathode 2 is connected to cathodes 5, 8, 11, . . . 200. This group of cathodes is called the phase-one ($\phi1$) group. Similarly, a $\phi2$ group consists of cathodes 3, 6, 9, . . . 201, and a $\phi3$ group consists of cathodes 4, 7, 10, . . . 199.

By driving these three phases of cathodes with a three-phase scanning clock, the neon glow can be made to "walk" along the entire length of the bar. When cycled fast enough, this scan presents a flicker-free dis-

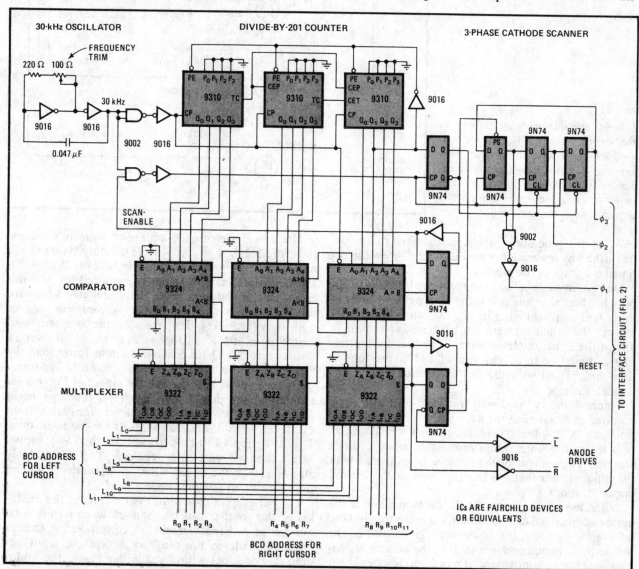

1. Scanner. Digital logic produces scanning signals that convert neon dual bar-graph display to dual addressable cursor display. Addresses of desired cursor locations are supplied as three-digit BCD codes between $(000)_{10}$ and $(200)_{10}$. Logic causes scan to pause at selected addresses for 25% duty cycle, producing a bright line that shows the value of a variable against a background that indicates full-scale value.

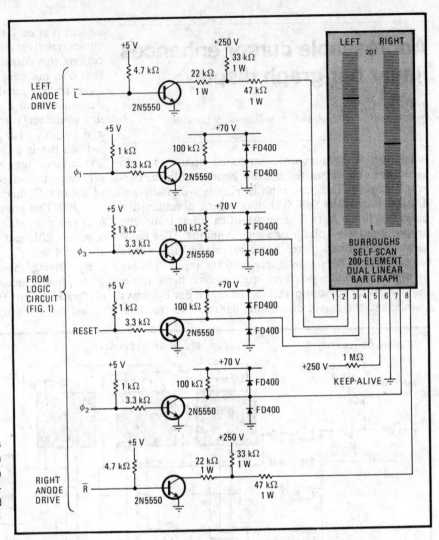

2. Driver and display. Six npn transistors interface the TTL logic of Fig. 1 to the neon bar-graph-display tube. All of the bar-graph segments glow dimly except for the two addressed segments, which glow brightly and show as cursors. Each cursor is one of 201 segments, so the resolution is ±0.5%.

play. At any time during the scan, the glow can be extinguished by lowering the anode voltage below the extinction voltage of the tube.

One addressable cathode segment can be made to appear brighter than the rest if the scan pauses briefly at that segment, showing it up as an addressable cursor. The bright segment can be caused to appear at any of the 201 cathode locations in the bar by controlling a digital address. The second bar in the tube is time-multiplexed with the first to provide a dual addressable cursor.

Figure 1 shows the digital transistor-transistor logic required to accomplish the scanning, pausing, and multiplexing. A 30-kilohertz oscillator drives a modulo 201 BCD segment counter and a reset/three-phase cathode scanner. The content of the counter is compared with the input signals that are the addresses of the desired cursor locations.

When the counter output is the same number as the cursor address, the cathode scanner is inhibited, and the neon glow pauses at the addressed segment. When the divide-by-201 counter again reaches the address, as determined by the comparator, the cathode scanner is enabled. When cathode No. 201 is reached, the alternate anode and address are selected, and the whole process is repeated.

The duty cycle of each addressed segment's glow is therefore 202/804 = 25.1% while the duty cycle of each nonaddressed segment is 1/804 = 0.124%. With a 30-kilohertz clock, each segment is energized for 33.3 microseconds, a duration more than adequate to ensure reliable operation of the device. A complete scan of both bars (including the pauses on the two addressed segments) is 804 × 33.3 μs = 26.8 ms, so the over-all display rate is 37.3 Hz. Since this rate is faster than the flicker rate of the human eye, the display is flicker-free.

Figure 2 shows how the TTL MSI circuit of Fig. 1 is interfaced to the dual linear bar-graph tube. Six high-voltage npn transistors provide level translation from TTL levels to 70-v and 250-v levels for the neon tube. The 70-v supply can be derived from the 250-v supply with a simple 1-watt zener regulator. The 250-v supply also biases on the "keep-alive" glow, which is hidden from view by its opaque anode.

For bar-graph tubes with fewer elements, the modulus of the counter can be changed to equal the total number of cathode segments. A corresponding change must be made in the range of acceptable input addresses. For tubes with a single bar graph, the multiplexer can be eliminated and the single anode can be wired permanently on by connecting it through a 75-kilohm 1-watt resistor to 250 v. □

Decoders convert binary code for hexadecimal display

by Robert F. Starr

National Oceanographic Instrumentation Center, Washington, D.C.

Hexadecimal code symbols can be shown cheaply and easily on a regular seven-segment display by two decoder/drivers and some logic circuitry. To keep the hex digits A through F completely recognizable, the circuit described here generates both upper-case and lower-case letters. The 7448 seven-segment decoder/driver displays a symbol for "6" that is identical to a "b". Therefore, the decimal point of the display is activated for the numbers 0 through 9, and extinguished for the letters A through F.

The circuit operation is quite straightforward. For binary inputs to the 7448 from 0000 to 1001 (0 to 9), the 7448 functions normally, displaying the appropriate digit on the light-emitting-diode display. As soon as the binary input exceeds 1001, the LT (Lamp test) input on the 7448 is brought low, lighting all segments, and extinguishing the decimal point (DP) on the LED. In addition, as soon as the D input (most significant bit) on the 7448 goes high, the 7445 binary-coded-decimal-to-decimal decoder/driver turns on.

With the D input of the 7445 grounded, the device sees only the three least significant bits of the input. When the binary input is 1011, for example, the 7445 sees a 011 (3) and brings the 3 output low. This output is decoded by the diode matrix, which turns off segments a and b of the LED display, forming a "b" on the display. The process is similar for all other binary inputs from 1010 to 1111 (A, c, d, E, and F).

An H-P 5082-7740 LED display is shown here, but other types can be used. For most of the larger displays, it may be necessary to pull the seven-segment lines to ±5 volts through 220-ohm resistors to achieve the desired brightness. □

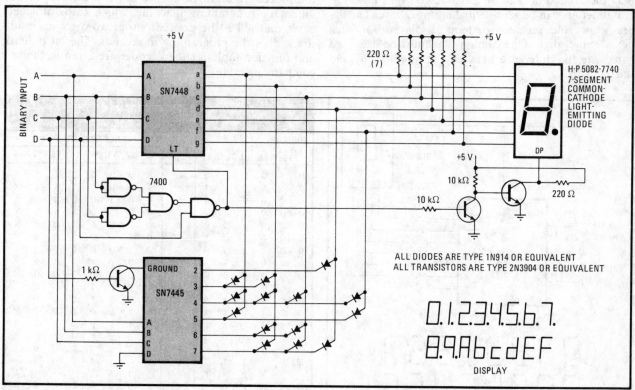

Hex signs. Binary inputs produce hexadecimal code on a standard seven-segment display with this circuit. To emphasize distinctions between numerals and letters, a decimal point is activated for numbers 0 through 9, as shown. Cost of parts (not including LED display) is less than $5. For more than one digit, the inputs can be multiplexed. Pull-up resistors may not be required for small displays.

PROM converts binary code for hexadecimal display

by Franklin E. Withrow III
Massachusetts Institute of Technology, Cambridge, Mass.

When designing and developing microcomputer systems, most engineers automatically include rows of lights to present information in binary format. However, when debugging the system, it can be frustrating and time-consuming to translate the binary data displayed into the hexadecimal format that many assemblers use. With a programable read-only memory and a seven-segment display, binary-to-hexadecimal conversion can be performed simply by hardware at very little cost over that of a binary display.

Usually, seven-segment displays are used to display only the numerals 0–9. In addition, they can also display the needed hexadecimal characters A–F; however, not all letters can be represented in upper case. The figure shows the segment patterns displayed for each hexadecimal digit. One caution that must be exercised is to note the difference between the number "6" and the letter "b".

To implement the hexadecimal-to-seven-segment decoder, a 74188 or N8223 PROM is used. Since the device has open-collector outputs, the light-emitting diodes in the display can be driven directly with a suitable current-limiting resistor. The PROM outputs should not be allowed to sink currents greater than 12 milliamperes. Each of the seven segments in the display is driven by a separate output of the PROM (one output is unused). The schematic for a single hexadecimal digit is given in the circuit diagram.

Locations 0–15 of the PROM are used to store the information that performs binary-to-hexadecimal conversion. For each word, a 0 in a bit position turns on the display segment at the output; if the bit is a 1, the segment is off. If locations 16–31 are left unprogramed (all 0s), the most significant address line performs a lamp-test function. When this line is high, a word in the range 16–31 is addressed and all segments of the display will light.

The PROM should be programed in accordance with the procedure outlined on the device's data sheet. An automatic programing machine, which reads punched cards that tell it the desired output word for each address, does the programing in seconds. The bit pattern and function table for the decoder are given in the accompanying table. □

TRUTH TABLE AND PROGRAM FOR THE HEXADECIMAL DISPLAY													
INHIBIT LAMP TEST	B8	B4	B2	B1	DISPLAY	Y1	Y2	Y3	Y4	Y5	Y6	Y7	Y8
0	0	0	0	0	0	0	0	0	0	0	0	1	X
0	0	0	0	1	1	1	0	0	1	1	1	1	X
0	0	0	1	0	2	0	0	1	0	0	1	0	X
0	0	0	1	1	3	0	0	0	0	1	1	0	X
0	0	1	0	0	4	1	0	0	1	1	0	0	X
0	0	1	0	1	5	0	1	0	0	1	0	0	X
0	0	1	1	0	6	0	1	0	0	0	0	0	X
0	0	1	1	1	7	0	0	0	1	1	1	1	X
0	1	0	0	0	8	0	0	0	0	0	0	0	X
0	1	0	0	1	9	0	0	0	1	1	0	0	X
0	1	0	1	0	A	0	0	0	1	0	0	0	X
0	1	0	1	1	b	1	1	0	0	0	0	0	X
0	1	1	0	0	C	0	1	1	0	0	0	1	X
0	1	1	0	1	d	1	0	0	0	0	1	0	X
0	1	1	1	0	E	0	1	1	0	0	0	0	X
0	1	1	1	1	F	0	1	1	1	0	0	0	X
1	X	X	X	X	(OFF)	1	1	1	1	1	1	1	1
0	1	X	X	X	8	0	0	0	0	0	0	0	X

1 = HIGH   0 = LOW   X = DON'T CARE

Remember the hex symbol. Binary inputs to the PROM produce a seven-segment representation of hexadecimal-code symbols. The PROM costs about $3, and can be programed quickly at practically no cost if an automatic programing machine is available.

Clip-on monitor unit displays count in IC

by John Okolowicz
Honeywell Inc., Fort Washington, Pa.

An integrated decoder/display, mounted on a standard test clip that fits onto a dual in-line package provides a quick means for monitoring the state of an integrated-circuit counter. This monitor is brighter than the LED-chip monitors now on the market, and can be custom-made to suit any purpose.

In the setup, the pins that correspond to the outputs of the counter to be monitored are wired to the inputs of the on-chip driver. The enable line (pin 5) is then tied to ground so that the chip always displays the latest state of the counter.

For each different type of counter or latch to be monitored, a new assembly must be made. However, by mounting a socket on the DIP clip, instead of soldering a display directly to the clip, a variety of monitor clips can be made without requiring a large number of display ICs.

The figure shows a Hewlett-Packard 5082-7340 hexadecimal decoder/light-emitting-diode-display IC mounted on a DIP clip; H-P 5082-7300 or 5082-7302 numeric displays may also be used.

This concept works best when the monitored counter can be single-stepped so that successive intermediate states are displayed. However, as long as the states are displayed for a sufficient time to be observed, any clocking arrangement is adequate.

This display technique provides a quick visual check of counters or latches with important outputs that need to be constantly monitored. The concept may be extended to monitoring of bus addresses or data-bus lines by using more than one display wired to a DIP clip with 24 or more pins and wiring only the first three inputs of each display so that an octal output format is displayed. Alternatively, all four inputs of each display may be used for a hexadecimal display. ☐

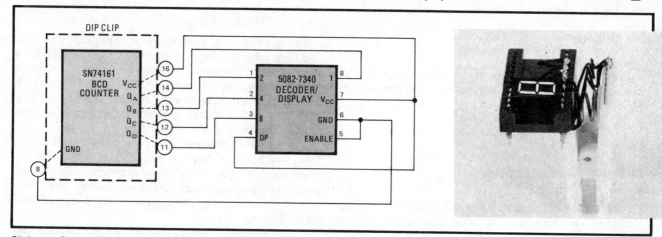

State monitor. LED decoder/display unit mounted on DIP clip is easily clipped to IC package to show the count on a counter such as the SN74161, the state of a latch, or the data on a bus. The unit draws power from the V_{CC} and ground pins of the package it is clipped to.

8. Graphical aids to design

Semilog paper is short cut to finding filter frequencies

by Marc Damashek
Clarke School for the Deaf, Northampton, Mass.

Semilogarithmic graph paper provides a handy way to estimate center frequencies and band-edge frequencies in the design of filter banks. It's also a convenient way of finding fractional roots and powers of numbers.

Both applications make use of the fact that a straight line on semilog paper represents the functional relation that can be stated as:

$$\log y = a + bx \tag{1}$$

or

$$y = y_0 k^x \tag{2}$$

where y is 10^a and k is 10^b.

For example, an engineer may want to design a filter bank in which the ratio of successive center frequencies $(f_0, f_1, \ldots f_{N-1})$ is constant:

$$f_1 = cf_0$$
$$f_2 = cf_1 = c^2 f_0$$
$$f_3 = cf_2 = c^3 f_0, \text{ etc.}$$

or, in general,

$$f_n = c^n f_0 \tag{3}$$

Equation (3) has the same form as Eq. (2), so a semilog graph of the frequency of each filter stage, plotted against the number of that stage, is linear. Therefore the frequency of the first stage can be plotted at abscissa zero, the frequency of the last stage can be plotted at abscissa (N – 1) where N is the total number of stages in the filter, and when the two points are connected by a straight line, the frequencies of all intermediate stages can then be read at a glance.

Thus in Fig. 1 the line A illustrates how to estimate center frequencies given a requirement for seven channels total, with a lowest-channel center at 80 hertz and a highest-channel center at 500 Hz. The line connecting points (0, 80) and (6, 500) shows that the intermediate frequencies are 109, 147, 200, 271, and 368 Hz.

It should be noted that this graphical technique circumvents the need for some fancy calculation. For instance, it is not necessary to compute c, which in this case is:

$$c = (500/80)^{1/6} = (5/2)^{1/3}$$

The method lends itself to quick appraisal of alternative filter schemes; for example, to find frequencies for a scheme with 10 channels instead of seven, line B is drawn connecting the point (0, 80) with the point (9, 500). Even if a calculator were at hand, it could not possibly give such a meaningful representation of the desired information in so short a time.

The line that connects the points (½, 80) and (6½, 500), which is labeled A' in Fig. 1, gives band-edge frequencies that equal the geometric means between successive center frequencies for the seven-stage filter. This sort of information is of interest in the design of constant-Q filters.

Use of semilog paper to estimate fractional roots and powers corresponds to letting y_0 equal unity in Eq. (2). Figure 2 illustrates the technique in finding the value of

1. Filter frequencies. As graphic aid in design of filter banks with constant frequency ratio between stages, line A determines frequencies for a seven-channel system and line B determines them for a 10-channel system, both covering the range from 80 hertz to 500 Hz. Line A' determines band-edge frequencies for the seven-channel system. The error in reading frequency values is about 0.5%.

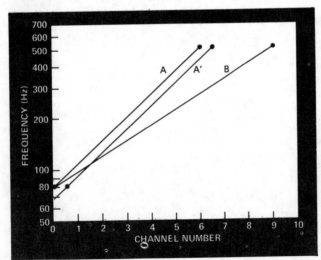

2. Roots and powers. Lines C and D illustrate use of semilog graph paper to provide quick solutions for values y and x in equations $y = 7^{0.37}$ and $10 = 3^x$, respectively.

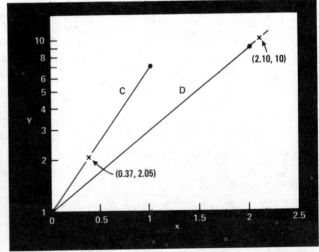

$7^{0.37}$. If:

$$y = 7^x$$

some known relations are:

$$1 = 7^0$$

and

$$7 = 7^1$$

Therefore $y = 7^{0.37}$ is found by drawing a straight line connecting $(0, 1)$ and $(1, 7)$ on the semilog paper. Where x is 0.37, y is found to have the value of 2.05.

As a final example, to find x in the equation $10 = 3^x$ (i.e., to find $\log_3 10$), draw line D to connect the points $(0, 1)$ and $(2, 9)$, and extend it out to $y = 10$. At $y = 10$, $x = 2.10$. □

Graphs aid selection of a-d converters

by Raymond J. Tarver
Raytheon Co., Equipment Division, Wayland, Mass.

Although analog-to-digital converters are widely used circuit components these days, they are frequently not specified properly by designers. In addition to the correct resolution, accuracy, speed, and temperature stability, a-d converters must be able to provide a given system dynamic range or signal-to-noise ratio.

Too often, designers neglect to take into consideration how converter quantization noise relates to other system noises. The result is a poor effective dynamic range or signal-to-noise ratio. The graphs given here make it easier to pick the right converter for the job.

For an ideal system, one that has no internal or external noise sources, and one in which the required variations on the signal are actually part of the signal, the signal-to-quantization noise power ratio is:

$$(SNR)_q = 12[S(t)]^2/Q^2 \qquad (1)$$

where $S(t)$ is the signal, and Q is the quantization increment. This latter variable is given by:

$$Q = R/N = R/(2\mu - 1) \qquad (2)$$

where R is the range or maximum magnitude of the signal being quantized, N is the number of available discrete quantization levels, and m is the number of bits (including the sign bit) provided by the converter.

In the real world, Eq. 1. is equivalent to defining any additive noise as part of the signal, or having a signal with noise-like variations. The signal-to-noise ratio of a real system having internal and external additive noise is given by:

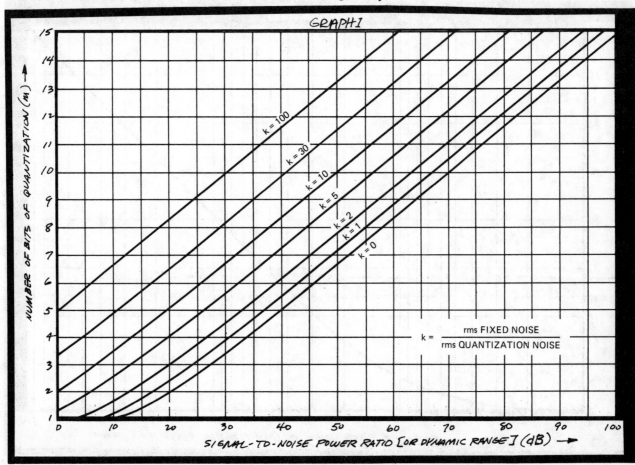

GRAPH 1

$$k = \frac{\text{rms FIXED NOISE}}{\text{rms QUANTIZATION NOISE}}$$

NUMBER OF BITS OF QUANTIZATION (m)

SIGNAL-TO-NOISE POWER RATIO [OR DYNAMIC RANGE] (dB)

$$SNR = [S(t)]^2 / [[N_i(t)]^2 + [N_a(t)]^2 + [N_q(t)]^2] \quad (3)$$

where $N_i(t)$ is the input noise, $N_a(t)$ is the internal noise, and $N_q(t)$ is the a-d quantization noise. This latter quantity can be expressed as:

$$N_q(t) = Q / \sqrt{12}$$

Naturally, the quantization noise can be made arbitrarily small by adding more bits to the a-d converter, although practical limitations, such as cost and availability, often limit the number of bits. In any event, if $N_q(t)$ is reduced to the point where $N_a(t)$ and/or $N_i(t)$ dominates the signal-to-noise ratio, obviously there is little reward in decreasing $N_q(t)$ further. This is another practical limitation on the number of converter bits chosen for a particular application.

Furthermore, cost and availability also enter in the reduction of $N_i(t)$ and $N_a(t)$. Hence, there must be a trade-off between the three noise sources. In high-data-rate radar applications, the remainder of the system is often designed around what value of $N_q(t)$ can be achieved with reasonable risk.

Equation 3 can be rewritten as:

$$SNR = S^2(t) / [[N_f(t)]^2 + [Nq(t)]^2]$$

where:

$$[N_f(t)]^2 = [N_i(t)]^2 + [N_a(t)]^2$$

Let:

$$N_f(t) = kN_q(t)$$

then, for values of k greater than or equal to 0:

$$SNR = S^2(t)/(k^2+1)[N_q(t)]^2 \quad (4)$$

where k represents the ratio of the root-mean-square value of fixed noise to the rms value of quantization noise:

$$k = \frac{rms\ fixed\ noise}{rms\ quantization\ noise}$$

Equation 4 can be further simplified by normalizing the signal, S(t), to unit range (R):

$$SNR = 12/(k^2+1)Q^2 \quad (5)$$

Substituting Eq. 2 in this last equation yields:

$$SNR = 12(2^m - 1)^2/(k^2+1) \quad (6)$$

Graph 1 is a plot of Eq. 6 with k as a parameter. As the nomograph shows, increasing values of k mean that more converter bits are needed to preserve a system's signal-to-noise ratio or dynamic range.

If dynamic range is defined as the ratio of the peak signal to the rms noise level, then Eqs. 5 and 6 also define the dynamic range as a function of the number of bits of quantization for a linear unipolar signal. For a bipolar signal, Eq. 6 is high by a factor of two, since half the range is expended quantizing the opposite polarity.

Graph 2 is a normalized plot of Eq. 6 that shows the degradation in dynamic range (or signal-to-noise ratio) as k departs from its ideal value of k = 0. At about k = 1, which corresponds to the knee of the curve, the dynamic range starts to deteriorate rapidly. □

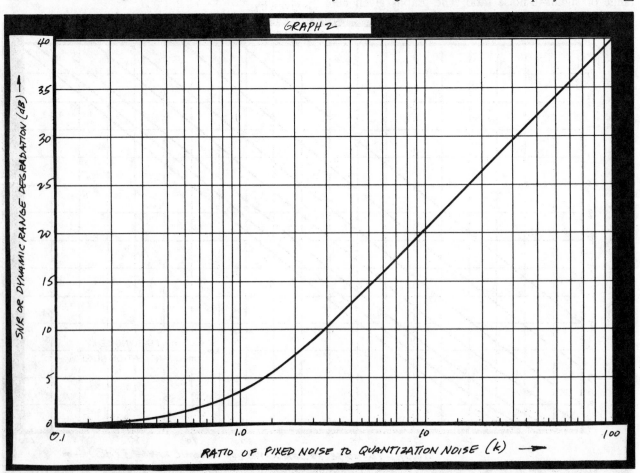

GRAPH 2

RATIO OF FIXED NOISE TO QUANTIZATION NOISE (k) ——➤

(vertical axis) SNR OR DYNAMIC RANGE DEGRADATION (dB) —➤

Convert coordinates and find SWRs graphically

by Vaughn D. Martin
Magnavox Co., Fort Wayne, Ind.

A relatively simple graphical procedure can reduce the error probability and the tedium of conventional mathematical approaches to finding standing-wave ratios, and converting admittance values in rectangular coordinates to impedance values in polar coordinates, including phase angles. The procedure requires only the known impedance, or admittance, and is executed with a pencil, a straightedge, and a compass. It involves just three steps and is more than 98% accurate.

For example, consider the circuit diagram (Fig. 1):

$R = Z_R = 50$ ohms
$G_R = 20$ millimhos
$C = 0.92$ microfarad
$X_C = 1/j(2\pi fC) = 1/j(5.78 \times 10^{-2})$ ohms
$B_C = 1/X_C = j57.8$ millimhos

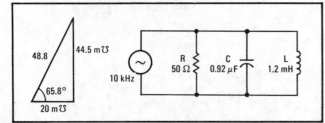

$L = 1.2$ millihenry
$X_L = j(2\pi fL) = j75.4$ ohms
$B_L = 1/X_L = 1/j75.4 = -j13.3$ millimhos
$Y = G + jB = 20 + j57.8 - j13.3 = 20 + j44.5$

In graphical computations, admittance is represented by the hypotenuse of the right triangle in which conductance is represented by the base, and susceptance by the altitude. In many applications, however, admittance is more useful when expressed in polar coordinates. Graphical conversion is accomplished as follows:

First, plot a point corresponding to the complex admittance on the chart (point A). Then, with a compass, draw an arc of a circle with center at the origin and passing through point A. The horizontal coordinate of point B, where the arc intersects the horizontal or conductance axis, is numerically equal to the total admittance; the impedance is indicated on the reciprocal scale by drawing a vertical line to that scale at point C, where the direct reading is 20.4 ohms. The phase angle is determined by the intersection of the graph's outer edge at point D with a line from the origin through point A. This value is about 66°. (Checking mathematically, the exact value is 65.85°.) The impedance, as determined from the chart, is

$$Z = 20.4 \underline{/66°}$$

If the value of the susceptance is negative in the rectangular-coordinate form, the polar version is plotted in the same way, but the sign of the angle is negative.

Converting polar to rectangular coordinates is the reverse of this procedure. The first step is to draw a vertical line from point C, representing the impedance,

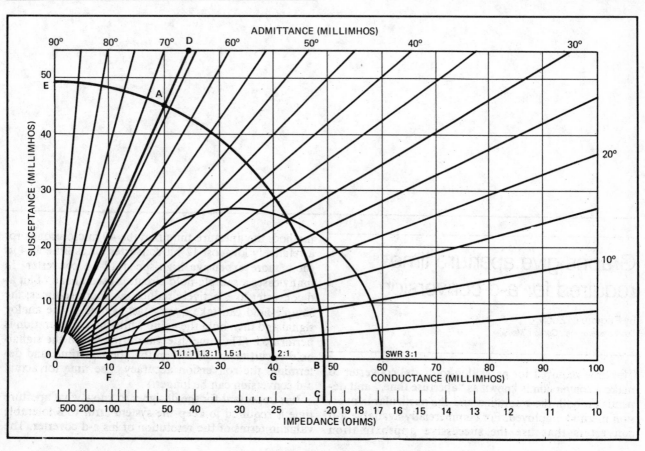

20.4, to point B on the X-axis. Then swing a 90° arc from point B to point E on the vertical axis, with the center point again at the origin. Finally, with a straight-edge, draw a line from the origin to the known phase angle (point D) at the top of the graph. The admittance is read in rectangular form where the arc and this line intersect (point A).

The same chart can be used to determine the standing wave ratio (SWR) on a transmission line of known characteristic impedance Z_o for a mismatched load. The semicircles sweeping out from the 20-millimho point on the conductance axis are lines of constant SWR for a transmission line with $Z_o = 50$ ohms. If such a transmission line has a load of 100 ohms, it should have SWR = 2. The reciprocals of 50 and 100 ohms are 20 and 10 millimhos respectively. The 20 millimho point on the conductance axis represents the 50-ohm characteristic impedance; the load resistance's conductance of 10 millimhos, at point F, is one end of the semicircle for SWR = 2. The other end of the semicircle is at 40 millimhos (point G), corresponding to a load of 25 ohms.

For loads that are not purely resistive, the compass is used again. For example, if the point A is the load admittance, the arc through that point centered on the origin, just as in the coordinate conversion, cuts the conductance axis at B, which is about halfway between the semicircles for SWR = 2 and SWR = 3. This indicates a SWR of about 2.5, which agrees with the computed impedance of 20.4 ohms (50/20.4 ≈ 2.5).

Other sets of semicircles can be drawn for transmission lines of different characteristic impedances. In each set, the centers are on the conductance axis. The center of the smallest one is at the point corresponding to the characteristic impedance; each successively larger circle is centered at a coordinate which is half the sum of the two intercepts of that circle with the horizontal axis. These two intercepts, in turn, are the characteristic conductance multiplied and divided, respectively, by the SWR for that circle.

In the chart, for example, the circle for $Z_o = 50$ and SWR = 3 intercepts the horizontal axis at G·3 and G/3, or 60 and 6.7; its center is at ½(60 + 6.7) = 33.3. Likewise, for $Z_o = 75$ and SWR = 2.5, G = 13.3, the intercepts are at 33.3 and 5.32; the center is at 19.3. □

Graphs give aperture time required for a-d conversion

by Eugene L. Zuch
Datel Systems Inc., Canton, Mass.

The time required for an analog-to-digital converter to make a conversion is known as "aperture time," and depends on both the resolution and the particular conversion method employed. For commercially available a-d converters that use the successive approximation method, the aperture time may be 40 microseconds for a relatively low-cost 12-bit converter, or as little as 4 μs for a more expensive high-speed 12-bit converter. In many cases a sample-hold circuit is used ahead of an a-d converter to effectively reduce the aperture times; the sample-hold can take a very fast sample of the analog signal and then hold the value while the a-d operation is performed. (The time interval during which the signal-hold circuit turns off is then the aperture time, and determines the conversion accuracy. The time for actual a-d conversion can be longer.)

It is important for the designer to know what aperture time is required to keep the system error to a tolerable value in terms of the resolution of his a-d coverter. The

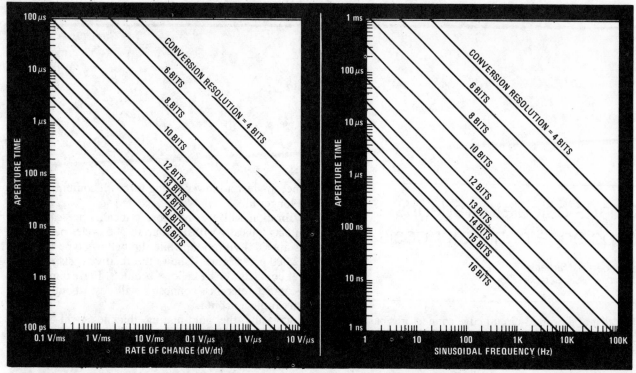

1. Sampling time. Aperture time for 1-bit accuracy at various resolutions in a-d conversion are shown here. Graph (a) gives aperture time as a function of signal rate of change for signals that are 10 volts full scale or 10 volts peak to peak. Graph (b) gives aperture time as a function of frequency for sinusoidal signals. Aperture times for larger allowed error can be found by reading on line for lower resolution, e.g., a 2-bit error and 8-bit resolution requires the same time as a 1-bit error and 7-bit resolution. Equations for these graphs are found in text.

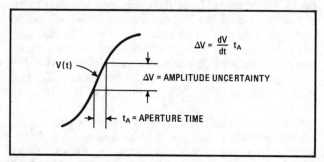

2. Error. Possibility of error in a-d conversion depends upon aperture time. The greater t_A is, the greater the uncertainty in value of an analog voltage that has been converted to digital level.

maximum aperture time that allows 1-bit accuracy in conversion of an analog signal to 4 bits, 6 bits, . . . or 16 bits is given here in two useful graphs. The graph in Fig. 1(a) shows this aperture time as a function of signal rate of change, for signals that are 10 volts full scale or peak to peak. Fig. 1(b) gives the aperture time as a function of the frequency of a sinusoidal signal.

The two graphs are derived with reference to Fig. 2, which shows a time-varying signal and the amplitude uncertainty ΔV associated with an aperture time t_A

$$t_A = \Delta V/(dV/dt)$$

If the fractional error ε is the ratio of ΔV to full-scale voltage V_{FS},

$$t_A = (\varepsilon V_{FS})/(dV/dt)$$

If ΔV is held to 1 bit, and V_{FS} is resolved into n bits, then $\varepsilon = 1/(2^n)$, and

$$t_A = V_{FS}/2^n(dV/dt)$$

This is the equation for the family of lines in Fig. 1(a), with $V_{FS} = 10$ volts and $n = 4, 6, . . . 16$.

For a sinusoidal signal, which has a maximum rate of change at its zero crossing,

$$\Delta V = t_A [d/dt(\tfrac{1}{2})(V \sin \omega t)]_{t-0} = \omega V t_A/2$$

where V is peak-to-peak signal value. This gives

$$t_A = (2\Delta V)/(\omega V) = \varepsilon/\pi f = 1/(2^n \pi f)$$

for a 1-bit error and n-bit resolution. This is the equation for the family of lines in Fig. 1(b).

If the allowed error is to be 2 bits instead of 1 bit, then $\varepsilon = 2/(2^n)$, so aperture times are doubled. An error of 3 bits gives $\varepsilon = 4/(2^n)$, and so on; thus a 1-bit increase in error is equivalent to a 1-bit decrease in resolution on the graphs.

As an example of the usefulness of these graphs, assume that a 1-kilohertz sinusoidal signal is to be digitized to a resolution of 10 bits. What aperture time must be used to give less than 1 bit of error? The answer, readily found from Fig. 1(b), is 320 nanoseconds. For ½ bit error the aperture time would have to be 160 ns. This is surprising, because a 1-kHz signal is really not very fast, and a 12-bit/320-ns converter is not to be found commercially available as a module. Therefore, a sample-hold circuit would be required ahead of a slower a-d converter. ☐

9. Tabular aids to design

Charts calculate tradeoffs in pc edge connector costs

by Robert R. Marker
Cinch Connectors, Elk Grove Village, Ill.

The cost of a printed-circuit edge connector is based primarily on the insulator and contact material, the number and type of contact, and the amount of gold plating used. These factors can be related to a standard reference connector, and percentage changes in cost for each option can be estimated.

The charts are based on actual cost figures developed over a long period of time, but care must be exercised in their use for cost estimating because other factors, such as the quantity and delivery time required, can have equal or greater impact on the price. The charts indicate, however, the possible economies in trading off cost for performance on several aspects of connector design.

All comparisons are made relative to an arbitrarily chosen reference connector commonly in use: a 22-position, dual-readout edge connector with diallyl phthalate insulator and wire-wrapping terminals, plus bellows-type contacts of phosphor bronze, grade A material, plated with 30 microinches of gold over the entire contact surface.

Cantilever contacts would decrease the connector cost, since such contacts are made in comb-like form and the carrier strip allows simultaneous loading of all contacts into the insulator. However, the cantilever contact will withstand fewer insertions and withdrawals (typically 50 cycles, versus the bellows contact's 100 cycles, if both have 30 microinches of gold). The bellows contact's longer engagement surface, more gentle en-

trance angle, and lower spring force all combine to give it a longer life.

Vibration will also be more critical, since cantilever contacts typically withstand up to 500 cycles per second of sinusoidal vibration, while the bellows type takes up to 2,000 cps. Figure 1 shows the relative costs of cantilever contacts versus bellows contacts. For example, the 22-contact reference connector will cost about 7% less with cantilever contacts.

Increasing the gold-plating thickness will increase contact life. Bellows-type contacts must be plated equally over the entire surface, but cantilever contacts can be selectively plated. Figure 2 shows relative costs of contacts that are barrel-plated (the bellows contacts) and selectively plated (cantilever contacts). The cost figures apply only to differences in gold thicknesses and do not cover the economies of simultaneous insertion of cantilever contacts. Thus, the chart indicates that to increase the life of the bellows contact from 100 to 500 cycles by applying 50 microinches of gold, rather than 30, would increase the cost by 16%. On the other hand, use of a cantilever contact selectively plated with 100 microinches to provide 500-cycle life would decrease plating costs to about 86% of the cost of the reference connector.

Contact material comparisons are shown in Fig. 3. Phosphor bronze costs about a third as much as beryllium copper, but is not recommended for use above 105°C, since it has a tendency toward stress relaxation. Beryllium copper can approach 150°C before encountering similar problems. Thus, from Fig. 3, using beryllium copper for the 22-contact connector will result in about a 7% increase in connector cost.

Another important factor in edge-connector performance and cost is the insulator material. The insulator must provide retention of the contact and electrical separation of the circuits under a variety of environmental conditions. Thermosetting compounds (diallyl phthalate and glass-reinforced or general-purpose phenolic) offer stability at high temperatures, but are relatively expensive, and can be difficult to mold and brittle in thinner wall sections. Thermoplastics (such as glass-reinforced nylon type 6/6, polycarbonate, and modified PPO—polyphenylene oxide) also can be used, but each has advantages and drawbacks.

Polycarbonate is stable and strong, but degrades when subjected to the chlorinated hydrocarbon cleaning solvents commonly used as flux removers. Nylon type 6/6 is resistant to these solvents but is hygroscopic, causing dimensional and electrical instability in moist

TABLE 1: MOLDED INSULATOR COSTS

Material	Relative Cost
Diallyl phthalate	100 %
Glass phenolic	93 %
General-purpose phenolic	59 %
Polycarbonate	58 %
Nylon 6/6	53.5 %
Modified PPO	53 %
Nylon 12	49 %
Celanex 917	36 %

TABLE 2: INSULATOR MATERIAL PERFORMANCE (96 HOURS AT 90/95% RELATIVE HUMIDITY AT 40°C)

INSULATION RESISTANCE (MEGOHMS)

Material	Before	During	30 min. after
Diallyl phthalate	20×10^6	20×10^6	20×10^6
Glass phenolic	10×10^6	1.5×10^5	2.5×10^5
G.P. phenolic	10×10^6	150	1000
Polycarbonate	20×10^6	20×10^6	20×10^6
Modified PPO	20×10^6	2.3×10^5	5×10^6
Nylon 6/6	20×10^6	9.8	1000
Celanex 917	20×10^6	5×10^6	15×10^6
Nylon 612	20×10^6	1×10^6	4×10^6

VOLTAGE BREAKDOWN (VOLTS RMS)

Material	Before	During	30 min. after
Polycarbonate	3144	2925	3125
Modified PPO	3075	2638	3006
Nylon 6/6	3000	2370	2410
Celanex 917	3183	3119	3160
Nylon 612	3244	3094	3150

(Thermosets not tested, but higher voltage breakdowns)

DIMENSIONAL STABILITY

Material	Length — before	Length — after
Polycarbonate	4.740	4.741
Modified PPO	4.741	4.741
Nylon 6/6	4.727	4.744
Celanex 917	4.730	4.732
Nylon 612	4.736	4.739

(Thermosets unaffected)

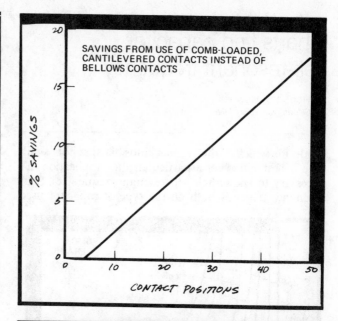

SAVINGS FROM USE OF COMB-LOADED, CANTILEVERED CONTACTS INSTEAD OF BELLOWS CONTACTS

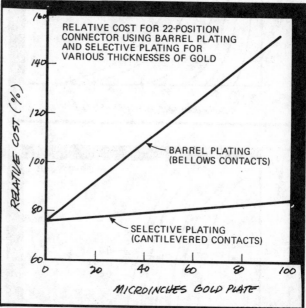

RELATIVE COST FOR 22-POSITION CONNECTOR USING BARREL PLATING AND SELECTIVE PLATING FOR VARIOUS THICKNESSES OF GOLD

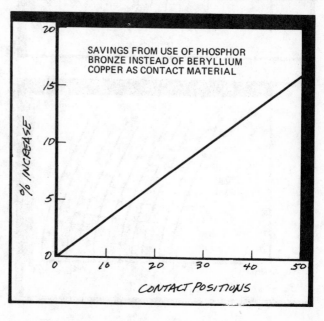

SAVINGS FROM USE OF PHOSPHOR BRONZE INSTEAD OF BERYLLIUM COPPER AS CONTACT MATERIAL

atmospheres. Glass-reinforced modified PPO is also susceptible to cleaning solvents, but is easily molded to close tolerances. New thermoplastic compounds, such as Celanex 917 and glass-reinforced nylon 612, are inexpensive to mold and are not subject to many of the disadvantages of other thermoplastics. Thus they can often be used in place of thermosetting compounds at considerable savings in cost.

Relative costs for molded insulators using various materials are based on molding in screw injection presses (see Table 1). Since processing time is a significant part of the insulator cost, these figures provide a much more accurate comparison than material costs alone would.

As an example, suppose the cost of the 22-position reference connector is known. For similar quantities and delivery times, assume that the engineer wants to estimate the cost of a connector that has the same number of contacts but uses polycarbonate insulation and cantilever contacts of phosphor bronze, selectively plated with 50 microinches of gold.

The cost-savings factor for polycarbonate insulation is 58%; for cantilever contacts, 93% (7% savings); for 50 microinches of selectively plated gold, 81%. Thus the cost of this connector would be (0.58)x(0.93)x(0.81), or about 44%, of the reference connector, according to the simple multiplication. However, the actual cost probably would not be precisely 44% of the reference cost—it would be safer to say around half the cost of the reference connector. □

Charts find capacitor self-resonant frequency

by Robert B. Cowdell
ITT Gilfillan, Van Nuys, Calif.

To decide which of the various kinds of capacitors available is best suited for a particular filter application, it's necessary to know their self-resonant frequencies. Self-resonance depends both on the type of capacitor used and the amount of lead length required. The charts plot the self-resonant frequency of several commonly used capacitor types for various values of lead length and capacitance.

For low-pass filter work, dry Mylar capacitors are the most popular because they are inexpensive, rugged, and fairly small. When capacitance values must exceed 5 microfarads, paper capacitors are a good choice. Ceramic units find use in miniature filters because of their high volumetric efficiency, and mica units are better suited for higher-frequency applications □

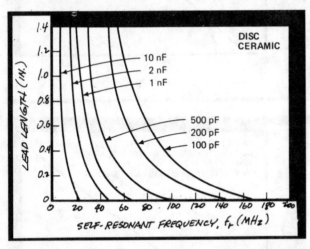

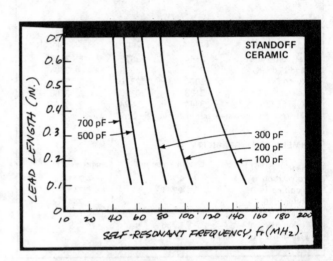

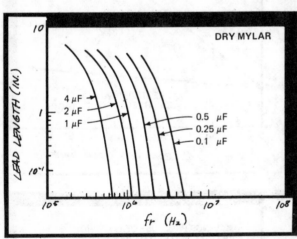

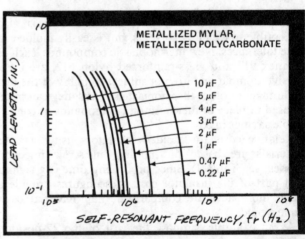

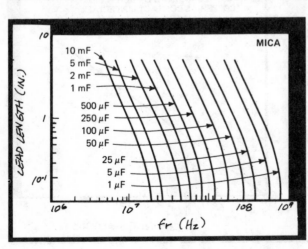

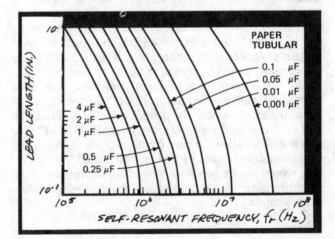

Equation table speeds design of symmetrical pi attenuators

by John J. Kush
General Electric Co., APO, San Francisco, Calif.

Attenuators are resistance networks used to reduce voltage, current, or power in controllable known amounts.

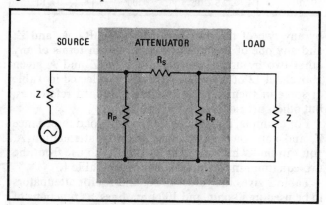

Easy. Symmetrical pi attenuator always presents matched load Z to source. Ratio of resistors R_P and R_S determines amount of attenuation, and Z determines their values. Any one of the four parameters A, Z, R_P, and R_S can be expressed in terms of any two of the others. Collection of expressions in Table 1 aids attenuator calculations.

One common type is the symmetrical pi attenuator shown in the figure.

In the symmetrical pi attenuator, the source and load impedances Z are equal, and the two parallel resistors R_P are equal. Values of R_P and series resistor R_S are selected so the impedance of the network with the load connected is equal to the source impedance. That is,

$$Z = \frac{R_P[R_S + R_P Z/(R_P + Z)]}{R_P + R_S + R_P Z/(R_P + Z)}$$

The attenuator and load form a voltage divider, so if the terminal voltage of the source is V_T, then the voltage across the load, V_L, is $R_P Z V_T/(R_P R_S + R_S Z + R_P Z)$. The total power output from the source, P_T, is V_T^2/Z whether the attenuator is in the circuit or not.

When the attenuator is in the circuit, part of the total power output from the source is dissipated in the attenuator, and the remainder of the power is delivered to the load. The ratio of the total output power to the power delivered to the load is the attenuation ratio, A.

$$A = P_T/P_L = (V_T^2/Z)/(V_L^2/Z)$$
$$= \frac{[R_S + R_P Z/(R_P + Z)]^2}{[R_P Z/(R_P + Z)]^2}$$

The power drop expressed in decibels is

$$dB\ attenuation = 10\ log_{10}A$$

A symmetrical pi attenuator is completely described

PARAMETER	AS A FUNCTION OF					
	Z, A	R_P, R_S	R_P, A	R_P, Z	R_S, Z	R_S, A
R_P	$\dfrac{Z(\sqrt{A}+1)}{\sqrt{A}-1}$				$\dfrac{Z}{R_S}\left[Z+\sqrt{Z^2+R_S^2}\right]$	$\dfrac{2\sqrt{A}}{(\sqrt{A}-1)^2}R_S$
R_S	$\dfrac{Z(A-1)}{2\sqrt{A}}$		$\dfrac{(\sqrt{A}-1)^2}{2\sqrt{A}}R_P$	$\dfrac{(\sqrt{A}-1)R_P Z}{R_P+Z}$		
A		$\left[1+\dfrac{R_S}{R_P}\sqrt{1+\dfrac{2R_P}{R_S}+\dfrac{R_S}{R_P}}\right]^2$		$\left(\dfrac{R_P+Z}{R_P-Z}\right)^2$	$\left[\dfrac{R_S}{Z}+\sqrt{\dfrac{R_S^2}{Z^2}+1}\right]^2$	
Z		$\dfrac{R_P}{\sqrt{1+2R_P/R_S}}$	$\dfrac{(\sqrt{A}-1)R_P}{\sqrt{A}+1}$			$\dfrac{2\sqrt{A}}{A-1}R_S$

TABLE 1: RELATIONS OF PARAMETERS FOR SYMMETRICAL PI ATTENUATOR

dB ATTENUATION = 10 LOG A

TABLE 2: SERIES AND PARALLEL RESISTANCE VALUES FOR SYMMETRICAL PI ATTENUATORS IN 50-OHM AND 100-OHM LINES							
Attenuation			R_S / R_P	For Z = 50 Ω		For Z = 100 Ω	
dB	A	$\sqrt{A}$		R_P (Ω)	R_S (Ω)	R_P (Ω)	R_S (Ω)
0	1.00	1.00	0	∞	0	∞	0
1	1.26	1.122	0.00663	870	5.77	1,740	11.5
3	2.00	1.413	0.0602	292	17.6	585	35.2
5	3.16	1.78	0.170	178	30.4	357	60.8
10	10	3.16	0.739	96.2	71.2	192	142
20	10^2	10.0	4.05	61.1	248	122	495
30	10^3	31.6	14.8	53.3	790	106	1,580
50	10^5	316	157	50.3	7,910	101	15,800
100	10^{10}	10^5	5×10^4	50	2.5×10^6	100	5×10^6

by any two of the four parameters R_P, R_S, A, and Z; and any one of them can be expressed in terms of any other two by use of the equations for Z and A given above. All 12 of the relationships are collected in Table 1; some of them can be found in standard references, but others are not readily available.

For example, if you know source and load impedance Z, and you want a particular value of attenuation A, you can find what values of R_P and R_S to use from the two equations in the first column of the Table 1.

Table 2 gives the values of R_P and R_S for attenuators to be used in 50-ohm and 100-ohm lines, as functions of dB attenuation. These attenuators are designed for the specific line impedances; if a different line impedance is used, the attenuation factor is not correct. □

Comparing coaxial cable shielding effectiveness

Radiation from coaxial cables has always been a concern of design engineers. That concern has been intensified by the most recent FCC document on cable TV systems radiation, which all CATV systems must now meet. And although these requirements apply to the CATV system as a whole (the cable, connectors, splitters, amplifiers, and other components), the allowable radiation levels for coaxial cables must be kept to a minimum for good shielding effectiveness.

Whether you're looking for a low-cost coaxial cable for short runs that will meet the FCC specification, or merely comparing effectiveness of the different shielding configurations, the following curves should prove helpful. The curves supplied by Belden Corp.'s Electronic division, Chicago, show the results of shielding effectiveness tests on RG/59/U-type CATV drop cable (for short runs from main cable to a subscriber's house) from 5 megahertz to 270 MHz.

The top curve illustrates the relative effectiveness of a shielding configuration consisting of Belden Duofoil film-sandwiched aluminum foil, plus a 61% shield coverage of tinned copper braid. The other two curves detail the isolation performance of 59/U-type CATV drop cables without foil and with different amounts of tinned-copper-braid shield.

The middle curve details isolation versus frequency for a cable with 94.5% coverage braid (this kind is usually specified by the military services). The lower curve illustrates the shielding effectiveness of the same grade and style of cable, but with a relatively open 55% coverage braid.

All the curves dip in their values of isolation at about 70 MHz and 200 MHz. These dips result from quarter-wave resonance inherent in the 3-foot cable sample. Changing the sample length does not eliminate these resonance dips—it only alters the frequencies at which they occur.   □

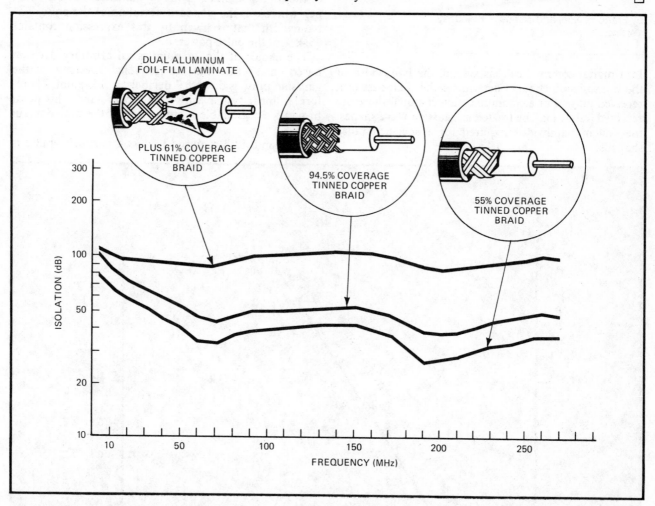

DUAL ALUMINUM FOIL-FILM LAMINATE

PLUS 61% COVERAGE TINNED COPPER BRAID

94.5% COVERAGE TINNED COPPER BRAID

55% COVERAGE TINNED COPPER BRAID

ISOLATION (dB)

FREQUENCY (MHz)

The Electromagnetic Spectrum Chart, published in the Sept. 25, 1972 issue of *Electronics,* contained several errors. Corrections for the more significant of these are listed in the table below, which can be clipped and affixed to the bottom of the chart for permanent reference.

FREQUENCY ALLOCATION	CORRECTION
640 & 1240 kHz	Delete reference to Civil Defense stations.
(21.870–22.0)MHz	Change note "Also aero fixed" to "Aero fixed only."
(121.975–123.075)MHz & (123.575–136)MHz	Should indicate both aeronautical mobile and aeronautical mobile satellite.
(137–138)MHz	Should show meteorological satellite instead of mobile satellite
(225–328.6)MHz	Add mobile satellite.
(335.4–399.9)MHz	Change amateur satellite to mobile satellite.
(406–406.1)MHz	Change note "Meteorological satellite" to "Mobile satellite."

FREQUENCY ALLOCATION	CORRECTION
466 MHz	Change to 460 MHz.
(460–470)MHz	Should indicate land-mobile and meteorological satellite. Delete mobile satellite allocation. Band is non-Government only.
(1535–1660)MHz	See correction to 15.4–15.7-GHz allocation.
(2500–2535)MHz	Should show broadcast satellite, fixed and fixed satellite uplink only. Delete amateur-satellite designation.
(15.4–15.7)GHz and (15.7–17.7)GHz	Notes should be applied to bands between 1535–1660 MHz. Notes "Proposed collision-avoidance systems" and "Radar altimeters" should be applied to band 1558.5–1636.5-MHz.

Nomograph shows bandwidth for specified pulse shape

by Franc E. Noel and James S. Kolodzey
IBM Corp., Poughkeepsie, N.Y.

In a digital communications system, the bandwidth of the transmission channel determines the sharpness of a received pulse. For a communication channel where the received pulses may be treated as gaussian wave shapes, the system bandwidth required for a specified pulse shape is:

$$F = (2/\pi T)[2\ ln(1/P)]^{1/2}$$

where, as in Fig. 2, T is the width of the time slot, P is the normalized height of the gaussian pulse at the ends of the time slot, and F is the 2σ bandwidth of the channel, where σ is the standard deviation of the pulse. The bandwidth that is given by this expression contains 95.45% of the pulse power.

The choice of the 2σ point is an arbitrary decision based on the fact that the frequency spectrum of the gaussian pulse is down 8.7 decibels at this point. Therefore, a linear system with a bandpass flat to this point provides a reasonable reproduction of the time-domain pulse.

The bandwidth required to pass a particular pulse is

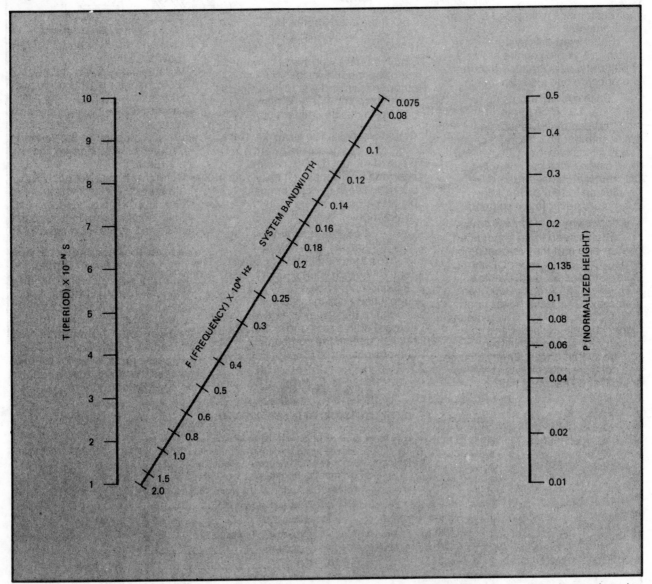

1. How wide the band? This nomograph shows the bandwidth F that contains over 95% of the energy in the spectrum of a gaussian pulse, where the duration of the pulse is T and the normalized amplitude of its end points is P (as shown in Fig. 2).

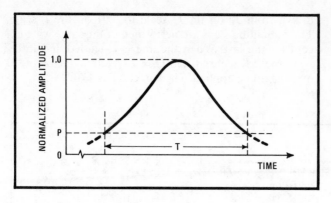

2. Pulse parameters. Time-domain representation of gaussian pulse shows normalized amplitude P at edges of time slot T. A low value for P gives low spillover into next slot, and therefore low error rate, but requires large bandwidth in transmission system.

given by the nomograph in Fig. 1. The values of the time slot, T, and normalized amplitude desired at the ends, P, are connected with a straight edge to determine the frequency axis crossover. For example, a time pulse that is down to $1/e^2$, or 0.135, at the edges of a 12.5-nanosecond time slot can be passed with a system bandwidth of 102 megahertz. □

A quick solution to conductive heat transfer problems

by International Electronic Research Corp. staff
Burbank, Calif.

Anyone looking for a shortcut to solving the conductive heat transfer equation should find this nomograph very useful. It is based on the more familiar units of watts and inches, and can help solve for any unknown within the equation. The accuracy of the result depends on how careful you are in plotting the points.

For example, suppose you wished to find the temperature drop across each segment of a one-inch-square sandwich of beryllium oxide and aluminum, separated by a 0.001-in. layer of air, that must conduct 30 watts.

The nomograph can be used to solve for ΔT across the 0.12-in. BeO layer once the heat conductivity, k, is found (table lists typical values).
■ Draw a line from 30 on Q scale to 0.12 on L scale, and note the point where it crosses reference line 1.
■ Draw another line from this reference point to 80 on k scale (exact value depends on the particular type of BeO). Note where this line crosses reference line 2.
■ Draw a third line from this point through 1 on the left side of A scale—and read 0.78°C on the left of the ΔT

THERMAL-CONDUCTION DATA FOR VARIOUS MATERIALS AT APPROXIMATELY 65°C			
Material	Density (lb/in.³)	Thermal conductivity, k (W/in.·°C)	(Btu/hr-ft-°F)
Silver	0.380	10.6	241
Copper	0.322	9.7	220
Gold	0.696	7.5	171
Aluminum, pure	0.098	5.5	125
Aluminum, 63S	0.100	5.1	116
Magnesium	0.063	4.0	91
Beryllium oxides	0.109 to 0.136	1.7 to 3.9	38.7 to 88.7
Red brass	0.316	2.8	63.7
Yellow brass	0.310	2.4	54.6
Beryllium copper	0.297	2.1	47.8
Pure iron	0.284	1.9	43.2
Phosphor bronze	0.318	1.3	29.6
Soft steel	0.284	1.18	26.8
Monel	0.318	0.9	20.5
Lead	0.409	0.83	18.9
Hard steel	0.284	0.65	14.8
Steatite	0.094	0.06	13.6
Pyrex	0.094	0.032	0.728
Grade A Lava	0.085	0.03	0.683
Soft glass	0.094	0.025	0.569
Water	0.0361	0.0167	0.380
Mica	0.101	0.015	0.341
Paper-base phenolic	0.0497	0.007	0.159
Plexiglas	0.043	0.0047	0.107
P-43 casting resin	0.045	0.0046	0.105
Maple	0.025	0.0042	0.096
Pine	0.018	0.003	0.067
Polystyrene	0.038	0.0027	0.061
Glass wool	0.001	0.001	0.023
Air	0.000043	0.0007	0.016

scale. (If the right side of the A scale were used, then the right of the ΔT scale would also have to be used).

The ΔT across the 0.09-in. thick piece of aluminum and the ΔT across the 0.001-in. air gap are found in similar fashion. But there is one correction that must be made for the air gap case: since the L scale does not extend to 0.001, a factor of 10 must be used and the line drawn from 30 on the Q scale to 0.01 on the L scale. The remaining steps are performed in the same way, except for the last. When the line is extended and intersects the ΔT scale at 430°C, a correction factor of 10 must again be applied. The corect ΔT is 43°C.

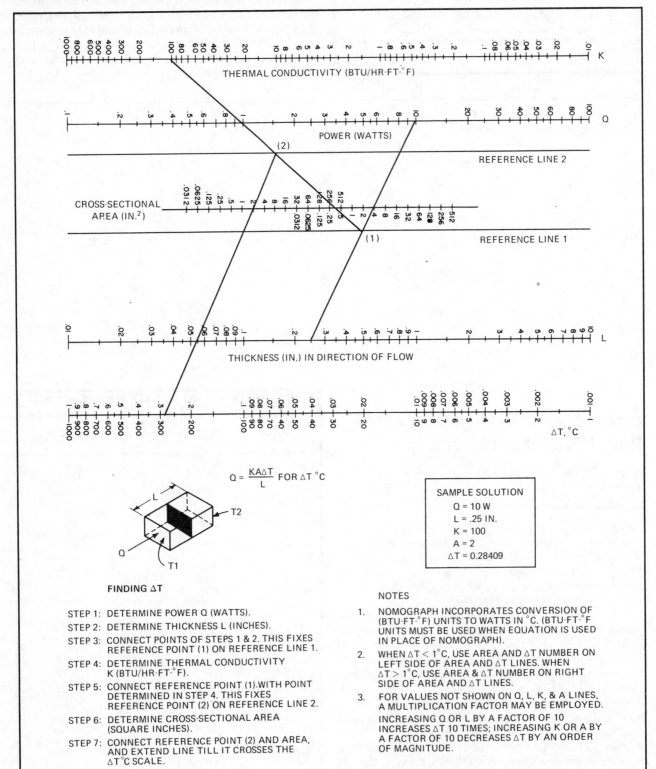

$$Q = \frac{KA\Delta T}{L} \text{ FOR } \Delta T \,°C$$

SAMPLE SOLUTION
Q = 10 W
L = .25 IN.
K = 100
A = 2
ΔT = 0.28409

FINDING ΔT

STEP 1: DETERMINE POWER Q (WATTS).
STEP 2: DETERMINE THICKNESS L (INCHES).
STEP 3: CONNECT POINTS OF STEPS 1 & 2. THIS FIXES REFERENCE POINT (1) ON REFERENCE LINE 1.
STEP 4: DETERMINE THERMAL CONDUCTIVITY K (BTU/HR·FT·°F).
STEP 5: CONNECT REFERENCE POINT (1) WITH POINT DETERMINED IN STEP 4. THIS FIXES REFERENCE POINT (2) ON REFERENCE LINE 2.
STEP 6: DETERMINE CROSS-SECTIONAL AREA (SQUARE INCHES).
STEP 7: CONNECT REFERENCE POINT (2) AND AREA, AND EXTEND LINE TILL IT CROSSES THE ΔT°C SCALE.

NOTES

1. NOMOGRAPH INCORPORATES CONVERSION OF (BTU·FT·°F) UNITS TO WATTS IN °C. (BTU·FT·°F UNITS MUST BE USED WHEN EQUATION IS USED IN PLACE OF NOMOGRAPH).

2. WHEN ΔT < 1°C, USE AREA AND ΔT NUMBER ON LEFT SIDE OF AREA AND ΔT LINES. WHEN ΔT > 1°C, USE AREA & ΔT NUMBER ON RIGHT SIDE OF AREA AND ΔT LINES.

3. FOR VALUES NOT SHOWN ON Q, L, K, & A LINES, A MULTIPLICATION FACTOR MAY BE EMPLOYED.

   INCREASING Q OR L BY A FACTOR OF 10 INCREASES ΔT 10 TIMES; INCREASING K OR A BY A FACTOR OF 10 DECREASES ΔT BY AN ORDER OF MAGNITUDE.

Graphic aids simplify low-pass filter design

by Robert B. Cowdell
ITT Gilfillan, Van Nuys, Calif.

Designing single-element low-pass interference filters for matched or mismatched systems can be reduced to the use of a few graphs and some simple equations. With this design technique, even the degrading effect of capacitor lead length on filter insertion loss can be easily determined.

The extent to which lead inductance influences filter insertion loss depends on the type of capacitor used. Since dry Mylar capacitors are used in approximately 75% of all filter applications, they will be characterized here. Their popularity can be attributed to their ruggedness, low cost, and small size for the capacitance values of interest (0.1 microfarad to 5 μF).

Both ideal and practical low-pass capacitor filters are shown in Fig. 1. The practical version, of course, includes a series inductance to account for capacitor lead length. Letting:

$F = f/f_o$ = normalized frequency ratio

where f is the frequency of interest (in hertz) and f_o is the filter cutoff frequency (also in hertz), and:

$A = R_L/R_S$ = mismatch ratio

where R_L is the load resistance, and R_S is the source resistance, the insertion loss for the ideal capacitor filter can be written as:

I.L. $= 10 \log[1 + F^2(4A^2/(1+A)^2)]$

For an ideal low-pass inductor filter, the equation for insertion loss is:

I.L. $= 10 \log[1 + F^2(4/(1+A)^2)]$

Capacitor radian cutoff frequency can be expressed as:

$\omega_o = 2/R_SC$

For inductors, this equation is:

$\omega_o = 2R_S/L$

Insertion loss curves (black lines) for the ideal capacitor filter can be plotted over a range of normalized frequencies for several values of mismatch ratio A, as is done in Fig. 1. The same curves will be obtained for an ideal inductor filter, but the values of A must be inverted. A nomograph (Fig. 2) can solve both radian cutoff frequency equations.

The insertion loss of the practical capacitor filter can be computed from:

I.L. $= 10 \log[1 + (F^2/(1 - F_r^2)^2)(4A^2/(1+A)^2)]$

where normalized resonant frequency $F_r = f/f_r$ and self-resonant frequency $f_r = 1/(2\pi LC)$. The equations for the practical and ideal cases differ only by the term, $(1 - F_r^2)^2$, which is, by definition, the universal reso-

1. Only ideal capacitor filters follow insertion-loss curves plotted for several values of mismatch ratio A. Self-resonant frequency curve (color) corrects for lead and internal-foil winding inductances. Ideal curves can also be used for ideal inductor filters.

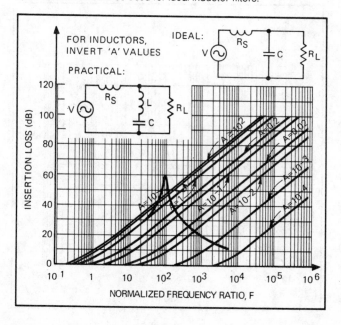

2. Low-pass cutoff frequency f_o, source resistance R_S, and L or C value can be found with straight-edge. Nomograph solves two radian cutoff frequency equations: $\omega_o = 2/R_SC$ and $\omega_o = 2R_S/L$.

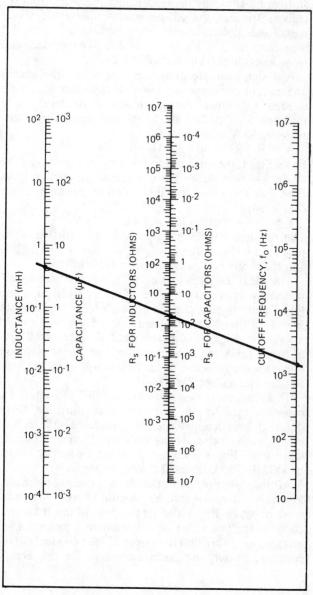

nance correction factor. For frequencies beyond cutoff, the practical insertion loss can be expressed as:

I.L. = $10 \log[F^2(4A^2)/(1+A)^2] - 20 \log(1-F_r^2)$,
permitting the correction factor to be added to or subtracted from the insertion loss of the ideal filter.

Plotting this last equation yields the universal resonance curve shown in Fig. 1. The departure of this curve from the ideal curves is the same for any value of capacitance and under any mismatch condition.

Although the curve's shape is always the same, its frequency location shifts with the value of capacitor self-resonant frequency f_r, and the curve's peak always occurs at f_r. Therefore, the practical filter's insertion loss follows one of the ideal curves (depending on mismatch ratio) until the self-resonance condition begins to dominate; then filter insertion loss follows the resonance curve.

A graph of the self-resonant frequency of dry Mylar capacitors is shown in Fig. 3 for various lead lengths and capacitance values. The shape of a capacitor, as well as its voltage rating (which dictates its size), alters capacitor internal inductance, but produces only a slight shift in f_r. Typically, as lead length increases from 0.1 inch to 3 inches, the self-resonant frequency of a 1-μF metallized polycarbonate capacitor shifts from 1.3 megahertz to 530 kilohertz for a 50-volt device, and from 1 MHz to 530 kHz for a 400-V device.

A design example illustrates how to use the graphs and equations. Suppose a low-pass capacitor filter were needed to reduce the conducted noise level on a matched 50-ohm line by 57 dB at 1 MHz. First, mismatch ratio A must be found:

A = R_L/R_S = 50 Ω/50 Ω = 1
From Fig. 1, the intersection of the A = 1 curve and the 57-dB loss line yields the normalized frequency ratio, F = 700; from this, the filter cutoff frequency is easily computed:

f_o = f/F = 1 MHz/700 = 1.4 kHz
The required capacitor value is found with Fig. 2 by placing a straightedge through the points f_o = 1.4 kHz and R_S = 50 ohms, which yields a value of C = 4.5 μF.

The ideal-insertion-loss curve of interest is now obtained by overlaying a piece of transparent paper on Fig. 1 and aligning cutoff frequency f_o = 1.4 kHz with F = 1 on Fig. 2. (Normalized frequency F = 1 should always be aligned with the desired filter cutoff frequency.) Trace the curve for A = 1 on the work paper to obtain the response of an ideal 4.5-μF capacitor in a 50-ohm system (see Fig. 4).

This ideal curve now must be modified to account for capacitor lead length. For illustration purposes, three different lead lengths will be considered—0.1 inch, 2 inches, and 4 inches. Using the curve for a 4-μF capacitance from Fig. 3 gives self-resonant frequency values of 640 kHz, 350 kHz, and 245 kHz, respectively.

All the data needed to sketch the practical-insertion-loss curve is now available. Again, overlay the same work paper on Fig. 1 and set the peak of the resonance curve at the first value of self-resonant frequency (640 kHz), making sure that the slopes of the two ideal curves coincide. Sketch the resonance curve for the first f_r

value, as well as the other two, as shown in Fig. 4.

Measured data for the 0.1-inch lead length curve agrees very closely with the computed results from 50 kHz to 2.5 MHz. For higher frequencies, computed insertion loss is inaccurate because of reactance effects.   □

■ *Self-resonant frequency curves for other capacitors will appear shortly in Engineer's notebook.*

3. Self-resonant frequency varies with capacitor type, as well as lead length. Curves shown are for dry Mylar capacitors.

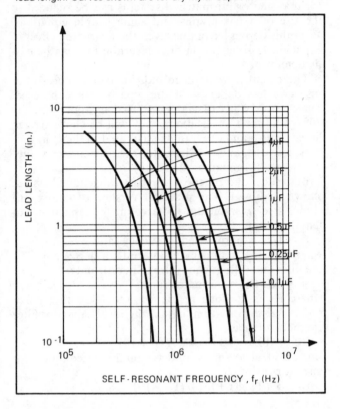

4. Design graph is generated by drawing appropriate ideal insertion-loss curve from Fig. 1. Self-resonance curve (color) can also be drawn, once correct self-resonant frequency is found with Fig. 3.

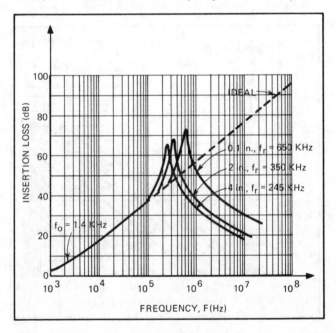

Filter bandwidth nomograph gives sweep-rate limits

by Roger T. Stevens
The Mitre Corp., McLean, Va.

Because it is convenient, the sweep frequency generator is commonly employed to obtain the bandwidth and bandpass characteristics of narrow-band filters. However, these characteristics will be seriously distorted unless the proper sweep width and sweep rate are used. The nomograph shows the maximum permissible values of sweep rate and sweep width allowable to assure that the measured filter bandwidth will be within 1% of the true bandwidth.

The illustrated filter "characteristics" demonstrate the effect of too fast a sweep rate. When a filter having an 11-kilohertz bandwidth is tested at the excessively fast rate of 7 kHz with a 70-kHz-wide sweep, the apparent filter bandwidth is much wider than the true bandwidth, and the bandpass curve is highly distorted. But if the same filter is swept with a 7-kHz-wide sweep at a rate of 41 hertz, the shape of the bandpass curve and the bandwidth produced are the same as would be obtained by point-to-point measurements.

The explanation as to why this occurs is complex, but it can be simplified. Roughly speaking, the filter responds in turn to each instantaneous frequency during a very slow sweep; but for very fast sweep speeds, the in-

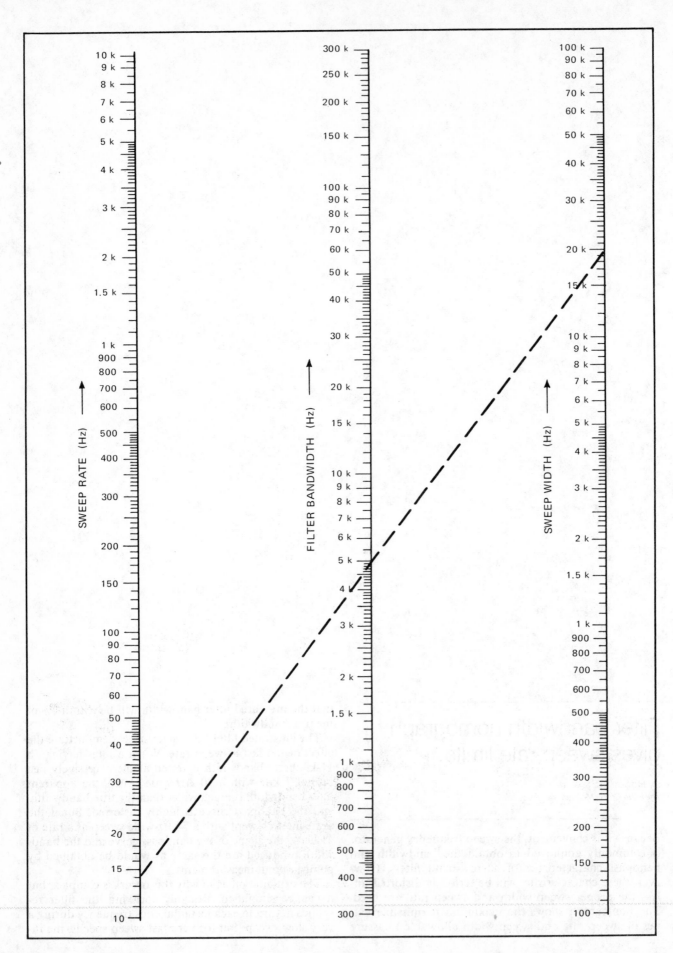

SWEEP RATE (Hz)

FILTER BANDWIDTH (Hz)

SWEEP WIDTH (Hz)

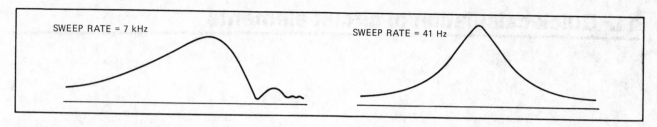

SWEEP RATE = 7 kHz

SWEEP RATE = 41 Hz

put that is applied to the filter begins to approach an impulse function, causing the filter to produce an output over the entire frequency spectrum.

The apparent bandwidth, B, of the swept filter is:

$$B = (4s^2 + b^4)/b$$

where s is the sweep rate in radians per second, and b is the true filter bandwidth in radians per second. From this equation, it can be seen that, as the sweep rate approaches zero, the apparent bandwidth is the same as the true bandwidth. For very fast sweeps, the apparent bandwidth is larger than the true bandwidth.

For most measurement applications, it is desirable to keep the apparent bandwidth within 1% of the true bandwidth. By substituting $B = 1.01b$ in the above equation (to achieve the 1% accuracy) and converting from radians per second to hertz, the product of the sweep width (W) and sweep rate (R) becomes:

$$W \times R = 0.01128b^2$$

This equation is represented by the nomograph.

To use the nomograph, simply draw a straight line connecting the desired points. Remember that the figures given for sweep rate and for sweep width are maximum permissible values, while those given for filter bandwidth are the minimum permissible values.

As an example, let expected filter bandwidth be 5 kHz, and, to show the significant portion of the bandpass curve, let sweep width be 20 kHz. The dashed color line drawn across the nomograph indicates that the maximum permissible sweep rate is 14.5 Hz. Therefore, if a commercial sweep generator with a 60-Hz sweep rate were used to check this filter's characteristics, the results would be highly distorted. ☐

Quick calculation gives filter-capacitor value

by Jerry J. Norton
LaBarge Electronics, Tulsa, Okla.

The minimum capacitance required for a given amount of ripple from a rectifier/filter power supply can be calculated simply from the expression:

Ripple voltage/peak voltage = T/RC

As illustrated in the figure, ripple voltage E_R is the difference between the peak and valley output voltages, (E_P – E_V). The ripple period, T, is the inverse of the power-line frequency for a half-wave rectifier, or half that value for the full-wave rectifier shown. Resistance R is the load through which current is being driven.

This short-cut technique for finding C holds to about 25% ripple. It assumes that the charging time for C is small, compared to its discharge time through R, so that T is virtually equal to t_d. In that case:

$$(E_P - E_V)/E_P = E_R/E_P = 1 - exp(-T/RC)$$

Note that as T/RC approaches zero, the ripple voltage also approaches zero, but especially note that for small values of T/RC, the right-hand side of the equation approaches T/RC.

Therefore the C value for 10% ripple is found by setting T/RC equal to 0.1, and if ripple must be held to 1%, T/RC must equal 0.01. The error from this approximation is less than the tolerance in the capacitors used.

For example, consider the circuit shown, and use the following circuit values:

Transformer: 12.6 v center-tapped rms, 50/60 Hz
Peak voltage: 8.9 v
Load: 8 v, 2 A
Diode drop: 0.9 v
Then E_P = 8.9 – 0.9 = 8.0 v peak, the load resistance is

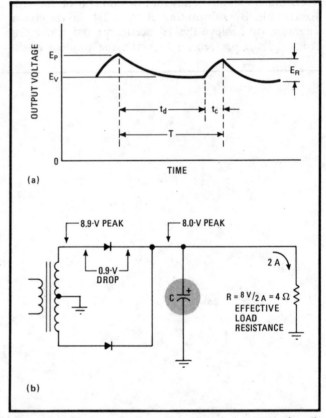

(a)

(b)

How much C? For a given amount of ripple in output of rectifier/filter power supply, the minimum value of capacitor C is closely approximated by expression E_R/E_P = T/RC. Output waveform is shown in (a), and full-wave rectifier circuit is shown in (b). Numerical values are those of example in text.

8 v/2 A = 4 ohms, and T is 0.01 second for 50 Hz or 0.00833 s for 60 Hz.

For 1% ripple, C = T/0.01R = 250,000 microfarads, yielding 0.08 v pk-pk ripple. For 10% ripple, C = T/0.1R = 25,000 μF, giving 0.8 v pk-pk ripple.

Allowing slightly more ripple saves considerably on capacitance in the filter, and the regulator can handle that ripple. □

Power rating calculations for variable resistors

by Randy Ragan
Mepco/Electra, Inc., San Diego, Calif.

A variable resistor's power rating is influenced not only by the voltage and current applied, but also by the position of its slider and the size of its load. The power rating limits the maximum uniformly distributed power that a variable resistor can dissipate at a given temperature. In effect, the power rating is established by the maximum hot-spot temperature that the resistive element can withstand when the slider is floating. With the circuit labels noted, the maximum unloaded limit can be expressed as:

$$W_{max} = E^2/R_P$$

If the variable resistor is used as a rheostat, the voltage applied across the unit's terminals must be limited to:

$$E_{max} = (1 - K)(W_{max}R_P)^{1/2}$$

where $(1 - K)$ is the smallest fraction of R_P that will remain in the circuit at the minimum resistance setting of the rheostat. The unit's slider current rating must also be respected. For a rheostat, this current is:

$$I_S = E/(1 - K)R_P$$

If the variable resistor is used as a potentiometer and is loaded, the power rating must be reduced because of the disproportionate amount of current drawn through the upper part of R_P and the slider. The degree of derating depends on how large K, the fractional setting, may be. Usually, it is assumed that there is no heat transfer from the more heavily loaded part of R_P to the less heavily loaded part. (This is also true for operation as a rheostat.)

Actually, there are two limitations on power rating when the potentiometer is operated with appreciable loading: power dissipation and slider current rating. The voltage across the upper part of R_P can be written as:

$$E_1 = E[R_P(K - K^2) + R_L(1 - K)]/$$
$$[R_P(K - K^2) + R_L]$$

This voltage may not exceed:

$$E_{1(max)} = (1 - K)(W_{max}R_P)^{1/2}$$

where W_{max} is the unloaded power rating of the potentiometer. Therefore, the maximum voltage that may be applied to a loaded potentiometer is:

$$E = (W_{max}R_P)^{1/2}[R_P + R_L(K - K^2)]/[R_P + R_L/K]$$

And the current through the slider is:

$$I_S = (E - E_1)/R_L = E/[R_P(1 - K) + R_L/K]$$

This value, of course, must not exceed the potentiometer's slider current rating.

Besides power rating, noise is another important consideration. For a film potentiometer, noise voltage is generally assumed to be generated in the signal-return leg. This voltage, therefore, is in series with the active portion of R_P and the load. (In practice, only a proportional part of the noise is generated by the active part of R_P.)

The interface between the slider and the film element generates a minute voltage because of a thermocouple (Seebeck) effect. This thermal emf is roughly proportional to temperature and can frequently be considered negligible. The graph indicates typical noise performance for carbon-film and metal-film potentiometers. □

Variable resistor. Slider position and slider current rating must be considered when the power rating is being computed.

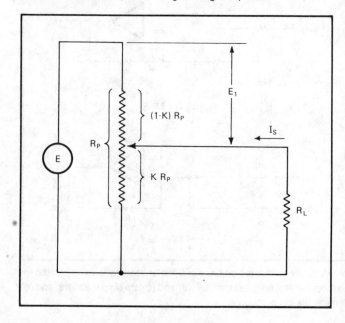

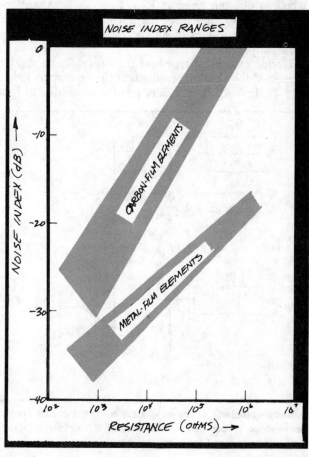

Calculating resistances for sum and difference networks

by D. Sheingold
Analog Devices Inc., Norwood, Mass.

Whenever signals must be added and/or subtracted, a few simple computations will yield resistance values that provide equal resistive loading at the two inputs of an operational amplifier to minimize offset-current errors. The loading resistance can have any desired value.

Figure 1 shows the general sum or difference network; it produces an output voltage given by

$$E_O = a_1 V_1 + a_2 V_2 + \ldots$$
$$- (b_1 V_{101} + b_2 V_{102} + \ldots)$$

where the Vs are input voltages. The voltages that are to be added ($V_1, V_2, V_3 \ldots$) are applied to the noninverting terminal of the operational amplifier through resistors $R_1, R_2, \ldots$, and the voltages that are to be subtracted ($V_{101}, V_{102}, \ldots$) are applied to the inverting terminal through resistors $R_{101}, R_{102}, \ldots$. Shunt resistor R_0 or R_L and feedback resistor R_F complete the network. The values of all the resistors are found by these simple rules:

■ Decide what composite load resistance, R_p, should be presented to the input terminals of the op amp. A value of 5 kilohms for R_p provides good bandwidth and low

noise pickup without too much loading of the input sources or the output.

■ Add up the positive coefficients (call this sum Σa).

■ Add up the negative coefficients (call this sum Σb), and add 1.00.

■ If Σa is greater than $(1 + \Sigma b)$, the network must include an R_L (for gain). If Σa is less than $(1 + \Sigma b)$, the network must include an R_0 (for attenuation). If Σa is equal to $(1 + \Sigma b)$, neither R_L nor R_0 is used.

■ Find R_F by taking the larger of Σa or $(1 + \Sigma b)$, and multiplying it by R_p. (The number that multiplies R_p here is called the closed-loop gain or "noise gain.")

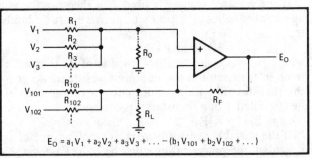

$$E_O = a_1 V_1 + a_2 V_2 + a_3 V_3 + \ldots - (b_1 V_{101} + b_2 V_{102} + \ldots)$$

1. Summing circuit. Output voltage from operational amplifier is sum of positive and negative terms that are related to input voltages by positive or negative coefficients. Signs of terms depend on which input terminal is fed, and magnitudes of terms depend on voltages and resistances. Simple procedure determines resistance values that yield the desired output while making op-amp input terminals see equal resistive loadings of any desired level. Circuit may include balancing resistor R_0 or R_L or neither, but never requires both.

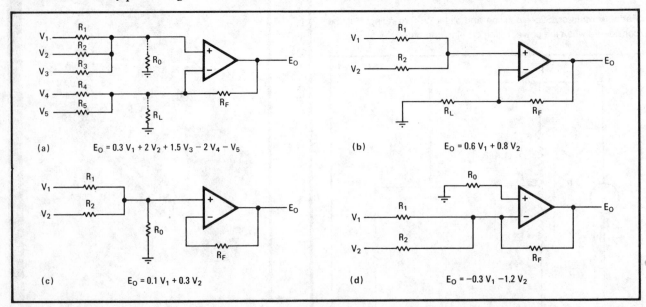

(a) $E_O = 0.3 V_1 + 2 V_2 + 1.5 V_3 - 2 V_4 - V_5$

(b) $E_O = 0.6 V_1 + 0.8 V_2$

(c) $E_O = 0.1 V_1 + 0.3 V_2$

(d) $E_O = -0.3 V_1 - 1.2 V_2$

2. Sample problems. Examples in text refer to these circuits. Resistor values are calculated on basis of 5-kilohm loading, a value chosen for convenience, at each input terminal of op amp. The circuit in (a) is the most general adder-subtractor; (b) and (c) are simple adders; and (d) is an inverting adder. Each example highlights a particular feature of the calculation procedure.

- R_L or R_0 is equal to R_F divided by the absolute value of $(1 + \Sigma b - \Sigma a)$.
- The value of each of the other resistances is found by dividing R_F by the associated coefficient: i.e. $R_1 = R_F/a_1$, $R_{102} = R_F/b_{102}$, and so forth.

As an example, the resistors for the network in Fig. 2(a) can be found by following the above rules:

> *Choose $R_p = 5\ k\Omega$*
> *$\Sigma a = 3.8$*
> *$(1 + \Sigma b) = 4.0$*
> *$(1 + \Sigma b) - \Sigma a = 0.2$ (An R_0 is needed.)*
> *$R_F = 4 \times 5\ k\Omega = 20\ k\Omega$ (Closed-loop gain is 4.)*
> *$R_0 = 20/0.2 = 100\ k\Omega$*
> *$R_1 = 20/0.3 = 66.7\ k\Omega$*
> *$R_2 = 20/2 = 10\ k\Omega$*
> *$R_3 = 20/1.5 = 13.3\ k\Omega$*
> *$R_4 = 20/2 = 10\ k\Omega$*
> *$R_5 = 20/1 = 20\ k\Omega$*

As a check, the parallel combination of R_1, R_2, R_3, and R_0 is 5 kΩ, and parallel combination R_4, R_5, and R_F is also 5 kΩ. (There is no R_L in the network.) The gains for V_4 and V_5 are $-20/10 = -2$, and $-20/20 = -1$, respectively. The gain for V_1 is the product of noise gain and attenuation (in the voltage divider that consists of R_1 and the parallel combination of R_2, R_3, and R_0); this product is $4 \times 0.075 = 0.3$. The gain for V_2 is $4 \times 0.5 = 2$, and the gain for V_3 is $4 \times 0.375 = 1.5$.

A second example is the summing circuit in Fig. 2(b).

> *Again choose $R_p = 5\ k\Omega$*
> *$\Sigma a = 1.4$*
> *$(1 + \Sigma b) = 1 + 0 = 1.0$*
> *$\Sigma a - (1 + \Sigma b) = 0.4$ (An R_L is needed.)*
> *$R_F = 1.4 \times 5\ k\Omega = 7\ k\Omega$ (Noise gain is 1.4).*
> *$R_L = 7/0.4 = 17.5\ k\Omega$*
> *$R_1 = 7/0.6 = 11.7\ k\Omega$*
> *$R_2 = 7/0.8 = 8.8\ k\Omega$*

A check of these results shows that both input terminals are loaded by parallel resistance combinations equivalent to 5 kΩ, the gain for V_1 is $1.4 \times 0.428 = 0.6$, and the gain for V_2 is $1.4 \times 0.57 = 0.8$.

Another summation problem is shown in Fig. 2(c).

> *Let $R_p = 5\ k\Omega$*
> *$\Sigma a = 0.4$*
> *$(1 + \Sigma b) = 1$*
> *$(1 + \Sigma b) - \Sigma a = 0.6$ (An R_0 is needed.)*
> *$R_F = 1 \times 5\ k\Omega = 5\ k\Omega$ (Noise gain is 1.)*
> *$R_0 = 5/0.6 = 8.3\ k\Omega$*
> *$R_1 = 5/0.1 \doteq 50\ k\Omega$*
> *$R_2 = 5/0.3 = 16.7\ k\Omega$*

The load on the inverting terminal is only R_F, which is 5 kΩ. The load on the noninverting terminal, consisting of the parallel combination of R_0, R_1, and R_2, is also 5 kΩ. The gain for V_1 is the product of noise gain multiplied by attenuation, or $1 \times 5.5/55 = 0.1$. The gain for V_2 is $1 \times 7.1/23.8 = 0.3$.

The last example, which is not as trivial as it looks, is the calculation of resistances for the inverting adder in Fig. 2(d).

> *Let $R_p = 5\ k\Omega$*
> *$\Sigma a = 0$*
> *$(1 + \Sigma b) = 2.5$*
> *$(1 + \Sigma b) - \Sigma a = 2.5$ (R_0 is needed.)*
> *$R_F = 2.5 \times 5\ k\Omega = 12.5\ k\Omega$ (Noise gain is 2.5.)*
> *$R_0 = 12.5/2.5 = 5\ k\Omega$*
> *$R_1 = 12.5/0.3 = 41.7\ k\Omega$*
> *$R_2 = 12.5/1.2 = 10.4\ k\Omega$*

A check of these results shows R_1, R_2, and R_F in parallel have a total resistance of 5 kΩ. Gain for V_1 is $-2.5 \times 0.02 = -0.3$, and gain for V_2 is $-2.5 \times 0.48 = -1.2$. □

Programable calculator performs spur analysis

by John R. Coleman
Harris Electronic Systems, Melbourne, Fla.

A programable hand-held calculator can identify spurious frequencies generated in the mixing of two signals. For instance, an HP-25 calculator can be used in place of a spur chart or a digital computer to calculate these values both accurately and quickly. The same HP-25 program is used for both up-conversion and down-conversion, and in contrast to many graphical methods, the maximum order of spur product need not be limited.

If frequencies f_1 and f_2 are mixed, some of the resulting frequencies are:

$$f_s = \pm Mf_1 \mp Nf_2$$

The arrangement of signs eliminates the trivial situations in which both terms are positive, and the meaningless cases where both are negative. M and N, which are positive integers, are called the coefficients of a spur, and the order of the spur is the sum $(M+N)$. The HP-25 program analyzes the situation sketched in Fig. 1. The lower input frequency, f_1, lies in the range from f_{11} to f_{12}; the higher input frequency, f_2, lies in the range from f_{21} to f_{22}, and the calculator finds all values of M and N that

yield frequencies f_s in the test range of interest between f_{B1} and f_{B2}.

The calculator begins the analysis with the order equal to 1. When both first-order spurs have been tested, the calculator tests all second-order spurs. The process continues until a spur falling in the test range is found or until the calculator is stopped; to conserve time, the program tests two products simultaneously. The calculator displays the coefficients in the form $M + N/100$ for the sake of brevity so that a -2×5 spur is shown as 2.05, as is a 2×-5 spur. The user decides, if he wishes, which coefficient is negative.

The calculator selects one set of positive values for M and N. Each set defines two mixer products, either or both of which may be spurs—i.e., in the output passband. The potential spurious product P_1 results when the term Mf_1 is positive and the term Nf_2 is negative. P_2 is the mirror image of P_1, in which the term Mf_1 is negative and Nf_2 is positive. Either or both products may be spurs, and if the calculator finds that P_1 does not fall in the output test range, it tests P_2. If P_1 does fall in the test range, the calculator displays the values of M and N. If P_1 and P_2 are not in the test band, the calculator proceeds to the next set of values. The program is shown in the table.

The program is run by following these steps:

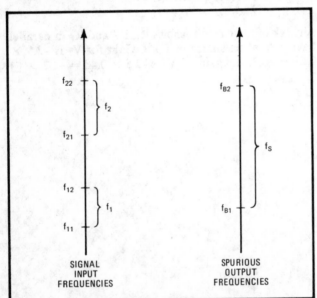

1. The ins and outs of spur analysis. In the program for finding spurious outputs from mixing of two input signals, the two input frequencies can lie anywhere within the ranges from f_{11} to f_{12} and from f_{21} to f_{22}, respectively. The program finds coefficients of any spurious frequencies that lie in the range from f_{B1} to f_{B2}.

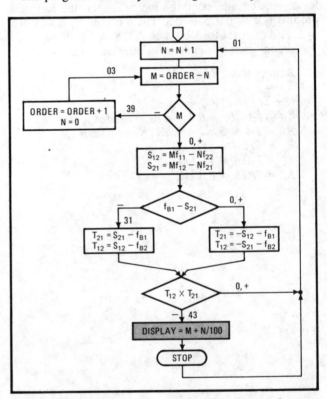

2. The light at the end of the program. Flow diagram for spur-analysis program shows that the calculator displays the coefficients for spurious outputs. Program then stops, but can be restarted with R/S button. The complete program is listed in the table.

LINE	CODE	KEY	LINE	CODE	KEY
00	—	—	25	13 31	GTO31
01	01	1	26	22	↓
02	23 51 07	STO+7	27	32	CHS
03	24 00	RCL 0	28	21	xoy
04	24 07	RCL 7	29	32	CHS
05	41	—	30	24 03	RCL 3
06	15 41	g x<0	31	41	—
07	13 39	GTO 39	32	21	xoy
08	24 01	RCL 1	33	24 06	RCL 6
09	61	X	34	41	—
10	24 07	RCL 7	35	61	X
11	24 05	RCL 5	36	15 41	g x<0
12	61	X	37	13 43	GTO 43
13	41	—	38	13 01	GTO 01
14	24 00	RCL 0	39	23 41 00	STO-0
15	24 07	RCL 7	40	34	CLRx
16	41	—	41	23 07	STO 7
17	24 04	RCL 4	42	13 03	GTO 03
18	61	X	43	24 07	RCL 7
19	24 07	RCL 7	44	01	1
20	24 02	RCL 2	45	15 21	g %
21	61	X	46	24 00	RCL 0
22	41	—	47	24 07	RCL 7
23	24 03	RCL 3	48	41	—
24	14 41	f x<y	49	51	+

REGISTER ASSIGNMENTS

7	N (init = 0)		
4	f_{12}	5	f_{22}	6	f_{B2}
1	f_{11}	2	f_{21}	3	f_{B1}
0	Order (= 0)		

- Load program into the calculator.
- Store the initial value of the order, 0, in register R_0; store the lower limits for each range, f_{11} in R_1, f_{21} in R_2, and f_{B1} in R_3, and store the upper limits for each range, f_{12} in R_4, f_{22} in R_5, and f_{B2} in R_6. Store 0 (the initial value of N) in register R_7.
- Press f, PRGM, and R/S.

The flow diagram in Fig. 2 shows what the program does. The first step is to increment N by 1. M is then calculated and tested, and the test is used to increment the order of the spur when required. After values are found for M and N, the end points of the frequency range of product P_1 are calculated. The highest possible frequency for P_1 is the value S_{21}. This value is compared with the lower limit of the output test range.

If the highest frequency of the mixer product P_1 is still less than the low end of the test range, then P_1 cannot be a spur and the calculator prepares P_2 for test. In both cases, the end points of the range of possible frequencies of the selected product are then compared with the output test range limits.

The test values T_{12} and T_{21} in the next step must have the same sign for the range of the selected product to be safely outside the output test range. If not, a spur exists and the calculator jumps to the display routine. The display routine retrieves the value for N and divides it by 100. This result is added to M to produce the displayed number.

The program stops when a number is displayed, but a push on the R/S button starts it again.
Example:
    Low input range: 11 to 12 MHz
    High input range: 21 to 22 MHz
    Test range: 31 to 35 MHz
Procedure:
    Load registers; initialize R_0 and R_7 to 0
Results:
    3.00 ($\pm 3f_1 \mp 0f_2$)
    1.02 ($\pm f_1 \mp 2f_2$)
    5.01 ($\pm 5f_1 \mp f_2$)   □

Programable calculator analyzes filter designs

by Tom Martin
Collins Radio, Dallas, Texas

An SR-56 calculator can provide a quick check on low-pass circuits laid out with the excellent filter-design programs in its applications library or on any other active or passive low-pass filter with up to four components. The calculator can be programed to analyze the performance of these filter circuits, giving the gain or

Circuits analyzed. The frequency responses of the active low-pass filter in a and the passive low-pass filter in b are quickly plotted by use of the programs given for the SR-56 calculator. The decibel value of A(f) is displayed at a chosen initial frequency f_1 and at successive incremented frequencies $(f_1 + \Delta f)$, $(f_1 + 2\Delta f)$ . . . as the R/S key is pushed repeatedly.

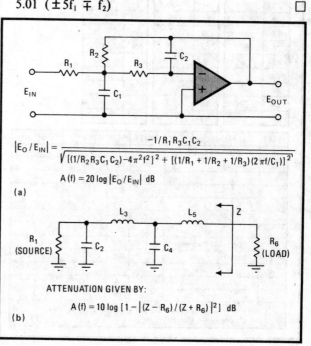

$$|E_O/E_{IN}| = \frac{-1/R_1 R_3 C_1 C_2}{\sqrt{[(1/R_2 R_3 C_1 C_2) - 4\pi^2 f^2]^2 + [(1/R_1 + 1/R_2 + 1/R_3)(2\pi f/C_1)]^2}}$$

$$A(f) = 20 \log |E_O/E_{IN}| \text{ dB}$$

(a)

ATTENUATION GIVEN BY:

$$A(f) = 10 \log [1 - |(Z - R_6)/(Z + R_6)|^2] \text{ dB}$$

(b)

attenuation at an incremental frequency each time the R/S key is pushed.

The theory of operation for the active-filter analysis is straightforward. It simply solves the gain-versus-frequency equations that are shown along with the circuit diagram in part a of the figure. The program (Table 1) includes provision for entering a starting frequency, f_1, and a frequency step size, Δf. Then simply pressing R/S repeatedly produces the data for plotting a linear frequency-response graph.

The passive-filter analysis works by calculating, at each frequency, the complex impedance that is seen looking back into the filter network from the load, as illustrated in part b of the figure. This filter impedance and the load resistance are then used in the equation given below to calculate the attenuation through the circuit.

The passive-filter program (Table 2) also provides for rapid plotting of frequency response curves, using f_1 and Δf. For filters with fewer than four reactive elements, zeroes should be inserted in place of the unused element values. The run time for this program is about 8 seconds for each frequency. □

TABLE 1: SR-56 PROGRAM FOR ANALYSIS OF ACTIVE LOW-PASS FILTER

LOC	KEY	LOC	KEY	LOC	KEY
00	STO	30	RCL	60	X
01	7	31	0	61	RCL
02	RCL	32	1/x	62	6
03	2	33	+	63	+/−
04	X	34	RCL	64	÷
05	RCL	35	1	65	RCL
06	3	36	1/x	66	0
07	X	37	+	67	=
08	RCL	38	RCL	68	|x|
09	4	39	2	69	LOG
10	=	40	1/x	70	X
11	1/x	41	=	71	2
12	STO	42	÷	72	0
13	6	43	RCL	73	=
14	÷	44	3	74	STO
15	RCL	45	X	75	8
16	1	46	2	76	RCL
17	−	47	X	77	5
18	RCL	48	π	78	SUM
19	7	49	X	79	7
20	x^2	50	RCL	80	RCL
21	X	51	7	81	8
22	4	52	=	82	R/S
23	X	53	x^2	83	GTO
24	π	54	+	84	0
25	x^2	55	RCL	85	2
26	=	56	9		
27	x^2	57	=		
28	STO	58	√x		
29	9	59	1/x		

REGISTERS	
0	R_1
1	R_2
2	R_3
3	C_1
4	C_2
5	Δf
6	temporary
7	temporary
8	temporary
9	temporary

STEP	PROCEDURE	ENTER	PRESS			DISPLAY
1	enter program, initialize		CLR	CMS	RST	
2	enter data	R_1	STO	0		
		R_2	STO	1		
		R_3	STO	2		
		C_1	STO	3		
		C_2	STO	4		
		Δf	STO	5		
3	enter initial frequency	f_1	R/S			$A(f_1)$
4	continue		R/S			$A(f_1 + \Delta f)$
						$A(f_1 + 2\Delta f)$

Note: For single-frequency analysis, enter the frequency and press RST, then R/S.

TABLE 2: SR-56 PROGRAM FOR ANALYSIS OF PASSIVE LOW-PASS FILTER

LOC	KEY	LOC	KEY	LOC	KEY	LOC	KEY
00	X	30	7	60	=	90	PROD
01	π	31	5	61	LOG	91	9
02	X	32	SUBR	62	X	92	RTN
03	2	33	8	63	1	93	x^2
04	=	34	1	64	0	94	+
05	SUM	35	RCL	65	=	95	RCL
06	0	36	6	66	R/S	96	9
07	RCL	37	INV	67	CLR	97	x^2
08	1	38	SUM	68	STO	98	=
09	1/x	39	9	69	8	99	RTN
10	SUM	40	X	70	STO		
11	8	41	2	71	9		
12	RCL	42	+	72	RCL		
13	2	43	RCL	73	7		
14	SUBR	44	8	74	RST		
15	7	45	=	75	X		
16	5	46	SUBR	76	RCL		
17	RCL	47	9	77	0		
18	3	48	3	78	=		
19	SUBR	49	1/x	79	SUM		
20	7	50	X	80	9		
21	5	51	(	81	RCL		
22	RCL	52	RCL	82	8		
23	4	53	8	83	SUBR		
24	SUBR	54	SUBR	84	9		
25	7	55	9	85	3		
26	5	56	3	86	1/x		
27	RCL	57	+/−	87	PROD		
28	5	58	+	88	8		
29	SUBR	59	1	89	+/−		

REGISTERS	
0	$2\pi f$
1	R_1
2	C_2
3	L_3
4	C_4
5	L_5
6	R_6
7	Δf
8	temporary
9	temporary

STEP	PROCEDURE	ENTER	PRESS			DISPLAY
1	enter program, initialize		CLR	CMS	RST	
2	enter data	R_1	STO	1		
		C_2	STO	2		
		L_3	STO	3		
		C_4	STO	4		
		L_5	STO	5		
		R_6	STO	6		
		Δf	STO	7		
3	enter initial frequency	f_1	R/S			$A(f_1)$
4	continue		R/S			$A(f_1 + \Delta f)$
			R/S			$A(f_1 + 2\Delta f)$

Note: For single-frequency analysis, press CLR, STO 0, STO 8, STO 9; enter the frequency, press RST, R/S.

Short program computes response of RLC networks

by Werner A. Schnider
Swiss Federal Institute of Technology, Zurich

When designing filters, amplifiers, and other circuits, the frequency response can be determined with a Fortran program that is very short and requires much less computation time than many common circuit-design programs such as ECAP-1. By introducing current-controlled current sources, the program can analyze transistor circuits directly, while with a little modification it works as well with circuits containing operational amplifiers. The program stores three matrixes—basically of resistance, capacitance, and reciprocal inductance—during the whole frequency-response computation, and from them builds the node-admittance matrix for each frequency.

The computational procedure for each frequency requires the set-up of a node-admittance matrix, [H], and the computation of two determinants, $|H_{io}|$ and $|H_{ii}|$ and the gain V_o/V_i. The gain is the quotient of the two determinants—a consequence of the equivalent current vector having only one non-zero element, corresponding to the input node. In the abstract, each of the two voltages that determine gain is the matrix product of the current vector and the inverse of the node-admittance matrix. Computing that inverse usually involves a great many determinants. But when the current vector has only one non-zero element, the matrix product becomes a scalar product, and, because the gain is a quotient of two such products, everything cancels out

INPUT DATA CARDS

```
                5,
             AR,1,2,1.E3
             AR,2,3,60.,
             AR,3,0,3.75E3,
             AC,3,0,90.E-12,
             AC,3,4,3.E-12,
             AR,4,0,1.E3,
             AC,4,0,50.E-12,
             AR,4,5,10.E3,
             AL,5,2,0.56E-3,
             AB,3,6,150.,
             A ,,,,,
             1,4,
             2.E5,7.E6,35,
```

PROGRAM

```
      PROGRAM AC(INPUT,OUTPUT)
      DIMENSION DC(20,20),BC(20,20),GM(30),NKA(30),NKB(30),EC(20,20)
      COMPLEX CO,CE,Q(20,20)
      DIMENSION A(100),P(100)
      INTEGER R,C,B,BLANK,TYPE
      DATA R,C,B,BLANK,LQ/1HR,1HC,1HB,1H ,1HL/
C INPUT-ROUTINE.
      PRINT 7
7     FORMAT(1H1,10(1H*),20H FREQUENCY RESPONSE ,10(1H*),/)
      DO 8 I=1,20
      DO 8 J=1,20
8     DC(I,J)=BC(I,J)=EC(I,J)=0.
      NZ=0
      CALL NREAD(NK)
2     CALL NREAD(TYPE,K1,K2,WERT)
      IF(TYPE.EQ.BLANK) GOTO 6
      PRINT 10,TYPE,K1,K2,WERT
10    FORMAT(1H ,A1,2(I4),4X,E12.4)
      IF(TYPE.NE.B) GOTO 3
      WERT=WERT*GM(K1)
      NA=NKA(K1)
      NB=NKB(K1)
      NBB=NKB(K2)
      NAA=NKA(K2)
      IF(NA.NE.0.AND.NAA.NE.0) BC(NA,NAA)=BC(NA,NAA)+WERT
      IF(NA.NE.0.AND.NBB.NE.0) BC(NA,NBB)=BC(NA,NBB)-WERT
      IF(NB.NE.0.AND.NBB.NE.0) BC(NB,NBB)=BC(NB,NBB)+WERT
      IF(NB.NE.0.AND.NAA.NE.0) BC(NB,NAA)=BC(NB,NAA)-WERT
      GOTO 2
3     CONTINUE
      NZ=NZ+1
      NKA(NZ)=K1
      NKB(NZ)=K2
      IF(TYPE.EQ.R) GM(NZ)=1./WERT
      IF(TYPE.EQ.B) CALL MATR(K1,K2,BC,GM(NZ))
      IF(TYPE.EQ.C) CALL MATR(K1,K2,DC,WERT)
      IF(TYPE.EQ.LQ) H=1./WERT
      IF(TYPE.EQ.LQ) CALL MATR(K1,K2,EC,H)
      GOTO 2
6     CALL NREAD(KA,KB)
      CALL NREAD(F1,F2,N)
      PRINT 20,KA,KB,F1,F2,N
20    FORMAT(/,11H I/O-PORTS ,2I4,/,1H ,8HF1-F2-N=,2E14.4,I8)
      PRINT 11,NZ,NK
11    FORMAT(/ ,1H ,I4,9H BRANCHES,10X,I4,6H NODES,//)
C COMPUTATION OF FREQUENCY RESPONSE.
      DEL=(F2-F1)/(N-1)
      DO 50 I=1,N
      FREQ=F1+(I-1)*DEL
      OMEGA=6.2831852*FREQ
      DO 51 K=1,NK
      DO 51 L=1,NK
51    Q(K,L)=CMPLX(BC(K,L),OMEGA*DC(K,L)-EC(K,L)/OMEGA)
      CALL CCDET(Q,KA,KA,NK,CO)
      CALL CCDET(Q,KB,KA,NK,CE)
      CO=CE/CO
      AMPL=CABS(CO)
      IF(REAL(CO).EQ.0.) CO=CO+1.E-16
      PHASE=ATAN2(AIMAG(CO),REAL(CO))
      PHASE=PHASE*180./3.1415926
      PRINT 60,FREQ,AMPL,PHASE
60    FORMAT(6H FREQ=,E10.3,5X,5HAMPL=,E12.4,5X,6HPHASE=,E12.4)
      A(I)=AMPL
      P(I)=PHASE
50    CONTINUE
      CALL FPLOT(A,P,N,F1,DEL)
      END


      SUBROUTINE MATR(K1,K2,DC,WERT)
      DIMENSION DC(20,20)
      IF(K1.NE.0) DC(K1,K1)=DC(K1,K1)+WERT
      IF(K2.NE.0) DC(K2,K2)=DC(K2,K2)+WERT
      IF(K1.EQ.0.OR.K2.EQ.0) GOTO 9
      DC(K1,K2)=DC(K1,K2)-WERT
      DC(K2,K1)=DC(K2,K1)-WERT
9     RETURN
      END


      SUBROUTINE CCDET(Q,IZ,IS,NK,VALUE)
      COMPLEX Q(20,20),CA(20,20),VALUE
      NKM=NK-1
      DO 10 K=1,NK
      DO 10 L=1,NK
10    CA(K,L)=Q(K,L)
      IF(IZ.EQ.NK) GOTO 3
      DO 2 K=IZ,NKM
      DO 2 L=1,NK
2     CA(K,L)=Q(K+1,L)
3     IF(IS.EQ.NK) GOTO 5
      DO 4 K=1,NK
      DO 4 L=IS,NKM
4     CA(K,L)=CA(K,L+1)
5     CONTINUE
      CALL CDET(CA,NKM,VALUE)
      VALUE=VALUE*(-1.)**(IZ+IS)
      RETURN
      END
```

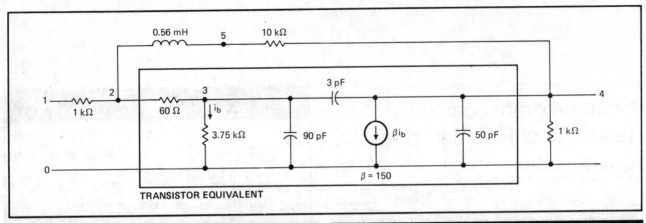

TRANSISTOR EQUIVALENT

OUTPUT LISTING

```
********** FREQUENCY RESPONSE **********

R   1   2      1.0000E+03
R   2   3      6.0000E+01
R   3   0      3.7500E+03
C   3   0      9.0000E-11
C   3   4      3.0000E-12
R   4   0      1.0000E+03
C   4   0      5.0000E-11
R   4   5      1.0000E+04
L   5   2      5.6000E-04
B   3   6      1.5000E+02

I/O-PORTS:    1    4
F1-F2-N=   2.0000E+05    7.0000E+06    35

   9 BRANCHES          5 NODES

FREQ= 2.000E+05   AMPL= 7.2734E+00   PHASE= 1.7903E+02
FREQ= 4.000E+05   AMPL= 7.3804E+00   PHASE= 1.7795E+02
FREQ= 6.000E+05   AMPL= 7.5590E+00   PHASE= 1.7664E+02
FREQ= 8.000E+05   AMPL= 7.8091E+00   PHASE= 1.7499E+02
FREQ= 1.000E+06   AMPL= 8.1295E+00   PHASE= 1.7287E+02
FREQ= 1.200E+06   AMPL= 8.5516E+00   PHASE= 1.7017E+02
FREQ= 1.400E+06   AMPL= 8.9594E+00   PHASE= 1.6677E+02
FREQ= 1.600E+06   AMPL= 9.4415E+00   PHASE= 1.6256E+02
FREQ= 1.800E+06   AMPL= 9.9313E+00   PHASE= 1.5748E+02
FREQ= 2.000E+06   AMPL= 1.0382E+01   PHASE= 1.5148E+02
FREQ= 2.200E+06   AMPL= 1.0732E+01   PHASE= 1.4464E+02
FREQ= 2.400E+06   AMPL= 1.0920E+01   PHASE= 1.3713E+02
FREQ= 2.600E+06   AMPL= 1.0898E+01   PHASE= 1.2925E+02
FREQ= 2.800E+06   AMPL= 1.0658E+01   PHASE= 1.2135E+02
FREQ= 3.000E+06   AMPL= 1.0231E+01   PHASE= 1.1378E+02
FREQ= 3.200E+06   AMPL= 9.6741E+00   PHASE= 1.0677E+02
FREQ= 3.400E+06   AMPL= 9.0501E+00   PHASE= 1.0047E+02
FREQ= 3.600E+06   AMPL= 8.4103E+00   PHASE= 9.4890E+01
FREQ= 3.800E+06   AMPL= 7.7896E+00   PHASE= 8.9997E+01
FREQ= 4.000E+06   AMPL= 7.2076E+00   PHASE= 8.5714E+01
FREQ= 4.200E+06   AMPL= 6.6730E+00   PHASE= 8.1960E+01
FREQ= 4.400E+06   AMPL= 6.1879E+00   PHASE= 7.8653E+01
FREQ= 4.600E+06   AMPL= 5.7503E+00   PHASE= 7.5721E+01
FREQ= 4.800E+06   AMPL= 5.3567E+00   PHASE= 7.3104E+01
FREQ= 5.000E+06   AMPL= 5.0026E+00   PHASE= 7.0749E+01
FREQ= 5.200E+06   AMPL= 4.6837E+00   PHASE= 6.8614E+01
FREQ= 5.400E+06   AMPL= 4.3958E+00   PHASE= 6.6666E+01
FREQ= 5.600E+06   AMPL= 4.1352E+00   PHASE= 6.4876E+01
FREQ= 5.800E+06   AMPL= 3.8986E+00   PHASE= 6.3221E+01
FREQ= 6.000E+06   AMPL= 3.6831E+00   PHASE= 6.1683E+01
FREQ= 6.200E+06   AMPL= 3.4863E+00   PHASE= 6.0245E+01
FREQ= 6.400E+06   AMPL= 3.3059E+00   PHASE= 5.8896E+01
FREQ= 6.600E+06   AMPL= 3.1401E+00   PHASE= 5.7624E+01
FREQ= 6.800E+06   AMPL= 2.9874E+00   PHASE= 5.6421E+01
FREQ= 7.000E+06   AMPL= 2.8462E+00   PHASE= 5.5283E+01
```

OUTPUT PLOT

```
FREQUENZGANG:

AMPLITUDE =  2.446E+00  4.46E+00  6.09E+00  7.69E+00  9.31E+00  1.092E+01
    PHASE =  3.528E+01  8.30E+01  1.05E+02  1.30E+02  1.54E+02  1.79CE+02
```

integers that denote the beginning and ending nodes of this branch, and a floating-point number that gives the value of the element in ohms, farads, or henries. The program numbers the branches automatically in the sequence the cards are read.

The branch cards are followed by cards giving the current-controlled sources with their amplification factors. Each of these begins with the letters AB, which identify this type of card. Then two integers specify the number of the controlling branch and the number of the controlled branch, and a floating-point number denotes the amplification factor. This is followed by the end card, which has only the letter A, one blank, and a series of commas, to signify that all the branches and sources have been listed.

Next comes an input/output card, with two integers that denote the numbers of the input and output nodes. The last data card carries two floating-point numbers that specify the frequency range and an integer that denotes the number of frequency steps—up to 100—to be calculated within the specified range.

The program uses five subroutines, three of which are

except the two determinants mentioned.

So, to establish the node-admittance matrix, number all the nodes, beginning with zero for the common-input-output port. Place the data cards—either punched cards or an equivalent data-entry medium—at the beginning of the program. The program includes a subroutine, NREAD, that eliminates all requirements for specific formats. All data elements are separated by commas.

The first data card specifies the number of nodes minus 1. It is followed by cards listing the branches with their elements. The first two characters on each branch card are alphabetics that specify the type of the passive element in that branch: AR for a resistor, AC for a capacitor, AL for an inductor. These are followed by two

available in most scientific computer centers, so are not listed here. They are NREAD (format-free reading of data cards), CDET (to compute the determinant of a complex matrix), and FPLOT (which plots the amplitude and phase of V_o/V_i. FPLOT is optional and if it is used, two arrays called A and R are required for storing the data to be plotted.

Two other subroutines are MATR, for setting up the matrixes, and CCDET, which computes the determinant $|H_{kj}|$ from the matrix [H] and the specified row and column. The program can handle any circuit with up to 20 nodes and 30 branches.

Here is an example. In a compensated rf amplifier (see drawing) the transistor is replaced by a current-controlled current source and by passive elements. The new program computes the frequency response of this circuit in 35 steps between 200 kilohertz and 7 megahertz on the Control Data 6400/6500 in less than 1.4 seconds. This includes use of the FPLOT subroutine and computation of the plotting values, but not the actual plotting itself. The same circuit computed with a modified ECAP took 3.4 seconds. (The output listing and the plot, prepared on a 1,200-line/min printer, comprise 94 lines, which take another 5 seconds or so to produce.)

The data cards that describe the circuit in this example are listed in the table.

□

Program analyzes all-resistive dc circuits

by Mark Jong
Wichita State University, Wichita, Kansas

Networks that are strictly resistive can be analyzed easily and quickly for dc conditions with a brief but effective computer program written in Basic. The circuit to be analyzed can also contain active devices, provided those devices can be represented by only resistive elements and voltage-dependent sources.

The standard circuit branch allowed by the program

1. Dc circuit analysis. Computer program, which is written in Basic, is useful for a speedy dc analysis of small resistive networks. The definitions for a standard circuit branch and the program listing itself are given here. Dependent sources must be voltage-controlled.

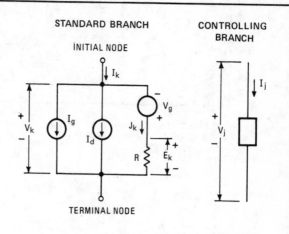

V_k, V_j = BRANCH VOLTAGES
I_k, I_j = BRANCH CURRENTS
E_k = ELEMENT VOLTAGE
J_k = ELEMENT CURRENT
V_g, I_g = INDEPENDENT SOURCES
I_d = $g_m \cdot V_j$ (VOLTAGE-CONTROLLED CURRENT SOURCE)

```
100    DIM A[7,15],Y[15,15],E[15],I[15],
       J[15],V[15],S[15],W[15,7],U[15,7]
110    PRINT "NUMBER OF NODES - 1 =";
111    INPUT N
120    PRINT "NUMBER OF BRANCHES =";
121    INPUT B
130    MAT A=ZER[N,B]
140    MAT Y=ZER[B,B]
150    MAT E=ZER[B]
160    MAT I=ZER[B]
170    FOR K=1 TO B
180    INPUT B1,F1,T1,R,E[B1],I[B1],Y1,C1
190    IF F1=0 THEN 210
200    LET A[F1,B1]=1
210    IF T1=0 THEN 230
220    LET A[T1,B1]=-1
230    LET Y[B1,B1]=1/R
240    IF C1=0 THEN 260
250    LET Y[B1,C1]=Y1
260    NEXT K
270    MAT S=ZER[B]
275    MAT J=ZER[B]
280    FOR K=1 TO B
281    LET S[K]=Y[K,K]*E[K]
282    NEXT K
290    MAT S=I+S
295    MAT S=J-S
300    MAT W=ZER[B,N]
310    MAT W=TRN(A)
320    MAT U=ZER[B,N]
330    MAT U=Y*W
340    MAT W=ZER[N,N]
350    MAT W=A*U
360    MAT U=ZER[N,N]
370    MAT U=INV(W)
380    MAT V=ZER[N]
390    MAT V=A*S
400    MAT J=ZER[N]
410    MAT J=U*V
420    PRINT
430    PRINT "NODE"," VOLTAGE"
440    FOR K=1 TO N
450    PRINT K,J[K]
460    NEXT K
470    MAT V=ZER[B]
480    MAT W=ZER[B,N]
490    MAT W=TRN(A)
500    MAT V=W*J
510    MAT J=ZER[B]
520    MAT J=Y*V
530    MAT J=J-S
540    PRINT
550    PRINT "BRANCH"," VOLTAGE"," CURRENT"," POWER"
560    FOR K=1 TO B
570    PRINT K,V[K],J[K],V[K]*J[K]
580    NEXT K
590    MAT V=V+E
600    PRINT
610    PRINT "ELEMENT"," VOLTAGE"," CURRENT"," POWER"
620    FOR K=1 TO B
630    LET J[K]=Y[K,K]*V[K]
640    PRINT K,V[K],J[K],V[K]*J[K]
650    NEXT K
660    END
```

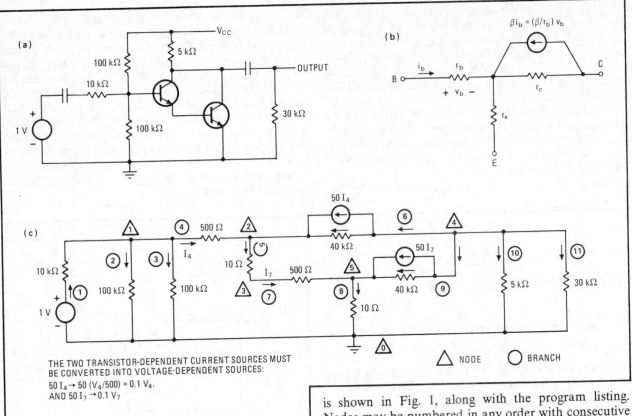

THE TWO TRANSISTOR-DEPENDENT CURRENT SOURCES MUST
BE CONVERTED INTO VOLTAGE-DEPENDENT SOURCES:

$50\,I_4 \rightarrow 50\,(V_4/500) = 0.1\,V_4.$
AND $50\,I_7 \rightarrow 0.1\,V_7.$

(d)

```
READY
RUN
NUMBER OF NODES - 1 =?5
NUMBER OF BRANCHES =?11
?1,0,1,10000,1,0,0,0
?2,1,0,100000,0,0,0,0
?3,1,0,100000,0,0,0,0
?4,1,2,500,0,0,0,0
?5,2,3,10,0,0,0,0
?6,4,2,40000,0,0,0,.1,4
?7,3,5,500,0,0,0,0
?8,5,0,10,0,0,0,0
?9,4,5,40000,0,0,0,.1,7
?10,4,0,5000,0,0,0,0
?11,4,0,30000,0,0,0,0
```

NODE	VOLTAGE
1	.428572
2	.404286
3	.400121
4	-82.2203
5	.191866

BRANCH	VOLTAGE	CURRENT	POWER
1	-.428572	5.71428E-05	-2.44898E-05
2	.428572	4.28572E-06	1.83674E-06
3	.428572	4.28572E-06	1.83674E-06
4	2.42857E-02	4.85713E-05	1.17959E-06
5	4.16505E-03	4.16505E-04	1.73477E-06
6	-82.4246	3.67952E-04	-3.03283E-02
7	.208255	4.16509E-04	8.67399E-05
8	.191866	1.91866E-02	3.68127E-03
9	-82.2122	1.87781E-02	-1.54314
10	-82.0203	-1.64041E-02	1.34547
11	-82.0203	-2.73401E-03	.224245

ELEMENT	VOLTAGE	CURRENT	POWER
1	.571428	5.71428E-05	3.26530E-05
2	.428572	4.28572E-06	1.83674E-06
3	.428572	4.28572E-06	1.83674E-06
4	2.42857E-02	4.85713E-05	1.17959E-06
5	4.16505E-03	4.16505E-04	1.73477E-06
6	-82.4246	-2.06062E-03	.169845
7	.208255	4.16509E-04	8.67399E-05
8	.191866	1.91866E-02	3.68127E-03
9	-82.2122	-2.05531E-03	.168971
10	-82.0203	-1.64041E-02	1.34547
11	-82.0203	-2.73401E-03	.224245

```
READY
```

2. Program at work. The transistor amplifier in (a) is analyzed for dc
conditions. The T-model equivalent circuit (b) can be used for the
transistors, provided that all dependent current sources are converted into voltage-dependent sources. In the complete amplifier
equivalent circuit (c), all nodes and branches are numbered consecutively. The program printout is shown in (d).

is shown in Fig. 1, along with the program listing.
Nodes may be numbered in any order with consecutive
integers beginning with zero. (The program always assumes that node 0 is the reference node.) Branches may
also be numbered in any order with consecutive integers, but this set of numbers must begin with the number one.

The program first asks to know the number of nodes
minus one, and then it requests the number of branches.
(A question mark is typed after each request.) The user
responds by typing in the data requested each time, and
pressing the RETURN key on his terminal.

After this preliminary input data is obtained, the program asks for the branch data by typing a question
mark each time for each branch. In response, the user
types in the data for each branch in a specific order and
on the same line. He gives the branch number, the initial node number, the terminal node number, the resistance value, the value of the independent voltage source,
the value of the independent current source, the trans-
conductance of the dependent current source, and the
number of the branch that is controlling the dependent
current source, finally pressing the RETURN key.

The polarity signs allotted to the voltage and current
sources must agree with the sign conventions defined by
the standard branch of Fig. 1. The various data inputs
must be separated by commas.

Once the program has all of the input data, it will
compute the circuit's output node voltages, as well as all
the branch and element voltages, currents, and power.
The element of a branch is the resistance of that branch.
When there is no current source associated with a
branch, the branch current is the same as the element
current. And when a branch does not have a voltage
source, branch and element voltages are the same.

Figure 2 shows an example analysis of a two-transistor amplifier (Fig. 2a). The simple T-model equivalent circuit (Fig. 2b) is used to represent each transistor. In the complete amplifier equivalent circuit (Fig. 2c), the node numbers are enclosed by triangles, and the branch numbers are encircled. The program printout (Fig. 2d) conveniently tabulates the input data, the output node voltages, the branch data, and then the element data.

On a 16-bit minicomputer with an 8,000-word memory, the program can handle a circuit having up to seven nodes and 15 branches. If a machine with more storage capacity is used, the dimensions of the arrays set up by statement 100 in the program listing can be increased to accommodate larger circuits. ☐

HP-45 calculator speeds rf amplifier design

by William J. Martin
Motorola Communications Division, Fort Lauderdale, Fla.

Important characteristics of an rf transistor amplifier can be evaluated quickly from the two-port scattering parameters of the transistor by using a Hewlett-Packard HP-45 scientific calculator. The calculations of stability, gain, and matching impedances use special programs for handling the complex terms in the amplifier analysis on the HP-45.

In using these programs, the designer should enter his data exactly as shown in the left-hand column and key it as shown in the center column. The result will appear as shown in the right-hand column after the last key in the center column is pressed.

The design of a 500-megahertz amplifier is carried through here to illustrate the procedure. This amplifier uses a Fairchild 2N2857 transistor with V_{CE} = 10 volts and I_C = 2 milliamperes; manufacturer's data give the S parameters in polar form (R,θ) as

$$S_{11} = 0.394 \; \underline{/ \; -158.7°}$$
$$S_{12} = 0.048 \; \underline{/ \; 63.5°}$$
$$S_{21} = 2.084 \; \underline{/ \; 79.2°}$$
$$S_{22} = 0.816 \; \underline{/ \; -20.4°}$$

The first step is to determine whether the transistor is stable under the given operating conditions. Calculation of the stability factor, K, requires complex quantity Δ, given by

$$\Delta = S_{11}S_{22} - S_{12}S_{21}$$

The program for obtaining Δ on an HP-45 calculator is as follows

$S_{11\theta}$	↑	
$S_{22\theta}$	+	
S_{11R}	↑	
S_{22R}	X, → R, Σ+	
$S_{12\theta}$	↑	
$S_{21\theta}$	+	
S_{12R}	↑	
S_{21R}	X, → R, Σ −,	
	RCLΣ, → P	Δ_R
	↔	Δ_θ

With the S parameters given above, this program yields

$$\Delta = 0.251 \; \underline{/ \; -164.8°}$$

Stability factor K is readily calculated from

$$K = \frac{1 + |\Delta|^2 - |S_{11}|^2 - |S_{22}|^2}{2|S_{21}S_{12}|} = 1.208$$

Because K has a positive value greater than unity, and S_{11} and S_{22} are less than unity, the 2N2857 is unconditionally stable; i.e., no source or load reflection coefficients exist that can cause instability. If the 2N2857 had not satisfied the stability criteria, the calculations would have been repeated for other transistors until a stable device was found.

To achieve the maximum possible power gain from this amplifier, the source and load impedances must be conjugately matched to the transistor. Therefore the next step in the amplifier design is to find these impedances. First a complex quantity, C_1, must be found. It is given by

$$C_1 = S_{11} - \Delta S_{22}*$$

(The asterisk indicates a complex conjugate.) The HP-45 routine for C_1 is

$S_{11\theta}$	↑	
S_{11R}	→ R, Σ+	
Δ_θ	↑	
$S_{22\theta}$	CHS, +	
Δ_R	↑ ↓	
S_{22R}	X, → R, Σ −,	
	RCLΣ, → P	$C_{1\,R}$
	↔	$C_{1\,\theta}$

In this example, the value of C_1 is

$$C_1 = 0.202 \; \underline{/ \; -173.2°}$$

Another necessary quantity is B_1, given by

$$B_1 = 1 + |S_{11}|^2 - |S_{22}|^2 - |\Delta|^2 = 0.427$$

The input reflection coefficient ρ_{MS} that is required to conjugately match the transistor is

$$\rho_{MS} = C_1* \left[\frac{B_1 \pm (B_1^2 - 4|C_1|^2)^{1/2}}{2|C_1|^2} \right]$$

The plus sign is used before the radical if B_1 is negative. The minus sign is used if B_1 is positive (as in this example). The value of ρ_{MS} here is

$$\rho_{MS} = 0.719 \; \underline{/ \; 173.2°}$$

To compute the output reflection coefficient that is required to conjugately match the output of the transistor, complex quantity C_2 must be found.

$$C_2 = S_{22} - \Delta S_{11}*$$

The HP-45 routine for C_2 is completely analogous to that for C_1 and yields

$$C_2 = 0.721 \underline{/\ -22.3°}$$

Quantity B_2 is also required. It is given by

$$B_2 = 1 + |S_{22}|^2 - |S_{11}|^2 - |\Delta|^2 = 1.448$$

The output reflection coefficient ρ_{ML} for conjugate match to the transistor is

$$\rho_{ML} = C_2* \left[\frac{B_2 \pm (B_2{}^2 - 4|C_2|^2)^{1/2}}{2|C_2|^2} \right]$$

The plus sign is used for negative values of B_2, and the minus sign for positive values of B_2. Here

$$\rho_{ML} = 0.910 \underline{/\ 22.3°}$$

Reflection coefficients ρ_{MS} and ρ_{ML} can be converted to

Matched circuit. Source and load impedances shown produce maximum possible power gain (13.6 dB) from 2N2857 operating at 500 MHz with V_{CE} = 10 volts and I_C = 2 milliamperes. Calculations of impedances and gain, as well as verification of amplifier stability, require only transistor S parameters and HP-45 scientific calculator.

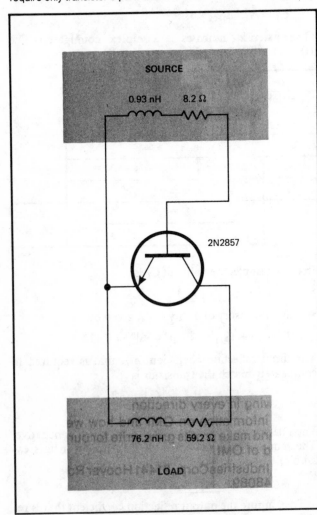

source and load impedances, respectively, by a graphical method (plotting on a Smith chart) or by the following HP-45 routine, which gives polar, series, and parallel forms for the impedance.

ρ_θ	↑	
ρ_R	→ R, 1, +, → P	
0	↑, 1, → R, Σ +, ↓, ↓	
ρ_θ	↑	
ρ_R	→ R, Σ −,	
	↓, ↓, RCLΣ +, → P,	
	↔, CHS, ↓, ÷,	
	↑, ↓, ↓, +, ↔, 50, X	MAG.
	↔	θ
	↔, → R,	R_S
	↔,	X_S
	↔, → P, ↓, ↑, ↓, COS,	
	÷, 50, X	R_P
	↓, ↔, SIN, ÷, 50, X	X_P

POLAR (MAG., θ)
SERIES (R_S, X_S)
PARALLEL (R_P, X_P)

The results, in series form, for this example are

$$Z_{source} = (8.19 + j\,2.91)\ ohms$$
$$Z_{load} = (59.23 + j\,239.15)\ ohms$$

Thus, the circuit shown in the accompanying diagram provides maximum possible power gain from this amplifier at the given values of frequency, voltage, and current.

The final step in the design analysis is to calculate the value of this maximum possible power gain. It is given in decibels as

$$G_{max} = \frac{|S_{21}|}{|S_{12}|} |K \pm (K^2 - 1)^{1/2}|$$

The plus sign is used in front of the radical if B_1 is negative. The minus sign is used if B_1 is positive. In this example the minus sign is used, and

$$G_{max} = 13.6\ dB$$

for a Fairchild 2N2857 transistor operated at 500 MHz with V_{CE} = 10 v and I_C = 2 mA.

This brief presentation has shown HP-45 routines for only the complex quantities Δ, C_1, and Z. Routines in the same format for the other quantities discussed (K, B_1, B_2, ρ_{MS}, and ρ_{ML}) are available from the author. Also available are routines for ρ_{MS}' and ρ_{ML}'. Quantity ρ_{MS}' gives the complex source impedance once the complex output impedance is known (from constant gain circles if a power gain other than G_{max} is desired). Quantity ρ_{ML}' gives the complex output impedance once the complex input impedance is known (e.g., for best noise match). □

13. Circuit aids to calculation

Computational module stresses applications versatility

by Lew Counts and Fred Pouliot
Analog Devices Inc., Norwood, Mass.

Multiplication, division vector calculations, solving for roots, and finding root-mean-square values are just a few of the jobs that can be done by a recently introduced multifunction module [*Electronics*, May 22, 1972, p. 125]. Sold by Analog Devices for $75 singly, the model 433 uses logarithmic computing techniques, so that its accuracy is maintained even with decreasing signal levels.

The small unit can accept three independent inputs—V_x, V_y, and V_z—of up to 10 volts each. They are related to the output by:

$$V_o = V_y(V_z/V_x)^m$$

Exponent m is adjustable over a 25:1 range, from 1/5 to 5, by appropriate selection of resistance values in a two-resistor divider network. This is illustrated in the block diagram and in the set of typical transfer functions. Programing resistors are not required for m = 1.0.

Of course, any conventional analog multiplier may be placed in the external feedback loop of an operational amplifier for use as an analog divider. However, such an arrangement increases error terms associated with the multiplier. Higher noise, offset drift, and over-all error result when the denominator signal decreases, thereby reducing loop gain.

For example, a 0.1% multiplier can operate as a 0.1% divider for a 10-v full-scale denominator input. But if this amplitude drops to 1 v, divider error increases from 0.1% to 1%. When denominator input levels reach 0.1 v, over-all error rises to 10%. In contrast, the model 433 functions as a logarithmic unit, so that errors emerge as a gain error and a fixed offset and are independent of the denominator signal amplitude.

One of the more sophisticated applications for the model 433 is computing the length of a two-dimensional vector. Only two external op amps must be outboarded, and this minimizes accumulated errors from amplifier offset, drift, nonlinearity, and noise. Ordinarily, such a vector computation requires a multiplier to square each input, an amplifier to sum the squared signals, and a multiplier/op-amp combination to extract

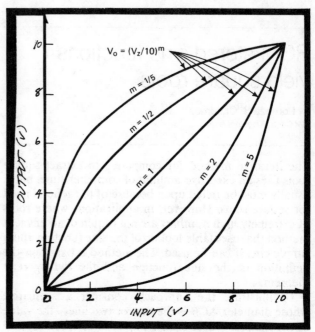

Voltage transfer curves show effect of varying index m from 1/5 to 5. Of course, when m = 1, the output is linear.

Handy logarithmic module has output that is function of three inputs: $V_o = V_y(V_z/V_x)^m$. Two resistors set value of exponent m.

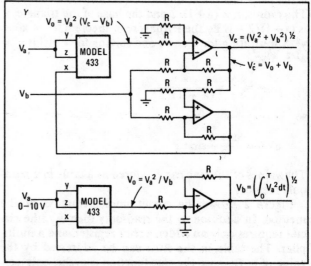

Outboarding one or more op amps permits module to find vector length (top) or solve for root-mean-square sygnal values (bottom).

the square root of the sum of the squared signals.

The closed-loop operation of the module's vector circuit broadens input signal dynamic range because circuit equations are solved implicitly, maintaining the output well within the module's operating range. Normally, the equations are solved explicitly, producing signals that quickly exceed a device's capability. Overall circuit accuracy is also improved to within 0.1% by closed-loop operation. When computing vectors, the accuracy of the model 433 depends primarily on the temperature stability of resistors in the external feedback loop and how closely their values are matched.

Another closed-loop application of the model 433 is finding true rms signal values. Here, only a single external op amp must be added. The standard approach requires an analog multiplier to square the input signal, followed by a separate integrator that drives a second multiplier (in an op amp's feedback circuit) that finds the square root for the final output.

As with the vector circuit, closed-loop operation for true rms computations permits a 100:1 input dynamic range to be realized for a 0.1% error. To obtain accurate results, the RC time constant must be large, as compared to the time constant of the input signal. □

ROM-stored sine functions yield square roots

by Lorenza S. Childress
IBM Corp., Kingston, N. Y.

The iterative method for computers to extract square roots uses an excessive amount of computer time, but it usually must be relied upon because of the general need for square roots. However, in applications where roots of extremely high numbers are not required, an efficient method that uses table lookup of the sine function and a simple circuit can be used. The method is based on the definition of the sine function and the Pythagorean theorem.

To illustrate the approach, consider a semicircle whose diameter ACB is the sum of two lines—the value of the number whose square root is to be taken (a) and a unit value (1). As shown in Fig. 1, the length AC is unity, and length CB is equal to quantity a. Quantity y is the perpendicular DC from the semicircle to the base. The radius, r, is $(a+1)/2$ and the base of the triangle, x, is $(a+1)/2 - 1$. By the Pythagorean theorem, $r^2 = x^2 + y^2$. Substituting for x and r and solving for y yields $y = a^{1/2}$. Also,

$$\sin\alpha = \frac{y}{r} = \frac{y}{(a+1)/2}$$

so

$$a^{1/2} = \frac{a+1}{2}\sin\alpha$$

The values of the sine can be stored as a table in a read-only memory.

Figure 2 shows the circuit implementation of the method. In addition to the read-only memory, the circuit requires only an adder, a shift register, and a multiplier. The table in the ROM can be addressed by the value of a. Because the sine function is cyclic, only certain values are required—those for angles between $\pi/2$ radians (90°) and 0.2 radians (11.5°), which handle val-

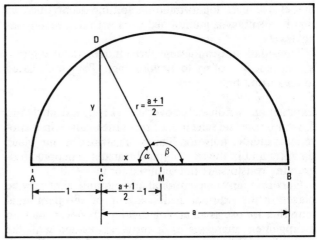

1. Getting to the root. Pythagorean theorem and sinα are used to calculate the square root of a number a with value between 1 and 100: $a^{1/2} = [(a + 1)/2] \sin\alpha$. Text tells how to handle values of a less than 1 or greater than 100.

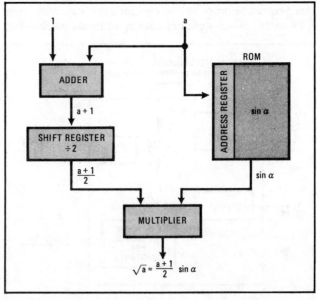

2. Arithmetic block. Schematic diagram of circuit for calculating $a^{1/2} = [(a + 1)/2] \sin\alpha$ using a table-lookup method. Note that table in read-only memory is addressed by the value of a.

ues of a between 1.0 and 100. For values of a requiring angles greater and less than these, modifications can be used.

Square roots of numbers smaller than one can be calculated by using the cosine function or the sine of the supplement, that is, $a^{1/2} = (\sin\beta)(a + 1)/2$, where β is less than $90°$. From the circuit standpoint, however, it appears to be easier to multiply the values of a by 100 or $10^{2(N-1)}$ where N is the number of decimal digits. After the table lookup, of course, a division is required. This can be handled as a negative multiply. A similar technique is used for numbers greater than 100.

For values of a less than one, the equation becomes

$$a^{1/2} = \frac{1}{[10^{2(N-1)}]^{1/2}}\left[\frac{a10^{2(N-1)} - 1}{2}\right]\sin\alpha$$

and for values of a greater than 100,

$$a^{1/2} = [10^{2(N-1)}]^{1/2}\left[\frac{(a/10^{2(N-1)}) - 1}{2}\right]\sin\alpha$$

The accuracy of the method depends on the accuracy of the sine calculation and the register length, or truncation. The multiply-divide process keeps register length reasonable with only a slight sacrifice in accuracy. □

Differential phase shifter speeds calculation of FFT

by Richard K. Dickey
California Polytechnic State University, San Luis Obispo, Calif.

The fast Fourier transform is an algorithm by which a computer can find the spectral components of a repetitive ac signal. And fast though it is, you can nearly halve the time many computer programs require for the FFT if you use a differential phase shifter in addition to the instrumentation that is normally associated with a computer.

The signal to be analyzed is expressed as

$$f(t) = \sum_{n=0}^{N-1} H_n exp(jn\omega_1 t)$$

where $\omega_1 = 2\pi$ times the repetition frequency of the waveform, N is the total number of harmonics used in the representation of function f(t), and Fourier coefficient H_n is a complex quantity that specifies the amplitude and phase of the nth harmonic component. The values of the coefficients are found by measuring the amplitude of f(t) at times $t = k\tau$, where k = 0, 1, 2, . . .(N – 1), and $N\tau$ is the period of the wave. Then each H_n is

$$H_n = (1/N) \sum_{k=0}^{N-1} f(k\tau)exp(-j2\pi nk/N)$$

The number of samples is usually taken as a power of 2, i.e., $N = 2^p$, because of the binary nature of computers.

In the simplest version of the FFT, the N samples are stored in a data field of memory capable of holding N complex variables. Further operations replace these original data samples with sets of complex numbers several times, until the final transform is generated. (For a detailed explanation of the FFT, see *Electronics*, April 15, 1968, pp. 124–129.)

According to the Nyquist criterion only N/2 final magnitude values can be computed from the original N points, even though the number of memory locations required is 2N. The reason is that all variables are assumed to be complex quantities and information would be lost if the imaginary components were neglected.

However, the input data is a real quantity, derived from sampling of a voltage, so the input field consists of only real numbers. The imaginary components must be set to zero. Therefore, if the computer is programed for complex quantities, it spends about half of its time proceeding unproductively through calculations with zero.

To realize the full capabilities of an N-point transform program on any given computer, the system in the block diagram can be used. Here the constant phase-difference (CPD) network produces two outputs of equal amplitude that differ in phase by 90° at all frequencies in the band of interest [as described in *Electronics*, Aug. 21, p. 82]. The two sample-and-hold circuits sample their input signals simultaneously at a command from the computer. Then the multiplexer, under computer control, introduces these samples, one after the other, via the a-d converter into computer memory. All of the circuit elements in the diagram except the CPD network are part of any good computer instrumentation system.

If one output of the CPD network is labeled as a real number, and the other output as an imaginary number, then the ensemble of outputs from the network is truly a complex quantity of the form

$$f(t) = \sum_{n=0}^{N-1} A_n exp[j(n\omega_1 t + \phi_n)]$$

for any repetitive input that is nonsinusoidal, where ω_1, is 2π times the fundamental frequency, and A_n and ϕ_n are the amplitude and phase, respectively, of the nth harmonic. Here the complex coefficient H_n has been replaced by $A_n exp(j\phi_n)$. If the input signal is a pure sine wave, this expression reduces to

$$f(t) = A_1 exp[j(\omega_1 t + \phi_1)]$$

With the simple N-point transform on a single-channel input, the sampling process modifies the original wave by introducing an image frequency: if f_c is the sampling rate and f_a is the frequency of the input signal, then the image frequency $(f_c - f_a)$ is produced and is displayed in the FFT output series. This image is what limits the allowable input frequency range to half the sampling rate, so that in the output display the image spectrum will not be confused with the input signal spectrum.

When the input signal is converted into a complex ensemble and sampled, the lower sideband, or image, is suppressed, allowing the analysis of input frequencies up to the full sampling rate. Note that the Nyquist criterion is not violated, because at each sampling time, two samples are taken, sufficient to supply both amplitude and phase information about the wave at a single time.

Use of the differential phase shifter to produce 2N words of data from N samples provides the same bandwidth and frequency resolution as 2N real samples; however, the computation time is halved if the program has been designed to treat all quantities as complex.

As an example of system operation, if a pure sine wave with zero relative phase, $f(t) = A_s exp(j\omega_s t)$, is applied to the input and sampled every τ seconds for $N\tau$ seconds total sampling time,

$$H_n = (1/N) \sum_{k=0}^{N-1} A_s exp(jk\omega_s\tau) exp(-j2\pi nk/N)$$

$$= (1/N) \sum_{k=0}^{N-1} A_s exp[jk(\omega_s\tau - 2\pi n/N)]$$

The function $exp[jk(\omega_s\tau - 2\pi n/N)]$ takes on various equally spaced angles, never summing to more than a value of one, for all values of n except $n = N\omega_s\tau/2\pi$. For this value of n, the angle of the complex exponential is always zero; the corresponding H is equal to A_s. □

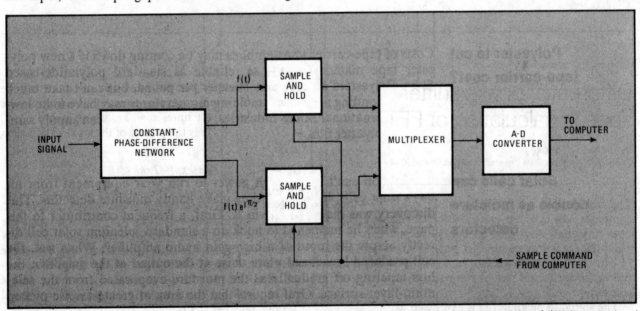

Speeding the FFT. Constant-phase-difference network and associated components shown here feed two samples of data to computer at each sampling of signal. Simultaneous sampling of the two quadrature-related signals identifies both amplitude and relative phase of each frequency component of the input wave. The multiplexer enables a single a-d converter to transmit both values to the computer. The computer program treats one value as a real number and the other as an imaginary number. Thus the bandwidth and frequency resolution obtained are the same as for twice as many real samples, but take about half the time to compute if the routine treats all variables as complex.

Module converts voltage to inverse square

by S. Ashok
Rensselaer Polytechnic Institute. Troy, N.Y.

Measurements of junction capacitance as a function of voltage are frequently used in semiconductor work to determine the doping profile of materials and the barrier potential of pn and Schottky junctions. The evaluation of these parameters actually requires a plot of the inverse square of the junction differential capacitance against reverse voltage, because the doping concentration is given by the slope of $1/C^2$ with voltage,

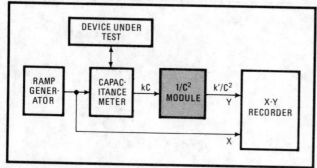

1. The secret is in the box. Block diagram shows arrangement for swept-voltage measurements of capacitance. The box that converts C to $1/C^2$ produces an X-Y plot that directly indicates the doping profile of a semiconductor junction.

2. Here's what's inside. The $1/C^2$ module of Fig. 1 is a multifunction converter IC, with appropriate external resistors added to give an output signal that's proportional to the inverse square of input signal. The proportionality constant is adjusted by R_1.

and the barrier potential is found by extrapolation of that line.

In the absence of sophisticated doping profilers, the plot of $1/C^2$ vs V is usually deduced point by point from swept C-vs-V data. However, the present availability of precision nonlinear-function modules at low cost enables one to obtain swept plots of $1/C^2$ against V directly by adding a simple circuit to the standard swept C-V setup.

Figure 1 shows the block diagram of the setup to obtain swept $1/C^2$-vs-V data. The ramp generator applies a linearly increasing reverse voltage to the device under test through the bias-input terminals of the capacitance meter. The recorder output of the meter gives a voltage that is proportional to the differential capacitance of the device. The $1/C^2$ module converts this voltage to its inverse square so that $1/C^2$ is plotted as a function of V directly on the X-Y recorder.

The schematic diagram of the $1/C^2$ module is shown in Fig. 2. It employs a Burr-Brown Model 4302 multifunction converter IC that gives an output voltage

$$V_{out} = V_y(V_z/V_x)^m$$

where the exponent m can be adjusted to any value from 0.2 to 5 by proper choice of R_4 and R_5 and their interconnection with the IC. The voltages V_x, V_y, and V_z should all be positive. For the $1/C^2$ plotter, V_x is the output of the C meter while V_y and V_z are constant voltages. Variable resistor R_1 controls the "gain" of the circuit and may be adjusted to give a V_{out} of $+10$ v for $V_z = V_x$. Since semiconductor-junction capacitance decreases with reverse voltages, V_z should be adjusted to equal V_x at the maximum sweep voltage. This is

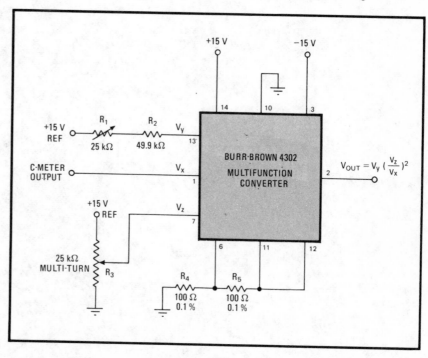

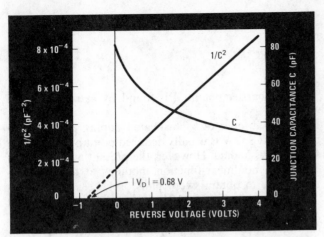

3. The plot revealed. X-Y plots of C and $1/C^2$ vs reverse bias are shown for a GaAs Schottky-barrier diode. The $1/C^2$ plot calculated from the C-V curve is practically coincident with the output of the $1/C^2$ plotter; the discrepancy of about 1.5% seen at the extremity (4 volts bias) is simply due to scaling error. Extrapolation of the $1/C^2$ plot gives the diffusion potential V_D, and the slope gives the doping.

achieved with the multiturn potentiometer R_3.

Typically, capacitance meters give a full-scale output of about 2 V, so an accuracy in $1/C^2$ of better than 1% has been obtained for C-meter readings down to a tenth of full-scale. The accuracy may be enhanced by using the voltage trimming features of the IC. Sometimes it is desirable to obtain a plot of $1/C^3$, and this is readily achieved by changing R_4 to 50 ohms.

A sample swept-voltage X-Y plot of C and $1/C^2$ for a gallium-arsenide Schottky-barrier diode is shown in Fig. 3. The net doping concentration, in donors per cubic centimeter, is calculated from the expression:

$$Doping = 1.1 \times 10^7/(A^2)(slope)$$

where A is the junction area in square centimeters and the slope is the rate of change of $1/C^2$ in picofarads with V in volts. Here A was 0.95×10^{-3} cm^2, so the doping concentration is 7.1×10^{16} per cm^3. The extrapolated $1/C^2$-vs-V plot yields a diffusion potential of 0.68 V. The deviation from linearity at low reverse voltages is due to traps in the material. □

14. Trouble detectors

Self-powered comparator warns when signal exceeds limits

by Roger Fell
Analog Devices Inc., Norwood, Mass.

An analog comparator circuit that indicates whether the signal measured by a digital panel meter is within programable limits is powered entirely by that same DPM. The circuit is particularly useful for system applications in which the voltages of process-control equipment or pollution have to be monitored.

The DPM displays all input signals, regardless of the limits, but flashes the polarity sign or digital display for inputs outside the desired range. The comparator works with any DPM that has blanking circuitry for the polarity sign or entire display; the Analog Devices AD2006 is suggested because it has, in addition to the blanking circuitry, ±15-volt dc and +5-v dc outputs that supply sufficient power for the comparator circuitry.

The reference output of the DPM is used here as a stable reference voltage for the comparator. It is buffered and attenuated by operational amplifiers A_1 and A_2 to levels of ±2.5 V. Potentiometer R_1 is set for the lower threshold and R_2 for the upper threshold, both at any value within the DPM's input range.

An analog input between the two thresholds drives the outputs of op amps A_3 and A_4 positive. The diode network at the outputs of A_3 and A_4 is a primitive AND gate, which turns on transistor Q_1 if both op-amp outputs are high. This short-circuits the timing capacitor C_1 of the NE555 timer, which is connected as an astable multivibrator. With pin 6 of the timer held at digital ground, the output of the timer at pin 3 is forced high. This signal, at the blanking input of the DPM, unblanks the polarity sign or display.

When the analog input signal of the DPM is above or below the preset thresholds, one of the two op-amp outputs is driven negative, turning off transistor Q_1, and removing the short circuit across C_1. This enables the astable multivibrator to operate; the resulting square wave at its output flashes the polarity readout of the DPM at a rate of about 5 hertz.   □

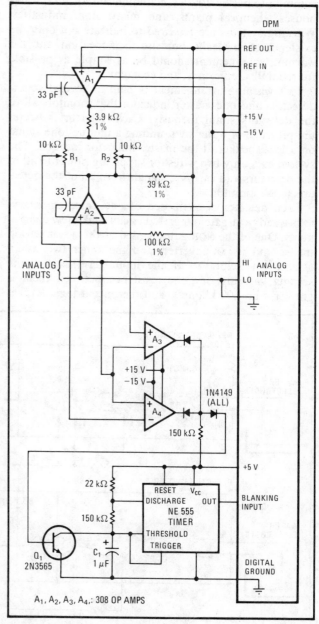

Limit checker. Potentiometers define upper and lower thresholds for permissible range of analog signal. When input is above or below the threshold range, the timer, connected as an astable multivibrator, begins to flash either the entire display or its polarity sign.

Multiplexed detectors isolate water leaks

by F.E. Hinkle
Applied Research Laboratories, University of Texas, Austin

The need to detect water leaks at any number of sites is common to public utilities, communications links, warehouses, chemical plants, and many other industries. Warning systems are required to indicate not only the existence of the leaks, but also their location, and the warning arrangement should be as simple as possible for reliability, efficiency, and economy.

This warning arrangement is built of several water-detectors and one master indicator that monitors all of the detectors simultaneously. Each detector indicates the presence of water by sounding a unique tone signal on a loudspeaker at the master-indicator location. The system uses only two wires for supplying power to all of the detectors and carrying signals from all of the detectors to the monitor.

Each detector is composed of one complementary-MOS quad NOR-gate integrated circuit and a few components. One of the NOR gates is used as the water sensor, the second as an inverter, and the other two as an astable multivibrator. If the input terminals of the sensing gate are dry, the resistance between them is greater than 500 kilohms, and the output logic level is low. Therefore the output from the inverter is high, and the multivibrator is disabled. But if water connects the input terminals of the sensor, the resistance between them is below 100 kilohms, the input to the inverter is high, and the multivibrator oscillates at a frequency determined by its RC time constant. Each detector has its own characteristic frequency, given by

$$f_n = 1/1.4\,R_n C_n$$

where the resistance R_n is in ohms and the capacitance C_n is in farads.

The oscillator signal is carried back to the indicator unit over the two wires that supply dc power to the detector. Since the signal oscillates between 0 and +9 volts with a 50% duty cycle, the average value of the supply voltage is reduced considerably. Therefore, diode D_P and capacitor C_P are used to detect the peak supply voltage and store it. The value of C_P in farads is chosen to be $1/1000f_L$, where f_L is the lowest frequency (in hertz) used by any of the detectors. This amount of capacitance allows less than 0.5-volt ripple on the C-MOS chips.

To isolate all of the detector oscillators from one another, a diode, D_S, is used at the output of each multivibrator. Collectively, these diodes in the detectors form a multi-input OR gate.

The indicator unit contains a C-MOS gate that detects voltage fluctuations on the two-wire interconnect line and feeds a transistor amplifier to drive the loudspeaker. Inductor L isolates the detector signals from the dc-power source. The inductance value is deter-

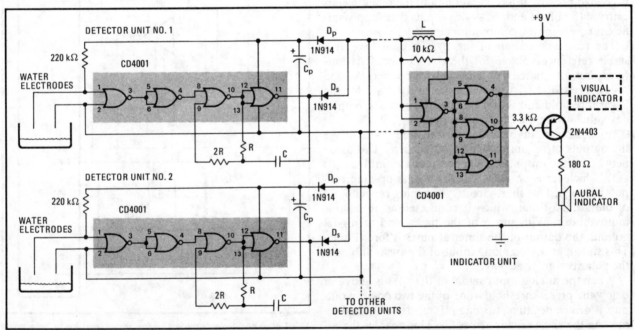

Handles water music. A variety of tones from a loudspeaker signals water leaks and their locations. Visual display can also be provided, if necessary or desirable. Each one of a large number of detectors is identified by its unique frequency. Only two wires are needed to connect all detectors to the monitoring location; the wires supply power to the detectors, and carry the warning signals back to the indicator.

mined by the lowest signal frequency and the maximum current permitted during the oscillations. If this current is taken to be 1 milliampere for C-MOS devices used, the value of L in henries is about $1600/f_L$. This value of inductance seems large if f_L is a few hundred hertz, but the low currents permit use of miniature types of coils. A resistor shunts the coil so that no signal will see an impedance greater than 10 kilohms.

In operation, the detectors normally are quiescent. If a leak is detected, the frequency corresponding to the particular location is generated and transmitted via the two-wire interconnect cable to the indicator unit. The indicator emits the tone that identifies the location of the leak.

In a large system with many detectors, the oscillating frequencies may be too close together to distinguish between them, but a visual display, such as an oscilloscope or frequency counter, can be used to measure the precise frequency of oscillation.

Because C-MOS integrated circuits are used, the standby power demand is extremely low. A 9-v battery can power the complete system.

This system can be adapted to many other applications besides water-leak detection. Various types of sensors can be connected to produce logic-level changes at the input gate of the detector; only two interconnect wires would still be required to tie all the detectors to the indicator unit. □

Flashing lamp reminds you to turn off equipment

by John Gibson
University of California, Berkeley, Calif.

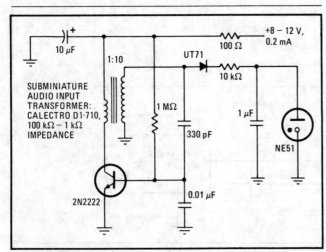

Warning light. Neon panel lamp flashes about every 5 seconds for as long as equipment is on. The circuit, which is intended for battery-operated units, keeps current drain to a low 200 microamperes.

Most battery-operated equipment lacks an indicator light to remind you to turn the unit off. Forgetting to flick the off switch can be an expensive oversight. For instance, if a dry-battery supply is left on so that it discharges completely, the highly corrosive fluid that oozes out of the cells may damage expensive components. Frequent replacement of run-down batteries can also be quite costly.

As a solution, you can easily install an incandescent indicator, but even the lowest-drain (and therefore dimmest) incandescent lamp requires appreciable power, often more than the rest of the equipment needs. On the other hand, the neon-lamp circuit in the figure holds current drain to a mere 200 microamperes. Moreover, the neon lamp flashes approximately every 5 seconds for a better warning indication.

The circuit employs a blocking oscillator whose output pulses are rectified and then used to pump-up the 1-microfarad capacitor in a staircase-generator fashion. When this capacitor's voltage reaches the firing voltage of the neon bulb, the bulb fires and discharges the capacitor. The cycle can now repeat.

Any neon bulb having a firing voltage of less than 90 volts can be used. Both the diode and the "firing" capacitor must be low-leakage devices. Correct transformer phasing is essential for proper circuit operation. The transformer is wired in reverse—that is, its secondary is used as the primary and vice versa. □

Continuous monitor for seven-segment displays

by Kenneth J. Wellington
Syracuse University, Syracuse, N.Y.

One of the major drawbacks of seven-segment displays is the ever-present possibility that one of the segments may fail and go undetected for some time. All the readings taken in the interim would, of course, be erroneous.

Here's a circuit that solves this problem by testing every segment automatically once every second. It is a full-time monitor that can be used with either incandescent or light-emitting-diode displays operating from a segment supply voltage of between 5 and 15 volts.

Unlike other failsafe circuits, this one does not require a separate differential amplifier for each segment being monitored. Instead, the circuit uses a resistor at each segment and a single multiple-input NAND gate to which the segment resistors are connected.

The gate is a complementary-MOS device that has its high-impedance inputs tied to the open-collector outputs of a decoder/driver. The segment resistors perform as the pull-down resistors for the multiple-input C-MOS NAND gate.

When the blanking-input/ripple-blanking-output (BI/RBO) line of the decoder/driver is activated, all seven of this device's outputs become open circuits, and the NAND gate checks the continuity between each segment and the segment supply voltage. An open filament or LED will result in a logic 1 at the gate's output.

The monitoring circuitry for each digit of the over-all display is identical to that drawn within the dashed color rule in the diagram. The outputs from all the digits drive the C-MOS NOR gate, whose output is inverted and shifted to TTL levels by the transistor. The translated gate output is then stored by the data latch.

A 555-type timer, operated in its astable mode, generates the waveform for controlling the BI/RBO line of each decoder/driver in the overall display. The inverters activate the BI/RBO output of each decoder/driver for 500 microseconds once every second. Since these inverters have open-collector outputs, the normal operation of an individual display's ripple-blanking is not affected.

The data latch is strobed at the end of the 500-μs pulse. Its Q output will normally be a logic 0, but will go to logic 1 if a segment failure is detected. This output can be used to turn off the display, turn on a warning light, or indicate in some other way when a segment has failed. □

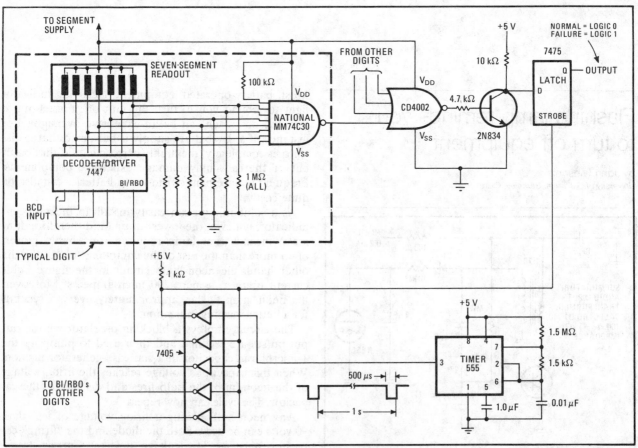

Watching for failures. Open segments in a seven-segment readout are detected by this failsafe circuit, which automatically checks the continuity of each segment once a second. As long as the segments are operating normally, the output of the latch remains at logic 0. If a segment fails, this output goes to logic 1. Either incandescent or solid-state readouts can be monitored by the circuit.

Gas and smoke detector uses low-leakage MOS transistor

by Al Pshaenich and Roger Janikowski
Motorola Semiconductor Products Inc., Phoenix, Ariz.

With metal oxide semiconductor field-effect transistors (MOS FETs) that have very low leakage current, combustion gas detectors can now be inexpensively built to run on battery power. This type of detector consists of an ionization chamber and a solid-state amplifier. Besides sounding an alarm in the presence of gas or smoke, the detector warns when the battery is dying.

An ionization chamber consists essentially of a collector electrode extending into a metal chamber, which forms the other electrode. A minute amount of radioactive material in the chamber emits alpha particles that bombard the air molecules and ionize some of them. When an electric potential is placed across the electrodes, the attracted ions produce an extremely small current—in the range of 10 to 30 picoamperes. Combustion-gas molecules that enter the chamber tend to attach themselves to the ions. The enlarged ions move more slowly in the electrical field, reducing the current across the electrodes of the detector.

If the ionization chamber is placed in series with a high-impedance reference, the pair forms a voltage divider. When the current decreases in the presence of gas or smoke, the voltage across the reference element decreases, and a comparator detects the change.

In the battery-operated detection circuit in the diagram, Q_1 and Q_2 form a MOS-bipolar differential amplifier. Q_1 is a high-impedance buffer, which has an input leakage current of about 1.0 pA—at least one order of magnitude less than the chamber current, so that it doesn't load the circuit. The reference resistor R_1 has an impedance approximately equal to that of the ionization chamber in the absence of smoke, thus setting the voltage at the FET gate to about 6 volts. The FET source current is about 30 microamperes, and the gate-to-source voltage is about 2 V, which places the source—the terminal connected to R_2—at 8 V. The threshold control, R_3, is set to back-bias Q_2, typically at about 500 millivolts.

Tests with smoke levels at 2% and 4% obscuration produced a negative voltage shift at the buffer gate of about 2 V and 3 V, respectively. This is enough to turn off Q_1 and turn on Q_2 and Q_3, which applies a logic 1 at one input of the NAND gate 1. This gate, together with inverter 2 and the associated discrete components, forms a nonsymmetrical astable multivibrator, which

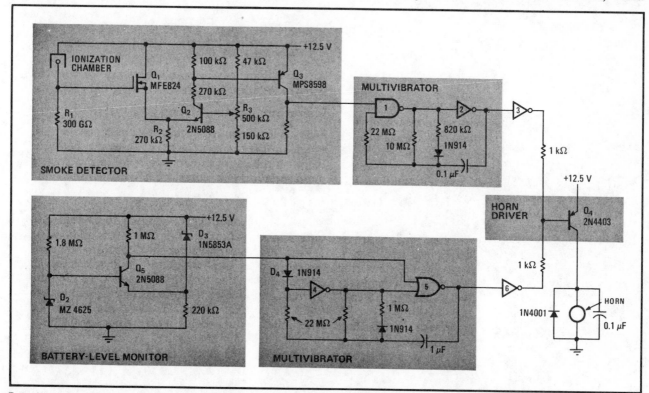

Detector. A MOS FET transistor, Q_1, with high input impedance monitors the voltage level at a divider, one half of which is an ionization chamber. Differential amplifier Q_1-Q_2 picks up any decrease in this voltage and triggers a multivibrator that sounds a pulsating alarm. Low battery voltage triggers a second multivibrator that uses the same horn to sound a "beep . . . beep . . . beep" warning.

begins to oscillate when Q_3 turns on. In the multivibrator, the capacitor charges quickly and discharges slowly; while it is discharging, it causes the horn to sound via the inverter 3 and driver transistor Q_4. The horn blows continuously for 2.5 seconds, then turns off for 0.2 seconds while the capacitor recharges. This pulsating alarm continues as long as smoke is present.

A comparator, consisting of one transistor and two zener diodes, determines when the battery is low. Diode D_2 carries only about $5\mu A$, so that the base voltage at Q_5 is about 3 V. The other diode, D_3, couples the full change in battery voltage to the emitter of Q_5. These diodes, which have zener breakdowns of about 4.5 V and 8.2 V, respectively, turn on and quickly saturate Q_5 when the voltage of the expiring battery sags to approximately 10.5 V. This drops its collector from near the battery voltage, maintained by D_4 at the input of inverter 4, to about 2.5 V, which is below the threshold of NOR gate 5. This is part of another astable multivibrator that also blows the horn via the same driver. But this capacitor is larger, and the network charges it slowly and discharges it quickly, so that the horn makes a 1-second toot every 23 seconds. This alarm is not only distinctly different from the smoke alarm, but it also conserves the energy remaining in the battery.

A single complementary-MOS integrated circuit, MC14572, can be used to build the four inverters, one NAND and one NOR, from which the two multivibrators are assembled. The other components in the multivibrators, and those in the smoke-detection and the battery-monitor circuits, are discrete. □

15. Five noise beaters

Choosing the best suppression network for your SCR converter

by L.R. Rice
Westinghouse Power Semiconductor Division, Youngwood, Pa.

Although a wide variety of schemes exists for suppressing the energy transients in semiconductor converters, unfortunately there is no single circuit that fits all needs. Instead, the design engineer must select that network that best suits his particular requirement.

Transients in most power systems arise from rapid electrical-circuit changes, such as energizing and de-energizing of a reactive circuit. Conventional RC suppression circuits will limit the magnitude or rate of rise of transient waveforms, but thyristor circuits generally require controlling the slope of transients. Diodes use shaping to reduce recovery losses.

Inductance is a convenient point to start looking for transient generation. In any practical circuit, a finite inductance exists. This may be caused by the wiring bus, transformer leakage reactance, or an inductance purposely designed into the circuit, such as the transformer windings or a filter choke used in the power supply.

Voltage transients can be caused by interruption of the power-transformer magnetizing current (either opening or closing the on-off switch in the primary winding) by a switching rectifier with an inductive load across the input, or by load switching. Also a dv/dt switch transient can be caused by closing of primary switch or when operating with a fuse, but without a filter network. Load-generated transients, such as overvoltage due to switching of motor load and resulting regeneration, however, pose less of a problem, since they can be easily suppressed by clamping diodes or a dissipative network.

In thyristor circuits, an inductor may cause false anode firing via dv/dt transients. For many circuits, simple RC filters may not sufficiently suppress the transient. This is especially true for converters operating from high-kVA transformerless connections. In these instances, the high device impedance and low bus inductance do not provide enough of a voltage drop, and dv/dt transients as high as 1,000 volts/microsecond can occur. □

BIBLIOGRAPHY
"Westinghouse SCR Designers' Handbook," 2nd ed., 1970.
John B. Rice, "Design of Snubber Circuits for Thyristor Converters," Proceedings of IGA, 1969, pp. 485-489.
J. B. Rice and P. G. Phillips, "A System for Recording Thyristor and Rectifier Current Waveforms," IGA Transactions, 1968.

FUNDAMENTAL SUPPRESSION AND PROTECTIVE SCHEMES FOR SCR CIRCUITS

Circuit								
Use	Clamps voltage across SCR to less than its rated forward blocking voltage, V_{DRM}	Varistor to increase dissipation with high voltage	Convert transient voltage to charging current and lower transient magnitude	Same as capacitor, but controls dv/dt shaping with lower di/dt	Similar to RC types, but on high kVA sources, the induction provides regulation to allow the RC to work and lower surge current	Similar to linear inductor but sat. reactor lowers size and cost	Same as RC types, but allows high charging current and low di/dt	Same as capacitor-type for series connection where $R1 \gg R$, and $C2 \gg C1$	Same as RC circuit, but with overvoltage protection that causes SCR to turn on before V_{DRM} is reached
Circuit limitations	Does not control dv/dt	Does not control dv/dt	Causes high di/dt and peak current, needs some line impedance to slow down dv/dt	Requires a compromise between allowable amounts of dv/dt and di/dt	If reactor must support large line voltage and current loads, it will be expensive and bulky	Usually requires large reactance to minimize initial current surge. This can be expensive and bulky	D1 recovery time must be < 1 μs or a high di/dt results	Diodes in the bridge must have recovery times < 1 μs to minimize di/dt	C1 and C2 must be selected to trigger SCR; large values of C2 can cause di/dt problems
Size[1]	6	7	9	8	1	3	5	2	4
Cost[1,2]	5	6	9	8	1	3	7	2	4
Complexity[1]	6	7	9	8	4	5	3	1	2

Notes: 1. Ranked in descending order   2. 100-A rms device

Ten ways to reduce noise pickup in ICs

by Peter A. Goodwin
Loblolly Associates, Wayland, Mass.

Engineers who struggle to minimize noise pickup in equipment built with integrated circuitry know that there is no magic procedure for eliminating interference caused by lightning hits on power lines, chattering relays, motor-starting transients, electrical discharges to or near the equipment, radio-frequency fields, and the like. Instead, they fight noise by meticulous attention to details of bypassing, grounding, shielding, decoupling, and circuit layout—all used with understanding of the particular characteristics of the ICs involved.

TTL devices exhibit low-impedance, current-mode characteristics and are particularly susceptible to potential differences between devices caused principally by conducted interference.

MOS devices exhibit high-impedance, voltage-oriented characteristics and are therefore susceptible to radiated interference. A secondary susceptibility to conducted interference arises by induction from a neighboring conductor that is carrying the current of an electrical discharge.

Linear integrated circuits have high input impedances and low output impedances, and lack the guaranteed-true voltage regions that are characteristic of digital circuits. Noise spikes can enter a high-gain amplifier through the supply-voltage bus.

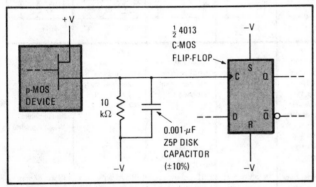

Noise suppression. Typical application of capacitor to bypass p-MOS output line that feeds edge-triggered C-MOS device. (Bypassing would be same for n-MOS device and pullup resistor, except that n-MOS would have V– supply and resistor would connect to V + .)

The following design practices will reduce the susceptibility of IC equipment to electromagnetic interference.

1. Bypass everything. An inexpensive general-purpose ceramic disk capacitor (0.01-microfarad) should be placed across the supply-voltage bus near each integrated circuit. TTL circuits are also improved by the presence of a 6.8-μF tantalum bypass capacitor for every 15 chips or so. Bypass MOS output lines that feed edge-triggered C-MOS devices, because only a passive device exists to provide the pullup or pulldown function. Use the minimum capacitance that gives acceptable rise time, and specify a temperature-stable 10% disk capacitor. See the figure for an illustration of typical components. No similar problem exists with C-MOS-driven devices, because C-MOS devices feature a totem-pole output structure.

2. *Allow sufficient printed-circuit conductor width.* Most interference is at radio frequencies, which travel on the surface of the conductors. Conductor width is particularly important in a TTL environment, where supply currents are substantial and the rate of change of current is on the order of 10^7 amperes/second. Supply-conductor widths of 100 mils or more are not uncommon in this environment. Use a ground plane wherever possible; the ground plane should be connected to the power-supply return.

3. *Distinguish between "earth" and "common" (system ground or power-supply return).* The earth conductor should never be used to transfer power. "Earth" and "common" conductors should be brought into contact at only one point in the system; otherwise a ground loop can radiate noise into the circuit.

4. *Run a separate supply bus for high-current devices.* This practice keeps transients off the busses that supply power to the logic circuitry. Remember also that conductors carrying current spikes couple inductively to neighboring conductors and that those carrying voltage spikes couple capacitively to their neighbors. Therefore, be careful in laying out these conductors.

5. *Keep pulldown resistors as small as possible* unless power consumption or other considerations are overriding factors. This is particularly true in MOS circuits.

6. *Don't overdo the fast-rise signals,* even though they are great for TTL devices. The lower the rise time, the less interconductor coupling.

7. *Don't let unused inputs float.* In the TTL discipline, connect them to V– or pull them up to V + through a 1-kilohm resistor, as appropriate. In the MOS discipline, pull to V– or V + as appropriate—a floating input is a true "maybe" condition.

8. *In general, use 1% resistors and capacitors in linear-circuit feasibility models.* The exceptions are pulldown resistors and bypass capacitors, where 20% variations can obviously be tolerated. After the design is optimized, then investigate the effects of component tolerance variations.

9. *Remember that decoupling is particularly suited to the low-current requirements of MOS circuitry.* A 1-ohm series resistor inserted in the supply bus on the supply side of the input bypass capacitor provides good isolation from high-frequency power variations.

10. *Avoid one-shots if pulse-width is critical.* The trouble is, their manufacturing tolerances are loose. Instead of

using one-shots, arrange to derive pulses from the clock.

If all else fails, line filtering and unit shielding offer attractive although more expensive possibilities. Metal or conductively coated nonmetallic equipment enclosures provide marked attenuation to external interference. Windows over displays, dials, and meters can be covered with copper screening. Line filters offer resistance to power-line-conducted noise, but generally should be matched to the equipment by enlisting the aid of the filter manufacturer. ☐

Eliminating stray signals in remotely gain-switched op amps

by Ernest J. Kacher & Forrest Fox
The Methodist Hospital, Texas Medical Center, Houston, Texas

When the gain switch for a variable-gain amplifier is physically distant from the amplifier itself, stray signal pickup and/or capacitance loading can affect circuit performance. A special switching arrangement, however, can eliminate both of these problems.

The circuits drawn in (a) show how cable capacitance can be introduced at the amplifier's input. While the circuits of (b) show where noise generators appear when the amplifier input leads remain open. (In all these circuits, the amplifier is connected in its non-inverting mode.)

In contrast, the switching arrangement illustrated in (c) has no current paths through unused resistors, and it eliminates switching at the amplifier input. All of the resistors are used with each gain configuration, and all of the lines to the switch are always connected either directly to signal ground or to the low-impedance output of the amplifier.

The maximum allowable cable capacitance, therefore, is now determined by the capacitance load that the amplifier can tolerate, rather than the signal phase shift. Another advantage of this switching arrangement is that the circuit's bias-current compensation remains optimum for each gain, as long as the correct value is selected for resistor R_0.

To make use of this type of switching, the resistors required, as well as the right switching arrangement, must be determined for the specific set of desired gains: G_0, $G_1, \ldots, G_n$. First, arrange the gains in ascending order according to magnitude (so that G_i is less than G_{i+1}), but let $G_0 = 1$ and $G_{n+1} = \infty$. Since there will be $n+1$ resistors required, they should be designated as R_1, $R_2, \ldots, R_{n+1}$. Compute the values of resistors R_2 through R_{n+1} sequentially, in terms of resistor R_1:

$$R_{i+1} = \frac{G_{i+1}(G_i - G_{i-1})R_i}{G_{i-1}(G_{i+1} - G_i)}$$

where i varies between 1 and n.

Next, arrange the switch so that, starting with the minimum gain of G_0, all the resistors connect from the amplifier's inverting input to the output. To obtain gain G_1, switch the end of R_1 from the output to ground, leaving everything else unchanged. To obtain gain G_2, switch the end of R_2 from the output to ground, leaving everything else unchanged. In general, then, to obtain gain G_i, resistors R_1 through R_i are connected to ground, and resistors R_{i+1} through R_{n+1} are connected to the output.

This same switching technique can be used for an inverting amplifier configuration. However, gain G_0 must be set equal to zero, and the values for resistors R_2 through R_{n+1} are found sequentially in terms of resistor R_1 from:

$$R_{i+1} = \frac{(G_{i+1} + 1)(G_i - G_{i-1})R_i}{(G_{i-1} + 1)(G_{i+1} - G_i)}$$

where i again varies between 1 and n.

Resistor R_0 can be computed as the parallel combination of all the gain resistors, R_1 through R_{n+1}. Or, for the non-inverting amplifier, it can be determined by:

$$R_0 = [(G_1 - 1)/G_1]R_1$$

And for the inverting amplifier, the value of R_0 is:

$$R_0 = [G_1/(G_1 + 1)]R_1$$

Circuits (d) and (e) give the resistor values for producing gains of 2, 5, and 10 when $R_1 = 1$. Amplifier (d) is noninverting, while amplifier (e) is inverting. □

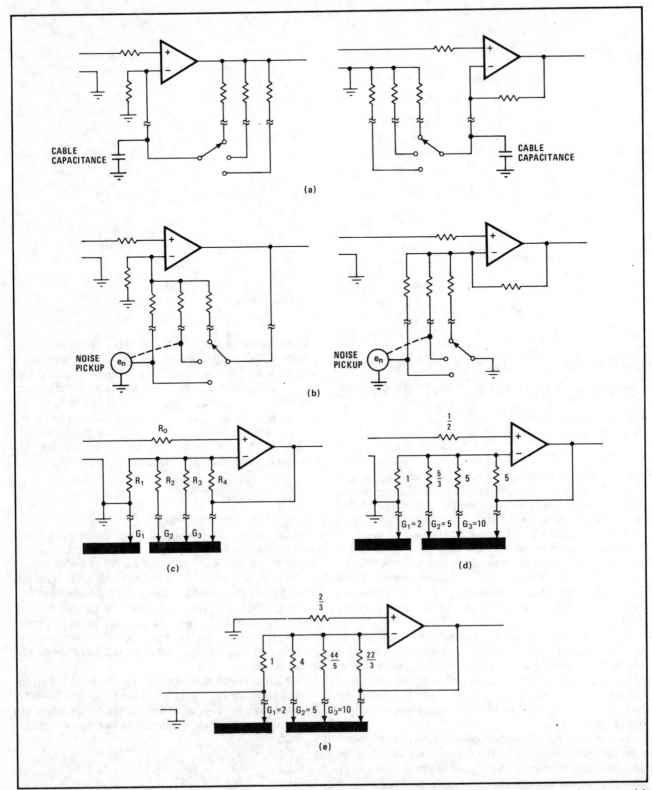

Switched-gain amplifiers. Remotely switched variable-gain amplifiers can suffer from the capacitance loading (a) of long wires or can pick up noise (b) through unused resistor paths. The switching arrangement of (c) doesn't have these problems because all of the switched points have low-impedance paths to ground. The noninverting (d) and inverting (e) amplifiers given here provide gains of 2, 5, and 10.

Circuit layouts minimize noise in digital systems

by Matthew L. Fichtenbaum
GenRad Inc., Concord, Mass.

Careful design of power and ground structures on printed-circuit boards and in multiboard systems can do much toward reducing the effects of noise from unwanted signal pickup. The layout techniques recommended here, which minimize ground inductance and stray capacitance, have contributed to the successful operation of many systems.

In Fig. 1, gates A and B, both of which are in one integrated-circuit package, drive gates C and D respectively. The ground path to A and B has some stray inductance, shown as L_{ground}, and each signal line has some capacitance to ground, such as C_{stray} on the output of A.

If A's output changes from high to low, the charge on C_{stray} causes a high instantaneous current to flow into A. The return path for this current is the ground lead, and the inductance in this path causes a voltage spike at the ground terminal. Output B, which should be in the low state, also carries this spike because the output cannot be lower than the ground level of the gate. So gate D, driven by B, sees an erroneous pulse at its input.

This effect may be lessened in several ways. Keeping tracks short, to decrease capacitance C_{stray}, reduces the spike amplitude. Although a resistor or inductor in series with the driver can limit the peak discharge current, they reduce system speed and can place unacceptable limitations on fanout. A better attack is to minimize the inductance in the ground lead through the use of a good ground structure.

An ideal solution is the full ground plane common to multilayer boards, which maintains minimal inductance and maximal amount of interconnection. Unfortunately, multilayer boards are expensive and difficult to justify for most circuitry.

The ground structure on a double-sided board in Fig. 2 gives a good approximation to a full ground plane. A V_{CC} bus runs up the right and left edges of the front surface of the board, and a ground bus runs up both edges on the back. Horizontal buses connected to the risers at the edges carry V_{CC} and ground for each IC. The buses' widely separated paths keep ground inductance low. Bypass capacitors, placed between the power and ground buses that feed a row of ICs, suppress the spikes in the supply current when an output switches. Because of the ample interconnection, few bypass capacitors are

1. Shaky ground. Gates A and B suffer unwanted coupling through inductance L_{ground} in the common ground lead. When gate A discharges C_{stray}, an erroneous signal appears at gate D.

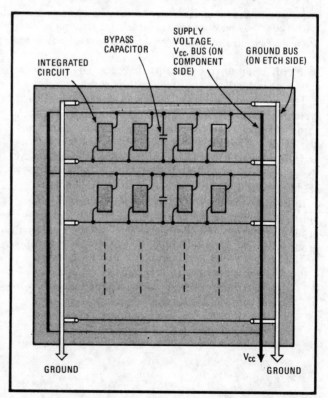

2. Grounds for confidence. The solid bar represents the supply voltage bus on the front of the circuit card, and the open bar is the ground bus on the back. The round holes allow back-to-front crossover. The grid structure of the bus lines approximates power and ground planes to keep inductance and noise low.

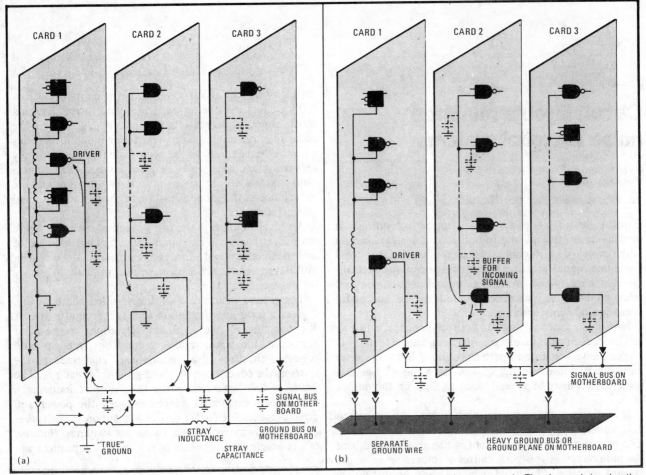

3. Cool bus. Stray inductance and capacitance in a multicard system (a) can cause noise problems between cards. The changed signal paths and ground structure in the arrangement shown on the cards (b) make the system less noisy and more reliable.

required; even so, the distance between any IC and a capacitor is small, so the spike path is short.

The same sort of noise problems exist in multicard systems where the logic signals communicate between cards. In Fig. 3a, the driver gate on card 1 must necessarily drive the stray capacitance on three cards and the motherboard. The resulting ground transients at the driver couple into other devices on card 1, so there could be serious noise.

In Fig. 3b, the system has been restructured to reduce noise. A ground plane or several widely spaced heavy ground tracks on the motherboard help keep all card grounds at the same voltage. Cards 2 and 3 buffer signals from the signal bus with a device near the bus connector. This buffering reduces the capacitive loading on the bus by shortening the length of track directly connected to it. It also keeps the heavy signal currents in the multiple loads local to the receiving card. Locating the driver near the bus connector keeps its paths short.

Perhaps most important, the driver receives its ground through a separate connection directly from the motherboard. This separate line keeps ground transients from affecting other devices on the card. It can dramatically increase the likelihood that the system will function properly, even with the long bus runs encountered when the card is on an extender. □

Coaxial buses help suppress power supply transients

by Herman Levin, Jeffrey O'Neil, and William Lord,
Colorado State University, Fort Collins, Colo.

The engineer using today's faster logic circuits may face the problem of power supply switching transients that have frequency components in excess of 1 gigahertz. Adding suppression networks to an adequately designed power supply will have little effect, but suppressing these transients along the power-supply feeder lines proves a viable technique.

Instead of using large parallel tubes just to satisfy the system's current requirements, try them in a coaxial configuration, and thus attenuate those transients, as well. A practical approach is to use copper tubes coaxially configured with polyvinylchloride tubing slipped over the inner tube and heat-shrunk tightly to it.

An experimental feeder-line section can be made easily by using copper tubing in sizes readily available from a hardware store. Connections to the section are

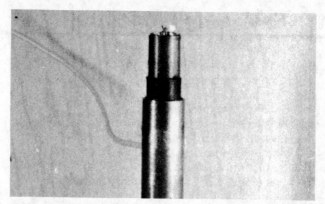

Experimental coaxial section uses standard copper tubes

TYPE L RIGID COPPER TUBES

Nominal size	Outside diameter	Inside diameter	Equivalent B & S wire size
1/4 in.	.375 in.	.315 in.	4
3/8	.500	.430	2
1/2	.625	.545	1
5/8	.750	.666	0
3/4	.875	.785	00
1	1.125	1.025	0000

made at the ends of the inner and outer tubes. For convenience, holes can be drilled prior to assembly in the outer tube at regular intervals, and connections to the inner tube can be made by drilling small holes through the sleeve and inner tube and using blind pop-type rivets to attach the leads. Connections to the outer tube can be made with clamps or presoldered connectors.

When production quantities are involved, most of the parameters can be optimized: the dielectric material and ratio of tube diameters can be chosen to increase the attenuation, and the inner tube connectors can be made with special feedthrough components for ease of fabrication.

Standard coaxial cable can be substituted for the copper tubes and sleeving. However, an excessively large cable would be needed to equal the current-carrying capacity of the tubes, and making connections to the inner conductor of standard coax isn't simple. Moreover, the ratio of the tube diameters can be adjusted to provide greater attenuation per unit length of the power supply feeder line.

TRANSIENT SUPPRESSION IN DECIBELS FOR A 3-FOOT SECTION (SOURCE RESISTANCE 50 Ω)

Bus No.	Frequency equivalent of transient		
	1 GHz	100 MHz	10 MHz
1	38	23	3.5
2	41	27	7.5
3	43	30	10
4	45	32	12
5	41	22	2

TYPICAL BUS CONFIGURATIONS

Bus No.	Outer tube nominal	Inner tube nominal	PVC tubing nominal
1	3/8 in.	1/4 in.	3/8 in.
2	1/2	3/8	1/2
3	5/8	1/2	3/4
4	3/4	5/8	3/4
5	1	3/4	1

16. Easy amplifier circuitry

Charting power losses for hybrid-combined amplifiers

by Ronald M. Sonkin
Electronic Navigation Industries Inc., Rochester, N.Y.

If a hybrid junction is used to combine the output power of several transistor amplifiers that are in phase and of equal magnitude, then it's easy to figure the total output power—simply multiply one amplifier's power by the total number. However, in the real world, outputs are seldom exactly equal in phase or magnitude. For such cases, the designer has to know how much gain and phase mismatch between amplifiers he can tolerate and still deliver the required output power. The accompanying curves show this latitude.

Hybrid junctions represent a class of four-port networks that have the properties of being matched, isolated, lossless, and reciprocal. In the basic hybrid connection for a two-transistor amplifier, a hybrid at the input splits the power for each transistor, and another hybrid at the output combines the transistor outputs.

The curves show the resultant loss in power at the output as a function of differences in phase and magnitude. The curves are derived from the scattering matrix of a magic-T hybrid junction. For example, if the ratio of the absolute values of the output voltages of the amplifiers is 0.8, the output power would drop by 0.05 decibel from the ideal level (where the two magnitudes and phases are equal). And, if the phases differ by, say, 30°, then an additional decrease of 0.3 dB would occur (the two effects are cumulative). For this example, output power thus would be 0.35 dB less than ideal.

Also shown is a curve that helps estimate the effects of a failure of one or more output transistors. For example, in the simple two-transistor case, if one transistor fails, the output power drops by 6 dB below the ideal level, since (N–M)/N is 0.5 (N is the total number of transistors that have their outputs combined, and M is the number of failed transistors). In this case, the output from the one transistor still operating is split by the hybrid—half to the output and half to the terminating resistor required on the hybrid's fourth arm. □

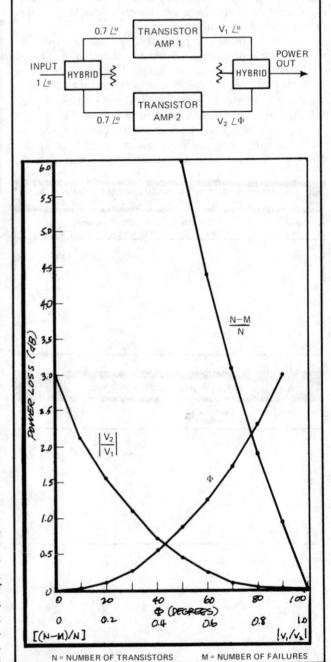

BIBLIOGRAPHY

Montgomery, Dicke, and Purcell, "Principles of Microwave Circuits," M.I.T. Radiation Laboratory Series, Vol. 8, 1948.
    L. Young et al., "Advances in Microwaves," Academic Press, Vol. 1, 1967.

Capacitance of twisted wire trims fast FET op amps

by Victor D. Roberts
General Electric Co., Large Lamp Dept., Cleveland, Ohio

High-speed FET-input operational amplifiers that have a large feedback resistor sometimes need a low-capacitance trimmer that can be adjusted to prevent oscillation without appreciably decreasing the op amp's frequency response. Try twisting together two short pieces of insulated wire to make a cheap and readily available trimmer capacitor. It's a technique that has been used for quite some time by builders of amateur radio equipment for neutralizing rf amplifiers.

Here is a typical application for this handy trimmer capacitor. A FET-input op amp is connected as a simple unity-gain inverter with a 1-megohm input impedance, as noted in the figure. Without a feedback capacitor, the circuit produces damped 200-kilohertz oscillations when driven by a fast-rise-time square wave. Employing 1½ turns of AWG #22 vinyl-insulated wire (0.4-millimeter wall) eliminates these oscillations without degrading the circuit's rise time. The twisted wire provides a capacitance of approximately 2 picofarads. □

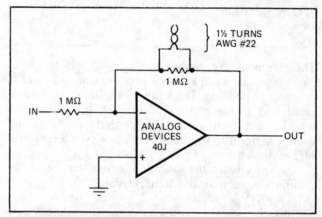

Twisting away oscillations. Short insulated wires make handy trimmer capacitor when twisted together. One or two turns can provide enough capacitance to stop fast FET op amps from oscillating.

Reducing IC FET op amp input bias currents

by Richard G. Jewell
Nova Devices Inc., Wilmington, Mass.

Adding a simple heat sink or operating at reduced voltage can significantly improve a field-effect transistor operational amplifier's input bias current over what the spec sheet says. Actually, both methods merely reduce the IC's junction temperature, but this is of great importance since FET input bias current doubles with every 10°C rise in temperature.

Either method of reducing the temperature requires the user to sacrifice very little. A heat sink isn't very expensive, if there's room for it; lowering the operating voltage has only a small effect on such parameters as input offset, slew rate, and gain. However, the maximum output-voltage swing will be limited to the operating voltage chosen.

Using a Wakefield model 209 or an equivalent heat sink can reduce the warmed-up bias current of an AD503 by 60%, typically to 1 picoampere. The model 205 reduces the bias current by 40%, and the model 204 provides a 10% decrease. Or reducing the operating voltage to ±5 volts would drop the AD503's warmed-up bias current by as much as 70%—to about 0.75 pA.

Although both methods can be used simultaneously to obtain subpicoampere bias currents, there is a practical lower limit of about 0.5 pA because of the finite leakage inherent in the IC's glass header. □

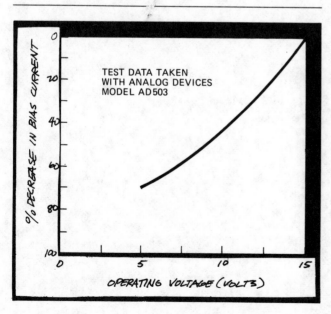

Trading larger output-voltage swings for lower input bias currents

Choosing MOSFET bias for minimum temperature drift

by D. William Baird
Redwood City, Calif.

There's now a way—and an easy way—to calculate what gate bias voltage will keep temperature drift in MOSFETs as small as possible. The analysis applies to both saturated and triode regions of MOSFET operation, and works out the gate voltage value that minimizes any change in drain-to-source current due to small temperature excursions.

The analysis for the saturated region starts with the familiar equation for the drain current,[1]

$$I_D = -K(V_{GS} - V_T)^2$$

To this, the actual (manufacturer's, not textbook) gate and channel temperature characteristics are added. The overall gain constant K is temperature-dependent:

$$K(T) = K_1(T_0/T)^{3/2}$$

where K_1 is the gain constant that's independent of temperature and T_0 is the ambient temperature. Both T and T_0 are in degrees Kelvin. The threshold gate voltage, V_T, also is temperature-dependent:

$$V_T = V_{T0} + K_2(T_0 - T)$$

where V_{T0} is the threshold gate voltage at the ambient temperature, and K_2 is the temperature-dependent gate characteristic, typically 0.004 for most MOSFETs. The expression for $K(T)$ and $V_T(T)$ is substituted into the equation for I_D. The resultant equation is differentiated with respect to temperature, and set equal to zero. This yields the two values of gate voltage that theoretically produce no change in drain current with temperature:

$$V_{GZ} = V_{T0} + K_2 + (T_0 - T/3);$$
$$V_{GZ} = V_{T0} + K_2(T_0 + T/9)$$

For the saturated region, there are two values of gate bias voltage which theoretically assure that $\Delta I_D/\Delta T = 0$ for small temperature excursions around ambient are:

$$V_{GZ0} = V_{T0} + 4 \times 10^{-3}(293 - 293/3)$$
and $V_{T0} + 4 \times 10^{-3}(293 + 293/9)$

At an ambient temperature of 20° C, $V_{GZ0} = V_{T0} + 0.78$ and $V_{T0} + 1.3$

The analysis for the triode region is similar:

$$V_{GZ0} = V_{T0} + 4 \times 10^{-3}(T_0 - T/3) + V_{DS}/2$$

At $T = T_0 = 20°C$; 293 K,

$$V_{GZ0} = V_{T0} + 4 \times 10^{-3}(293 - 293/3) + V_{DS}/2$$
$$= V_{T0} + 0.78 + V_{DS}/2$$

where V_{DS} is the drain-to-source voltage.

These equations were used to calculate V_{GZ0} for one half of a dual MOSFET, Siliconix M108, and the results verified experimentally. The change in I_D represented by changes in V_{DS} for a resistive drain load was measured at several values of V_{GS} for small temperature changes around an ambient temperature. This was carried out for three different values of I_D (0.5 mA, 0.75 mA, and 0.93 mA) to show that V_{GZ} is not a function of I_D. So that V_{GS} wouldn't be affected by variations in I_D, the gate was grounded and a constant-voltage source connected between gate and source.

Both halves of the MOSFET match very closely, and measured threshold voltages were 2.9 V. The zero temperature gate bias voltages for the saturated case were 3.68 V and 4.2 V; for the triode condition, $3.68 + V_D/2$. The 3.68 bias point offers better signal handling range at smaller I_D currents than the other points, and remains constant for changes in V_{DS}.

Finally, differentiating V_{GZ0} with respect to temperature provides the thermal drift rate (−1.3mV/°C) so that a compensating circuit[2] can be selected. □

REFERENCES
1. R.H. Crawford, "MOSFET in Circuit Design," McGraw-Hill Book Co., New York, N.Y., 1967, p.46.
2. Arthur Chace, "IC transistor array compensates for temperature," Electronics, Dec. 6, 1971, p.77.

17. Novel uses of timers

Timer ICs control life-test cycling

by Joseph E. Fleagle
St. Louis, Mo.

Life tests on electromechanical devices like solenoids and relays can be automated by a simple astable multivibrator that uses two 555 timers (or one 556 dual timer). The on and off times for the device under test are independently adjustable to any value between 10 milliseconds and 1 second for a wide range of testing rates and duty cycles. These times are adjusted by the settings of 10-turn potentiometers; the dial readings in milliseconds are accurate to within ±5%. Supply-voltage fluctuations have negligible effect on the timing.

When power is initially applied to the circuit, timer 1 triggers immediately because the trigger terminal of timer 1 is low, since C_1 is uncharged, and the trigger terminal of timer 2 is high. Upon expiration of the output pulse from timer 1, the negative-going pulse triggers timer 2. The output from timer 2 turns on transistor Q_1, thus grounding the reset terminal of 1 to prevent retriggering until the output of 2 expires. When Q_1 goes on, it also turns on Q_2, which boosts the output current to 2 amperes. Diode D_1 and zener diode D_2 form a suppression network to protect Q_2 from destructive back voltages from inductive loads.

Adjustment for direct reading of the on and off times is straightforward. To set the off time, connect a scope to the output of timer 1 and adjust potentiometer R_8 for minimum resistance.

While holding the shaft of the pot so that it cannot rotate, set the dial to display the time measured on the scope; for example, if the scope shows the output-pulse duration is 10 milliseconds, adjust the dial to read 10. Then tighten the set screw. Next, adjust R_8 until the dial reads 999, and change R_2 until the pulse width is 999 milliseconds. These two adjustments interact slightly, so it may be necessary to repeat the steps once again.

The on time is calibrated in the same fashion, using potentiometers R_{11} and R_5. □

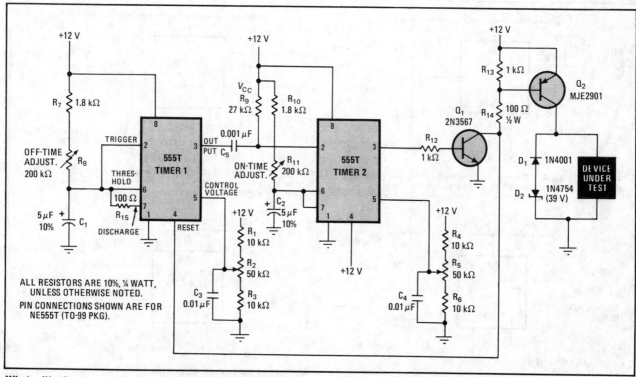

What a life. Device undergoing life test is cycled on and off by simple astable multivibrator that uses two 555 timers or one 556 dual timer. The on and off times, which are read directly from dials of potentiometers R_8 and R_{11}, can be set independently to any value from 10 milliseconds to 1 second. Diodes shunting device under test protect Q_2 against back voltages from inductive loads.

Low-cost IC timer handles a lot of jobs

by Hans R. Camenzind
Interdesign Inc., Sunnyvale, Calif.

If you're in the market for a low-cost compact timer, try a new commercial integrated circuit—you may like it. This adaptable IC, internally compensated for component tolerances and temperature drifts, requires only an external resistor and capacitor for time delays ranging from a microsecond to an hour with maximum deviation of only 1%.

Designed by Interdesign Inc., the IC is available from Signetics Corp., in either an 8-pin plastic package (NE555) or an 8-pin metal package (SE555). The plastic version costs 75¢ in quantities of 100 and has a timing accuracy within 5%. The temperature coefficient of both circuits is typically only 25 ppm/°C.

In addition to one-shot timing chores, the IC can be converted simply into a free-running pulse generator. The IC can be used for simple time delay, missing-pulse detection, frequency-division, pulse-width and pulse-position modulation, and test sequencing.

The output of the IC can supply about 200 milliamperes to a load, which can be connected either to V_{CC} or ground. This is achieved by using two high-current transistors in a inverting output stage, which allows the load to be connected for either normally on or normally off operations. At load currents less than 50 ma, the IC delivers a pulse with a maximum rise and fall time of 50 nanoseconds at any time setting, and the voltage levels are TTL-compatible.

When connected as a one-shot the timing cycle of the IC starts when the trigger voltage drops below $1/3V_{CC}$ and continues undisturbed, even if the circuit is triggered repeatedly. This eliminates contact bounce or can serve as a pulse stretcher.

Initially, the external capacitor is discharged by the transistor from pin 6 to ground. The negative trigger sets the flip-flop output to zero, which removes the short-circuit from across the capacitor and raises the IC output (pin 3) to V_{CC}. The capacitor then starts charging toward V_{CC} at a rate proportional to the time constant established by $R_A C$. The cycle ends when the ca-

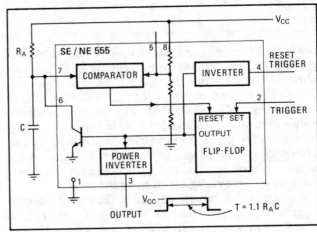

Functional diagram shows setup for one-shot operation; adding another resistor between pins 6 and 7 makes it astable.

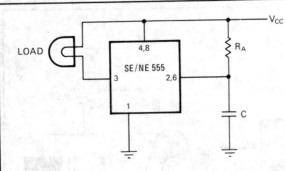

(a) BASIC TIMER. Circuit provides an initial time delay in which the lamp will turn on 1.1 R_AC seconds after the supply voltage is applied. Circuit resets every time the power is turned off.

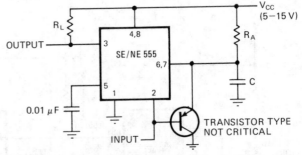

(b) MISSING PULSE DETECTOR. A change in frequency or a missing pulse shifts the output level. For proper operation, the time delay should be slightly longer than one expected pulse spacing.

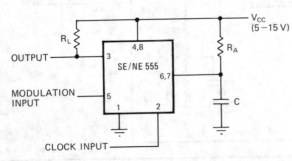

(c) PULSE-WIDTH MODULATOR. Modulating the control voltage terminal (pin 5) and triggering the timer with a continuous pulse train produces an output of different pulse widths.

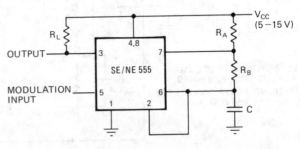

(d) PULSE-POSITION MODULATOR. With the modulating signal applied to the control voltage terminal and the timer free-running, the output pulse positions can be varied depending on the modulating signal.

pacitor is charged to $2/3V_{CC}$. The time that the IC remains in the high state is given by: $T = 1.1R_AC$.

The circuit incorporates a high-input impedance comparator so that large timing resistors (several megohms) can be used. The comparator is referenced to $2/3V_{CC}$ by three resistors of equal value. When the voltage across the external timing capacitor reaches this level, the flip-flop is reset, and the capacitor is discharged. The IC output level is then in the low state.

Both the charging current and the end-of-cycle voltage ($2/3V_{CC}$) are proportional to the supply voltage, which makes the timing accuracy independent of that voltage. The circuit operates from 4.5 v to 15 v, with less than 1% long-term drift in timing accuracy.

Timing can be adjusted in any of three different ways: resistor R_A provides a four-decade range; capacitor C offers more than an eight-decade coverage, and applying an external control voltage to terminal 5 produces a 3:1 timing variation. This terminal also provides an ideal point in which to add filtering to reduce noise on the supply-voltage line.

The basic one-shot circuit is easily triggered manually by a switch that connects the trigger input (pin 2) to ground to initiate the timing cycle. For example, using a 10-microfarad capacitor and a 91-kilohm fixed resistor

in series with a 5-megohm variable resistor can provide preset timing from a second to an hour.

In addition to monostable operation, the IC timer can be made to trigger itself and free-run. An extra terminal (pin 6) is provided so that a second resistor (R_B) can be used to help set the duty cycle. The timing capacitor charges through both resistors, but discharges only through R_B. The total period, $T = 1.46/(R_A + 2R_B)C$, is the sum of the charge time (output high), $0.685(R_A + R_B)C$, and discharge time (output low), $0.685R_BC$. The duty cycle, however depends only on the timing resistors: it is the ratio of either the charge or discharge time to the sum of both.

A quite different triggering mode is possible by connecting pin 4 and pin 2 (trigger input). In this arrangement, the timer is reset each time a trigger pulse is present, and the output will only go low if the circuit is not retriggered within the set time. Such a configuration could be used as a missing-pulse detector or a pulse-width discriminator. Other applications requiring any sort of a timing cycle can be easily accommodated by the IC timer. Frequency dividers, pulse-position modulators, and pulse generators with a frequency from 0.00001 hertz to 500 kHz and a duty cycle from 0.1% to 50% are possible. □

IC timer's duty cycle can stretch over 99%

by Michael S. Robbins
Los Angeles, Calif.

The duty-cycle range of the 555-type timer IC can be extended by providing independent charging and discharging paths for the timing capacitor.

With the circuit (a) suggested by the manufacturer for an astable rectangular-pulse generator, the duty cycle can be adjusted from about 0.01% to almost 50%. The charging path for the capacitor is the series network of resistors R_A and R_B to the supply, V_{CC}; the discharge path is through resistor R_B to ground.

The addition of two diodes, as done in (b), makes the capacitor's charging and discharging paths independent of each other so that the timer's duty cycle can be extended to more than 99%. The charging path is now through resistor R_A and diode D_1 to the supply, while the discharging path is through R_B and D_2 to ground.

For the component values shown, the timer's duty cycle can be adjusted from less than 10% to greater than 90% with only a 1% variation in the output period, which, in this case, is 1 millisecond. The output pulse frequency is 1 kilohertz. □

More duty cycle. Usual configuration for astable multivibrator (a) limits output duty cycle to about 50%. Adding two diodes, as shown in (b), separates the capacitor's charging and discharging paths, allowing duty cycles of greater than 99% to be achieved.

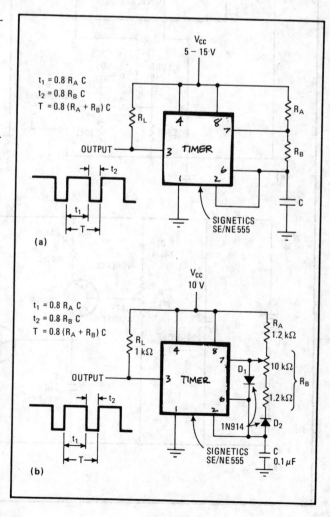

115

All-electronic metronome provides accurate beat rate

by Dennis R. Morgan
General Electric Co. Electronics Laboratory, Syracuse, N.Y.

For the engineer who is also a music enthusiast, here is a precision electronic metronome that can be adjusted to the desired beat rate, is accurate to within 1 beat per minute, and can be assembled from standard parts. The circuit, which can be powered from any garden-variety 9-volt transistor-radio battery, can generate audible clicks (beats) even beyond the standard metronome range—from about 15 to 380 times a minute.

A 10-turn potentiometer that has a turns-counting dial is used to set the metronome's beat rate. The circuit can be calibrated so that the setting of this potentiometer is accurate to well within 1 beat per minute over the standard metronome range of 40 to 208 beats per minute. Furthermore, the circuit is relatively insensitive to variations in battery voltage, in particular to the reduced voltage that results from aging.

The figure shows two versions of the circuit—the one given in (a) is a pocket-sized metronome that has an 8-ohm earphone output, and the one given in (b) is a more powerful metronome with a regular 8-ohm speaker output. This latter circuit develops a hefty output power level of approximately 0.01 joule.

In both circuits, a constant-current generator (transistor Q_1) is used to charge capacitor C_1. When this capacitor's voltage reaches the firing point (above 6 v) of the

Rhythm reminder. Electronic metronome circuits are accurate to within 1 beat per minute over the standard metronome range of 40 to 208 beats per minute. Circuit (a) has an earphone output, while circuit (b) has a speaker output. In each case, a 10-turn potentiometer is used to set the beat rate. Both circuits are battery-operated. A typical calibration curve shows the linearity of the output beat rate.

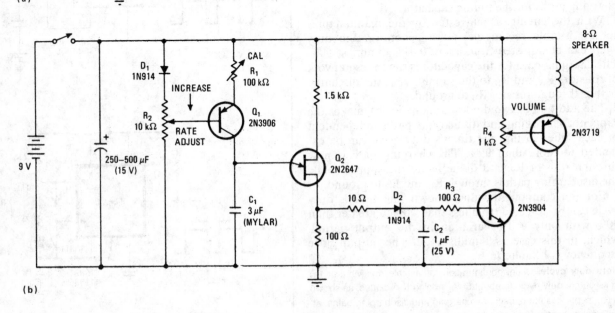

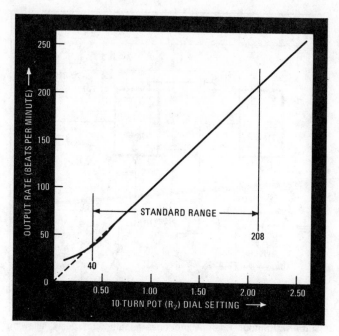

unijunction transistor (Q_2), the capacitor is discharged and an output pulse is generated. The capacitor's charging current, and hence the operating frequency, is directly proportional to the voltage across variable resistor R_1, a voltage that varies linearly with the setting of potentiometer R_2. Diode D_1 compensates for the base-emitter drop of transistor Q_1.

Either circuit is calibrated by adjusting resistor R_1 to obtain the upper standard beat-rate limit (208 beats per minute) and then adjusting the stop on potentiometer R_2's turns-counting dial to get the lower standard limit (40 beats per minute). A typical calibration curve is given in the figure. (Plenty of patience and a good stopwatch are also needed for good calibration results.)

Metronome (a) includes a loud and soft control over volume within its on/off switch. Metronome (b) employs a pulse stretcher, made up of diode D_2, capacitor C_2, and resistor R_3, to increase the available energy from the 9-v battery. This circuit's volume control, resistor R_4, can be replaced with a fixed resistor to obtain maximum output, if desired. □

Electronic timer circuit improves welder performance

by Alex W. Sivan
Orpak Ltd., Tel Aviv, Israel

Point welders are widely used in industry, but many of them have no timers. Without an automatically controlled welding pulse, only skilled operators can weld thin metal parts that require a current-pulse duration of less than a second; if the equipment is automatically timed, however, almost anyone can weld such parts successfully. And even skilled personnel can probably perform repetitive production operations more quickly and efficiently with the aid of a timed current pulse.

A simple timing circuit that can be added to a welder is shown in the figure. When the ac line voltage is turned on and switch S_2 is closed, current through the relay coil holds K_1 open and K_2 closed. When the operator wants to weld, switch S_2 is opened, and the current through the relay coil thereupon decreases so much that K_1 closes and K_2 opens.

With K_1 closed, welding current flows in the secondary of T_1, and because K_2 is open, C_1 charges through R_1 and R_2. When the voltage across C_1 reaches the firing voltage of the silicon-controlled rectifier (about 2 volts), the SCR carries enough current to let the relay open K_1 and close K_2 again to stop welding and discharge C_1. The SCR continues to conduct until the operator lets S_2 close again. The welding current flows for a time returned by $(R_1 + R_2)C_1$ and the line voltage.

One of the most important features of this circuit is that the welding cycle is immune to noise from the relay spikes and transformer surges.

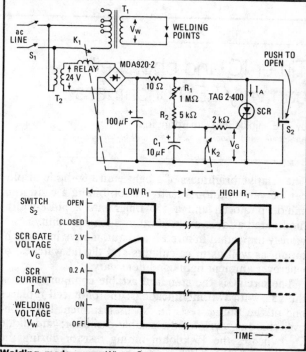

Welding made easy. When S_2 is pushed open, welding current flows and gate voltage starts to rise. Once gate voltage becomes high enough to let SCR conduct, welding current ceases. SCR continues to conduct until operator allows S_2 to close; thus, duration of welding pulse is determined only by charging time for V_G to reach SCR firing voltage, not by how long S_2 is open.

The timing diagrams in the figure illustrate the operation of the circuit and indicate some typical values of current and voltage. □

117

Pair of IC timers
sounds auto burglar alarm

by Michael L. Harvey
Ropat Corp., El Segundo, Calif.

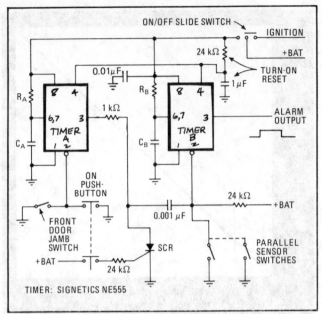

An inexpensive car burglar alarm system can be built with only two low-cost 555-type timer circuits. The timers are connected as indicated in the diagram.

Timer A serves two purposes: it provides a time delay (roughly $1.1R_A C_A$) for arming the system and allowing the driver to exit the car, and it also permits the driver to enter the car and disarm the alarm. This time delay eliminates the need for an inconvenient and vulnerable arming switch on the outside of the car. The on/off switch for the alarm can be hidden somewhere under the car's dashboard.

When the alarm goes "off," timer B is triggered on by the falling edge of the output from timer A. After the initial turn-on, however, the SCR prevents timer B from triggering until one of the grounding-type sensor switches fires this timer. □

Auto watchdog. Timer A produces a safeguard delay, allowing driver to disarm alarm and eliminating vulnerable outside control switch. The SCR prevents timer A from triggering timer B, unless timer B is triggered by strategically located sensor switches.

Timer IC and photocell
can vary LED brightness

by F. E. Hinkle and Jim Edrington
Applied Research Laboratories, University of Texas, Austin

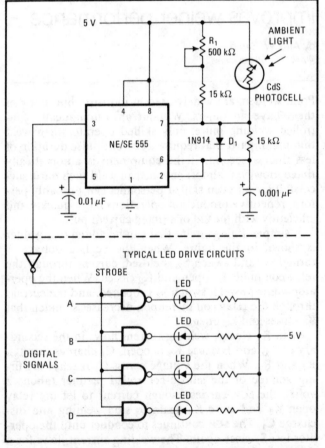

The relative brightness of a light-emitting-diode display can be varied automatically by combining a cadmium-sulfide photocell and a 555 timer into a pulse-width-modulated astable multivibrator. Such variability is obviously important in aircraft and automotive instrumentation, as well as in calculators and digital watches, or wherever ambient light conditions vary.

The circuit is the standard astable configuration for the 555, with two modifications: the photocell replaces one of the timing resistors, so that ambient light controls the duty cycle of the astable oscillator; and diode D_1 bypasses the 15-kilohm timing resistor during the charging of the timing capacitor, increasing the maximum duty cycle of the 555 beyond the normal 50% limit, and allowing the display to obtain full brightness.

As increasing ambient light level decreases the photocell's resistance, the timer's duty cycle increases. The varying duty cycle controls the length of time the display drivers are on, and this controls the brightness.

This circuit varies the duty cycle from less than 5% in total darkness to more than 90% in sunlight. Manually setting control R_1 establishes the minimum brightness level in total darkness; if such adjustment is considered unnecessary in a particular application, R_1 could be replaced with a fixed resistor. □

Fader. Brightness of LED display is varied by using a photocell in place of one timing resistor in a 555 timer, and bypassing the other timing resistor to boost the timer's maximum duty cycle. Result is brighter display in sunlight, fainter in the dark.

Oscilloscope triggered sweep: another job for IC timer

by Robert M. McDermott
U.S. Army Korea Support Command, San Francisco, Calif.

For less than $10, you can add a triggered sweep to upgrade the low-cost type of oscilloscope. The circuit, which essentially consists of an IC timer and an op amp, can be powered from the scope's supply and fits on a small pc board that can be placed inside the scope.

When an input signal from the scope's vertical amplifier rises above the circuit's trigger-level voltage setting, the op amp switches, causing its output to go from $+V_{CC}$ to $-V_{CC}$. This voltage change is coupled to the trigger input of the IC timer as a negative spike, which sets the flip-flop and cuts off the discharge transistor.

The switch-selected timing capacitor, C, now charges exponentially through timing resistance R until capacitor voltage reaches the level of control voltage existing at pin 5 of the timer. (Timing period is 0.4RC, and control voltage level is $0.33V_{CC}$.) The circuit's output frequency will be 2.5/RC and, in this case, can be varied from 1 hertz to 1 megahertz.

Once capacitor voltage is equal to the timer's control voltage level, the flip-flop resets and the output transistor discharges timing capacitor C. Pulses occurring before the flip-flop resets do not affect the circuit's output voltage. The flip-flop controls the discharge transistor and can only be reset by the timer's comparator, which is operated by the capacitor and control voltages.

Over-all cost can be reduced still further if the variable controls for trigger level and input sensitivity are replaced with fixed components. ☐

Add-on triggered sweep. IC timer holds down the cost of adding a triggered sweep to an economy oscilloscope. The circuit's input op amp triggers the timer, setting its flip-flop and cutting off its discharge transistor so that capacitor C can charge. When capacitor voltage reaches the timer's control voltage ($0.33V_{CC}$), the flip-flop resets and the transistor conducts, discharging the capacitor.

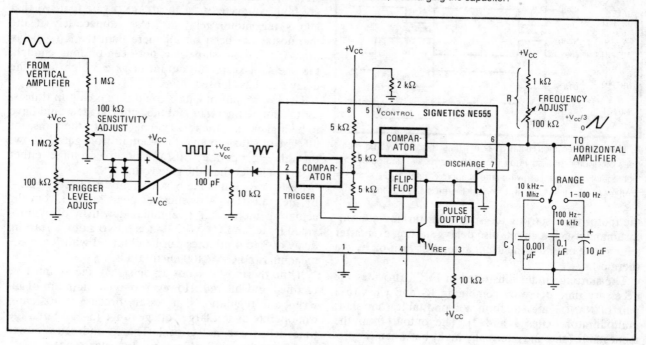

Adaptive motor starter delays when necessary

by Alan R. Miller
New Mexico Institute of Mining and Technology, Socorro, N.M.

The potential starting load on the compressor motor of an air conditioner or freezer is greatest immediately after the motor has been shut off. But after the motor has been off for a few minutes, the pressure in the system has equalized and the motor can safely be started again. Therefore a starting circuit need not provide delay if the motor has been off for several minutes, but it should if the motor has been off only momentarily (as might occur when lightning causes a brief loss of power, or when someone improperly turns the thermostat down and then right back up again).

An RC time-delay network coupled to a unijunction transistor and a silicon controlled rectifier will prevent

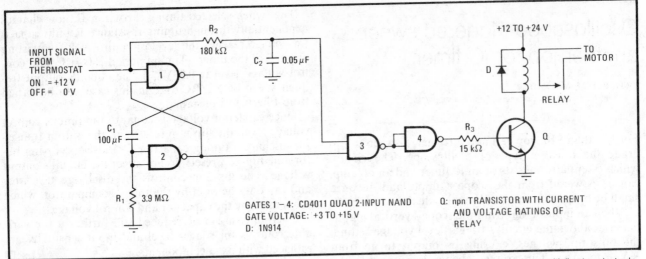

1. Restart delay. Motor is held off for a minimum time given by R_1C_1 in this circuit arrangement. NAND-gate one-shot multivibrator starts delay pulse when thermostat goes off, so delay is not added to thermostat off-time. Quad NAND gate keeps component count low, and npn transistor allows flexibility in gate voltages. The time constant of C_2 and R_2 smooths over any contact bounce in the actuating relay.

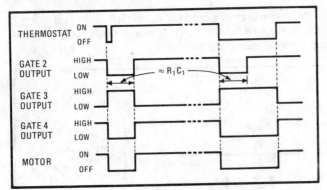

2. Timing. When thermostat goes off, gate 2 goes low and motor goes off. Motor then stays off until both thermostat and gate 2 are high again; gate 2 stays low for time of approximately R_1C_1, so motor is off for at least that long, and longer if thermostat is off longer.

the motor from starting too soon after turning off. Unfortunately such a circuit also delays starting even after a long time or under the usual automatic turn-on by the thermostat.

The starting circuit illustrated in Fig. 1 provides the necessary time delay by combining R_1 and C_1 with a pair of NAND gates to form a monostable (one-shot) multivibrator (gates 1 and 2). The output from the monostable (gate 2) is normally high; but when the signal from the thermostat goes to zero, the monostable goes to zero for a time of approximately R_1C_1 and then returns to its high level (as shown in Fig. 2). This output from the one-shot and the signal from the thermostat are both connected to a third NAND gate (gate 3) that allows the motor relay to close immediately if the thermostat has been off for more than the R_1C_1 delay time. If the input signal has not been off long enough, the one-shot keeps the output of gate 3 high until the delay time has elapsed.

The low output of gate 3 could turn on a pnp transistor to actuate the relay, but the gate voltage would have to be higher than the relay voltage to turn the transistor off. Use of gate 4 to invert the output from gate 3 allows the relay to operate with any positive voltage, either higher or lower than the gate voltage.

Resistor R_3 limits the base current drawn from gate 4 by the transistor. Any effect of point bounce from the actuating thermostat is eliminated with a delay provided by R_2 and C_2. With C-MOS NAND gates, a starting delay of 3 to 4 minutes can be obtained with $R_1 = 3.9$ megohms and $C_1 = 100$ microfarads.

If the thermostat sends an ac signal, the ac must be rectified and filtered. However, only a minimum of filtering and regulation is necessary because C-MOS gates can operate over a large voltage range (3–15 V) and the time delays are not critical. The IC and relay power could even be supplied by the thermostat signal. □

IC timer automatically monitors battery voltage

by Edward J. McGowan, Jr.
Stoelting Co., Chicago, Ill.

The 555-type timer IC can conveniently function as the heart of an automatic battery charger. The circuit is intended to maintain a full charge on a standby battery supply for an instrument that is always connected to the ac power line, whether in use or not. This charger uses the timer's two on-chip comparators, its set-reset flip-flop, and its high-current driver amplifier.

The zener diode, D_1, provides a reference voltage for both comparators through the timer's internal resistive divider network. The output of the timer (pin 3) switches between 0 and 10 volts.

The circuit is calibrated by substituting a variable dc power supply for the nickel-cadmium batteries. The OFF adjustment potentiometer is then set for the desired battery cutoff voltage, which is typically 1.4 V per cell; and the ON adjustment potentiometer is set for the desired turn-on voltage, around 1.3 v per cell.

Resistor R_L limits the circuit's operating current to less than 200 milliamperes under all conditions. Diode D_2 prevents the battery from discharging through the timer when the timer is in its off state. The capacitor stops oscillation during the circuit's off transition. The feedback divider can be decoupled for better load transient immunity, if desired. □

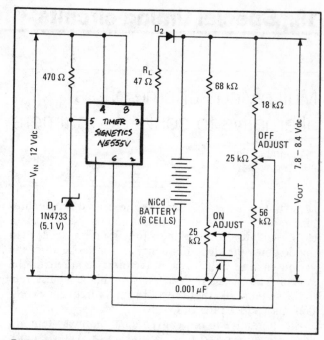

Battery charger. Integrated timer functions as the command post for automatic battery-charging circuit. The zener diode sets the reference voltages for the timer's on-chip comparators. Desired turn-on and turn-off battery voltages are determined by the potentiometers.

IC timer drives electric fuel pump

by Sudarshan Sarpangal
ISRO Satellite Systems Project, Bangalore, India

A 555 integrated-circuit timer and a transistor provide an efficient driving system for a high-speed electric fuel pump. This arrangement allows the pumping rate to be adjusted and can be used with any pump of the solenoid-plunger type.

As the schematic diagram shows, the timer and components R_1, R_2, and C form a basic square-wave oscillator circuit. The output at pin 3 drives transistor Q on and off and so operates the solenoid-driven plunger of the pump. Commutating diode D protects the transistor from surges at turnoff.

The components shown are used to drive a Bendix fuel pump at 16 strokes per second, with the speed adjustable by change of R_2. If a different pump is used that requires current of more than 1 ampere, a different transistor must be chosen. □

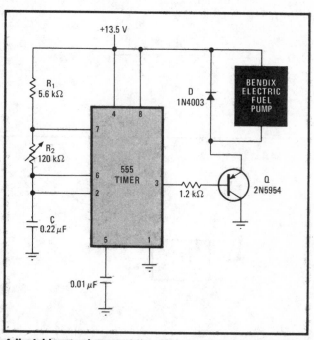

Adjustable-speed pump driver. This IC timer arrangement drives the Bendix plunger-type electric fuel pump at a rate of 16 strokes per second. Adjustment of R_2 permits other pumping rates.

Multiplying scheme offers alternative to count-down timers

by Elbert L. Cole
Westinghouse Systems Development division, Baltimore, Md.

Most timing networks, such as those used to synchronize radar and digital communications systems, use a clock oscillator at the highest timing rate needed, then divide down the clock frequency to synthesize all of the various gating pulses and waveforms required in the system. The clock thus generates the highest pulse rate in the system; all other waveforms have frequency components at clock rates or lower.

An alternative to this conventional timing system has been proved successful at Westinghouse. A lower clock frequency is used, and the waveforms required are generated by multiplying up from the clock frequency.

The frequency-multiplying, or count-up, technique is of particular advantage when used at frequencies higher than about 20 MHz, where inexpensive MSI count-down circuits are not available. The multiplying approach is also highly desirable when used in subsystems that get their fundamental timing from a low-frequency clock at some central location in the system.

Key to the count-up approach is a simple and inexpensive multiplying scheme, based on fundamental properties of the binary-numbering system. The basic frequency-doubling circuit (Fig. 1), consists of a delay line, followed by an exclusive-OR gate, which has the following truth table:

	0	1
0	0	1
1	1	0

The timing diagram (Fig. 2) for the multiplication circuit illustrates the circuit's operation. As can be seen, the delay line must be adjusted so that its propagation delay $\tau = 1/4f_o$, when f_o is the frequency of the waveform to be doubled.

Any number of frequencies can be generated by cascading the multipliers, limited only by the operating speed of the circuitry used. Thus, n multipliers will generate n + 1 frequencies, each of which is a 2^n multiple of f_o.

The amount of delay required, of course, varies with each cascaded stage. Screwdriver-adjustable dual in-line delay packages are readily available to provide variable delays from less than 1 millisecond (corresponding to a clock frequency of 1 kilohertz) to devices with delays of 0 to 2 nanoseconds (corresponding to frequencies higher than 100 MHz). Integrated-circuit delay-line costs range from about $2 for nanosecond delays to $8 for delays of as long as 1 millisecond.

TTL exclusive-OR gates that operate at speeds to several tens of megahertz are readily available in TTL packages at costs well under $1 per gate.

Two important performance parameters for timing circuitry are frequency stability, which is determined by the stability of the clock oscillator, and pulse-to-pulse jitter, a little of which is introduced in each multiplier stage. For a single multiplier stage, this jitter is typically 500 picoseconds peak-to-peak, and the jitter adds randomly as multiplier stages are cascaded.

The frequency-multiplying scheme has been used in several operating systems, including a ground station for the synchronous meteorological satellite network scheduled for launching early next year, and a drone-tracking radar for range instrumentation installed at White Sands Missile Range.

In the radar system, 22 cascaded frequency doublers are used to multiply a 23-Hz clock frequency up to 96 MHz. The wide range of frequencies generated is needed in tracking missiles of widely varying speeds. A target range resolution of less than 5 meters is maintained by keeping the over-all system-timing jitter below 30 ns. □

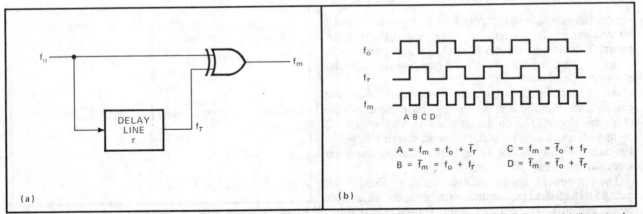

1. Frequency doubler. Basic multiplier circuit (a) consists of a delay line and a single exclusive-OR gate. Timing diagram (b) illustrates frequency-doubling operation. Any 2^n multiple of f_o is generated by cascading multiplier circuits.

Building timing circuits for noisy environments

by T.C. Matty
Transportation Division, Westinghouse Electric Corp., Pittsburgh, Pa.

It's true that it's easy to use pre-packaged one-shot circuits for timing and time-delay tasks, but be prepared to cope with problems ranging from excessive charging current to false triggering from external noise. This type of circuit is susceptible to false triggering because of its high gain and use of positive feedback. However, two extensively used circuits have an inherent noise immunity—the capacitor dump timer and the digital monostable.

The capacitor dump circuit (Fig. 1) is useful where low cost and moderate accuracy is important, but where external-frequency or clocking sources are not available. Noise immunity is achieved by discharging the energy stored by the timing capacitor through the input transistor. This makes the input requirements depend on the energy stored in the capacitor, as well as the input-transistor characteristics. Moreover, the RC timing circuit forms an inherent low-pass filter that further rejects noise signals.

Timing of up to 1 minute is possible with this circuit. Timing accuracy depends on several factors: the RC product, the relative variations of the reference voltage and supply voltage, and the level-sensing transistor Q_1. But since the sense transistor is reverse-biased during the timing period, its effect is negligible. Of course, a small amount of leakage current (about 10 nanoamperes) flows, but that in most cases can be neglected.

However, when a zener diode is used for the reference voltage, a resistor should be inserted in either the base or emitter circuit of the sense transistor to prevent excessive zener current from affecting the timing accuracy.

This circuit can be improved by eliminating the zener and using a resistive divider network as the reference voltage. This now establishes the decision point as the ratio between the timing RC and the resistor network. And adding a diode in the base or emitter circuit of the sense amplifier will compensate the circuit for most temperature effects. With these additions, the timing function becomes independent of the supply voltages. The timing accuracy depends only on the difference between the base-emitter turn-on voltage of Q_1 and the diode voltage drop. It's therefore important that the diode be chosen so that its characteristics match the base-emitter characteristics of the sense transistor. And, if the accuracy must be maintained over a wide temperature range, these characteristics also should track over that range.

This type of circuit has been tested over a 100°C change in temperature with less than a 2.5% total change in timing. For the diode-compensated case, the output time is equal to 0.7 RC; when no diode compensation is used, the base-emitter voltage of 0.5 V is added, and the output time will increase by the ratio of the base-emitter voltage drop to supply voltage.

Another approach that provides high noise immunity and accurate timing, if clocking frequencies are available, is the digital monostable circuit. The circuit (Fig. 2) can provide an output pulse duration of one clock period for every low-to-high input transition. Another feature of this circuit is that its output will have a width of a full clock pulse or no output at all. This feature virtually eliminates outputs caused by noise of false inputs because an output is generated only when an input is coincident with the transition of the clock line. Thus, if the clock input frequency is selected to be the lowest available or allowed by the system, the probability of coincidence between a clock-line transition and input is reduced (assuming that false inputs are random).

For example, if a Poisson distribution is assumed for noise inputs of sufficient amplitude and width to enable an input, then the average rate of coincidence is:

$$P = \lambda\tau \exp(-\lambda\tau)$$

As the clock-pulse width τ is reduced, the probability is also reduced and in the limiting case goes to zero. If τ is taken as 100 ns (the rise time of the clock) and λ as unity (the average rate of noise inputs), then P can be

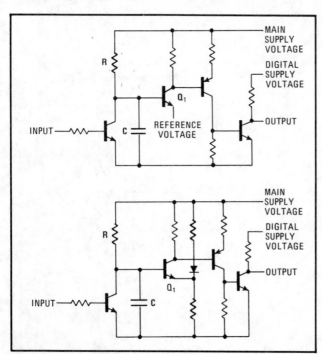

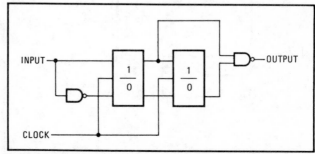

1. Good noise immunity. Capacitor dump circuit gives moderate accuracy without external clocking; improved version uses divider.

2. Improved accuracy. Digital monostable timer offers high noise immunity with improved accuracy, but needs clocking frequencies.

calculated.

$$P = 10^{-7} \exp(-1 \times 10^{-7})$$
$$= 10^{-7} \times 0.999999$$
$$= 10^{-7}$$

The calculated value for P is for the probability of coincidence between the random input and the edge of the clock input. There are, however, f edges per second (equal to the clock frequency), and this gives f chances per second for coincidence to occur. Therefore, the improvement in noise immunity is found by multiplying the probability of occurrence and the rate at which it might occur to give true probability, or rate R.

$$R = fp$$

If, for instance, an enabling noise pulse occurs once per second, then a standard monostable will generate a false output once per second. Using a digital monostable with the same noise input, a clock input of 1 kilohertz and a rise time of 100 ns, a false output will occur at the following rate:

$$R = 10^3 \times 10^{-7}$$
$$= 10^{-4} \text{ false outputs/s}$$

This is an improvement of 10^4, or an 80-dB improvement in signal-to-noise ratio. □

Design chart identifies intermodulation products

by Helmut Lobenstein
General Electric Company, Aircraft Equipment Div., Utica, N.Y.

Frequency conversion in receiving, transmitting, or synthesizer systems frequently causes undesirable in-band mixing products to be produced. A rapid and handy design aid—the often-forgotten mixer intermodulation chart—can help the designer predict which of these unwanted frequency components will be troublesome to his system.

This type of chart is generated by considering what frequency products are created by mixing an rf input at frequency α with a local oscillator (LO) signal at frequency ω, producing an i-f output at frequency β:

$$\beta = |\pm n\omega \pm m\alpha|$$

where m is the harmonic number of the rf input frequency and n is the harmonic number of the LO frequency. This equation can be rewritten as:

$$\beta/\omega = |(\pm m\alpha/\omega) \pm n|$$

which has the form of a linear equation (for instance, y = mx + b), permitting straight lines to represent any desired harmonic number.

The chart is easy to use. Suppose an rf input of 8–9 gigahertz is to be mixed with an LO frequency of 10.5 GHz, producing an i-f output of 2.5–1.5 GHz. To find the intermodulation products that can be expected, first tabulate the data:

α	ω	β	α/ω	β/ω
8-9	10.5	2.5-1.5	0.762	0.238
			0.857	0.143

On the chart, the frequency ratios of $\alpha/\omega = 0.762$ and $\beta/\omega = 0.238$ intersect the $\alpha = \omega - \beta$ line, as they should, since this is the desired down conversion. Any other lines that cross the $\omega - \beta$ line within the range plotted will produce an in-band mixing product. In this case, the product:

$$\alpha = (3\omega + \beta)/4$$

which is the fourth harmonic of the rf input minus the third LO harmonic, is produced. The other product produced is:

$$\alpha = (4\omega + \beta)/5$$

which is the fifth harmonic of the rf input minus the fourth LO harmonic. The higher the harmonic number of the mixing product, the lower is its power level. There are several ways to determine this level[1].

The choice of a mixer significantly influences the harmonics that occur. A simple single-diode mixer, for example, will produce all the harmonic mixing products. But a single-balanced mixer will suppress one of its in-

TABLE 1 INTERMODULATION PRODUCTS FOR SINGLE BALANCED MIXER					
Signal harmonic (mα) \ Local oscillator harmonic (nω)	1	2	3	4	5
1	$\omega \pm a$	$2\omega \pm a$	$3\omega \pm a$	$4\omega \pm a$	$5\omega \pm a$
2 a					
3 $3a$	$3a \pm \omega$	$3a \pm 2\omega$	$3a \pm 3\omega$	$4\omega \pm 5a$	$5\omega \pm 3a$
4					
5 $5a$	$5a \pm \omega$	$5a \pm 2\omega$	$5a \pm 3\omega$	$5a \pm 4\omega$	$5a \pm 5\omega$

TABLE 2 INTERMODULATION PRODUCTS FOR FULL WAVE DOUBLE BALANCED MIXER					
Signal harmonic (mα) \ Local oscillator harmonic (nω)	1	2	3	4	5
1 a	$\omega \pm a$	—	$3\omega \pm a$	—	$5\omega \pm a$
2					
3 $3a$	$3a \pm \omega$	—	$3\omega \pm 3a$	—	$5\omega \pm 3a$
4					
5 $5a$	$5a \pm \omega$	—	$5a \pm 3\omega$	—	$5\omega \pm 5a$

put signals and its even-order harmonics, while a double-balanced mixer will suppress both input signals and all of their even-order harmonics. Tables 1 and 2 indicate the intermodulation products generated by these latter two types of mixers, assuming perfect mixer balance.

For the example given here, the spurious mixing products should be more than 80 decibels below the desired output whenever a double-balanced mixer, which is properly matched for impedance[2], is to be used in the system. □

REFERENCES
1. James W. Steiner, "Rfi due to Intermodulation Products," IEEE Transactions on Electromagnetic Compatibility, January, 1964.
2. Peter Will, "Reactive Loads, the Big Mixer Menace," Microwaves, April, 1971.

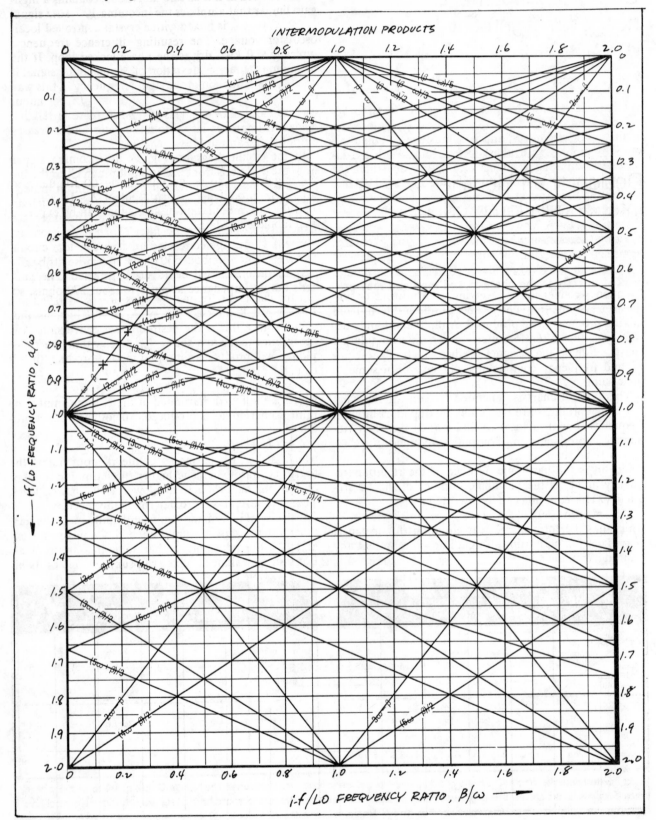

INTERMODULATION PRODUCTS

— r-f/LO FREQUENCY RATIO, α/ω

i-f/LO FREQUENCY RATIO, β/ω ⟶

One-chip fm demodulator needs no alignment

by J. Brian Dance
University of Birmingham, England

A complete i-f amplifier and demodulator for an fm receiver uses a single integrated circuit that requires no inductors or alignment, and it avoids use of tuned circuits by employing a phase-locked loop. With a 1-kilohertz modulating frequency and 75-kHz deviation, the input sensitivity is about 9 microvolts for a 30-decibel signal-to-noise ratio at 10.7 megahertz. The audio-output voltage is 280 to 480 millivolts, and total harmonic distortion is 0.4%. However, this demodulator won't operate satisfactorily when the input signal contains spurious frequencies, because any beat frequencies formed with the local oscillator signal or its harmonics are fed directly to the phase-locked loop and may pre-

vent the circuit from locking onto the desired signal.

The IC used in this circuit, an NE563, contains a high-gain limiter that amplifies the incoming 10.7-MHz signal before the latter is mixed with a crystal-controlled local-oscillator voltage. The resulting difference frequency, typically 900 kHz, drives the phase-locked loop. If the maximum frequency deviation of the incoming signal is 75 kHz, the reduction of the signal frequency in this way increases the relative maximum deviation from about 0.7% to more than 8%. This 10-fold increase in relative deviation improves signal-to-noise ratio and increases output-signal amplitude.

In the circuit diagram (Fig. 1), an incoming signal from the receiver's front end is fed through C_1 to the input of the high-gain limiter at pin 7. The input impedance is 135 ohms. The signal, amplified by as much as 60 dB, is taken from pin 5 to the filter F. This filter is a standard 10.7-MHz ceramic filter (Toko, Vernitron, or Murata). It must be connected on each side to a circuit with impedance of about 330 ohms; otherwise, its bandpass characteristic will be adversely affected. The limiter's output impedance at pin 5 is about 270 ohms, so

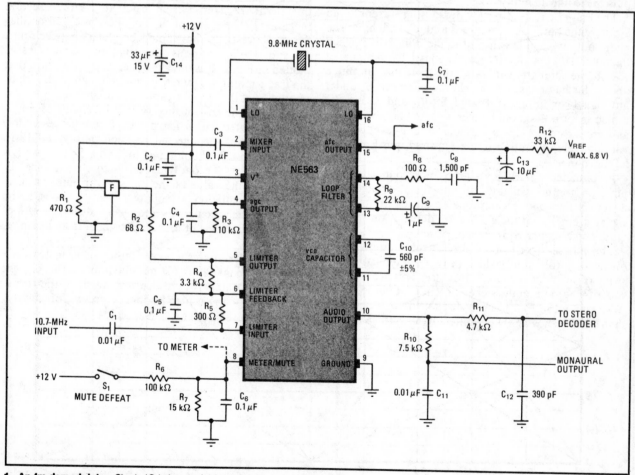

1. An fm demodulator. Single IC is heart of this i-f amplifier and demodulator for fm receiver. The NE563 IC uses phase-locked loop to replace inductors, tuned circuits, and alignment. Resistors, capacitors, ceramic filter, and local-oscillator crystal are only external components; crystal can be replaced with ceramic resonator if preferred. Input sensitivity is about 9 µV for 30-dB signal-to-noise ratio.

the value of R_2 should be about 68 ohms. Similarly, the mixer's input impedance at pin 2 is about 1,250 ohms, so the value of R_1 in parallel should be 470 ohms.

The 9.8-MHz crystal, connected between pins 1 and 16, is part of the local-oscillator circuit. The 900-kHz difference frequency is fed internally to the phase-locked-loop section of the NE563. The free-running frequency of the loop is determined by C_{10}; it is desirable that this capacitor have a tolerance of about ±5%.

The bandwidth is controlled by the loop filter connected between pins 13 and 14. The filter's output impedance is typically 6.2 kilohms. If R_9 is reduced in value, the bandwidth, and hence the noise level, is reduced.

The low-pass filter, consisting of R_{10} and C_{11}, provides the normal deemphasis. C_{11} should have a value of 0.01 microfarad for use in the U.S., where the deemphasis time-constant is 75 microseconds. For use where the required time constant is 50 μs, C_{11} should be 0.0068 μF. The filter formed by R_{11} and C_{12}, with time constant of 1.8 μs, attenuates radio frequencies before the signal is fed to the decoder.

The limiter circuit feeds the stage that provides automatic gain control from pin 4. The potential at pin 4 remains at about 2.7 volts until the input signal exceeds about 600 μv, and then falls with increasing signal level until it becomes fairly constant at about 0.65 V for inputs exceeding 20 millivolts.

The limiter circuit also provides muting current to pin 8, where the output impedance is about 20 kilohms. The audio-output stage is switched to the muted state when the potential at pin 8 falls below about 1.1 V. A signal of reasonable strength will raise the potential of pin 8 above this value, as will the closing of switch S_1 under any signal conditions. If desired, S_1, R_6, and R_7 may be replaced by a 47-kilohm potentiometer between pin 8 and ground to provide a variable muting-level control. Alternatively, if muting is not required, pin 8 may be left unconnected.

A voltmeter of fairly high impedance, connected from pin 8 to ground, will indicate the signal strength; the meter's deflection is proportional to the logarithm of the signal strength, but the calibration depends on whether mute-defeat switch S_1 is open or closed.

The phase-locked loop drives the automatic-frequency-control circuit, which provides a typical output swing of 1.5 V for a 200-kHz increase. This afc output is superimposed upon the steady potential at pin 15.

The circuit in Fig. 1 can be used at frequencies other than those shown. The limiter bandwidth is about

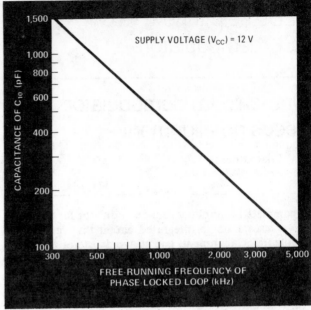

2. Loop frequency. Free-running frequency of phase-locked loop is determined by capacitor C_{10}. Plot shows value of capacitor for various values of free-running frequency. This frequency must be close to the difference between the incoming-signal frequency and the local-oscillator frequency if signal capture is to occur.

22 MHz at –3 dB, and the phase-locked loop itself can operate at frequencies from less than 1 kHz to several megahertz. The value of the voltage-controlled oscillator capacitor (C_{10}) that should be placed between pins 11 and 12 for various free-running frequencies is plotted in Fig. 2. It is obviously necessary to ensure that the free-running frequency is close enough to the input frequency of the loop for capture to occur.

To avoid the cost of the crystal, the circuit of Fig. 1 can be operated with a Taiyo CR-9.8 ceramic resonator. This resonator is connected between pins 1 and 16 in parallel with a 2.2-kilohm resistor and a 5-pF capacitor. The capacitor C_7 is omitted. Satisfactory results are obtained, but the value of the parallel capacitor is fairly critical if oscillation at spurious frequencies is to be avoided. Such oscillations produce a distorted output and may even prevent the wanted signal from being received at all.

The circuit requires a power supply of 10 to 15 V at a current of about 38 mA (42 mA maximum). This current is enough to make the device feel warm to the touch. Some drift of the center frequency occurs for about a minute after the power is first applied. □

LEDs help tune FSK demodulators

by C. Clay Laster
Kelly Air Force Base, San Antonio, Texas

Light-emitting diodes make excellent tuning aids for frequency-shift-keyed (FSK) demodulators. They can replace cathode-ray tubes or meters in both single-frequency-shift-keyed demodulators and dual-frequency-shift-keyed (DFS) demodulators. The LED display can be easily incorporated in existing demodulators or in yet-to-be-designed demodulators.

Many conventional FSK and DFS demodulators use CRTs to provide vector-like displays of the teleprinter mark (binary 1) and space (binary 0) signals. FSK and DFS modulation techniques normally make use of frequency shifts on the order of 200 to 800 hertz. One popular standard is to use a frequency shift of 850 Hz, with the space centered at 2,125 Hz and the mark centered at 2,975 Hz. The FSK demodulator, therefore, will have selective filters of 2,125 and 2,975 Hz to detect the respective space and mark signals.

In radio-communications circuits, the mark and space signals are transmitted as individual signals that shift below and above the transmitter's center frequency. Thus, if a radioteletype signal is transmitted at a center frequency of 7,100 kilohertz with a total frequency shift of 850 Hz, the space signal will be transmitted 425 Hz below the center frequency (at 7,099.575 kHz), and the mark signal will be transmitted 425 Hz above the center frequency (at 7,100.425 kHz). For proper signal reception, the receiver must be tuned so that the space and mark signals are centered at 2,125 and 2,975 Hz.

With a CRT vector-like tuning monitor, the space signals are displayed horizontally, while the mark signals are displayed vertically. When the receiver is tuned to the teleprinter signal and the receiver's beat-frequency oscillator is adjusted so that the space and mark signals are centered, the CRT will display the space and mark vectors.

Light-emitting diodes, along with the appropriate logic-interface circuitry, can be substituted for this more expensive and less reliable CRT tuning aid. Three LEDs, when arranged as indicated for the FSK demodulator, provide a display for the tuning function. (Other arrangements may be more desirable in some instances.) When the receiver is tuned to the signal center frequency, LED-1 lights; when it is below the center frequency, LED-2 lights; and when it is above the center frequency, LED-3 lights.

The block diagram shows how this simple LED tuning aid can be added to a conventional FSK demodulator. The dc outputs from both filter/detector stages are applied to a resistive divider network that acts as a threshold detector for the LEDs. The isolating diodes are connected as an OR gate to allow these dc signals to be applied to LED-1 when the demodulator is tuned to the signal's center frequency. If the output level from either filter/detector stage is not sufficient to drive the LEDs, appropriate transistor switches or digital logic ICs may be used as interface devices.

The same sort of LED tuning aid can be devised for DFS demodulators. In this case, five LEDs are required to replace the CRT display. Most DFS demodulators use switchable filters and have individual outputs for each teleprinter channel. They also sometimes have combining circuits (different antennas) for use with space and frequency-diversity schemes. In any case, the LED interface circuitry can be connected to the individual detector outputs, and the display can be arranged to show the space-space, space-mark, mark-space, and mark-mark combinations. □

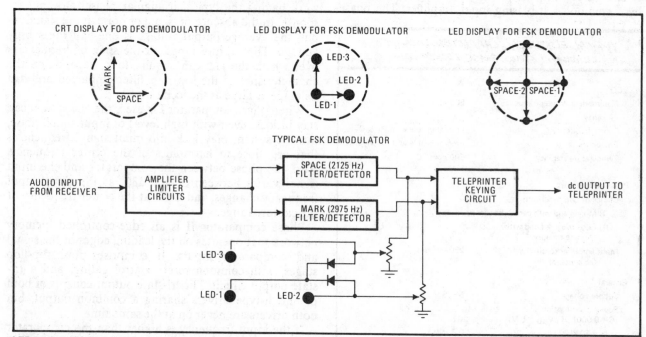

LED tuning aid. Light-emitting diodes can replace the vector-like CRT display commonly used for tuning a receiver to the signal center frequency. Three LEDs do the job for a single-frequency (FSK) demodulator, while five are needed for a dual-frequency (DFS) demodulator.

Micro-power phase-locked loop widens designer's choice

by David Morgan
RCA Solid State Division, Somerville, N.J.

Monolithic phase-locked loop (PLL) ICs have found wide acceptance in both analog and digital systems since they were first introduced. However, these bipolar ICs, which cover a wide band of frequencies, typically consume upwards of 100 milliwatts of power.

Now a monolithic complementary MOS phase-locked loop may change all that. The C-MOS IC used as an fm demodulator consumes only 600 microwatts of power when operating at 6 volts and a frequency of 10 kilohertz—less than 1/160 the power needed by its bipolar counterparts.

A basic functional diagram of the CD4046A PLL is shown in Fig. 1. The PLL structure consists of a low-power linear voltage-controlled oscillator (VCO) and provides the designer a choice of two digital-type phase comparators. Both comparators share a common signal-input amplifier and a common comparator input. A 5.4-V zener diode is provided for supply regulation, if necessary. The VCO can be connected either directly or through frequency dividers to the comparator input of the phase comparators. And an external low-pass filter is used to handle any configuration changes that are needed for different applications.

The phase comparators shown in Fig. 2a are driven by a common self-biasing input amplifier. The phase-

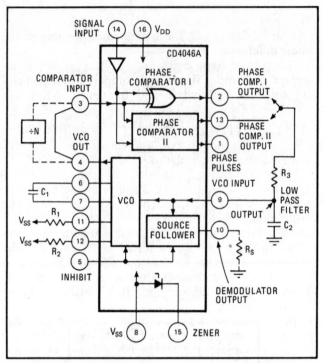

1. C-MOS phase-locked loop offers a choice of comparators.

comparator signal input (terminal 14) also can be directly coupled for signal swings within C-MOS logic levels— logic 0 is equal to or less than 30% of $(V_{DD}-V_{SS})$, logic 1 is equal to or greater than 70% of $(V_{DD}-V_{SS})$. Smaller input-signal levels must be capacitively coupled to the input signal terminal.

Phase comparator I is basically an exclusive-OR network having the typical triangular phase-to-output response. In the absence of signal or noise at the signal input, the average output voltage is one-half the supply voltage. The capture range, or the span of frequencies over which the PLL can acquire lock, depends on the characteristics of the low-pass filter employed and can be made as large as the lock range.[1]

When phase comparator I is used, the PLL system can stay in lock, even with high levels of input signal noise, but the system may lock into input signal frequencies that are close to harmonics of the center frequency. Also, the phase between the comparator and the input signal varies between 0° and 180° as the signal-input frequency changes, and is 90° at the center frequency of the capture range.

Phase comparator II is an edge-controlled memory network that operates on the leading edges of the signal and comparator inputs. It comprises four flip-flop stages, with common reset, control gating, and a tri-state output circuit. The tri-state output consists of both p- and n-type drivers sharing a common output, but both drivers are never on at the same time.

If the input frequency is higher than the comparator frequency, then the p-type output driver is on continuously; if the input frequency is lower than the com-

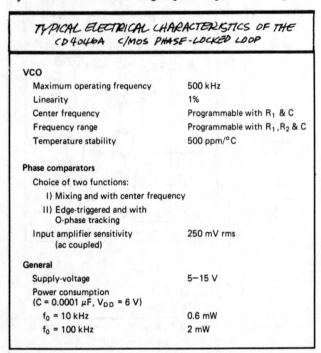

TYPICAL ELECTRICAL CHARACTERISTICS OF THE CD4046A C/MOS PHASE-LOCKED LOOP

VCO

Maximum operating frequency	500 kHz
Linearity	1%
Center frequency	Programmable with R_1 & C
Frequency range	Programmable with R_1, R_2 & C
Temperature stability	500 ppm/°C

Phase comparators

Choice of two functions:

  I) Mixing and with center frequency

  II) Edge-triggered and with 0-phase tracking

Input amplifier sensitivity (ac coupled)	250 mV rms

General

Supply-voltage	5–15 V
Power consumption ($C = 0.0001 \mu F$, $V_{DD} = 6$ V)	
$f_0 = 10$ kHz	0.6 mW
$f_0 = 100$ kHz	2 mW

parator frequency, the n-type output driver is kept on. If these frequencies are the same, but the phase of the input signal lags that of the comparator, the n-type output driver would remain on for a time that corresponds to the phase difference. If the frequencies are equal, but the signal phase leads that of the comparator, the p-type driver is kept on for a time corresponding to the phase difference.

This type of phase comparator adjusts the VCO input voltage until input signal and comparator frequencies are equal in both phase and frequency. When this stable condition occurs, both driver stages are off. In the absence of an input signal, phase comparator II adjusts the VCO to its lowest possible frequency. This comparator has a lower signal-to-noise ratio than phase comparator I and could lock on noise signals. However, it will not lock on harmonics of the VCO signal, as will phase comparator I.

The VCO shown in Fig. 2b, unlike its conventional phase-locked counterparts, is a square-wave oscillator with a 50% duty cycle. This allows the unit to directly interface with other C-MOS devices, such as the PLL's digital phase comparator, counters, and so on. Not only does the C-MOS VCO consume significantly less power than bipolar types, but an "inhibit" input is provided, which enables the VCO and the source follower or turns both off to minimize standby power consumption. The high input impedance (10^{12} ohms) of the VCO simplifies the design of low-pass filters by permitting a rather wide choice of resistor-to-capacitor ratios.

As in conventional VCOs, the frequency range and frequency offset are adjustable. Resistor R_1 and capacitor C_1 determine the frequency range of the VCO, and resistor R_2 will provide a frequency offset, if required. A source follower allows monitoring of the VCO input voltage without loading of the low-pass filter.

REFERENCES
1. Floyd M. Gardner, "Phaselock Techniques," John Wiley & Sons Inc., N.Y., N.Y., 1967.

2. Digital route. Diagram details phase comparator (a) and voltage-controlled oscillator (b) circuits of phase-locked loop.

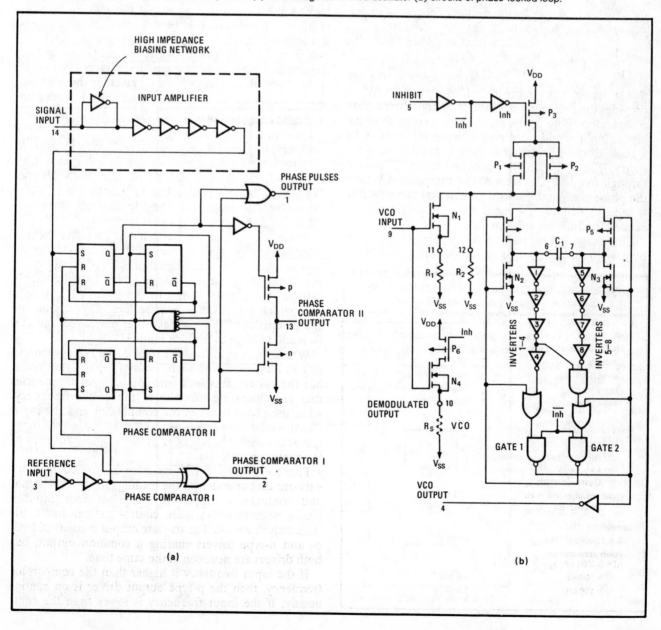

131

Dual-bandwidth loop speeds phase lock

by A.T. Anderson, D.E. Sanders, and R.S. Gordy
Electronic Communications Inc., St. Petersburg, Fla.

A phase-lock loop with two filters of different bandwidths, and the capability of achieving a gradual transition from one to the other, can satisfy the conflicting requirements of noise rejection and fast signal acquisition. Having acquired the signal, the loop then serves as a local source that matches the remote source of the incoming signal, which may be intermittent because of imperfections in the transmitting channel. Essentially, the loop is a voltage-controlled oscillator that forces the output into a fixed phase with the input.

If the input signal has noise or phase jitter riding on it, the loop will try to follow the disturbance as well as the signal. Noise effects on the loop can be reduced by lowpass filtering of the error. The narrower the filter, the less the noise affects the VCO, but the harder it is for the loop to achieve lock.

In fact, if the frequency-offset—the difference between input frequency and VCO rest frequency—is too large, the loop may never lock. In this case, an external voltage may be applied to sweep the VCO rest frequency over the range of input isgnals; the maximum sweep rate depends on the filter bandwidth.

Even if the frequency-offset is small, the slow transient response of the narrow filter slows the loop's signal acquisition. Loop-filter design must often compromise between large bandwidth for fast acquisition and small

bandwidth for noise-free tracking.

To avoid this compromise, two discrete bandwidths can be used. A large bandwidth is used until the signal is acquired; after acquisition, a small loop bandwidth is switched in. This technique, which is shown in Fig. 1, has three significant disadvantages.

First is the voltage step which results from switching the VCO control line, point C, from point A to point B. The step change in voltage at point C which results from switching the VCO-control line from point A to point B can cause loss of lock.

The second disadvantage is the voltage transient that can result from abrupt switching with real circuit devices even when the voltages at the two inputs are equal. This transient can also cause the loop to lose lock. A third disadvantage is that the ratio of large to small filter bandwidth is limited if a frequency-offset exists in the phase-lock loop.

A slow bandwidth-switching technique shown in Fig. 2 eliminates these disadvantages. Switchover from point A to point B is accomplished gradually by varying resistance R from zero (or a low value) initially, to a high value at the end. When the R is low, the VCO-control line is essentially connected to A because of the low impedance drive at A. The output of the narrow (slow) filter is also connected to A initially. The low impedance of A forces the narrow filter output to follow the fast response of the wide filter, effectively giving the narrow filter a fast response time while also forcing the voltages at points A and B to be equal. The slow, controlled switchover, together with the equal voltages, prevents transients at point C which might cause loss of acquisition.

During switchover, the VCO-control line, point C, is effectively connected to a combination of both filter outputs, resulting in

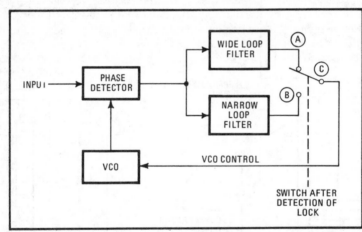

1. Switchable bandwidth. A phase-lock loop requires two different switched loop filters for acquisition (lock) and tracking (narrow).

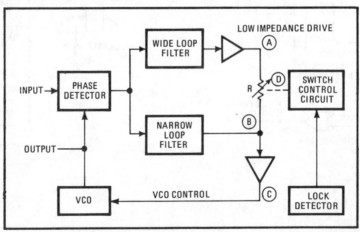

2. Slow switching technique. Slow bandwidth switching with a variable resistor eliminates the disadvantages of conventional bandwidth-switching.

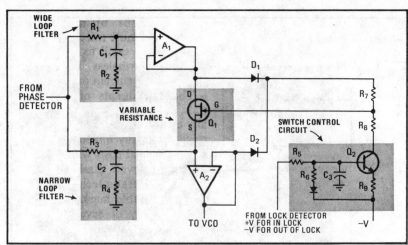

3. FET control. Signals from a lock detector gradually vary resistance of Q_1 from a low to high value. This smoothly changes the loop filter bandwidth.

gradual reduction of bandwidth from large to small. The shape of the switch-control waveform, at point D, can be designed to optimize acquisition under given conditions such as signal-to-noise and frequency offset, and can easily be changed as these conditions change. The gradual change forces the loop to remain in lock at all times so that the ratio of large to small bandwidth can be much higher than with conventional switching. Actual circuitry for Fig. 2 is relatively easily realized, with the exception of the slow switch and its switch-control circuitry. A desired feature of these two elements is that the R should be strictly controlled by the switch-

control line and not be affected by the voltage at A or C.

An example of a circuit that meets this criterion is given in Fig. 3. In this circuit, a junction FET, Q_1, is the variable resistance. Initially, no current flows in Q_2, so Q_1 is closed (low resistance). This forces the voltage on C_2 in the narrow filter to follow C_1 and charge to approximately the correct value during acquisition.

When lock is detected (by an external circuit), the "lock-detector" input switches from $-V$ to $+V$. The time-constant of the parallel combination of R_5, R_6 and C_3 causes the current in Q_2 (initially zero) to increase at an exponential rate in response to the lock's signal change. Q_2 is a current source and is unaffected by the filter outputs or switch. Current will flow through R_7 and either CR_1 or CR_2, depending on which side of Q_1 is more negative. This allows the voltage on the gate of Q_1 to follow the more negative voltage on the drain or source. Therefore, noise at the drain and source of Q_1 has no effect on the resistance of the J-FET, since the resistance of this type of FET is determined by the voltage on the gate in relation to the voltage on the drain or source. CR_2 is connected to the output of A_2 rather than to the FET source. Voltages at these points are essentially equal, and location shown prevents current through CR_2 from loading the FET.

Low-frequency discriminator utilizes analog delay

by Satoru Tanaka and William L. Brown
Reticon Corp., Mountain View, Calif.

Low-frequency discriminators, which translate frequency-modulated signals having center frequencies from a few hundred to a few thousand hertz into direct analog signals, are vital components in equipment such as doppler tracking systems and servo motor control systems. But they have been cumbersome because of the requirement for very large inductors and capacitors. That no longer need be true, however, with the advent of the discrete time analog delay.

The approach employed here (Fig. 1) is a low-fre-

quency equivalent of a technique that is common at much higher frequencies. The amplitude of the incoming signal is clipped by the limiter, becoming, in essence, a square wave. The square wave is then split in two; one signal goes directly to one input of a four-quadrant multiplier; the other is first delayed, then applied to the other input of the multiplier. The output voltage of the multiplier is inversely proportional to the

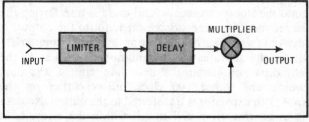

1. Principle. Clipped input, multiplied by a delayed form of itself, produces an averaged output proportional to input frequency.

133

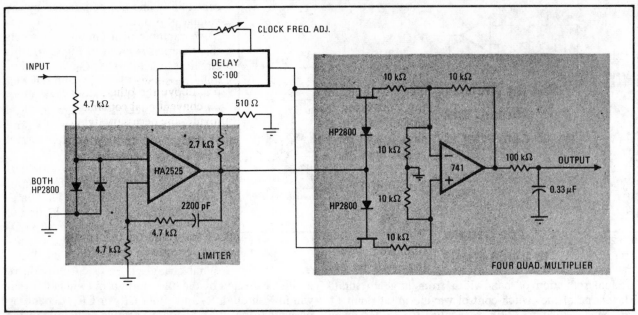

2. Implementation. Discriminator circuit is based on principle of clipping, delaying and multiplying, as shown in Fig. 1.

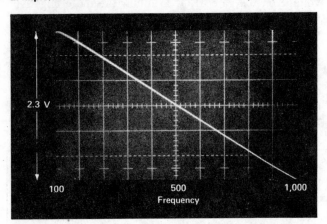

3. Result. Output voltage decreases linearly with swept frequency.

phase difference of the two signals. But since the time delay is fixed, the change of phase imposed by the delay line is directly proportional to the frequency; therefore, when the phases are compared in the multiplier, the output is inversely proportional to the frequency.

The delay line, one of the two key elements of the circuit, is a monolithic integrated circuit: Reticon Corp.'s SAD-100, fabricated with MOS silicon-gate technology and packaged in a 16-lead dual in-line package. The SAD-100 is essentially an array of 100 sample-and-hold circuits. It stores analog information sequentially in an array of 100 storage capacitors. Each capacitor has two multiplex switches—one for reading a sample of data onto the storage capacitor, and one for transferring the stored data from the storage capacitor to the output. A dynamic shift register operating as a ring counter sequentially activates the two multiplex switches. As the nth capacitor acquires a new data sample, the data which was stored 100 clock pulses earlier on the $(n + 1)$th capacitor is transferred to the output. No data is transferred from cell to cell within the array, as is done with charge transfer devices, in which the multiple transfer can cause signal degradation.

The total delay range of the SAD-100 is from 700 nanoseconds to 50 milliseconds; it is controlled by its sampling frequency. Its delay-to-rise-time ratio is 98, its video bandwidth exceeds 5 megahertz, and under certain conditions its signal-to-noise ratio is greater than 65 dB. The SAD-100 is obtainable separately, or as a component in a network, designated the SC-100, which includes clocking and signal extraction circuits.

The four-quadrant multiplier, as a phase comparator, is used in the conventional way. Its two input values are +1 and –1; it multiplies the two signals to obtain one of four products: +1 × +1, +1 × –1, –1 × +1, and –1 × –1. If two square waves that switch between +1 and –1 with identical frequency and phase are continuously multiplied, the product would be +1 at all times. Likewise, if the signals' phases are 180° apart, the product is –1 at all times. Thus, if the phase is continuously shifted between 0 and 180°, the average output is somewhere between these extremes, proportional to the phase. If the amplitude is some value other than unity, a corresponding constant factor is included.

In the actual circuit (Fig. 2), the time delay depends on the clocking frequency, which is continuously variable from 3 kilohertz to 10 mHz. For this discriminator the clock was set to produce a delay of approximately 500 microseconds, which shifts the phase of a 1,000-hertz signal by 180°. Lower frequencies down to 100 Hz are shifted proportionally. This circuit's linearity over a range of 10:1 is better than 99%; its maximum frequency can be shifted as high as 100 kHz by adjusting a single resistor. No tuned circuits, bulky coils, or capacitors have to be changed.

Figure 3 is a photograph of the output voltage as the frequency is swept from 100 Hz to 1,000 Hz. The output does not change noticeably as the input to the limiter is varied between 0.5 v and 30 v peak-to-peak. □

134

Varactor pair in new stripline circuit improves modulation

by Donald Neuf
RHG Electronics Laboratories, Farmingdale, N.Y.

Modulation linearity is a most important consideration for designers of color television transmitters—any variation in the phase or amplitude of the transmitted signal will distort both hue and saturation at the viewer's end. Here is a design approach for modulating an fm transmitter that uses two tandem varactor diodes for improved linearity and a novel stripline design that provides tight radio-frequency coupling and diode bias isolation.

With the more conventional single-varactor lumped-element tuning circuit, the frequency of oscillation normally varies as the fourth root of the tuning voltage—hardly a linear relation. However, if the series inductance of the tuned circuit could be changed without adding stray capacitance, then the frequency could be made to vary as the square root of the tuning voltage. The required variable inductance is easily achieved by adding a varactor diode and an impedance inverter, such as a quarter-wavelength transmission line (the sec-ond varactor stage in the pi network, Fig. 1).

The stripline design has two center conductors in different planes (one above the other, instead of the two side by side as in conventional coplanar stripline). This arrangement provides the necessary tight coupling without the critical tolerances inherent in the conventional coplanar structure.

The color TV transmitter must supply typically 250 milliwatts at 7 gigahertz, with a maximum frequency deviation of ±4 megahertz. The transmitter must handle baseband modulating signals from 0.1 hertz to 10 megahertz and hold the differential amplitude and phase variation across the 8-MHz deviation range to within ±0.5 dB and ±0.5°, respectively.

The varactor-modulated Impatt transmitter was constructed in a stripline package with a built-in circulator (Fig. 2). In addition to isolating the load and providing an input port for an external locking signal, the circulator simplifies measuring external Q and the optimizating of the oscillator first as an amplifier.[1]

A gallium-arsenide Impatt diode was chosen for its lower noise qualities.[2] The Impatt diode has an equivalent Q low enough to provide the desired frequency deviation. In general, oscillation occurs at a frequency at which the net circuit reactance is zero and the negative diode resistance is equal to the positive source resistance. And although oscillation is possible when the diode's negative resistance is greater in magnitude than

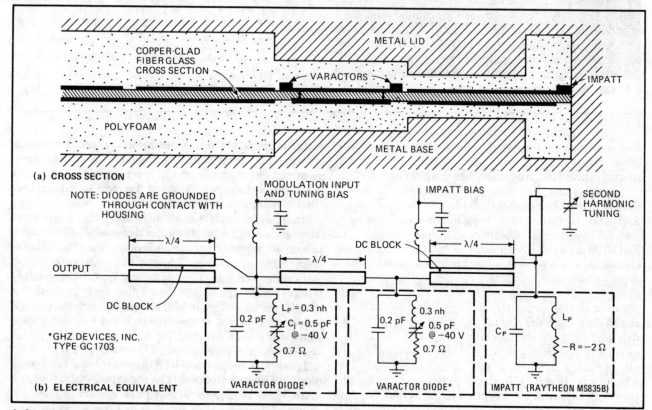

1. A cross-section of the Impatt transmitter (a) details the stripline construction with center conductors in two planes. An equivalent circuit for the varactor-modulated transmitter (b) illustrates the quarter-wavelength coupling techniques with dc blocking.

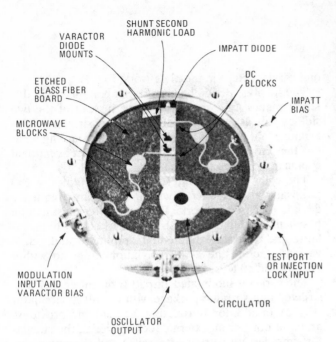

2. **A built-in** three-port circulator isolates the load from the varactor-modulated Impatt-diode oscillator, provides a convenient test port, and can also serve to inject an external locking signal. The complete fm transmitter is shown without the cover (top ground plane) and the top layer of polyfoam.

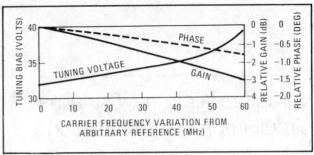

3. **Differential gain and phase** are held to within ±0.5 dB and ±0.5°, respectively, over any 8-MHz segment within the varactor tuning range. A bias of 32 to 40 volts (a compromise between diode breakdown and tuning control) provides about a 60-MHz tuning range.

the source resistance, an optimum operating point was chosen where the oscillator has the highest efficiency and the lowest noise spectrum.[3]

The oscillator circuit construction uses both sides of a copper-clad glass fiber board for the stripline dual center conductors (Fig. 1). This stripline design offers more predictable impedance control and higher Q than does microstrip. A polyfoam material (dielectric constant of 1.2) is then used to support the stripline center conductors. The stripline design also provides a means of si-

multaneously filtering the second harmonics and isolating the varactor modulation and dc bias voltages from the avalanche diode. Equivalent characteristic impedances of the quarter-wavelength sections are determined by using "odd" and "even" propagation-mode analyses.[4]

The avalanche diode is also loaded by a separately adjustable half-wavelength line. This circuit controls the second harmonic loading and helps to reduce fundamental noise.[5]

The final package power output, in the 100 to 200 mW range, increases about 1 dB with an increase in tuning voltage. A varactor bias in the 32- to 40-volt range produces an rf frequency variation of some 60 MHz. The total fm noise of the oscillator, measured with a standard EIA TV noise-weighting filter, was 8 kHz rms. □

REFERENCES
1. J. Ashley and F. Palka, "A Modulation Method for the Measurement of Microwave Oscillator Q," PGMTT, November 1970, pp. 1002–1004.
2. M. Gupta, "Noise in Avalanche Transit-Time Devices," Proc. IEEE, December 1971, pp. 1674–1687.
3. A. Cowley et al., "Noise and Power Saturation in Singly Tuned Impatt Oscillators," IEEE Journal of Solid-State Circuits, December 1970, pp. 338–345.
4. G. Matthaei, L. Young and E.M.T. Jones, "Microwave Filters, Impedance-Matching Networks, and Coupling Structures," McGraw-Hill, p. 221.
5. F. Sullivan and W. From, "Second-Harmonic Tuning Effects on Impatt Diode Oscillator Noise Characteristics," 1971, IEEE-GMTT International Microwave Symposium Record.

Data transmission is faster with ternary coding

by T. Bruins
Cern European Organization for Nuclear Research, Geneva, Switzerland

Although data is usually transmitted in binary form, much faster bit rates can be realized, even over long distances, if the data is converted to ternary form. With optimized filters and sensitive receivers, for instance, a ternary data transmission system can achieve an effective rate of up to 6 megabits per second over a 1-mile line of ordinary twisted-pair cable.

Although twisted-pair drivers have been around for quite some time, they have only been used to carry binary information. Here, logic 1s and logic 0s are defined by the two opposite polarities on the two trans-

mitter outputs. Decoding these voltage differences into ordinary TTL levels is normally done with voltage comparators. The common-mode noise immunity that this system offers has made it one of the most popular transmission techniques in recent years.

Strangely enough, however, nobody has considered the usefulness of a third state, which would still retain a certain immunity to common-mode noise. This state is defined by the absence of any voltage difference at the transmitter outputs. It is primarily useful for sending ternary-coded data over long distances. In case bit speeds are of no great importance, binary data could still be transmitted in the conventional way. The third state would then be used for status information or for system synchronization.

There are several ways of implementing a ternary data transmission system. Over distances of a mile or more, special-purpose balanced line drivers providing a choice of differential or single-ended operation must be used. In these cases, a tristate line driver like National

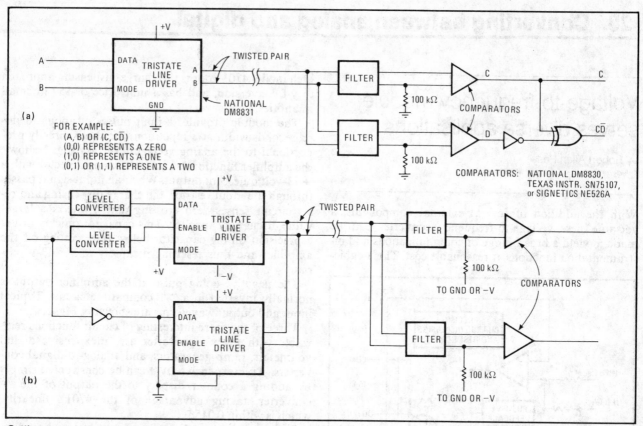

Getting more out of a twisted pair. Ternary-coded data can be transmitted at megabit rates through ordinary twisted pairs over long distances. A single integrated tristate line driver can be used to send the data at low bit rates, as in (a); or two drivers can be employed, as in (b), for higher bit rates. If desired, the third state can be used for synchronization purposes or to transmit status or control information.

Semiconductor's DM8831 unit is a good choice. The single-ended state may be detected with biased voltage comparators.

If two comparators are used, biased, for example, to different polarities, the third state can be decoded with a mere exclusive-OR logic operation, as shown in (a). This is a simple scheme for low bit rates. It is particularly useful if status or control information is transmitted on the same twisted pair as the data but must nevertheless be distinguished.

For very long lines or for transmission rates of greater than 1 megabit per second, it is best to use two tristate line drivers, establishing a grounded symmetrical transmission system. The three states are easily generated with two line drivers, as in (b). One driver operates differentially (at –2½ and +2½ volts, instead of the usual 0 and 5 v), while the other driver operates in its single-ended mode at normal voltage in a complementary fashion.

To change binary-coded data into ternary-coded data does not require an excessively complicated conversion circuit. Consider, for example, that a fully decoded 16-bit binary word reduces to 10 ternary bits—$(1\ 111\ 111\ 111\ 111\ 111)_{base2} = (1\ 022\ 220\ 020)_{base3}$. In this case, full code conversion provides a bit reduction of 10/16. This means that a ternary-coded transmission system that is able to carry 4 megabits per second of binary-coded data now can effectively carry 16/10 times more information, or 6.4 megabits per second.

Code conversion can be simplified greatly if the binary bits are coded in subgroups. If two binary bits are taken as a subgroup, two ternary bits are required to convert each subgroup. But if subgroups of three binary bits are used, again only two ternary bits are needed (since $111_{base2} = 21_{base3}$) and, therefore, 16 binary bits can be coded into 11 ternary bits.

One application for a ternary transmission system is the use of ternary parity bits. Since there are three states (instead of two), two flip-flops (instead of one) are required. The parity check, then, can just be the modulo-3 addition of the information bits. In this way, a large number of even errors will be detected, but not all odd errors.

With k free binary bits as information carriers and n – k dependent ternary error detection bits, there are 2^k information words out of $2^k \times 3^{n-k}$ possible bit combinations. Therefore, the ratio of nondetectable errors to all possible errors will be: $(2^k – 1)/(2^k 3^{n-k} – 1)$, which approximately equals $\frac{1}{3}^{n-k}$. If one single ternary parity check is used, then two thirds of all possible errors will be detected, instead of only half the errors, as in the case of the modulo-2 parity. □

Voltage-to-frequency module serves diverse applications

by Robert Allen Pease
Teledyne Philbrick, Dedham, Mass.

With the addition of several external components, a versatile new voltage-to-frequency converter can be made to yield a broad range of communications and instrumentation functions at reasonable cost. The 1-cubic-

inch model 4701 adopts the charge-dispensing approach to v-f conversion, and has a unit price of $59 in small quantities.

The module provides output pulses of about 30 microseconds width at a repetition rate that's directly proportional to the analog voltage level. As Fig. 1 shows, the amplifier functions as a zero crossing detector with a + 13-volt quiescent output. When an input signal passes through the input resistor, the charge dispensing and reset circuit senses zero crossing and connects a large-value discharge capacitor. This capacitor quickly drives a precision timing capacitor below zero, cutting off the amplifier and thus resetting it rapidly to a + 13-v output.

The negative-going pulse at the amplifier output is normally inverted in a TTL-compatible circuit. Typical input and output waveforms are shown in Fig. 2.

Three of the more interesting of circuit functions realizable with the v-f converter are: inexpensive digital voltmeters, ramp generators, and analog-to-digital converters. An inexpensive DVM can be constructed simply by adding a counter/display to the output of the v-f converter, taking advantage of the 4701's linearity, which is within 0.015%.

Programable, very linear ramp generators based on v-f techniques (Fig. 3) overcome a major difficulty of conventional designs—they do not suffer from charge leakage of the timing capacitor under temperature extremes. By driving a ripple counter with an R-2R ladder connected to its output, the 4701 converter generates a highly linear 10-v ramp that operates at frequencies to 80 hertz. Output impedance is 51 kΩ ±5%.

An analog-to-digital converter is constructed from a 4701 and several inexpensive components. In Fig. 4, the converter output feeds a counter which is reset by a 1-

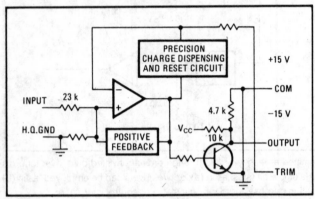

1. Converter. Frequency-to-voltage module follows charge-dispensing design approach. Output is buffered and TTL-compatible.

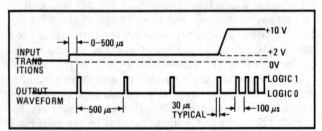

2. Proper timing. Typical waveforms show timing relationships between input and output for input levels of 2 and 10 volts.

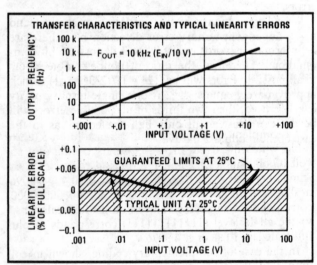

TRANSFER CHARACTERISTICS AND TYPICAL LINEARITY ERRORS

$F_{OUT} = 10 \text{ kHz } (E_{IN}/10 \text{ V})$

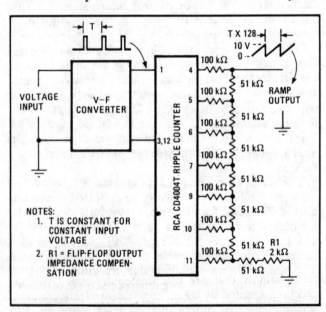

NOTES:
1. T IS CONSTANT FOR CONSTANT INPUT VOLTAGE
2. R1 = FLIP-FLOP OUTPUT IMPEDANCE COMPENSATION

3. Better ramp. Voltage-controlled ramp generator doesn't share the charge-leakage problem of conventional generators.

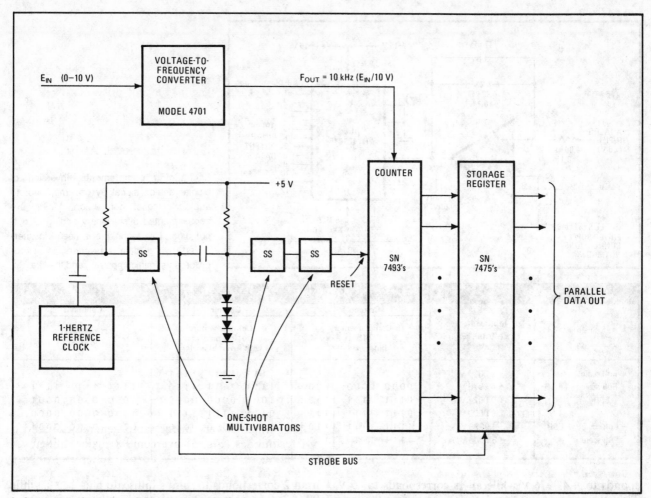

4. Low-cost conversion. Analog-to-digital conversion is inexpensive with the voltage-to-frequency converter and several other components. For fast computer processing, the output data is available in parallel from a single strobing.

Hz clock pulse. Just before reset, the peak counted value of the input frequency is strobed into the storage register. The data can be read out of the register (or a following parallel-to-serial shift register) in a few microseconds, so that processing may be performed on virtually any digital computer on a time-shared basis. □

Op amp complements a-d converter output code

by Eugene L. Zuch
Datel Systems Inc., Canton, Mass.

In many cases where an analog-to-digital converter has data outputs that are complementary-coded (highest level represented by 00 . . . 0), the interfacing requires uncomplemented coding (highest level represented by 11 . . . 1), and vice versa. Conversion from one form to the other can of course be done with logic inverters, but if the input analog signal is bipolar, a single operational amplifier can perform all of the inversions.

The approach also works with minicomputers, some of which require complementary input coding while others require uncomplemented coding.

Uncomplemented coding is shown in column 3 of the table, which illustrates the offset binary coding of a ±5-volt bipolar analog signal. A 12-bit a-d converter is assumed here, so the least significant bit is 10 v ÷ 4,096, or 0.0024 v. In this code the all-0s level (000000000000) corresponds to an analog value of minus full scale, or –5 v; the all-1s level (111111111111) corresponds to plus full scale less 1 LSB or +4.9976 v.

In the case of complementary coding, shown in column 1 of the table, the reverse is true. All-0s corre-

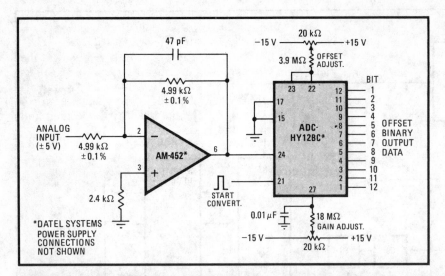

Exchanging complements. Inversion of bipolar analog signal by op amp, prior to analog-to-digital conversion, yields uncomplemented offset binary coding of output data. This technique is useful in interfacing hybrid data converters to microprocessors, minicomputers, and the like.

Scale	Input voltage (± 5 V full scale)	Column 1 Complementary offset binary coding	Column 2 Complementary offset binary with inverted analog	Column 3 Offset binary coding
+ Full scale	+ 5.0000 V		1111 1111 1111	
+ Full scale − 1 LSB	+ 4.9976 V	0000 0000 0000	1111 1111 1110	1111 1111 1111
+ 1 LSB	+ 0.0024 V	0111 1111 1110	1000 0000 0000	1000 0000 0001
0	0.0000 V	0111 1111 1111	0111 1111 1111	1000 0000 0000
− Full scale + 1 LSB	− 4.9976 V	1111 1111 1110	0000 0000 0000	0000 0000 0001
− Full scale	− 5.0000 V	1111 1111 1111		0000 0000 0000

CODING TABLE

sponds to +4.9976 V while all-1s corresponds to –5 V. Thus the codes in column 1 and 3 are simply the logic complements of one another.

The obvious way to go from one code to the other is to add a logic inverter to each output line. This is relatively inexpensive, requiring only two hex inverters for 12 output data lines, but it may often be quite inconvenient because 12 data lines must be connected to 12 dual in-line pins on a circuit board. And if the data output from the converter is tri-state, two strobe connections must be handled in addition to the data lines.

For bipolar operation, the inverting-op-amp method requires connection to only one pin of the a-d converter, the analog input. The gain of the inverting amplifier must be set close to –1, although small variations can be taken care of by the a-d converter gain adjustment. The circuit of Fig. 1 shows a fast integrated-circuit op amp connected to the input of a fast hybrid 12-bit a-d converter. After the amplifier is connected, the converter is calibrated for offset and gain, as is normally done for the coding of a bipolar signal (i.e., offset binary coding). Because the ADC-HY12BC converter normally has complementary offset binary coding, use of the inverting amplifier in this case results in offset binary coding.

The table shows how the coding transformation works. Starting with the complementary offset binary coding in column 1, inversion of the analog input in effect rotates the coding about the analog 0 axis, as shown in column 2. Now, column 2 is almost identical with column 3, except that column 2 is 1 LSB higher in analog value than column 3. In other words, 00 . . . 0 in col-

umn 2 corresponds to minus full scale plus 1 LSB, while 00 . . . 0 in column 3 corresponds to minus full scale. But this difference in analog value is easily taken care of by the offset adjustment of the a-d converter.

The technique works in both directions, from offset binary to complementary offset binary or the reverse. It also works between two's-complement coding, in which the most significant bit is complemented from its value in offset binary coding, and complementary two's-complement coding. (Most newer modular or hybrid a-d converters have an output that is the complement of the MSB output for use in two's complement output coding.)

In applications of the op-amp inversion technique, the settling time of the inverting amplifier must be added to the conversion time of the a-d converter. In the circuit shown, the settling time of the AM-452 amplifier is 3 microseconds to 0.01%. Added to the 8-μs conversion time of the ADC-HY12BC, this gives a total conversion time of 11 μs.

The conversion technique is useful in interfacing a-d converters to microprocessors, minicomputers, or other digital-input devices. Most of the earlier modular a-d converters used uncomplemented coding, but many of the newer converters, such as the new low-priced hybrid units, use complementary coding. The change derives from the popularity of the quad current switch technique and the use of a monolithic successive-approximation register inside the converters. □

DAC differential linearity: it makes a difference

by Ron Gadway
Burr-Brown Research Corp., Tucson, Ariz.

Though digital-to-analog converters are frequently found in CRT displays or in digital plotting systems, it's not as frequently realized that a specification called differential linearity can significantly affect the converter's output and the resulting display presentation.

In a d-a converter, linearity error is usually called out as ±½ the least significant bit (LSB). There are two ways in which it is often defined: either as a straight line drawn between the end points or as a best-fit straight line drawn between all codes. In either case, linearity error means that the actual output voltage will not vary from the ideal output by more than ±½ LSB.

But don't count on this specification alone to take care of linearity problems. If a d-a converter is linear to ±½ LSB, as shown in Fig. 1, its differential linearity can still vary by as much as 2 LSB from one successive digital input code to the next. Differential linearity can be thought of as the maximum or minimum increment in the converter's analog output for a change between two successive digital input codes (for example, from 1101100 to 1101101).

Figure 2 shows the outputs of two different d-a converters, one having an unspecified differential linearity and the other having a specified differential linearity. Both graphs represent the vector form of the monotonic output that is produced in response to an increasing digital input code. Although both outputs are linear to ±½ LSB, only the converter with a specified differential linearity of ±½ LSB confines all possible linearity errors to ±½ LSB.

In a CRT display application, the imperfections in the output of the converter having an unspecified differential linearity will be visible and, most likely, intolerable. Therefore, when choosing a d-a converter for a display, be sure its differential linearity is specified and meets design requirements. □

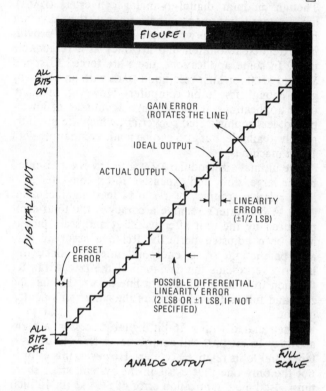

FIGURE 1

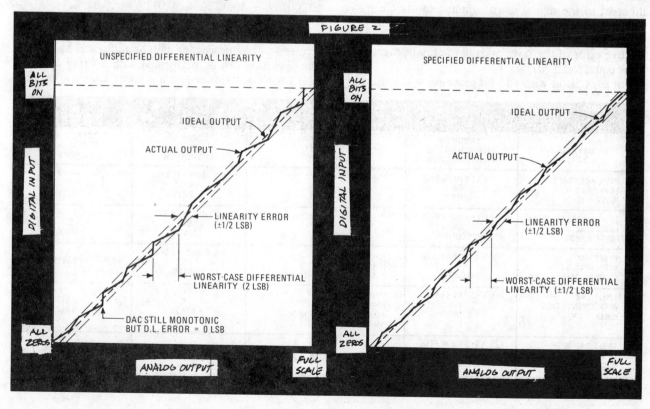

FIGURE 2

141

Economical approaches to 16-bit d-a conversion

by David Atkins
Hybrid Systems Corp., Burlington, Mass.

Though modular digital-to-analog converters (DACs), are constantly improving in performance, they have not been able to keep up with digital processors in providing extended resolution and accuracy at a reasonable price. In some applications, users are forced to spend $400 to $500 for high-resolution DACs with an accuracy good enough for 16-bit computers. However, in many other applications, users can take advantage of lower-priced, less sophisticated converters, which are not only readily available, but also can be made compatible with 16-bit machines.

The ultimate in modular DAC accuracy is represented by the large, slow, and expensive 16-bit converter having a relative accuracy of ±½ to ±1 least significant bit (LSB). A converter's relative accuracy is the total error produced by the unit after its offset and scale factors have been adjusted perfectly. Relative accuracy may also be thought of as end-point linearity, since this linearity represents the deviation of the DAC's transfer function from an ideal straight line drawn through the zero and full-scale end points of the converter's analog output.

When mated with a 16-bit digital processor, a high-accuracy 16-bit DAC will contribute an error to the system equal to its relative accuracy. However, this error is not the only one that exists in the system, since there must also be a quantization error of ±½ LSB (in 16 bits) inherent in the digital word supplied to the converter. The total error in converting to an analog voltage, then, is the sum of the ±½-LSB quantization error and the relative error of the DAC, making the total peak system error equal to ±0.0015%.

But a DAC user with a 16-bit processor will only rarely need this kind of accuracy at a price of $500. He can get adequate accuracy by going to alternate, less expensive approaches. The table summarizes four other methods of converting digital information from a 16-bit source into an analog signal with good accuracy and at relatively low cost.

The first method involves a simple, but cost-effective, modification to the high-performance approach just described—buy a 16-bit DAC with a poorer accuracy specification. Most manufacturers of high-performance 16-bit d-a converters offer the identical model with a relative accuracy of 14 or 15 bits (an error of ±2 LSBs in 16 bits) at a price reduction of 15% to 25%. The resulting system error will then be a ±½-LSB quantization error plus a ±2-LSB analog error, or a peak output error of ±2½ LSBs (in 16 bits). Of course, the other disadvantages of the high-performance DAC, namely slow speed and large size, still remain.

A second, more drastic, alternative is to change the very nature of the DAC. Just because the digital word is 16 bits is no reason to force the DAC to be 16 bits. A 12-bit DAC, which is both small and fast, can be used instead, but the user must then decide what to do with the four LSBs that have no connection to the 12-bit DAC. One possible solution is to simply drop them (this is called truncation). A second solution is to use the 4 LSBs to correct the digital number to the nearest 12 bits (this is called rounding off).

Rounding off to 12 bits is equivalent to quantizing to 12 bits, so that the digital quantization error becomes ±½ LSB in 16 bits plus ±½ LSB in 12 bits, or ±0.00075% + ±0.012%. In addition, a typical 12-bit DAC has a relative accuracy of ±½ LSB in 12 bits, or ±0.012%. Therefore, when a 12-bit DAC is used with round off, the total output error for the system becomes ±½ LSB in 16 bits plus ±½ LSB in 12 bits plus ±½ LSB in 12 bits, or ±0.00075% + ±0.012% + ±0.012% = ±0.025%.

This approach produces more error than the previous two methods, but it costs much less, even though it does involve an extra processing step or additional hardware. The operation can be performed with a string of three 4-bit adders or a slower and less costly analog approach

METHOD	ERROR OF DIGITAL PROCESS (FROM COMPUTER)	ERROR OF INTERMEDIATE PROCESS	ERROR OF D-A CONVERTER	TOTAL PEAK SYSTEM ERROR
HIGH-ACCURACY 16-BIT DAC (COST ≈ $500)	± ½ LSB IN 16 BITS OR ± 0.00075%	—	± ½ LSB IN 16 BITS OR ± 0.00075%	± 1 LSB OR ± 0.0015%
LOWER-ACCURACY 16-BIT DAC (COST ≈ $400)	± ½ LSB IN 16 BITS OR ± 0.00075%	—	± 2 LSBs IN 16 BITS OR ± 0.003%	± 2½ LSBs OR ± 0.00375%
12-BIT DAC WITH ROUND OFF (COST ≈ $75)	± ½ LSB IN 16 BITS OR ± 0.00075%	ROUND OFF (FROM 16 TO 12 BITS) ± ½ LSB IN 12 BITS OR ± 0.012%	± ½ LSB IN 12 BITS OR ± 0.012%	± 0.025%
12-BIT DAC WITH TRUNCATION (COST ≈ $75)	± ½ LSB IN 16 BITS OR ± 0.00075%	TRUNCATION (DROP 4 LSBs) + 0 LSB, − 1 LSB IN 12 BITS OR + 0%, − 0.012%	± ½ LSB IN 12 BITS OR ± 0.012%	+ 0.013%, − 0.037%
16-BIT DAC WITH 12-BIT ACCURACY (COST ≈ $75)	± ½ LSB IN 16 BITS OR ± 0.00075%	—	± 0.01%	± 0.01075%

ERROR COMPARISON FOR 16-BIT D-A CONVERSION

DAC = DIGITAL-TO-ANALOG CONVERTER   LSB = LEAST SIGNIFICANT BIT

can be used instead. Since rounding off requires that 1 LSB (in 12 bits) be added to the DAC input any time the 2^{-13}th bit is true, an analog voltage equivalent to 1 LSB can be added to the DAC output each time the 2^{-13}th bit is logic 1.

Truncation is similar to rounding off, but it has a somewhat different error pattern. Since the unused bits are simply dropped in truncation, no additional hardware is involved. However, truncation also means that the 12-bit representation of a 16-bit quantity may be in error by -1 LSB (in 12 bits), or -0.024%. If the error were centered by adding ½ LSB (in 12 bits) and then truncating, the resulting error would be $\pm0.012\%$, which is equivalent to the error obtained when round off is used. However, this addition would force the DAC's zero and full-scale end points to be in error, and the converter would be difficult to calibrate.

The fourth method of mating a d-a converter to a 16-bit processor at reasonable cost lies somewhere between the other approaches. This method makes use of a DAC having a relative accuracy of 12 bits but a resolution of 16 bits, like the model DAC328 made by Hybrid Systems Corp. With such a converter, the user can preserve the low digital error from the computer, while obtaining an analog accuracy of $\pm0.01\%$, which is consistent with the accuracy of a regular 12-bit DAC. The system error again is the sum of the digital error ($\pm0.00075\%$) and the converter error ($\pm0.01\%$), for a total peak error of $\pm0.01075\%$. Further, it costs no more to use this higher-accuracy approach than to use a regular 12-bit DAC. □

IC timer converts temperature to frequency

by Donald DeKold
Santa Fe Community College, Gainesville, Fla.

When wired as an astable multivibrator, the 555-type IC timer may be used to generate a square-wave output voltage whose frequency has a one-to-one correspondence with temperature. A negative-temperature-coefficient thermistor is used in the IC's charging network.

The circuit's output frequency varies in a nearly linear manner from 38 to 114 hertz as temperature changes from 37°F to 115°F. At no point in this temperature range does the frequency count differ by more than ±1 Hz from the corresponding temperature. Due to the small parts count, low cost (about $3), and low power requirements (9.3 milliamperes at 10 volts dc), this temperature-to-frequency converter makes an inexpensive temperature transducer that can be used for telemetry applications.

The conventional astable configuration for the 555-type timer employs two fixed resistors. In place of one of these, the converter circuit uses a thermistor/resistor series combination. The other fixed resistor is replaced by transistor Q_1, which is turned on during the charging interval and off during the discharging interval. This transistor's near-zero on-resistance and very large off-resistance result in equal charge and discharge intervals that depend on only R_T and R_R. Operating frequency can then be given by:

$$f = 1/[2(R_T + R_R)C \ln(2)]$$

or:

$$f = k/(R_T + R_R)$$

Frequency variation with temperature, therefore, is similar to the voltage variation of a thermistor/resistor divider network. (This type of divider is often used in a bridge arrangement to produce a linearized voltage output with temperature.) The divider's output voltage can be expressed as:

$$V_{OUT} = [R_R/(R_R + R_T)]V_S$$

Since the denominators of this equation and the frequency equation are the same, the frequency/temperature relationship of the converter circuit will have the same shape and degree of linearity as that of the voltage

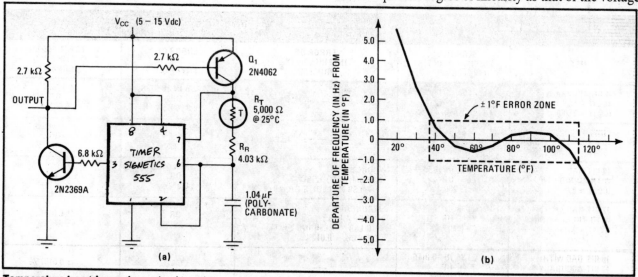

Temperature transducer. A couple of transistors and a thermistor in the charging network of the 555-type timer enable this device to sense temperature and produce a corresponding frequency output. The circuit is accurate to within ±1 hertz over a 78°F temperature range.

output of a conventional thermistor/resistor divider.

When a thermistor having an R_o value of 5,000 ohms at 25°C and a resistance ratio of 9.06:1 over the temperature range of 0°C to 50°C is used, the converter circuit produces a linearity error of less than ±1° over a 78°F range. The figure contains a plot of this temperature/frequency performance.

It is purely coincidental that the frequency count of the circuit is the same as the useful fahrenheit temperature range (37°F to 115°F) for which the circuit is nominally designed. In general, the frequency will be linear with respect to temperature in any interval of interest, but the frequency count will probably be different from the absolute value of the temperature being sensed.

To minimize circuit error, it may be necessary to use temperature-stable polycarbonate capacitors. For this circuit, off-the-shelf capacitors having nominal ±5% tolerances were employed, with the final capacitance being a number of parallel capacitors hand-selected to give the correct frequency count at a given temperature.

The IC timer itself contributes negligible error to the frequency output over temperature. Without adequate power-supply bypassing, the circuit is somewhat sensitive to supply-voltage variations. □

Time-delay sampling simplifies settling-time measurements

by Robert E. Gagnon
Raytheon Co., Sudbury, Mass.

Problems arise when the settling time of large-magnitude nanosecond step functions has to be measured to within ±1 millivolt, regardless of the driving source. A differential comparator amplifier plug-in for commercially available oscilloscopes can measure settling time directly, but the scope's overload-recovery capability limits resolution to microseconds. This method falls short when faster settling times must be measured, because the scope may be showing its own settling time, rather than that of the device under test.

One way around these problems is to use a time-delayed sampling technique that effectively "freezes" the waveform to be measured. This allows viewing any portion of the waveform with the oscilloscope on a repetitive basis and measuring the settling time by simply using the scope delay and a dc voltmeter. Although a digital type can be used, a differential voltmeter gives more accurate results.

To measure the settling time of a digital-to-analog converter, the DAC under test is cycled periodically between the voltage levels; the level of interest is then

Measuring settling times with good resolution and accuracy requires a fast one-shot and a sample-and-hold with small aperture time.

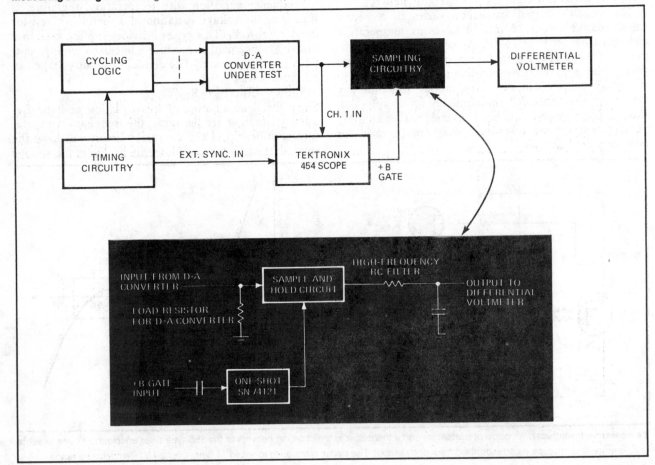

sampled at the same rate, but with a fixed amount of delay (provided by the scope). The resultant output of the sample-and-hold circuit is a dc level equal to the amplitude of the step at that point in time. When the amount of delay is varied, the meter, having been zeroed at the level of interest, will move back and forth around zero, in effect tracing the DAC's settling-time waveform.

The timing and cyclic logic circuits are set so that the DAC's output alternates between the two levels at which settling-time measurements are to be made. The cycling period should be at least 10 times longer than the DAC's expected settling time. This assures that the DAC output will have completely settled at the final value before the testing sequence is repeated.

The oscilloscope used to view the waveform is set for "A-intensified-by-B" operation; the B sweep is triggered by the timing circuitry after a fixed amount of delay, controlled by the scope. What is seen on the scope is a source wave with a small spot or section of it intensified. The scope delay is then adjusted so that the intensified spot is positioned almost at the final-voltage level end of the waveform. The dc differential voltmeter is then zeroed at that level, and the scale set to handle the value of settling-time voltage tolerance. The scope delay is then reduced until the voltmeter reading deviates from the zero setting by an amount equal to the settling-time voltage tolerance. This value of delay is recorded. The amount of delay is further reduced (with an appropriate increase of voltmeter scale to avoid pegging the meter) until the intensified spot is at a level equal to the initial voltage level plus 10% of the total change in voltage between the initial and final voltage step. This can be done with good accuracy by observing the wave-form.

Measurement resolution and accuracy depend on the minimum width of the sampling pulse. This is determined by the output pulse width of the one-shot and the aperture time of the sample-and-hold circuit. To handle very fast settling-time measurements, an ECL one-shot can be substituted for the SN74121 (which is capable of providing 40-nanosecond pulses).

As long as the delay of the scope +B gate remains constant, the sample-and-hold circuit samples only a dc level. Switching transients are minimized by a simple RC filter. □

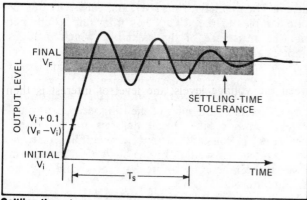

Settling-time characteristics of a typical waveform.

Precision sample-and-hold stores voltage for a week

by B. K. Lunde and F. A. Schmidt
Iowa State University, Ames, Iowa

A voltage can be sampled and held for a week or more with at least 99.9% precision by an analog-to-digital converter followed by a digital-to-analog converter. The a-d converter is triggered when the voltage is to be sampled, and its output is used by a d-a converter to set a programable power supply. The supply then continues to furnish that voltage for as long as desired.

This circuit is useful in automating the electrotransport process for purifying metals. In this process, a direct current passes through a metal rod, heating it by internal resistance and producing charge carriers that sweep impurities along with them to one end of the rod. The current necessary to reach a specific temperature is known at the beginning of the run, and the voltage necessary to provide this current should be held for the remainder of the run.

The circuit to do this is shown in the figure. The timer, a spring-driven or motor-driven clock mechanism to control some switches, first connects the current control of the power supply to R_1, which holds the current at the desired level of 86.5 amperes. An override constant-voltage control is also used to put an upper limit on the output voltage of the supply during this time.

After three minutes, when the sample has reached a stable condition at about 1,600°C, the a-d converter is triggered to read the voltage across the rod. This voltage is about 3.1 volts for a rod resistance of 0.037 ohm. The signals from the a-d converter are fed into a d-a converter, and, after the conversion is complete, the timer applies the output of the d-a converter to the power supply. This commands the supply to furnish the same voltage it was applying at the time of the trigger. The inverting amplifier is necessary in the system to correct the polarity, because a control voltage of about –2 v is applied to the supply to provide a +3.1-V output. For safety of the sample rod, the timer switches the current control resistor to R_2, somewhat larger than R_1, which puts an upper limit on the current supplied.

This program of applying a chosen current and then continuing to furnish the voltage which that current requires is necessary because purification is optimum at a particular temperature. The most accurate automatic way of attaining this temperature is to apply a specified current. The diameter, resistivity, and emissivity of separate samples of metal vary less from one to another than the resistance of the assembly, which includes adaptors and vacuum feed-throughs. It is therefore necessary to specify the current, rather than the voltage, at the start of the purification experiment. However, it is desirable to keep the voltage, rather than the current, constant for the remainder of the run, because, as purification continues, the sample deforms and the resistance rises. If constant current were applied, the increased resistance would cause enough of an increase in power and temperature to melt the metal and end the run prematurely.

The circuit shown holds the voltage across the metal rod constant and equal to that required for a specified current at the beginning of the experiment. This voltage is held for the remainder of the run, about a week, by the digital number stored in the d-a converter. □

Holds the voltage. A-d and d-a converters sample and hold a voltage for a week at a time. Timer triggers a-d converter to measure voltage, and d-a converts it back to analog signal that controls output voltage of power supply. This control signal can be held indefinitely, stored as a precise digital number. Entire process of purifying metal rod is started by timer.

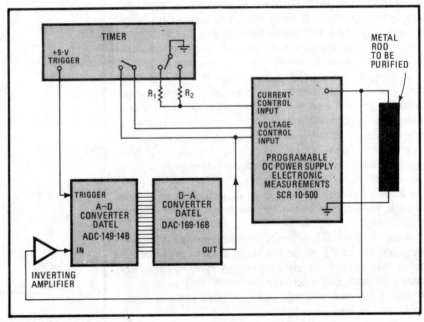

Inductor simplifies
memory-driver circuit

by Robert Johnson, Paul Feldman, and Edwin Fisher
Honeywell Information Systems, Billerica, Mass.

Designing memory systems with 4,096-bit n-channel random-access memories poses a number of problems with the associated interface circuitry. But a small inductance can at least eliminate the headache of having an extra power supply in the memory driver.

While most of such RAMs on the market today have inputs—all addresses, data-in, chip-select, and read/write—that are compatible with transistor-transistor logic, the clock or chip-enable clock input requires 0 to 12 volts for proper memory operation. Of particular concern is the memory's clock input, where a minimum high level of 11.4 v is required.

A common totem-pole output driver circuit—similar to the SN75365 or MC3960 initially used with p-channel RAMs—tied to a number of n-channel-RAM clock inputs, is shown in (a). Capacitive loading is typically 390 picofarads per clock driver. When $V_2 = V_3 = V_{DD}$, the outputs appear degraded, and $V_{OH} = V_{DD} - 1$ v at $I_{OH} = 50$ μA. Increasing V_3 to $V_{DD} + 3$ v changes the output to a more acceptable level, normally $V_{DD} - 0.3$ v at $I_{OH} = 100$ μA.

However, in n-channel systems, the values of V_{DD} and V_{CC} are usually 12 v and 5 v, respectively. If the method of increasing V_3 is used, V_{DD} must be raised to 15 v for V_3 and then dropped back down to 12 v for V_2 and other parts in the system to generate a separate supply voltage on each array card. The alternative is for a separate supply voltage to be bused in for V_3. These methods, while feasible, are not very practical because of increased power consumption and cost.

A way to provide the correct output levels for both chip and driver with only a + 12 v supply is to place an inductor from V_3 to V_2. The inductor overcomes the drawbacks of operating with $V_3 = V_2$ without adding a supply greater than V_{DD} to the system, as shown in (b). The inductor provides an energy source in the form of a voltage "kick" whenever the output totem pole is in a transition state. The increased voltage on V_3 supplies the additional current needed as E_{out} changes from low to high, resulting in a smooth and uninterrupted transition to V_{OH}.

A small value of L will not provide an adequate voltage increase at V_3, while too large a value will not recover fast enough at high repetition rates. Values between 36 and 100 microhenries work well at a pulse width of 500 nanoseconds and repetition rates of 1 microsecond or less. ☐

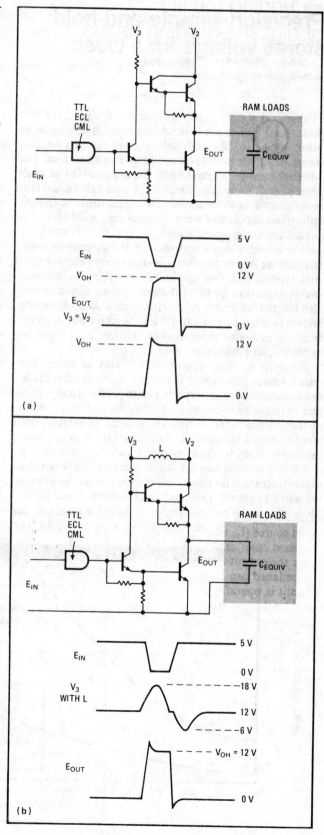

Extending the life
of digital recording heads

by Greg J. Ehalt and M. J. Grundtner
Nortronics Co., Minneapolis, Minn.

High-speed digital tape transports with tape speeds of 100 to 250 inches per second and rapid start-stop operation wear out conventional channel digital recording heads much too fast. Generally made of aluminum with Mumetal cores, these heads remain usable for only about 2,000 hours. Their surface imperfections also tend to accelerate tape wear, and the signal dropout that results from deposits of wear debris is very troublesome in digital computer applications.

Worse still, today's high-density data storage systems make it necessary to minimize the space between head and tape in order to maximize resolution. In commercial systems (except those designed for air-film support), this has meant living with continuous sliding contact between tape and head—and with the concomitant problems of excessive maintenance, a short and unpredictable life, and inaccurate data storage.

Analysis of tape microstructure and of worn computer heads has shown that wear is essentially caused by abrasion. Magnet tape is like superfine emery cloth, the abrasive particles on its surface being 5 to 10 microinches in diameter. When these come in contact with the recorder head surface, they either cut into it, removing chips from it like a machine tool, or make shallow furrows that may cause fatigue, localized corrosion and microfracture. The rate of wear depends on the amount of contact between tape and head surface, which in turn depends partly on the degree of aerodynamic lift (air bearing action) as the tape passes over the head and partly on the action of the individual magnetic particles, as affected by binder and tape resilience, particle angularity, and surface plasticity.

Consequently, any factor that reduces abrasion by magnetic particles will enhance head life. For instance, surface chemical reactions producing thin organic or oxide films on the head surface can buffer the contact between magnetic particles on the tape surface and the metal face of the head—but these films are regrettably not controllable, and their origins poorly understood. Again, as the abrasive medium and the material being abraded approach each other in hardness, wear rate becomes negligible, and surface cutting no longer occurs.

With all these factors in mind, Nortronics investigated numerous materials for digital head coatings. The equation used for abrasive wear was $V = KWL/3H$, where V = volume of material being removed, W = load, L = distance slid, H = indentation hardness of the softer material, and K = wear coefficient.

Several approaches were evaluated (Table 1) in terms of gap erosion, core material cost, ease of manufacturing, core efficiencies, differential wear rates, head life, crosstalk rejection, and basic wear capability.

Twelve of the hard-coat materials tested were charted (Table 2) in terms of application method, porosity, obtainable finish after grinding and lapping, and tape wear. An aluminum oxide alloy applied by plasma torch was selected for development of a LifeTime Ceramic (LTC) head, because it had low porosity, good hardness and surface finish, and caused no apparent tape wear after 10,000 passes of dynamic testing.

The design adopted achieves long life by contouring or relieving the face of the Mumetal magnetic core to within 0.010 in. of the gap on either side. The nonmagnetic ceramic coating is then applied to the face of the head to fill in the relieved areas, and the head is recontoured to the desired shape. The LTC coating is significantly harder and more wear-resistant than the core

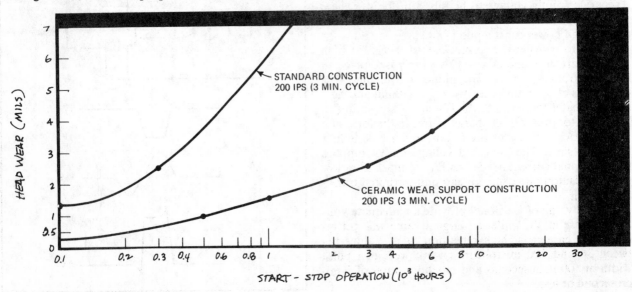

HARD-COAT MATERIALS AND PROCESSES

Material	Application method	Porosity	Finish (μin. AA)		Tape wear at 200 ips
			After grinding with 400 grit wheel	After lapping	
Aluminum oxide (Union Carbide type LA 1 or equiv.)	Detonation gun	5 – 6 %	10 – 12	1 – 2	Pores fill with foreign matter and start tape wear.
Tungsten carbide (Union Carbide type LW 1 or equiv.)	Detonation gun	4 – 5 %	12 – 15	2 – 3	Pores fill with foreign matter and start tape wear.
Tungsten carbide (Union Carbide type LW 4 or equiv.)	Detonation gun	½ – 1 %	4 – 5	1 – 2	Small wear after 10,000 tape passes.
Tungsten carbide (Union Carbide type LW 5 or equiv.)	Detonation gun	2 – 3 %	10 – 12	1 – 2	Small wear after 10,000 tape passes.
Aluminum oxide (Coors type Rokide A or equiv.)	Oxyacetylene torch	15 – 20 %	45 – 50	30 – 35	Too rough for use.
Chrome oxide (Coors type Rokide C or equiv.)	Oxyacetylene torch	15 – 20 %	45 – 50	30 – 35	Too rough for use.
Chrome oxide (Metco type 106 NS or equiv.)	Plasma torch	10 – 15 %	40 – 45	25 – 30	Too rough for use.
Chrome oxide (Union Carbide type LC 4 or equiv.)	Plasma torch	2 – 3 %	10 – 14	1 – 2	Small wear after 10,000 tape passes.
Tungsten carbide (Union Carbide type LW 10 or equiv.)	Plasma torch	6 – 8 %	10 – 15	2 – 3	Slight marking of tape, probably due to porosity.
Tungsten carbide (Metco type 72 F or equiv.)	Plasma torch	10 – 12 %	10 – 15	6 – 8	Slight marking of tape, probably due to porosity.
Hard chrome	Electrolytic plating	None apparent	2 – 3 (80 grit wheel)	1 – 2	No apparent wear after 10,000 tape passes.

Design approach	Gap erosion	Core material costs	Ease of head manufacture	Core efficiencies at frequencies of		Differential wear rates	Head life	Crosstalk rejection	Basic material hardness (assume Mumetal = 1)
				≤ 300 kHz	≥ 300 kHz				
Nortronics hard coat process	Good	Low	Low	Good	Average	Good	Good	Good, shields exposed	10
Ferrite cores Mumetal or aluminum spacers	Poor	Medium	Medium	Average	Good	Poor	Average	Average, shields wear below ferrite	6
Ferrite cores and nonmagnetic ferrite spacers	Poor	High	High	Average	Good	Good	Good	Average, shields recessed below spacer	7
Alfenol cores Alfesil cores Sendust cores	Good	High	High	Average	Average	Average	Average	Good	3
Alfenol-tipped cores Alfesil-tipped cores Sendust-tipped cores	Good	High	High	Average	Average	Average	Average	Good	3
Chrome-plated over Mumetal cores	Good	Low	High	Good	Average	Good	Good	Good	8

it surrounds. Because of the differential wear rate, the height of the core relative to the ceramic rapidly stabilizes at the level of the ceramic surface. With an adequate tape wrap and tension, the tape bridges the core area at the gap, riding primarily on the hard ceramic surface. This provides a design whereby the actual head wear—the pole pieces at the gap—is almost entirely determined by the nonmagnetic surface of the head.

The average digital drive becomes obsolete before it wears out—it has an operational life of perhaps 10 to 15 years. Yet a conventional all-metal digital head lasts only two or three years. LTC not only should extend head life ten times, but does not require any changes in core or shield structure, so that electrical performance remains unchanged. And for greater efficiency under limiting conditions, the gap depth of an LTC head may be reduced without shortening its life. Just as important, it eliminates expensive field maintenance. □

Listening to magnetic fields can be useful, as well as fun

by Calvin R. Graf
Kelly Air Force Base, San Antonio, Texas

Magnetic fields created by an alternating current are radiated by many electrical and electronic devices, including power transformers, motors, electronic wristwatches, pocket calculators, lamp dimmers, and electric clocks. Listening to what these various devices sound like in the audio-frequency range can be not only interesting, but also quite useful.

With the simple sensing circuit drawn in the figure, you can detect changing magnetic fields—even the field created by the tuning-fork oscillations of an electronic wristwatch powered by as little as 8 microwatts. The telephone pickup coil functions as the circuit's antenna, the loudspeaker as its transducer, and the audio amplifier, which can be of the transistor-radio variety (for strong magnetic fields), as its receiver. The circuit's audio response for magnetic fields ranges from 40 hertz to 10 kilohertz. All the parts are readily available and will easily fit into a small hand-held case, loudspeaker and all. And parts cost is low— only about $10.

What can you do with this magnetic-field sounder? Well, in your home, you can locate electrical wiring in walls to within a fraction of an inch. Or, you can find buried water pipes, either copper or iron ones, to within a few inches because there is a 60-hertz power frequency induced into a buried water-pipe system.

You can also enjoy the musical sounds made by your pocket calculator as you press its keys or when the unit is computing, but you'll find it far more informative to tune in your automobile. You can listen to: the high-frequency whine of the alternator, the low-frequency hum of the alternator field, the voltage regulator, the distributor timing, the firing of an individual spark plug, the click-click of the fuel gage and gas tank sensor, the engine starter, the windshield-wiper motor, the air-conditioner's magnetic clutch or blower motor, and the

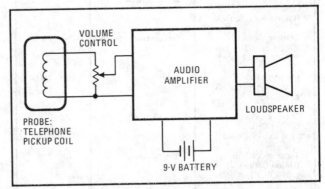

Sounding out magnetic fields. Simple sensing circuit enables you to eavesdrop on the interesting world of magnetic fields. An ordinary telephone pickup coil acts as the circuit's probe, serving as the antenna for the audio amplifier, which can be a garden-variety transistor radio. You can listen to the sounds created by an automobile, the ac line in your home, and many other sources.

left-turn/right-turn directional signal flashers.

Here are a few more ideas. You can check the 30-pulse-per-second vertical synchronization signal in your television set, as well as locate and isolate fluorescent light ballasts. And natural very-low-frequency emissions caused by lightning and other phenomena make for interesting listening, too—you'll be able to hear all sorts of clicks, pops, and tweets.

The magnetic field created by a small permanent magnet can also be detected (heard) as the field is moved back and forth across the sensor's probe. Additionally, the circuit can be used to amplify both ends of a telephone conversation by placing its probe near the induction coil of the telephone receiver. Radiation from nearby radar sets and microwave ovens can also be picked up.

The magnetic-field sounder can even aid in determining the operating condition of an implanted cardiac pacemaker. Better yet, it could prove very useful to the wearer of a pacemaker by alerting him to the presence of electromagnetic interference that might affect the implanted device adversely. □

DIP switches and diodes form programable ROM

by Louis E. Frenzel
Heath Co., Benton Harbor, Mich.

Microprocessor-based equipment depends more on software than on hardware for its operation, and therefore the design of such equipment consists largely of program development. If the memory in which a program is stored can be changed easily and quickly, program writing and debugging are simplified. The programable read-only memory described here speeds up these program-development processes, and thus facilitates physical breadboarding with the microprocessor in the initial stages of design.

The PROM shown in Fig. 1 is a switchable diode matrix organized into 16 8-bit words. Each bit is implemented with a single-pole, single-throw switch and a diode. To simplify construction and minimize size, the PROM uses the new 8-switch/16-pin dual in-line packages. Each DIP unit thus represents one 8-bit word.

Instruction words and data words are loaded into the

1. DIP-switch memory. Microprocessor programs can be tested with read-only memory, consisting of eight-switch DIPs used as 8-bit binary words. This memory, which is simple to set or change, can be checked visually. Diodes in the ROM isolate words from one another. The decoder connects the DIPs to the data bus.

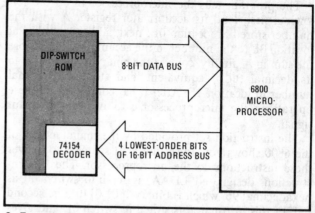

2. Example. This arrangement of a DIP-switch ROM with a 6800 microprocessor is used for the program shown in the accompanying box. (Other microprocessors may have different means for address input.) Programs can be set up, tested, and modified more simply with the switch memory than with integrated-circuit ROMs or RAMs.

memory by setting the switches; a closed switch produces a low (binary 0) output, while an open switch generates a high (binary 1) output.

Instruction words are loaded into sequential memory locations. Data words can be placed in any convenient memory location that is available. If the DIP switches are arranged in address sequence with the switch levers properly oriented (up = 1, down = 0), the memory contents can be determined at a glance. The ability to see the memory content and to change it in seconds will greatly expedite program development. It becomes possible to modify and debug a program in a fraction of the time that would be required if a conventional ROM or RAM were used.

The use of only 16 words may seem severely limiting in a ROM, but it is usually more than adequate to test and exercise a microprocessor. The memory is sufficient to try all instructions and to test short subroutines. The flexibility of being able to quickly and conveniently change a program and to actually see the program stored in memory makes it easy to design microprocessor systems and to learn programing.

A 74154 TTL 1-of-16 decoder is used to address the memory words. The decoder input lines are connected to the four lower-order bits of the microprocessor address bus or data bus.

The box (top, right) shows a sample program using DIP-switch ROM with a 6800 microprocessor, as in Fig. 2. For this application the 16 switches are numbered consecutively in hexadecimal notation: 00, 01, 02 . . . 09, 0A, 0B, . . . 0F. The program contains five instruction words and two data words. Three of the instructions (LDAA, ADAA, and STAA) occupy two sequential 8-bit locations. Instructions DAA and WAI each occupy a single 8-bit location. The instruction words are loaded into the first eight DIP switches because the microprocessor operates on instructions sequentially. The two data words can go into any of the eight remaining switches; here the data words are put into the last two

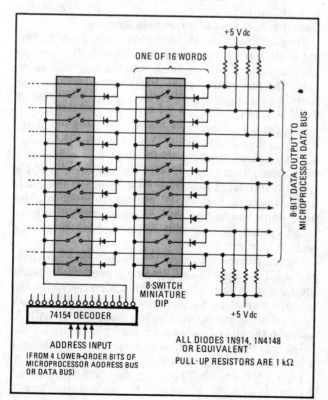

ONE OF 16 WORDS

+5 V dc

8-BIT DATA OUTPUT TO MICROPROCESSOR DATA BUS

8-SWITCH MINIATURE DIP

74154 DECODER

+5 V dc

ADDRESS INPUT
(FROM 4 LOWER-ORDER BITS OF MICROPROCESSOR ADDRESS BUS OR DATA BUS)

ALL DIODES 1N914, 1N4148 OR EQUIVALENT
PULL-UP RESISTORS ARE 1 kΩ

switches (0E and 0F). The data stored for this example are the numbers 48 and 37, which are set on the switches as 0011 0000 and 0010 0101, respectively.

The program tells the microprocessor to do the following: first, load its accumulator register A with the number stored at location 0F; next, add the number at location 0E to the number in the accumulator, and store the sum in A; finally, convert the binary number in A to its decimal (BCD) equivalent, and store the decimal number in location 1F. After it has completed all these operations, the microprocessor is to await an interrupt signal.

The instruction set provided by the manufacturer of the 6800 shows how to set the ROM switches to deliver these instructions to the microprocessor. The first instruction, designated LDAA, is set into switch 00 as hexadecimal 96, which is binary 1001 0110. The second half of this instruction is stored in switch 01, and gives the location of the data to be loaded; that location is hexadecimal 0F, or 0000 1111. The next instruction, ADDA, is found from the 6800 instruction set to be hexadecimal 9B, or binary 1001 1011. The remaining steps are similarly set into the DIP switches by use of the 6800 instruction set.

The result of adding 37 to 48 could be displayed by an output device that showed the content of location 1F. It would show 85, because decimal notation was specified. □

ROM address	Instruction or Data	Operation performed	Hex	Binary
		SAMPLE PROGRAM		
00	LDAA	Load accumulator A with the contents of	96	1001 0110
01	F	memory location 0F.	0F	0000 1111
02	ADDA	Add contents of memory location 0E to the	9B	1001 1011
03	E	number in accumulator A and store the sum in A.	0E	0000 1110
04	DAA	Convert the binary number in A into BCD.	19	0001 1001
05	STAA	Store contents of accumulator A in memory location	97	1001 0111
06	1F	1F.	1F	0001 1111
07	WAI	Wait for interrupt.	3E	0011 1110
08				
09				
0A				
0B				
0C				
0D				
0E	48	Data	30	0011 0000
0F	37	Data	25	0010 0101

Computer program reduces fusible-PROM errors

by Shlomo Waser
Monolithic Memories Inc., Sunnyvale, Calif.

A brief computer program written in Basic saves time and minimizes errors in the fuse-blowing process used to store information in a programable read-only memory. The procedure for programing a PROM employs momentary current pulses to selectively open fusible links between diodes and the internal memory array. Thereafter, whenever an input address selects a bit with an open fuse, the output voltage is low (0 to 0.4 volt). When a bit with an unblown fuse is selected, the voltage is high (2.4 V).

The machine used to blow these fuses selectively is called a PROM programer, which usually has two operating modes—manual and automatic. Using the manual mode entails a three-step operation after the machine has been attached to the PROM:

■ The address word is set on the address-line dials.

■ The output word to be stored at that address is set on the output-line dials.

■ A button is pushed to make the machine blow the fuses that store the output word in memory.

For example, if the PROM is required to have an output of 0110 when location 8 is addressed, the operator sets the address dial to 1000, sets the output dials to 0110, and pushes the "blow fuses" button. Then he repeats the three steps to store the next memory word in location 9, and so forth.

Because use of the manual mode for PROMs containing more than 21,048 bits is tedious and highly susceptible to human errors, it is desirable to use the automatic mode whenever possible. The automatic mode is typically interfaced to a paper-tape reader, which reads in the tape containing the information to be stored. The paper tape, which goes through all of the addresses in order, applies the output word and blows the fuse for each, at high speed.

Manufacturers who provide PROMs that are programed from input information on a paper tape specify the format to be used. Monolithic Memories specifies the tape format shown in Fig. 1. The letter S indicates the start of the storage-instruction data, and the letter E indicates the end of the whole procedure. The data is divided into fields (the output words). Each output word is preceded by the letter B for begin and is followed by the letter F for finish. The actual data to be programed is either H for high voltage or L for low voltage. The use

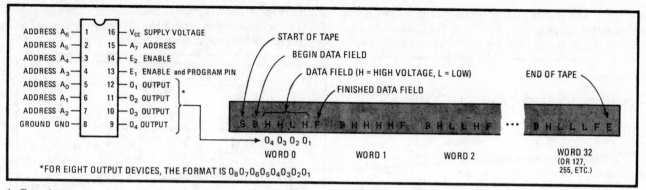

*FOR EIGHT OUTPUT DEVICES, THE FORMAT IS $O_8O_7O_6O_5O_4O_3O_2O_1$

1. Tape format. Automatic Monolithic Memories PROM programer is fed by a punched paper tape that gives the desired output word for each input address in sequence. In this tape format, H and L are used instead of 1 and 0 to avoid ambiguity of positive or negative logic.

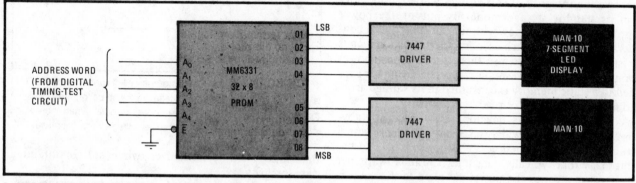

2. PROM at work. The PROM converts the output from the digital tester into a form suitable for input to the display driver. Text describes how to generate a tape for programing the PROM automatically. Note that output is in BCD to drive the two seven-segment displays.

```
100  !/PROM-PROG/
110  INTEGER T,B,K
120  OPEN /FILE/,OUTPUT,1
130  J='' 'B' 8W 'F'/'' ! OUTPUT FORMAT
140  WRITE ON 1:''S''!START OF DATA
150  FOR I=0 TO 31!START OF LOOP CALCULATIONS
160  T=5+(I*3)  !CALCULATE DECIMAL VALUE
170  K=T/10
180  B=T+(K*6)!  CONVERT IT TO BCD
190  WRITE ON 1 IN FORM J:B!OUTPUT TO A FILE
200  NEXT I
210  WRITE ON 1:''E''!END OF DATA
220  CLOSE 1
230  END
```

3. Basic program. This little computer program, written in Basic, calculates the output data to be stored in the memory, which is given by the equation $T = 5 + (3 \times I)$, where I is the address location. Results are converted into the format required by the automatic PROM programing machine. Line 180 converts the representation to BCD code; thus, 98 is 1001 1000 (i.e., the first 4 bits are the 9, and the second 4 bits are the 8).

```
S                 S
B00000101F        BLLLLLHLHF
B00001000F        BLLLLHLLLF
B00010001F        BLLLHLLLHF
B00010100F        BLLLHLHLLF
  .                 .
  .                 .
  .                 .
  .                 .
B10001001F        BHLLLHLLHF
B10010010F        BHLLHLLHLF
B10010101F        BHLLHLHLHF
B10011000F        BHLLHHLLLF
E                 E

    (a)               (b)
```

4. Output. The output file, (a) above, is from the Basic program, while (b) in the format of Fig. 1 is obtained from (a) by use of the text editor. Each of the 32 data words represents two binary-code-decimal digits: the first word is 05, and the last word is 98.

of H and L avoids the possibility of confusion resulting from using 1 and 0, which have different meanings in positive and negative logic.

The program is punched on the paper tape by the teletypewriter interface from the computer that prepares the program for the PROM. The complete procedure for generating the program and tape is illustrated by the following example:

Figure 2 shows a PROM used to translate timing information from a digital testing circuit into a 2-digit binary-coded-decimal output to drive a display. The pa-

rameter measured by the tester is a time, which is quantized in 3-nanosecond steps from 5 to 98 ns. Therefore, the 32 possible outputs from the PROM are BCD codes for 5, 8,11 . . . 95, 98. The outputs for successive inputs (addresses) 0, 1, . . . 31 are:

$$T = 5 + (3 \times I) \quad I = 0, 1, 2. \ . \ .31$$

Once a functional relationship like this is established, it is an easy matter to convert it to a program. The Basic program in Fig. 3 executes the above equation in a loop controlled by I, the address; it converts the results into

BCD form, and it files the conversion in a binary format with control characters S, B, F, and E as shown in Fig. 4a. This file is then edited by a text-edit routine to substitute H for 1 and L for 0. The edited file, shown in Fig. 4b, is punched on the paper tape, which then is used to control the PROM programing machine. □

Reducing the power drain of semiconductor static RAMs

by B.W. Martin and J.A. Roberts
Microsystems International Ltd., Ottawa, Canada

A semiconductor memory requires continuous power to preserve the integrity of stored data while the memory is in its standby storage mode. By pulsing the power supply, the memory's power drain can be reduced considerably. This approach is particularly advantageous for static memories because their normally low power drain can be made even smaller. Most of the power supplied to a static memory is consumed in its storage array and not in its decoders or read/write circuitry.

As an example, let's develop a low-drain standby-power circuit for the widely used type-2102 n-channel static random-access memory. This device is a 1,024-by-1-bit array that typically consumes 150 microwatts per bit. Because most of the power supplied to this RAM is needed by its storage circuitry, techniques that simply switch off the power to its peripheral circuitry are of little use.

As shown in Fig. 1, the RAM's basic storage cell is a bistable flip-flop that has a dc path to ground on one side. To reduce standby power, the current consumed in

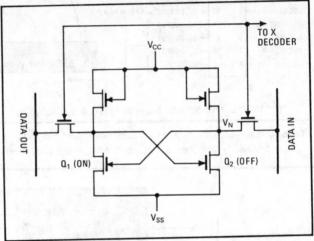

1. Memory storage cell. Basic storage cell of n-channel static RAM is a bistable flip-flop. Node voltage V_N must be greater than the threshold of transistor Q_1 to prevent loss of data. When there is no standby power, leakage current causes voltage V_N to decrease.

this path must be minimized while still maintaining data integrity.

Because leakage current increases with rising temperature, data integrity is most severely threatened at elevated temperatures. During the off-time of a power pulse, node voltage V_N decreases due to leakage current, particularly leakage from the node to the substrate. If this node voltage approaches or falls below the

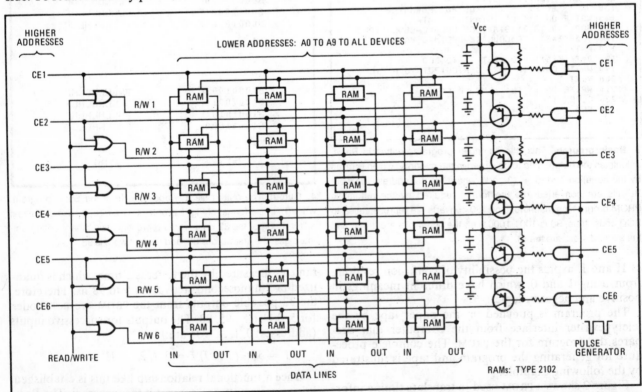

2. Minimizing standby-power drain. Pulsing standby power for memory array maintains data integrity while significantly decreasing power consumption. To reduce noise pickup on the pulsed power line, the switching transistors are mounted on the same board as the memories.

threshold voltage of transistor Q_1, the data is lost.

When supply voltage V_{CC} is 4.75 volts, data integrity can be maintained if the on-time of V_{CC} is 5 microseconds and the off-time is 145 μs. At room temperature, the RAM will draw a typical current of 1.1 milliamperes, which represents a power consumption of only 5.2 milliwatts and a power reduction of 96%.

If V_{CC} is decreased to 3.5 v, with an on-time of 10 μs and an off-time of 70 μs, the integrity of the data can still be maintained. Now, the average current drawn at room temperature is 1.5 mA, the power consumed is 5.25 mw, and the power reduction is still 96%. This latter approach is useful in emergency situations because it permits a lower standby battery voltage to be used.

In many systems, decoupling capacitors are connected across the memory power rail to reduce noise. While this is acceptable when the rail voltage is not pulsed, certain factors should be considered when dealing with a pulsed rail supply.

In the standby mode, the magnitude of the supply-voltage pulse height and pulse width are critical. A typical type-2102 RAM has a maximum capacitance of 500 picofarads from the V_{CC} supply line to ground. The addition of decoupling capacitors on the order of 0.01 microfarad could increase the power-rail capacitance to such an extent that the pulsed power supply cannot drive the load fast enough to reach the required voltage in the time allowed by the input pulse.

A practical solution is to mount the switching transistors that are used to get the pulsed power on the same board as the memory; this reduces noise pickup on the pulsed line. To reduce noise, decoupling capacitors can be mounted on the unswitched side of the switching transistors, where the V_{CC} supply voltage remains constant.

A typical standby power system for a 6,144-by-4-bit memory array is shown in Fig. 2. The CE1 through CE6 inputs are the higher address lines that select the major array row desired. (A major row is selected when a CE line is logic 0.) Since all other rows are deselected, the read/write lines to these minor rows are in a read mode (logic 1.) The CE lines also control the V_{CC} supply to the over-all array so that only the unselected rows are pulsed at the required duty rate. The lower address lines, A0 through A9, run to all the memories in the array. Therefore, when a particular row is being addressed, the same address will appear at all unselected rows. (A changing address has little effect on the power consumption of a type-2102 RAM.)

The duty cycles suggested here for the pulsed standby power are the minimum allowable if the memory is to operate over a temperature range of 25°C to 70°C. Even shorter duty cycles can be used if the memory is not expected to encounter high ambient operating temperatures. And if complementary-MOS devices are employed for the logic gates, additional power savings can be realized. Naturally, the duty cycles selected should be appropriate for the specific devices being used. □

22. Generating wave shapes to order

Approximating waveforms with exponential functions

by Robert G. Durnal

Systems Development Division, Westinghouse Electric Corp., Baltimore, Md.

Many engineering applications require generating a waveform that matches a characteristic curve of some device or physical law. Some examples of such waveforms are hyperbolic ground-range radar sweeps, fast automatic-gain-control functions, and automatic light-level compensation waveforms for television cameras. The most useful and easily generated waveform for approximating such functions is the decaying exponential. And using the graphical exponential approximation technique demonstrated here permits an accurate fitted curve to be obtained in less than two hours.

To illustrate the technique, an approximation will be developed for a typical waveform—a logarithmic voltage function that must be generated to compensate a particular process. The function is:

$$V = 2 \log_{10}(t_{max}/t)$$

Voltage V must be accurate to within 0.05 volt for values of time t between t_{max} and 0.25% of t_{max}. The curve should be plotted on semilogarithmic graph paper be-

TABLE 1: ERROR IN FIRST APPROXIMATION

t/t_{max}	Translated curve (V)	First approximation (V)	Difference error (V)
0.05	3.002	2.384	0.618
0.1	2.40	2.162	0.238
0.2	1.798	1.777	0.021
0.3	1.446	1.460	0.015
0.4	1.196	1.200	0.005
0.5	1.002	0.987	0.015
0.6	0.844	0.811	0.033
0.7	0.710	0.667	0.043
0.8	0.594	0.548	0.046
0.9	0.492	0.450	0.041
1.0	0.400	0.370	0.030

TABLE 2: ERROR IN SECOND APPROXIMATION

t/t_{max}	Translated curve (V)	Second approximation (V)	Difference error (V)
0.005	5.002	4.233	0.769
0.01	4.400	4.053	0.347
0.02	3.798	3.735	0.063
0.03	3.446	3.468	−0.022
0.04	3.196	3.240	−0.045
0.05	3.002	3.047	−0.045
0.06	2.844	2.880	−0.037
0.07	2.710	2.737	−0.027
0.08	2.594	2.612	−0.018
0.09	2.492	2.502	−0.011
0.1	2.400	2.405	−0.005

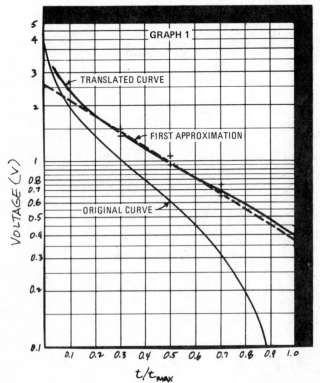

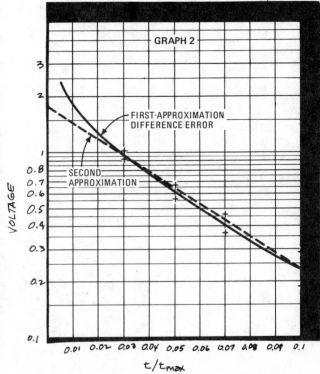

cause the decaying exponential, the function to be used to approximate voltage V, can then be drawn as a straight line.

Voltage V is plotted as a solid black curve in Graph 1. It can be seen by inspection that this curve is inflected—the direction of curvature reverses at the midpoint. Inflected curves are difficult to generate with a series of straight-line approximations, which is the method to be used here.

The difficulty can be removed by simply adding a constant along the entire curve of voltage V. The value of the constant is not critical, but if it is too large, the curve will flatten out. (As a rule of thumb, the constant can be one-half to two-thirds the value of the curve at the inflection point.)

Graph 1 shows, as a solid color line, voltage V translated by adding a constant offset voltage of 0.4 v. In this case, the right-hand portion of the translated curve is nearly linear. The envelope of the ±0.05-v limits is represented by crosspoints (shown in color on the graph) to aid in choosing the approximation curve.

The first approximation should cover the greatest possible range of voltage V. Larger errors can be tolerated for higher values of t/t_{max}, since the tolerance band is wider for the rightmost section of the curve than for the leftmost. Additionally, the first approximation should be drawn below the translated curve to avoid negative difference errors (between the translated and approximation curves), which are difficult to plot.

As shown in Graph 1, the first approximation is drawn for a best fit graphically within the restrictions already cited. The exponential function of this first approximation can be written as:

$$V_1 = 2.63 \exp(-t/0.51 t_{max}) - 0.4$$

where the voltage intercept is 2.63 v, the added constant is 0.4 v, and $V_1 = 2.63/e$ (here, e represents the base for the natural logarithm) when $t/t_{max} = 0.51$.

Table 1 lists the voltage levels of the translated curve and the first approximation curve for several values of t/t_{max} from 0.05 to 1.0. The difference error between these two curves is computed and then plotted (Graph 2) for values of t/t_{max} between 0.01 and 0.1, where the error is largest. Again, the ±0.05-v limits are inserted as an approximating aid.

When the difference-error curve is approximated, care must be taken not to disturb the accuracy of the first approximation. Therefore, absolutely zero error is introduced at $t/t_{max} = 0.1$ by locating the straight-line second approximation at the same point as the first-approximation difference-error curve. The best fit for the second approximation is then determined graphically. Voltage V can now be expressed as a sum of two exponentials and a constant:

$$V_2 = 2.63 \exp(-t/0.51 t_{max})$$
$$+ 1.8 \exp(-t/0.05 t_{max}) - 0.4$$

where V_2 is the entire second approximation. The leftmost portion of this approximation, which is shown in Graph 2, has a voltage intercept of 1.8 v.

Table 2 shows the voltage levels of the translated curve and the second-approximation curve for values of t/t_{max} between 0.005 and 0.1. The difference errors between these two curves are within the allowable limits (of ±0.05 v) when t/t_{max} is greater than 0.01. The second-approximation difference error curve, therefore, is plotted (Graph 3) for t/t_{max} from 0.001 to 0.01.

The same graphical technique can now be used to arrive at a third approximation for the leftmost portion of voltage V. The accuracy of the second approximation is preserved by making the difference error equal to zero at $t/t_{max} = 0.01$. The best fit for the third approximation of voltage V yields:

$$V_3 = 2.63 \exp(-t/0.51 t_{max})$$
$$+ 1.8 \exp(-t/0.05 t_{max})$$
$$+ 1.88 \exp(-t/0.006 t_{max}) - 0.4$$

Table 3 gives the difference errors between the translated curve and the third straight-line approximation curve. The desired accuracy of ±0.05 v is now met for the specified 400:1 time range—from $t/t_{max} = 0.0025$ to $t/t_{max} = 1.0$.

The circuit needed to produce voltage V, therefore, must consist of three exponential generators and a constant voltage. □

TABLE 3: OVER-ALL ERROR			
t/t_{max}	Translated curve (V)	Third approximation (V)	Difference error (V)
0.0015	6.0500	5.833	0.217
0.002	5.798	5.696	0.102
0.0025	5.622	5.573	0.049
0.003	5.446	5.450	−0.004
0.004	5.196	5.236	−0.040
0.005	5.002	5.050	−0.048
0.006	4.844	4.887	−0.044
0.007	4.710	4.744	−0.035
0.008	4.594	4.619	−0.025
0.009	4.492	4.507	−0.015
0.01	4.400	4.408	−0.008

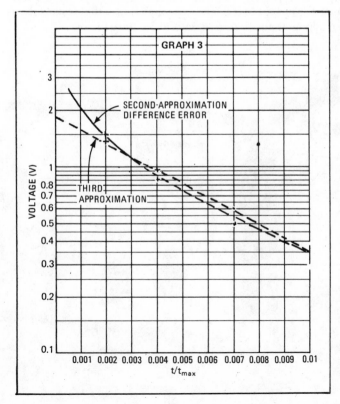

GRAPH 3

SECOND-APPROXIMATION DIFFERENCE ERROR

THIRD APPROXIMATION

VOLTAGE (V)

t/t_{max}

Two tandem pulse generators provide waveform flexibility

by Sandford Jacobson
Cober Electronics Inc., Stamford, Conn.

Whether in testing components like pulse transformers or in studying how bipolar molecules behave in chemical birefringence and similar phenomena, it's necessary to use trains of bipolar pulses, with both positive and negative polarities relative to ground. The quickest and most economical method of generating these pulse sequences is by connecting two standard pulse generators in tandem, with opposite polarities.

The tandem generators can also be connected with like polarities to double the pulse width and thus double the average power delivered to a load. Series and parallel arrangements are also possible, giving twice the voltage or twice the current of a single unit.

A pair of standard 10-volt generators, such as the Datapulse 101 or the Tektronix 114, can be used to generate bipolar waveforms at low voltages. For high-voltage/high-power requirements, Cober 605-P pulse generators are excellent.

In setting them up, it is better not to use pulse trans-formers but to employ generators capable of providing both positive and negative outputs, or to select one generator with a positive output and the other with a negative output. Reversing pulse polarity with a transformer degrades the pulse shape, so that the waveforms are not symmetrical.

This technique for generating bipolar pulses is illustrated in Fig. 1. One generator determines the polarity, amplitude, and width of the first pulse. The other, triggered from the back edge of the first output pulse, provides the reverse-polarity pulse with its own amplitude and width. The pulse rate is determined by the first generator.

In practice, this general technique is somewhat tempered by the internal impedance of the particular generators used. The maximum outputs are obtained when the pulse generators have high internal impedance during their off stage and provide low internal impedance during their on stage. In this way, the loading effect of one generator upon the other is minimized, and maximum energy is developed across the load. The 605-P, with essentially infinite output impedance in the off state, can provide bipolar pulses of up to 2,200 volts and 11 amperes peak; each generator can produce a pulse from 50 nanoseconds to 3 milliseconds long at a duty rate of 1.5%. Figure 2 shows two of these generators applying a bipolar pulse train to a pulse transformer.

If the two generators are set so that both deliver the same polarity, and the second is triggered by the first, the output to the load is a single pulse that lasts twice as long—up to 6 milliseconds at 3% duty factor.

1. Bipolar testing. Two high-power pulse generators are connected to test a pulse transformer with pulses of alternating polarity. Tandem, series, and parallel connection of pairs of generators allows a variety of useful pulse-testing arrangements.

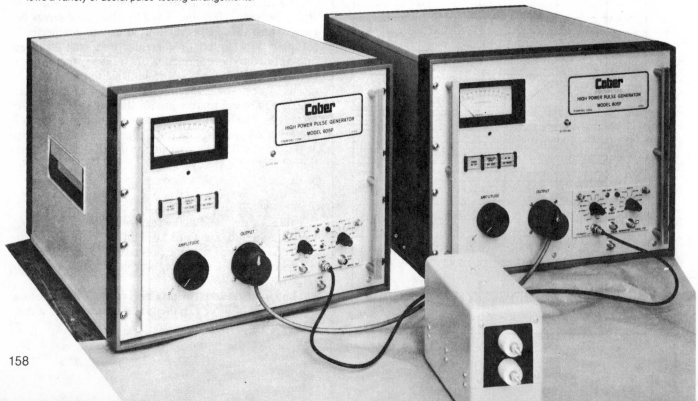

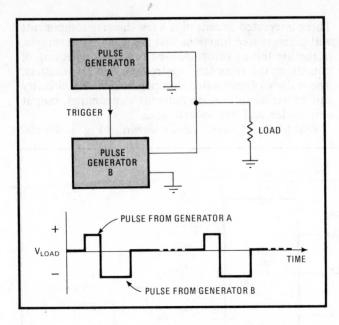

2. Tandem cycle. Here two pulse generators are connected so that the second is triggered by the falling edge from the first. If the two have opposite polarities, as shown, the resulting pulse train is bipolar. If the two have the same polarity, the pulse length is doubled.

If the two generators are set so that both deliver the same polarity and are triggered simultaneously, the output to the load is then a single pulse with current capability up to 22 A. And if the two generators are connected in series and triggered simultaneously, the output voltage may be as high as 4,400 v. The voltage isolation of the upper generator, which is not grounded, must be sufficient to withstand the sum of the voltages of the series pair.

For many applications, the two pulse generators need not be identical or of the same manufacture to be operated in these various modes. Thus, complicated waveforms can be achieved without any degradation of rise time or fall time by the hookup of pulse generators for series, parallel, or tandem operation. □

IC timer plus resistor
can produce square waves

by S.A. Orrel
Ellicott City, Md.

An inexpensive square-wave generator can be put together quickly by using the 555-type timer. With only one external resistor, this circuit can be made to generate fairly accurate square waves.

The generator of (a) produces square waves because the output voltage is essentially 180° out of phase with capacitor voltage, making capacitor voltage change in a direction that forces the output to change state. The circuit of (b) works identically and may be used where it is necessary to eliminate the slight ringing that occurs with circuit (a) just prior to positive output transitions.

The output symmetry of the generator depends on the accuracy of the timer's internal resistor string which produces the device's comparator reference voltages. These errors can be eliminated by adding the trimming resistor, R_T, as shown in (c). (The trimmer goes to the positive supply line or to ground, depending on the correction needed.) The value of the trimmer is determined by the timing resistance used, how much asymmetry can be tolerated, and the specifications of the particular timer being used.

If a variable pulse width is desired, the circuits drawn in (d) and (e) may be used. In circuit (d), the output varies from a symmetrical square wave to a negative pulse train as resistor R_W ranges from infinity to zero. In circuit (e), the output varies from a symmetrical square wave to a positive pulse train. The minimum pulse width is, of course, a function of the timer's propagation delay and capacitor size. □

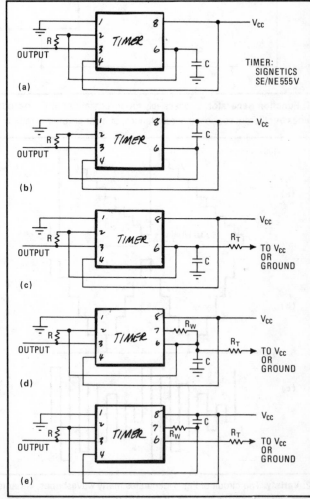

Choice of generators. Timer IC (a) generates symmetrical square-wave output. Slight output ringing can be eliminated with circuit (b). Output symmetry can be adjusted with external trimmer (c), or output pulse width made variable, as in circuits (d) and (e).

Simple step-function generator aids in testing instruments

by Michael M. Lacefield
Honeywell Inc., New Orleans, La.

Three integrated circuits plus a few discrete components will generate step functions that are useful, for example, in the life testing or unattended functional checking of potentiometric recorders, controllers, and transmitters. The values of individual components in the circuitry can be varied to provide different step timings, output amplitudes, and step-to-step ratios.

With the component values shown in Fig. 1, the cir-

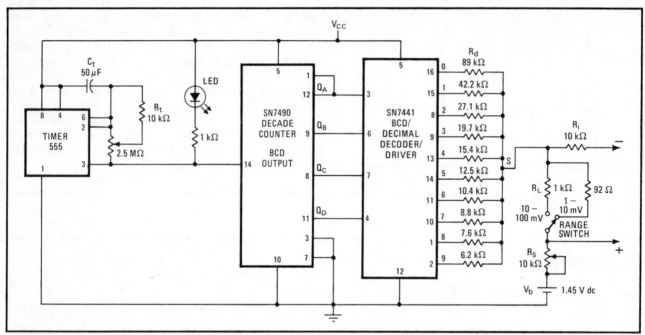

1. Function generator. Successively lower resistances at the decoder outputs create a stairstep function for testing instruments of various kinds. A different sequence of resistances, or a set of variable resistors, generates different kinds of step functions.

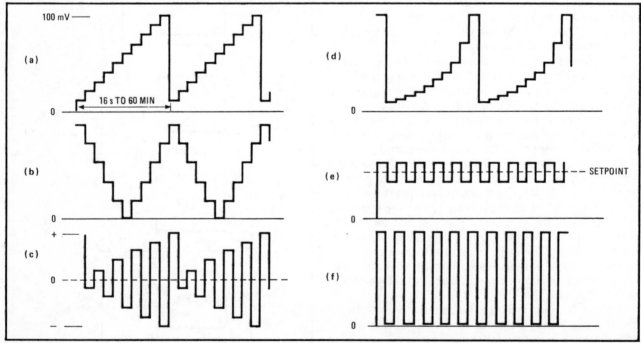

2. Variety. The circuit of Fig. 1 generates many waveshapes, variants of the basic stairstep waveform (a), which ranges from 5 to 120 millivolts and lasts anywhere from 16 seconds to 60 minutes. Increasing and decreasing steps (b) test electrical and mechanical balancing functions. Ever-increasing step amplitudes, either with a center zero (c), or all positive (d), test the response to such steps. Ordinary square waves of large (e) and small (f) amplitudes check positive and negative excursions from setpoints, large-scale process-variable changes, and mechanical drive assemblies. Waveshapes (c), (d), and (f) also check for response to full-scale retrace of function.

cuit generates a stairstep function with 10 equally spaced, ascending steps of equal height, covering a total range of either 5 to 12 or 50 to 120 millivolts, depending on the setting of the range switch and potentiometer R_s. The spacing between steps ranges from 1.6 seconds to 6 minutes, so that the total time for the complete staircase is 16 s to 60 min, depending on the setting of the potentiometer on the timer.

The circuit is based on the 555 timer configured as an astable multivibrator. In this configuration, the timer's output remains low for about a third of the complete cycle and high for the other two thirds; the length of the cycle is determined by the value of the capacitor C_t and the setting of the 2.5-megohm potentiometer; the minimum length, as mentioned, is 1.6 s. The 10-kilohm resistor R_t is added to the potentiometer wiper so that the total resistance tapers properly for particular instruments that need it. The light-emitting diode is a visual indicator that the timer is operating; it is on whenever the time output is low.

Every negative-going transition from the timer increments the decade counter, which steps from 0 to 9 repeatedly and produces its outputs in binary-coded decimal form, on lines Q_A through Q_D. These are translated into the low state on the 10 individual outputs of the BCD-to-decimal decoder/driver. Thus the 10 progressively lower resistance values R_d are successively coupled into the divider network R_d:R_L:R_s, so that the voltage at the summing point S is a stairstep waveform, developed across R_L. This waveform is fed to the device under test through the isolation resistor, R_i.

The diagram shows a reference voltage V_b generated by a mercury cell at 1.45 volts, but any convenient battery or power supply can be used, provided only that it meets the requirements of the application and does not overload the decoder. The decoder's rating of 70 v and 7 milliamperes leaves plenty of latitude in the choice of power sources.

The component values shown provide fixed 10% increments in the stairstep, which is suitable for testing most instruments. However, different values of resistors at R_d will change the increments. In fact, variable resistors can be used if the shape of the waveform is to be frequently changed—for example, in testing recorder inking systems, intermittent amplifiers or transmitters, or worn mechanical servo assemblies. The basic waveform and a few variations are shown in Fig. 2. □

Jitter generator tests bit synchronizer

by M. Harikumar and N. Gopalan Nair
Vikram Sarabhai Space Center, Trivandrum, India

To test bit-synchronizer performance in the presence of frequency jitter, it is often necessary to produce random variations in the frequency of a square-wave oscillator. A sinusoidal voltage can be used to vary the oscillator frequency within a specified range, but the sinusoidal variation is a poor approximation of discrete frequency changes. However, a circuit can be built to shift the output frequency among four levels in a noise-like jitter in such a way that the known and repetitive properties of the jitter help in a realistic evaluation of the system performance.

In this circuit, the outputs from all four stages of a four-stage shift register are summed and applied to a voltage-tunable oscillator. Each shift-register stage can have a logic level of either 0 or 1, but the all-zero state is suppressed. The summed output can range from 1 to 4, which would result in voltages of 5, 10, 15, and 20 volts for 5-v logic. The input to the register consists of the outputs from the third and fourth stages, fed back through an exclusive-OR arrangement to generate a pseudorandom sequence of 15 states. The 4-input NOR gate suppresses the all-zero state after turn-on.

TABLE 1. SEQUENCE OF SHIFT-REGISTER STATES AND THEIR SUMMED VALUES	
Shift-register state	Sum of outputs from register stages
⋮	⋮
1111	4
0111	3
0011	2
0001	1
1000	1
0100	1
0010	1
1001	2
1100	2
0110	2
1011	3
0101	2
1010	2
1101	3
1110	3
⋮	⋮

The successive shift register states and their sum outputs are given in Table 1. It can be seen that the summed output has a binomial distribution, which is an approximation of a gaussian distribution. The summed value 1 occurs four times, which is just the number of possible combinations of four things taken one at a time

161

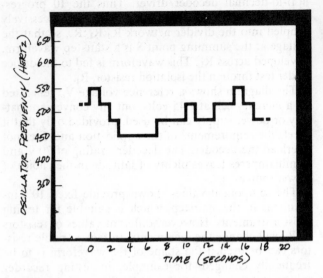

1. Frequency jitter. Pseudorandom jitter of frequency from voltage-controlled oscillator is generated by using the sum of the outputs from individual stages of a four-stage shift register to tune VCO. Oscillator's output frequency has more possible values, with more noise-like distribution, when more shift-register stages are used.

TABLE 2. FEEDBACK STAGES FOR LONGER SHIFT REGISTERS	
Number of stages in shift register	Feedback stages
4	3, 4
5	2, 5
6	5, 6
7	6, 7
8	4, 5, 6, 8
9	4, 9
10	7, 10

(C_1^4). The value 2 occurs six times, which is C_2^4, the value 3 occurs four times (C_3^4), and value 4 occurs only once (C_4^4). The shift register is activated by clock pulses that have a repetition frequency of only 1 hertz or whatever jitter rate is desired.

The outputs from the individual stages of the shift register are summed in an adder circuit, producing a stepped sequence of voltages that is used to tune the voltage-controlled oscillator. If the synchronizer bit rate is 500 Hz and a variation of ±10% is required, the VCO is adjusted to oscillate at 450 Hz for the lowest voltage

from the adder, and to oscillate at 550 Hz when the summed voltage is a maximum.

In this example, with a 4-stage shift register, the output-frequency variation is limited to four steps. But a longer shift register can provide more voltage levels for a better approximation of noise-like properties in the jitter introduced. Table 2 shows what stages should be fed back to the input of longer registers. □

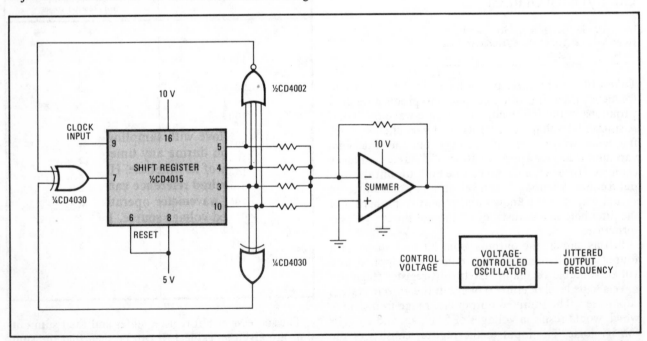

2. Random oscillator. Output voltages from individual stages of shift register are summed and used to determine output frequency from VCO. Feedback arrangement in shift register makes summed voltages vary among four levels in pseudorandom, repeating 15-step sequence. Four-input NOR gate suppresses all-zero condition in register after turn-on, so that exclusive-OR gates can generate sequence of voltage levels. Longer registers produce more levels, longer sequences, and a more nearly gaussian distribution.

Waveform generator chips help the circuit designer

by Bill O'Neil
Intersil Inc., Cupertino, Calif.

Ready-made monolithic waveform generators are versatile building-block components that can simplify many circuit-design tasks. For instance, they are easily inserted into phase-locked loops as voltage-controlled oscillators because of their inherent frequency and temperature stability and because they ease the job of matching loop elements.

At least two of these packaged generators-on-a-chip are now available—the model 8038 from Intersil, and the model XR-205 from Exar Integrated Systems Inc., Sunnyvale, Calif. [*Electronics,* Feb. 14, p. 127]. Both units can produce sine, square, and triangular wave outputs, as well as a sawtooth output and a pulse train. Additionally, both devices can accept modulation voltages, and they offer a broad operating frequency range from less than 1 hertz to 1 megahertz.

A block diagram of Intersil's model 8038 waveform generator is shown in Fig. 1. External capacitor C is charged and discharged by current source A, which is on continuously, and current source B, which is switched on and off by the flip-flop. While current source B is off, the capacitor charges with a current of magnitude I, causing its voltage to rise linearly with time. When this voltage reaches the switching level of comparator 1 (two-thirds of the supply voltage), the flip-flop triggers and switches on current source B.

Since this current source normally carries a current of magnitude 2I, the capacitor is discharged with a net current of magnitude I, and the voltage across it decreases linearly with time. When capacitor voltage reaches the switching level of comparator 2 (one-third of the supply voltage), the flip-flop is triggered into its original state, and the cycle can start again.

Both comparators are made from Darlington transistor pairs to raise input impedance to a high level, permitting the waveform generator to operate with small timing currents. Furthermore, the comparators only draw current at or near each switching threshold level so that any errors created by loading can be neglected.

To achieve the highest possible operating speed, the flip-flop is built with transistors that are kept out of saturation by individual Schottky-barrier diodes. Also, the flip-flop is forced to change state before switching on current source B to avoid potential false triggering or hang-up problems.

Four basic waveforms are readily obtainable from this fundamental generator circuit. With current sources A and B set at levels of I and 2I, respectively, capacitor charge and discharge times are equal, creating a triangular waveform across the capacitor and a square wave at the flip-flop output. Both waveforms are fed to buffer stages.

The levels of the current sources can be varied over a wide range of values with two external resistors. When these levels are set at values other than I and 2I, a linearly rising or falling sawtooth can be generated, along with a train of pulses having a duty cycle from less than 1% to greater than 99%. In addition, a sine-wave output is obtained by feeding the triangular wave into a conversion network.

Either a single power supply (10 to 30 volts) or a dual power supply (±5 to ±15 v) can be used to run the generator. With the single power supply, the average voltage levels of the triangular wave and the sine wave are exactly one-half the supply voltage, while the square wave alternates between the positive supply level and ground. The split power supply moves all waveforms symmetrically about ground.

What's more, the load resistor for the square-wave

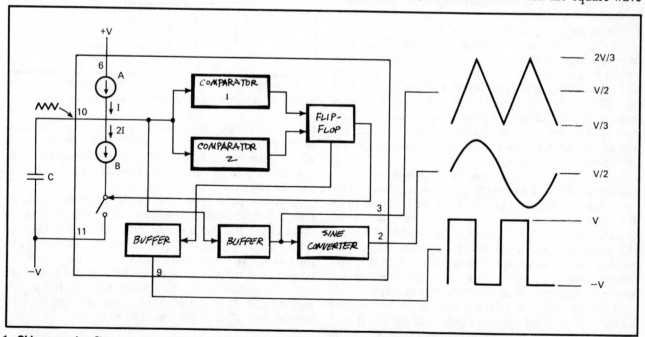

1. Chip generator. Sine, square, triangular, and sawtooth outputs can be produced, in addition to pulses with a variable duty cycle.

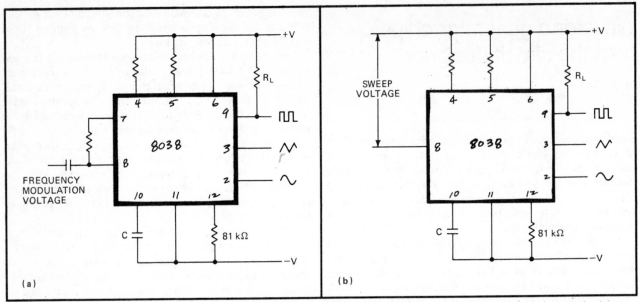

2. Modulation schemes. Generator outputs can be frequency modulated or swept over 1,000:1 frequency ratio with dc control voltage.

output can be connected to a different power supply altogether, as long as that supply's voltage remains within the waveform generator's 30-v breakdown capability. This arrangement permits the square-wave output to be made compatible with TTL circuits by connecting the load resistor to a 5-v supply, while the waveform generator itself is powered from a much higher voltage.

An external dc voltage (measured from the supply voltage), as well as the traditional external RC timing network, can be used to control the frequency at which these waveforms are generated. Altering this dc voltage produces either frequency modulation or sweeping.

For small (±10%) fm deviations, the modulating signal can be applied directly, as shown in Fig. 2a, with a capacitor to provide dc decoupling. The resistor inserted between package pins 7 and 8 increases device input impedance, which is nominally 8 kilohms when pins 7 and 8 are shorted together.

For larger fm deviations or for frequency sweeping, the modulating signal is applied between the positive supply voltage and pin 8 (Fig. 2b). This means that all of the bias voltage for the current sources is created by the modulating signal, permitting a sweep ratio as high as 1,000:1 to be obtained. However, the supply voltage must now be regulated, because capacitor charging current is no longer a function of the supply voltage, and the operating frequency becomes dependent on the power-supply voltage level.

Since the waveform generator exhibits good frequency stability, it can serve as the voltage-controlled oscillator in a phase-locked loop. Figure 3 illustrates an fm demodulator circuit, where, along with the waveform generator, a phase detector and an amplifier are the other building blocks in the loop. The circuit provides a free-running output frequency, offers very low temperature drift, and produces a large reconstituted sine wave having the same frequency as the input.

Naturally, the three building blocks must be matched to each other. For large-amplitude VCO signals, it may be necessary to use two different supply voltages and to return the square-wave output to the supply line of the

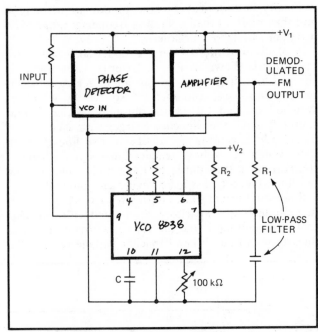

3. Fm demodulator. Employing monolithic generator in phase-locked loop simplifies the job of matching loop building blocks.

phase detector. This prevents the VCO signal from exceeding the input levels acceptable to the phase detector. To attenuate the VCO signal, a simple resistive voltage divider can be connected between the VCO's output and the phase-detector's input.

Also, the dc output level of the amplifier must be compatible with the dc level required at the modulation input of the waveform generator. A direct solution is to set up a voltage divider to the generator's supply (like the one shown for resistors R_1 and R_2) if the amplifier's output level is lower than desired. Or, if the amplifier's output is higher, place the divider between the supply and ground. One of the divider resistors can even be used as part of an output low-pass filter. □

23. Logic techniques

DIPs verify strobe within time window

by Robert A. Dougherty
RAD Technical Consulting, Dunedin, Fla.

It is often necessary, in testing digital equipment, to ascertain that the equipment under test can deliver a pulse (strobe) during a particular time interval (window). The circuit shown here can verify the presence of a strobe pulse coming from equipment under test during a window pulse from the test set; if the strobe does not appear, an error signal goes high. This circuit operates with no external clock, and uses only two dual-in-line-packaged integrated circuits.

As shown in the diagram, one of the ICs is a dual edge-triggered J-K flip-flop; the other is a quad NOR gate. Assume that both J-Ks are initially in the reset condition—that is, Q_1 and Q_2 are both low. In this case the falling leading edge of a window complement pulse, $\overline{W}$, sets Q_1 high. Also, the low condition of $\overline{W}$ enables gate G_1. Therefore if a strobe complement pulse, $\overline{S}$, appears while $\overline{W}$ is low, G_1 goes high and resets J-K_1 through G_2.

The output from inverter G_3 is the window pulse, W. Its falling trailing edge clocks the condition of Q_1 (which is also J_2) to Q_2, which is the error latch. Therefore, if Q_1 is low, the error latch stays low. If Q_1 is high, the error latch goes high and remains high until cleared by the error reset or the master reset.

The master reset initializes both J-Ks. The error reset clears the error latch through G_4.

The timing diagram illustrates the operation of the circuit. Note that the error latch stays low if a strobe is totally within the window, or if it overlaps the beginning and/or end of the window. But if a strobe does not coincide with any portion of the window, the latch goes high; it can ring a bell, light a light, or otherwise indicate that the equipment under test has failed to deliver a pulse when one was required. □

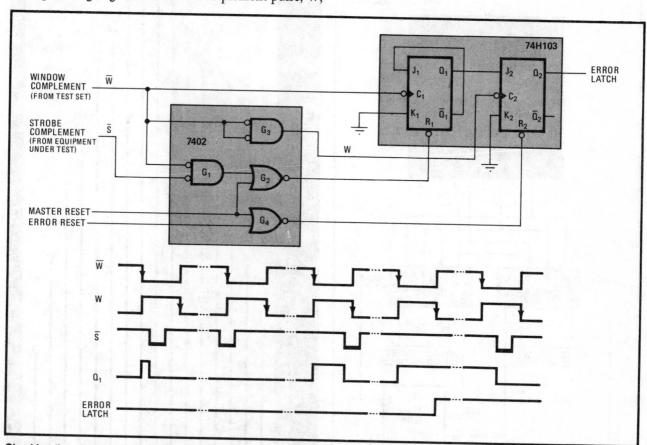

Checking the windows. Indicating whether digital equipment can deliver a pulse at the proper time, this circuit signals an error if a strobe pulse does not coincide with a window pulse generated by the test station. Note that 74H103 J-K flip-flops are clocked by falling edge of pulse. Gates in the 7402 quad NOR are drawn to indicate their function; by DeMorgan's Theorem, a negative NAND is equivalent to a NOR. Timing diagram shows that error latch goes high on falling edge of window pulse (W) unless strobe pulse has occurred some time during W.

Increasing an instruction set without increasing word length

by C. W. Moser Jr.
Western Electric Co., Winston-Salem, N.C.

The number of instructions in a system-instruction set can be increased without increasing the word length. Normally, a 4-bit instruction word can be decoded as one of 16 possible instructions (i.e., $2^4 = 16$). If more than 16 instructions are required for a particular application, the instruction word can be lengthened, or the technique described below can be used.

Figure 1 shows an N-by-4-bit memory in which each

1. Decoder circuit. Instruction words in memory can have either of two meanings, depending upon state of flip-flop. With this two-set technique, each 4-bit word provides 30 possible instructions.

2. More sets. Maximum number of instructions obtainable from a 4-bit word is plotted as a function of the number of instruction sets (or decoders). Optimum area has fewest components per instruction.

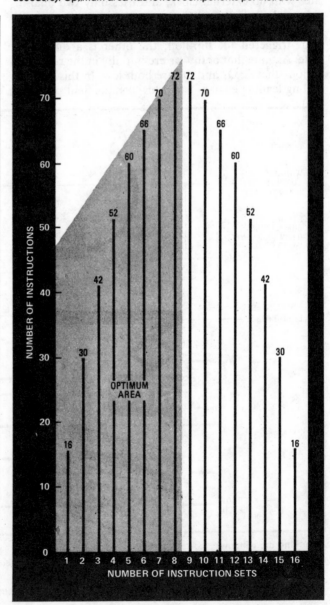

4-bit instruction word can be decoded as one of 30 possible instructions; these instructions are divided into two sets of 15 instructions each. A 4-bit instruction word in the memory can have either of two meanings, depending on the state of the flip-flop. If the flip-flop is clear, decoder 2 is disabled and decoder 1 is enabled; therefore the instructions in set 1 can be performed.

If it is necessary to perform an instruction that is in set 2, the flip-flop must be set to provide an enabling pulse to decoder 2. For this purpose, line No. 15 from decoder 1 is connected to the set lead of the flip-flop; thus a 1111 instruction from decoder 1 sets the flip-flop, disables decoder 1, and enables decoder 2 so that the instructions in set 2 can be performed. Similarly, line No. 15 from decoder 2 is connected to the clear lead of the flip-flop; thus, a 1111 instruction from decoder 2 clears the flip-flop, disables decoder 2, and enables decoder 1 so that instructions in set 1 can be performed.

If the number of instruction sets is increased, the total number of possible instructions increases up to a point, and then actually decreases as more sets are added. Figure 2 shows the number of possible instructions obtainable from a 4-bit word as a function of the number of instruction sets (or number of decoders). The total number of instructions decreases for more than nine instruction sets, because every set must include commands for enabling every other set. The shaded region of the graph is optimum in that fewer components are required per instruction than in the unshaded region.

This technique is most valuable in operations where one group of instructions (for example, instruction set 1) is performed many times and the second group is performed after the first group. Of course, this technique can be applied to systems that use words other than 4 bits long.

In some applications, a decrease in the total number of bits and an increase in the total number of words can be realized in comparison with similar applications that make use of longer words. This technique slightly lengthens the microprogram and the execution time because time must be allocated when accessing a different set of instructions. □

Weigh-counting technique is faster than binary

by Patrick F. Howden
Sydney University, Sydney, Australia

A system of counting that is more condensed and much faster than binary can easily be implemented with tristate integrated circuits. It is based on the fact that all rational numbers can be represented through a series such as . . . 243, 81, 27, 9, 3, 1, $1/3$, $1/9$, $1/27$, . . . , assuming any of these "weights" can be put on either "pan" of a "scale." This weigh-counting scheme is not related to tertiary counting, though it uses the same number of digits as does tertiary with a sign bit.

A weight digit is designated by a plus sign in a circle if it is in the pan opposite the number to be measured, and by a minus sign in a circle if it is in the same pan. Then the integers 1 through 15 can be represented as shown in the table.

As can be seen, n digits of weigh-counting reach

WEIGH-DIGIT FORMAT AND COUNTING RULES

	27	9	3	1
1				⊕
2			⊕	⊖
3			⊕	○
4			⊕	⊕
5		⊕	⊖	⊖
6		⊕	⊖	○
7		⊕	⊖	⊕
8		⊕	○	⊖
9		⊕	○	○
10		⊕	○	⊕
11		⊕	⊕	⊖
12		⊕	⊕	○
13		⊕	⊕	⊕
14	⊕	⊖	⊖	⊖
15	⊕	⊖	⊖	○

ADDITION

RULES

○ + ○ = ○
⊖ + ○ = ⊖
⊕ + ○ = ⊕
⊕ + ⊖ = ○
⊖ + ⊖ = ⊕ AND CARRY ⊖
⊕ + ⊕ = ⊖ AND CARRY ⊕

EXAMPLE

```
    ⊕  ⊖  ⊖  =   5
 +  ⊕  ⊖  ○  = + 6
 ─────────────────
    ⊕  ⊕  ⊖  =  11
```

MULTIPLICATION

RULES

○ X ○ = ○
⊖ X ○ = ○
⊕ X ○ = ○
⊕ X ⊖ = ⊖
⊖ X ⊖ = ⊕
⊕ X ⊕ = ⊕

EXAMPLE

```
        ⊕  ⊖  ⊖     =   5
  X     ⊕  ⊖  ○     = X 6
 ──────────────────────
        ○  ○  ○
     ⊖  ⊕  ⊕
  ⊕  ⊖  ⊖
 ──────────────────────
  ○  ⊕  ○  ⊕  ○      =  30
```

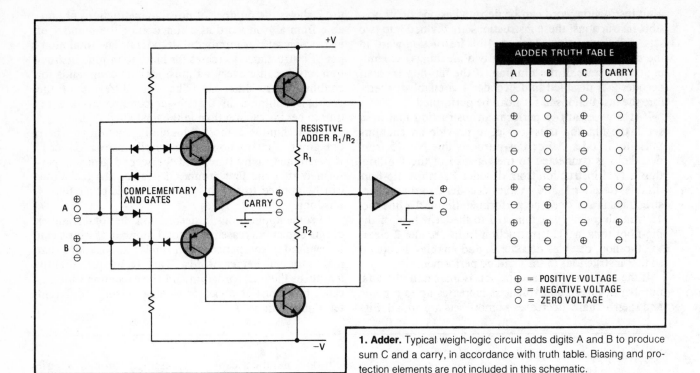

ADDER TRUTH TABLE			
A	B	C	CARRY
$\bigcirc$	$\bigcirc$	$\bigcirc$	$\bigcirc$
$\oplus$	$\bigcirc$	$\oplus$	$\bigcirc$
$\bigcirc$	$\oplus$	$\oplus$	$\bigcirc$
$\ominus$	$\bigcirc$	$\ominus$	$\bigcirc$
$\bigcirc$	$\ominus$	$\ominus$	$\bigcirc$
$\oplus$	$\ominus$	$\bigcirc$	$\bigcirc$
$\ominus$	$\oplus$	$\bigcirc$	$\bigcirc$
$\oplus$	$\oplus$	$\ominus$	$\oplus$
$\ominus$	$\ominus$	$\oplus$	$\ominus$

$\oplus$ = POSITIVE VOLTAGE
$\ominus$ = NEGATIVE VOLTAGE
$\bigcirc$ = ZERO VOLTAGE

1. Adder. Typical weigh-logic circuit adds digits A and B to produce sum C and a carry, in accordance with truth table. Biasing and protection elements are not included in this schematic.

2. D-a converter. Weigh-system converter uses 10 resistors with 3-position switches to sink or source any combination of 10 different currents to summing amplifier. Each switch can be set for positive, negative, or zero positions. Thus, for a fixed magnitude of voltage V, 29,524 positive and negative current outputs are possible—a total of $3^{10} - 1$ levels. A binary converter with this many levels requires 16 bits.

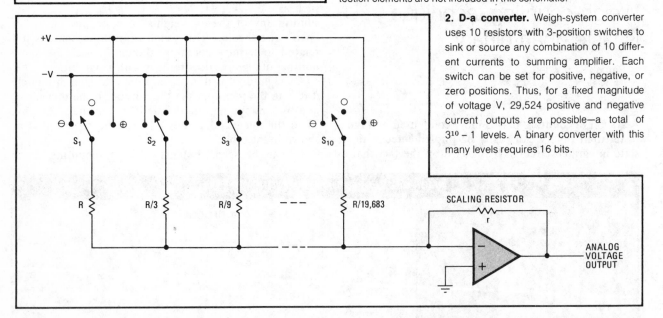

$\frac{1}{2}(3^n - 1)$, whereas an n-bit binary system counts only to $2^n - 1$. Therefore seven weights are approximately equivalent to 10 bits, and 10 weights are equivalent to 15 bits (or 16 bits with sign). This allows a dramatic compression of registers, counters, and wiring. Power consumption is also reduced, and speed is increased, especially if three-state devices are used.

The rules for addition in weigh-digit format are shown in the table. Subtraction is simple. All weighted symbols are reversed in the number to be subtracted, and the result is then added. Long columns of addition and subtraction can therefore be performed simultaneously; the "carries" do not tend to accumulate (as they do in binary or other addition), but rather cancel because two oppositely weighted symbols equal zero.

Parallel multiplication is also simple. As shown in the table, a negative-weight digit in the multiplier reverses all the digits in the multiplicand, and multiplication by successively more significant digits (1,3,9, . . .) merely shifts the multiplicand to the left by 0,1,2, . . . places.

Fast low-power digital-logic packages to perform these arithmetic functions are easy to assemble. Figure 1 shows a typical basic one-digit adder.

Another example is the 10-bit digital-to-analog converter shown in Fig. 2. Only 10 resistors are required to span 59,048 levels, which is almost 16 bits in binary operation. Resistors R and r set the scale factors, and S_{10} is the most-significant-resistor switch. □

Capacitance-coupled logic fills unusual jobs

by Stephen R. Pareles
Cook College of Environmental Science, New Brunswick, N.J.

Capacitively coupling logic signals may prove to be a simple way to do several not-so-simple jobs. For instance, capacitive coupling can make short work of bidirectional pulse-edge detection, as well as comparison of an analog signal and a digital signal.

With the circuit of Fig. 1 and a single-trace oscilloscope, an analog signal and a digital signal can be displayed at the same time, allowing the two signals to be compared or synchronized. The circuit's output is the analog signal with superimposed digital cursors.

The capacitor serves as a bidirectional edge-detector for the buffered arbitrary logic train. Analog-level transients are produced by the capacitor from this input logic train. They are positive for leading pulse edges and negative for trailing pulse edges.

These transients are then cross-coupled with the analog signal through resistors that provide cross-current isolation (100-kilohm resistors are sufficient for most applications). A capacitance of 500 picofarads is ideal for slow horizontal sweep rates of up to about 100 hertz. Smaller capacitance values should be used for faster sweep rates to prevent the trailing edges of the transients from becoming observable.

Capacitive coupling can also be used to perform bidirectional edge-detection when a logic-level output is desired. The detector circuit, which is drawn in Fig. 2, can even handle variable pulse widths.

Normally, a 74121-type one-shot is only triggered by a positive transition at point D, following a low condition at points D and Q. When the input first goes high, point A1 goes high. Since point A2 is still high, point C momentarily remains low. When A2 goes low and C high, the one-shot is triggered by the positive edge at D. Point B is kept high throughout.

When the input goes low, A1 goes low before A2 goes high, so that C remains high. Point B, however, is momentarily low. When B goes high again, the one-shot is triggered by the positive edge at C, as before. The tables in Fig. 2 detail the circuit's operation at key points. ☐

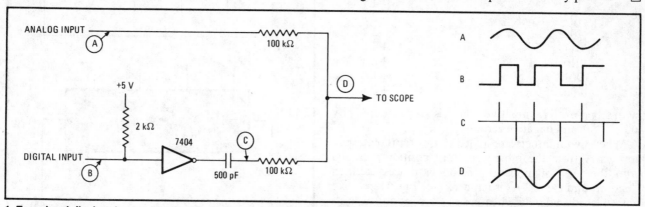

1. Two-signal display. A capacitor simplifies the task of observing two signals on a single-trace oscilloscope. The circuit's output becomes the analog input with superimposed digital timing cursors. The two 100-kilohm resistors provide the necessary cross-current isolation.

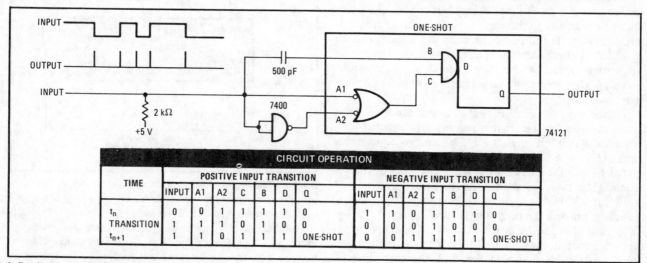

	CIRCUIT OPERATION												
TIME	POSITIVE INPUT TRANSITION							NEGATIVE INPUT TRANSITION					
	INPUT	A1	A2	C	B	D	Q	INPUT	A1	A2	C	B	D	Q
t_n	0	0	1	1	1	1	0	1	1	0	1	1	1	0
TRANSITION	1	1	1	0	1	0	0	0	0	0	1	0	0	0
t_{n+1}	1	1	0	1	1	1	ONE-SHOT	0	0	1	1	1	1	ONE-SHOT

2. Dual edge-detection. Both the leading and trailing edges of the input-pulse train are detected by this capacitively coupled circuit.

One's complement adder eliminates unwanted zero

by John F. Wakerly
Digital Systems Laboratory, Stanford University, Stanford, Calif.

0011 +3 0010 +2 ―――― 0101 +5	0000 +0 0000 +0 ―――― 0000 +0	1111 −0 1111 −0 ―――― 11110 −1 └→ 1 +1 ―――― 1111 −0
0110 +6 1001 −6 ―――― 1111 −0	0111 +7 1001 −6 ―――― 10000 +0 └→ 1 +1 ―――― 0001 +1	1011 −4 0111 +7 ―――― 10010 +2 └→ 1 +1 ―――― 0011 +3

1. One's complement addition. Examples show the one's complement representation in which a negative number is just the bit-by-bit complement of the positive number; the "end-around carry" rule for addition, and the two forms of zero.

To enable an adder to subtract, a binary system can use the one's complement representation for negative numbers. However, since the negative of a number is created by replacing 1s by 0s and 0s by 1s, two forms of zero result—00 . . . 0 and 11 . . . 1—to the complication of later zero-checking operations. Fortunately, it's possible to eliminate the 11 . . . 1 version if a NAND gate is included in the adder circuitry.

In a one's complement binary system, the most significant digit in a positive number must be 0 and in a negative number must be 1. Thus the eight possible values that can be represented by 3-bit number are no longer 0, 1, . . . 7. Instead, they are −3, −2, −1, −0, +0, +1, +2, +3. The following table shows why both +0 and −0 occur:

One's complement form	Value represented
111	−0
110	−1
101	−2
100	−3
011	+3
010	+2
001	+1
000	+0

More generally, positive zero is represented by 00 . . . 0, and negative zero by 11 . . . 1.

When two numbers are added in this representation, any carry from the most significant position is added into the least significant position—a process termed "end-around carry." As it happens (see Fig. 1), positive zero is produced only when positive zero is added to itself.

The standard implementation of a one's complement adder uses a conventional binary adder with the carry output connected to the carry input to achieve the end-around carry. This direct connection of the carry output to input in effect turns the adder into an asynchronous sequential circuit, whose state depends on its previous state. (A D-type flip-flop is a familiar example of a sequential circuit.)

To see this, consider Fig. 2(a), which shows a 4-bit one's complement adder that can be implemented with a single MSI circuit such as a 7483. The two input numbers are $A = a_3a_2a_1a_0$ and $B = b_3b_2b_1b_0$, the carry input is c_i, and the carry output is c_o. The state of the sequential circuit is the state of the carry line C.

In Fig. 2(a), A equals 0110, B equals 1001, and C equals 0, making the output is 1111 as expected. In Fig. 2(b), A is changed by one bit to 0111, C changes to 1, and the output changes to 0001. When A is changed back to 0110, as shown in Fig. 2(c), the carry line C, which was 1 before the change, produces the sum of

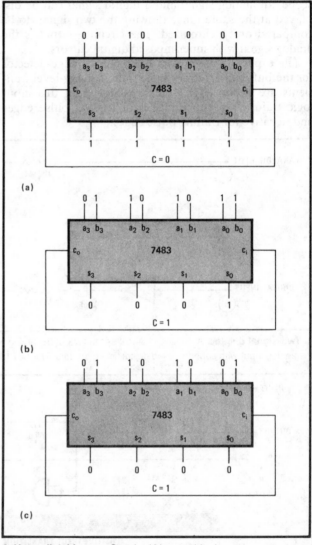

2. Unpredictable zero. Standard binary adder has carry output connected to carry input for "end-around carry" in adding one's complement numbers. A result that is zero may come out as 1111 (negative zero) or 0000 (positive zero), depending upon prior condition of circuit. In both (a) and (c), computation of (6 − 6) is represented by (0110 + 1001); results are 1111 and 0000, respectively, because intervening computation in (b) changed state of circuit.

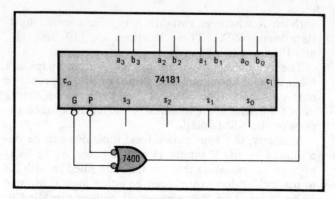

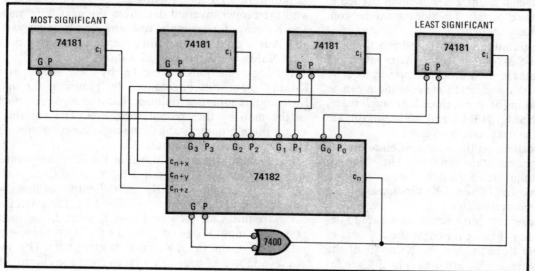

3. Eliminates negative zero. This 4-bit one's complement adder has only one form of zero—0000. The 1111 representation of zero is eliminated by use of NAND gate and arithmetic logic unit that has carry-generate (G) and carry-propagate (P) outputs.

4. More bits. Here a 16-bit one's complement adder uses NAND gate to assure that zero appears as 00 . . . 0. NAND-gate arrangement introduces no more delay than the conventional end-around carry.

0110 + 1001 + 1 = 10000 after the change, so that C remains 1 after the change.

Thus the circuit has two stable states, either C = 0 or C = 1, for any input combination having exactly one 0 and one 1 at each bit position (that is, a number and its one's complement are being added). Which state the circuit attains for a particular input combination depends on the state of the carry line C for the previous operation. Unless the inputs of the adder are set to a known value (say 0) before each operation, it is quite impossible to predict which form of zero will be produced by adding a number and its complement.

Nevertheless, despite its unpredictability, the unwanted form of zero (11 . . . 1) can be eliminated very easily with most MSI and LSI arithmetic logic units (ALUs) and data path slices. MSI circuits such as any 74181, 74S281, and 74S381 ALUs, and LSI circuits such as Monolithic Memories' 6701, Intel's 3002, and Advanced Micro Devices' 2901 data path slices, all have carry-generate (G) and carry-propagate (P) outputs for fast carry lookahead, in addition to the normal ripple carry output (c_o). Examination of the carry-propagate equations shows that P equals 1 if a number and its one's complement are being added, i.e., the sum equals 11 . . . 1. Therefore the 11 . . . 1 representation of zero can be eliminated by producing a carry input of 1 whenever a carry is generated (G = 1) or P equals 1. For typical devices this process requires a single two-input NAND gate, as shown in Fig. 3 for a 4-bit one's complement adder using one 74181.

For larger adders, the G and P outputs of the carry lookahead generator may be used, as shown in Fig. 4 for a 16-bit one's complement adder using four 74181's and one 74182 lookahead carry generator. In all cases the resulting circuit is no longer a sequential circuit, because generate and propagate outputs do not depend on the carry input.

The total propagation delay of a one's complement adder using a conventional end-around carry is $t_{ADD} = t_{ICO} + t_{CIS}$, where t_{ICO} is the propagation delay from any data input to the carry output and t_{CIS} is the propagation delay from the carry input to the sum output.

For the scheme illustrated in Fig. 3, the delay is $t_{ADD} = t_{IPG} + t_N + t_{CIS}$, where t_{IPG} is the delay from any data input to the P and G outputs and t_N is the NAND-gate delay. Typical values for standard 7400-series parts are $t_{ICO} = 28$ ns, $t_{CIS} = 13$ ns, $t_{IPG} = 17$ ns, and $t_N = 11$ ns. Hence the total delay for both schemes is the same: $t_{ADD} = 28 + 13 = 17 + 11 + 13 = 41$ ns.

For larger adders, as in Fig. 4, the delay for both schemes is still approximately the same, since the delay of the external NAND gate is comparable to the delay of the internal gate used to compute the ripple carry output from P, G, and c_i in the ALU or lookahead generator.

The scheme of Fig. 3 or Fig. 4 automatically converts all arithmetic results of 11 . . . 1 to 00 . . . 0. However, it should be noted that in logic operations a result of 11 . . . 1 is not converted. In most applications this is the desired behavior. □

Nonsequential counter design makes use of Karnaugh maps

by Glen Coers
Texas Instruments, Components Group, Dallas, Texas

The design of a nonsequential binary counter—one that does not count in a 0-1-2-3-4-5-6-7 sequence—can be considerably simplified by the use of Karnaugh mapping techniques. Such a counter is sometimes needed in digital systems where certain functions must be controlled in a nonbinary sequence.

To illustrate the technique, we will design a three-bit counter for a 0-2-4-5-3-7-1-6 sequence. After listing the desired counter states in their proper sequence, as done in (a), the present-state and next-state conditions can be compiled, as shown in (b). Next, three Karnaugh maps, the ones labeled NSM_A, NSM_B, and NSM_C in (c), are used to represent the next-state conditions.

The minterm locations on the next-state maps are determined by the present-state variables. The value for that location is obtained from the next-state table. Since three bits are involved, three J-K flip-flops will be needed to implement the counter.

Six other maps are now constructed—three are to determine the logic functions required at the J inputs of the flip-flops, while three are for the K inputs of the flip-flops. These maps, which are drawn in (d), are labeled J_A, J_B, J_C, K_A, K_B, and K_C, where J_A and K_A represent the inputs of flip-flop FF_A, J_B and K_B the inputs of flip-flop FF_B, and J_C and K_C the inputs of flip-flop FF_C. (TTL flip-flops will be used.)

The locations of the variables that are true are noted on the J-input maps by Xs, indicating that the state of the variable can be either logic 0 or logic 1. (This permits maximum reduction of circuitry.) For example, on the J_A map, the true locations of variable A are marked with an X wherever variable A is logic 1 on its next-state map, NSM_A. These locations are 110, 100, 111, and 101.

The remaining locations on the J-input maps are filled in with the remaining values on the appropriate next-state map. The leftmost four locations on the J_A map, for instance, are identical to the leftmost four locations on the NSM_A map.

Similarly, the appropriate logic functions can be determined for the K inputs. For these however, the locations of the variables that are false are filled in with Xs to mark the "don't care" (can be either logic 0 or logic 1) positions. And the remaining locations are filled in with the proper inverted data from the next-state map. The K_A map, for example, contains Xs whenever variable A is logic 0 on the NSM_A map, and inverted data from NSM_A in the remaining locations.

The logic functions represented by these J-input and K-input maps can be reduced by grouping through Karnaugh mapping techniques. These groups are noted on the map by the colored enclosures. The variables within these groups establish the logic function needed at a particular flip-flop input.

The J_A input requires a signal of $B + C$, which means that the Q output of flip-flop FF_B must be ORed with the Q output of flip-flop FF_C and the output of that OR gate applied to the J input of flip-flop FF_A. Likewise, input J_B requires an OR gate ($\overline{A} + C$), input J_C an AND gate ($A\overline{B}$), input K_A an OR gate ($B + C$), input K_B an OR gate ($A + \overline{C}$), and input K_C an AND gate ($\overline{A}\,\overline{B}$). The negated variables, of course, are taken from the $\overline{Q}$ outputs of the flip-flops.

Now the nonsequential binary counter design is complete. The circuit of (e) shows what the final configuration looks like. The states of its three output lines agree with the truth table in (b) and proceed in the nonbinary sequence of (a). □

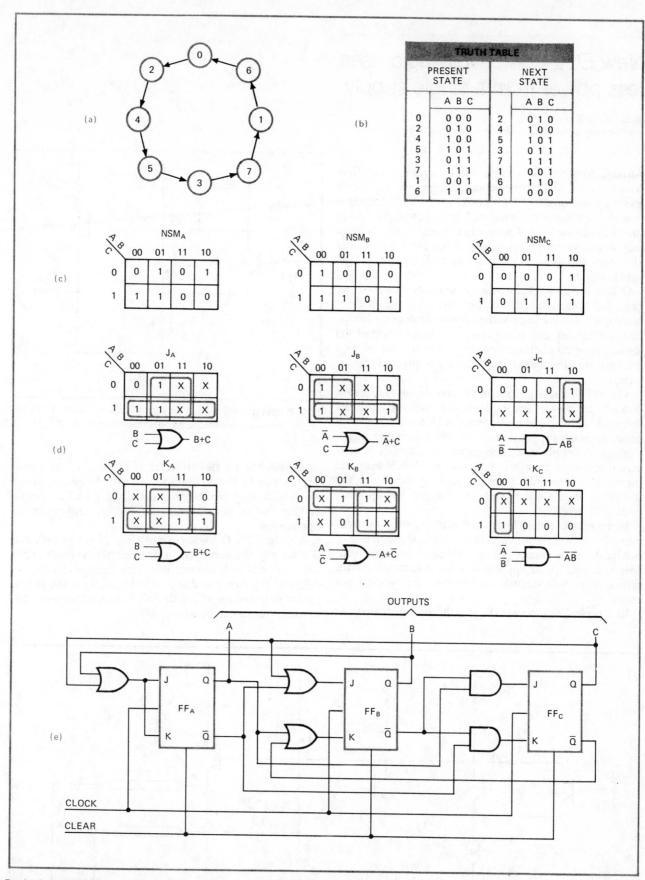

Designing a counter. Karnaugh mapping, a design procedure that is normally applied only to binary designs, can also be used for synthesizing a nonsequential counter. The three-bit binary counter designed here has a 0-2-4-5-3-7-1-6 sequence (a). From the truth table (b) of this counter's next-state outputs, the next-state map (c) can be drawn for each of its three output lines. The next group of maps (d) establish the logic function required at each input of the three J-K flip-flops needed to build the counter. The final circuit is shown in (e).

New ECL-compatible logic uses less power from a single supply

by Bohumir Sramek
International Peripherals & Computer Corp., Santa Ana, Calif.

Anyone looking for a logic family that's compatible with conventional emitter-coupled logic, but dissipates less than one-quarter of the power at the same propagation delay should be interested in a new logic family called 2½-diode logic. Circuits in the new family require only one power supply voltage, with a potential of only 2½ times the voltage drop across a diode; hence the name, 2½-D.

Other advantages include: fewer components per gate, and therefore less area per gate on a silicon chip; more gates per package within power dissipation limits; better reliability and lower cost, as a direct result of the lower power dissipation; and the ability to operate with a single standby battery cell during a primary power outage.

The 2½-D family does have two disadvantages: it doesn't have an uncomplemented output, and its threshold is temperature-dependent. A temperature-dependent power supply should overcome the latter disadvantage. A supply that changes by -3 millivolts per degree Centigrade change in temperature should keep the threshold in the middle of the logic swing, since the transistor base-emitter voltage changes by approximately -2 mV/°C.

In emitter-coupled logic—sometimes called current-mode logic—a constant current is steered through one of two paths by a current switch. These circuits are suitable for high-speed applications because no transistor saturates in these circuits, and carrier storage does not occur.

In a typical ECL circuit (Fig. 1) the power dissipation

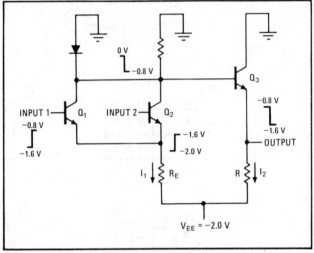

2. 2½-D circuit uses only a 2-volt supply and only one of two output circuits; reference transistor cuts power by factor of 5 to 8.

is established by the collector resistance R, the power supply V_{EE} of -5.2 v, and the value of the emitter resistors, which may be at either the driving end or the receiving end of the transmission line, depending on the application.

A simple 2½-D logic current (Fig. 2) needs only one 2-v supply, the same as the termination voltage in the conventional ECL circuit. But with the same value of collector resistance and the same logic levels, the propagation delay is not affected. This reduces the power dissipation per switch by about 60%.

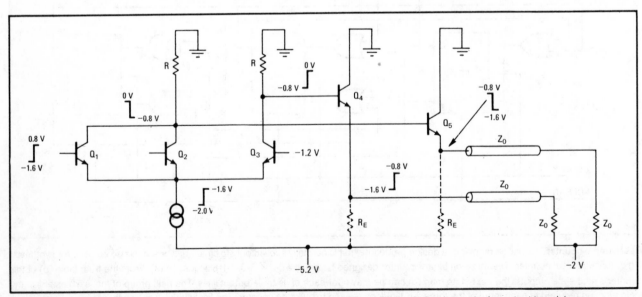

1. Conventional ECL circuit requires a relatively high 5.2-volt power supply, in addition to a 2-volt supply, for output transistors.

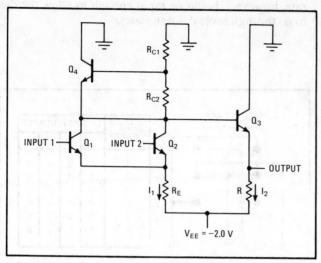

3. For matched performance, transistor clamp Q_4, instead of diode, assures logic levels and transfer characteristic are the same as ECL.

A further power reduction of 50% to 70% below this already low level (to a point 12% to 20% of the original) is possible by eliminating the noninverting output while keeping the same current from the V_{EE} supply. This is possible by removing the noninverting emitter follower circuit and the reference transistor (Q_3 in Fig. 1).

When circuit elements are removed, the natural properties of the semiconductor material establish the reference, as they do in saturating-logic families such as DTL and TTL. However, the logic capability of the 2½-D circuit is only slightly affected—the OR/NOR function of the original ECL circuit is changed to a NOR function, from which any larger digital function can be assembled.

When the circuit in Fig. 2 has a binary 0 at both inputs, both input transistors Q_1 and Q_2 are non-conducting and the only current path from the power supply is through the output transistor Q_3. If a binary 1 appears at either input, the corresponding transistor turns on, and current flows through R_E, having a value such that the sum of the two currents through the two branches with a 1 at the input equals the current through the output branch and Q_3 when both inputs were at logic 0.

In this simple circuit, the diode prevents the input transistors from saturating by clamping the collector at 0.8 V, the drop across the diode. But a more practical circuit (Fig. 3) uses a transistor as a clamp instead of a diode; the proper choice of R_{C1} and R_{C2} allows an adjustment of logic levels. Meanwhile, the ratio of R_{C1} + R_{C2} to R_E can be varied (as it can in the diode version) to make the transfer characteristic of the gate match that of standard ECL. □

Electronic dice ease tough decisions

by Glen Miranker*
Yale University, New Haven, Conn.

A pair of electronic dice can help you make decisions. Many people in management positions are often faced with decisions that appear to be impossible to make, based on the information provided them. In an attempt to decide among the choices that confront them, some flip a coin, thus using a statistical method to select one of two courses of action.

*Now with IBM Corp., Yorktown Heights, N.Y.

Generally, however, there are more than two possible choices, and then a pair of dice is better, allowing you to choose one out of up to 36 separate alternatives.

A die face can be considered as shown in (a); a table of the desired states is also given. The two tables of (b) indicate how a standard binary counter can be modified slightly to produce these desired states. In fact, if the counter is reset at a "normal" count of six and the "modified" zero state is detected and decoded properly, a popular type 7493 four-bit binary counter will do.

The wiring scheme of (c) will serve as a single die—with seven incandescent bulbs representing the die face. Naturally, if you build two of these circuits, you will have a pair of dice.

All that remains to be done is to clock the counters to some random state to simulate a roll of the dice. The leftover flip-flops and inverters can be used to do this, as shown in (d). Just about any capacitor value will do, provided it produces a pulse repetition rate of less than 10 megahertz. A capacitance of 1 microfarad is fine, although you may want to use a larger value so that the clocking of the counters is readily apparent. The clock rate, however, should be rapid enough to allow the dice to go through several dozen states. ☐

Manager's helper. A statistical decision maker—a pair of electronic dice—can be simulated by logic gates, a binary counter, and a series of miniature lamps. Desired states (a) for seven-bulb die face can be realized by modifying a four-bit binary counter as noted by the table in (b). Hookup for single die is shown in (c), while circuit (d) makes use of leftover logic gates to simulate a roll of the dice.

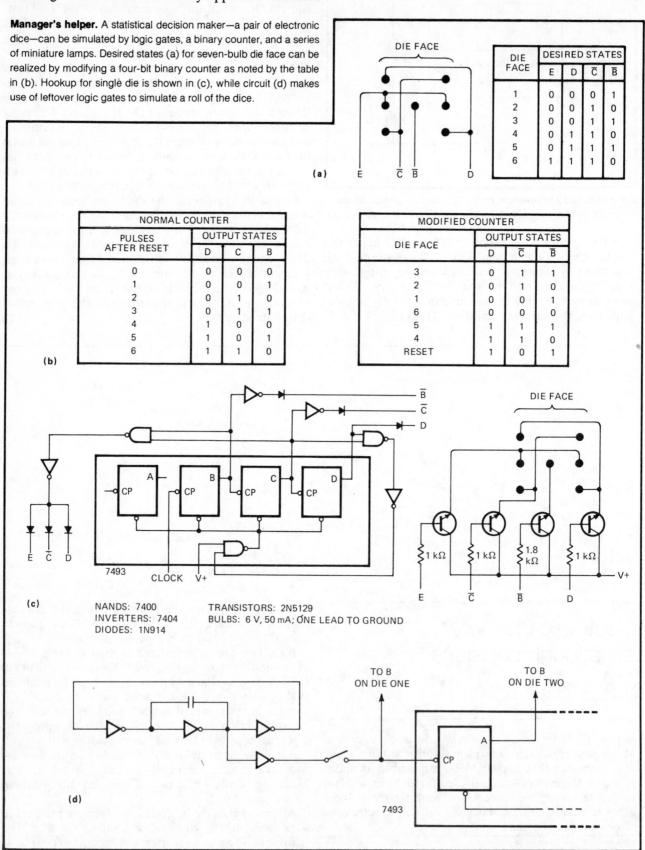

(a)

DIE FACE	DESIRED STATES			
	E	D	$\overline{C}$	$\overline{B}$
1	0	0	0	1
2	0	0	1	0
3	0	0	1	1
4	0	1	1	0
5	0	1	1	1
6	1	1	1	0

(b)

NORMAL COUNTER			
PULSES AFTER RESET	OUTPUT STATES		
	D	C	B
0	0	0	0
1	0	0	1
2	0	1	0
3	0	1	1
4	1	0	0
5	1	0	1
6	1	1	0

MODIFIED COUNTER			
DIE FACE	OUTPUT STATES		
	D	$\overline{C}$	$\overline{B}$
3	0	1	1
2	0	1	0
1	0	0	1
6	0	0	0
5	1	1	1
4	1	1	0
RESET	1	0	1

(c)

NANDS: 7400
INVERTERS: 7404
DIODES: 1N914

TRANSISTORS: 2N5129
BULBS: 6 V, 50 mA; ONE LEAD TO GROUND

(d)

TO B ON DIE ONE

TO B ON DIE TWO

176

24. Interfacing to logic circuits

C-MOS Schmitt trigger can be more than an interface

by R.L. Morris
Audichron Co., Atlanta, Ga.

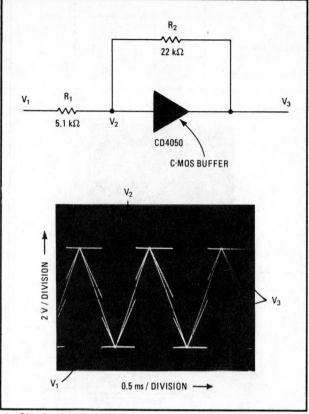

1. Simple circuit. C-MOS buffer and two resistors form a Schmitt trigger circuit that provides a high input impedance, fast output transitions, and a wide range of hysteresis voltage. The scope display illustrates the circuit voltages when the input is a triangular wave.

A Schmitt trigger makes a convenient interface between any type of logic family and signals that have slow transition times and possibly contain some noise component. When complementary-MOS circuits are being used to take advantage of their high input impedance and convenient switching threshold level, it is particularly necessary to employ an interface circuit that provides sufficient hysteresis.

A versatile C-MOS Schmitt trigger can be built with a minimum of parts—with only a couple of resistors and a conventional C-MOS noninverting buffer, such as the type CD4050 device. The circuit, which is drawn in Fig. 1, is actually quite similar to a standard comparator circuit having hysteresis. Unlike a comparator, however, the source impedance required to drive the C-MOS Schmitt trigger can be considerably lower than the value of its input resistor (R_1). If the source resistance is a relatively fixed value, it can even be added to R_1 for calculation purposes.

To see how the C-MOS Schmitt trigger operates, first let output voltage V_3 be at ground level. As input voltage V_1 increases from below the circuit's positive-going threshold point, voltage V_2 is divided by resistors R_1 and R_2. When the threshold point of the C-MOS buffer is reached, the output of the buffer will begin to increase, producing positive feedback through resistor R_2. This causes a fast transition at the circuit's output and latches the circuit into its other state.

Now, let output voltage V_3 be at the V_{DD} supply level. The same circuit action takes place, but it occurs in the opposite direction. The scope display in Fig. 1 shows the superimposed waveforms for V_1, V_2, and V_3 for typical values of these voltages. The total circuit hysteresis, in this case, is approximately 2.3 volts.

Only a few circuit equations are needed to describe circuit behavior with reasonable accuracy. The feedback factor can be expressed as a resistance ratio:

$$K = (R_1 + R_2)/R_2$$

The circuit's positive-going threshold voltage is then given by:

$$V_{T+} = V_T K$$

where V_T is the threshold voltage of the C-MOS buffer being used. The negative-going threshold voltage can be written as:

$$V_{T-} = K(V_T - V_{DD}) + V_{DD}$$

And the total hysteresis of the circuit is the difference between the two threshold voltage levels:

$$V_H = V_{T+} - V_{T-} = (K - 1)V_{DD}$$

These equations can be further simplified by assuming that $V_T = 0.5V_{DD}$, which is a good approximation for a C-MOS buffer. Then, the positive-going and negative-going threshold voltages can be expressed as:

$$V_{T+} = 0.5V_{DD}K$$
$$V_{T-} = (1 - 0.5K)V_{DD}$$

Of course, there are a number of ready applications for the C-MOS Schmitt trigger of Fig. 1. One is as a delay element to generate time delays with a simple RC integrator network. The delay may be desired for logic timing functions or for filtering noise. Figure 2a shows the configuration for a delay element. In this circuit, as long as resistance $10R_3$ is less than or equal to resistance $(R_1 + R_2)$, the circuit's hysteresis and time constant can be considered to be independent of each other. A word of caution, though—the threshold point for a type CD4050 buffer is only specified to within ±40% of the ideal V_T threshold of $0.5V_{DD}$. However, the stability of V_T with temperature for any particular device is very good.

Another possible application for the C-MOS Schmitt trigger, one which is based on the delay element of Fig. 2a, is as an edge detector or differentiator (Fig. 2b). Three different outputs can be obtained from this circuit. With a NAND gate at the output, the circuit detects only the leading edge of the positive input pulse.

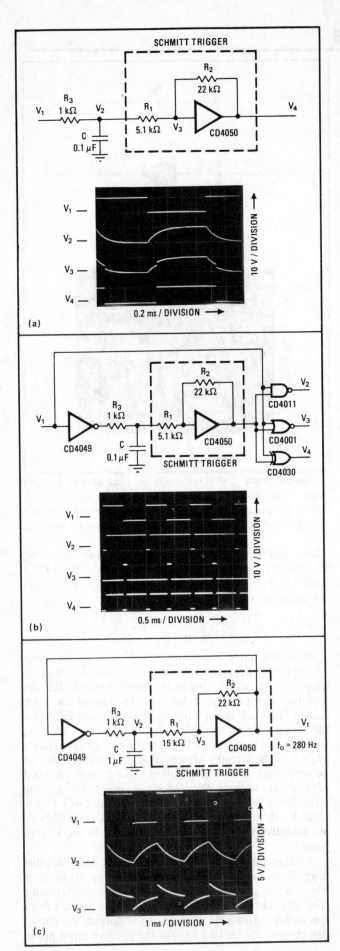

(a)

(b)

(c)

2. Applications. With an RC network at its input, the C-MOS Schmitt trigger can operate as a delay element (a), an edge detector (b), or an oscillator (c). Depending on the output gate employed, the edge detector will mark leading and/or trailing pulse edges.

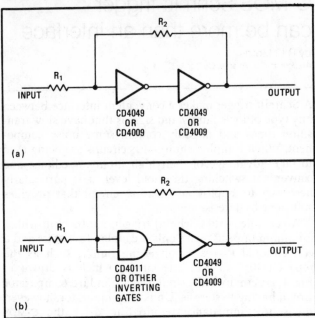

(a)

(b)

3. Alternate implementations. Instead of a buffer, two inverting-type C-MOS gates can be used to obtain a Schmitt trigger, as long as very fast output transitions are not needed. Two inverters can be substituted, as in (a), or, as in (b), a gate and an inverter.

With a NOR gate at the output, the circuit detects only the trailing edge of the positive input pulse. And with an exclusive-OR gate at its output, the circuit will detect both edges of the input pulse, as well as doubling the input pulse frequency. Output pulse width for this edge detector is controlled by the delay introduced by the RC network.

The delay element can also be used to construct a simple RC oscillator, as shown in Fig. 2c. Because of the Schmitt trigger circuit, the slow transition from the RC network is never applied directly to the device being driven by the oscillator. In this circuit, the hysteresis range of the C-MOS Schmitt trigger is expanded to make use of the RC time constant. By increasing the value of resistor R_1, the hysteresis voltage of the Schmitt-trigger portion of the oscillator is raised to 6.4 V.

For designs where only one or a few Schmitt triggers are needed, it may be desirable to use some other C-MOS device, rather than the CD4050 buffer. Any two inverting-type gates can be substituted, as indicated in Fig. 3. Although a buffer is preferable for driving resistor R_2, a gate-type device, which has a lower output drive, will do, provided that the proper values are selected for resistors R_1 and R_2. The lower-gain gate-type device will result in slower output transition times.

If several Schmitt triggers are needed for a design project, dual-in-line packaged resistor networks, instead of discrete resistors, can be used to help conserve circuit board space. ☐

Touch switch enters data without extra components

by Kim Rubin
University of California, Berkeley, Calif.

A clocked touch switch provides a convenient way to enter data into a microcomputer because no additional circuitry is required. And, since touch switches don't bounce, debounce software routines are unnecessary. If a finger is on the switch when it is clocked, the switch produces a short output pulse. No pulse is produced if the switch is not being touched.

A microcomputer receives data through an input in-struction that typically entails the use of a negative-go-ing input pulse $\bar{I}$. This pulse strobes the latch that con-nects the data bus or data source to the computer. When the data source is the clocked touch switch, the $\bar{I}$ pulse can be used to clock the switch. The output data pulse from the switch has a duration of about 2 micro-seconds, which is long enough for the computer to ac-cept the data.

The figure shows a touch switch interfaced to a micro-computer through an Intel 8212 latch. While the switch is touched, the strobe pulse appears on the data line as a logic 0. When the switch is not touched, no pulse ap-pears on the data line in response to the strobe, so a logic 1 is read in.

Although an Intel 8212 I/O port is shown, a Motorola MC6820 peripheral input adapter or an Intel 8255 pro-gramable peripheral interface may be used. □

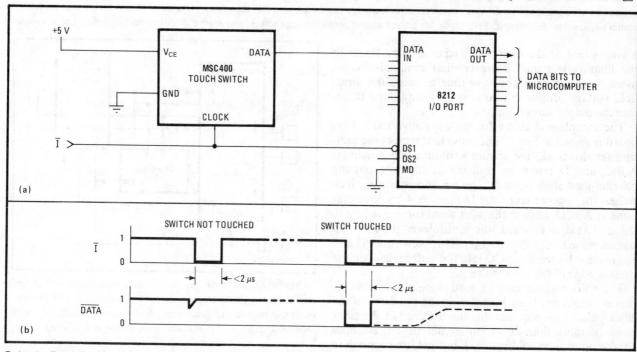

Data at a fingertip. Clocked touch switch feeds logic 1s or 0s into computer through I/O latch (a). Strobe that enables latch also clocks the touch switch and appears on data line as a logic 0 if switch is touched (b). Dashed line indicates what happens when the strobe stays low.

TTL IC serves as touch keyboard.

by David Cockerell
Electronic Music Studios (London) Ltd., London, England

The terminals of a $2 multiplexer IC can be used as a contactless keyboard to produce binary-coded output. The IC is mounted on a printed-circuit board, and its terminals are connected to finger-tip-size touch pads. During scanning of the 16 multiplexer inputs, which are actually NAND-gate terminals, a number is generated at the output only when the corresponding pad is touched by an operator's finger.

The transistor-transistor-logic NAND gate in Fig. 1 il-lustrates the operating principle of this keyboard. If one input of the gate is pulsed high while the other input terminal is allowed to float, the stray capacitance of the floating terminal (typically 3 picofarads) is charged by a current of about 1 milliampere. This makes the floating terminal also go high, and the two high inputs result in

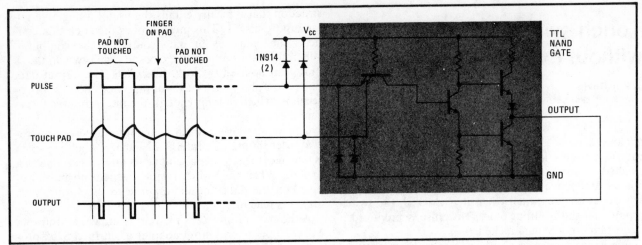

1. Touch control. Operator's finger on terminal of TTL NAND gate makes output stay high when other input is pulsed. Output is generated by addition of capacitance from finger—no switches or leads are required. Using this technique, 16-terminal IC can be contactless touch-control keyboard for BCD output. External diodes protect against positive voltage spikes, and internal diodes protect against negative spikes.

a low output. If the operator touches a 30-pF finger to the floating terminal, however, that terminal charges more slowly; it does not have time to reach the threshold voltage (unless the pulse is very long), and therefore the output stays high.

The complete circuitry for the capacitive touch keyboard is shown in Fig. 2. The pulse that strobes the multiplexer also clocks the scanning counter, which delivers A,B,C, and D inputs to both the multiplexer and the parallel-load shift register. During 16 successive clock pulses, the counter scans the 16 possible 4-bit combinations at ABCD, and, at the 4-bit word corresponding to the pad that is touched, the multiplexer produces an output pulse to the shift register. This pulse (into S1 and S0) loads 4-bit word ABCD into the shift register on the trailing edge of the clock pulse.

The shift register can be loaded only if the multiplexer output has been high during the last 20 ns of the clock pulse. This requires that the duration of the clock pulse be more than 20 ns (to let untouched terminals charge up to threshold voltage), but not long enough to let the touched pad charge. A pulse duration of 50 ns has been used successfully.

If the input current to a pad were unusually low, the pulse might have to be longer. Manufacturers of TTL specify only a maximum value for input current, but in fact, the spread in values is less than two to one from one device to another, and is even less between terminals on the same chip. To minimize the effect of this spread without having to adjust each circuit, fixed capacitance of the touch pads should be kept low.

The clock frequency is not critical. It merely must be

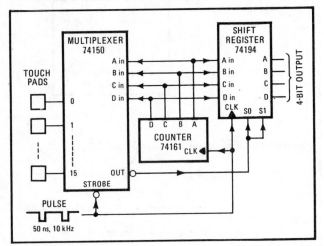

2. Keyboard. Complete circuit for contactless touch-control keyboard uses multiplexer, counter, and parallel-load shift register. Pulse that strobes multiplexer also clocks scanning counter into shift register on its trailing edge. Output from register is 4-bit word.

low enough to allow 10-nanoampere inter-emitter leakage to discharge the touch pads between scans. A clock frequency of 10 kilohertz has operated satisfactorily.

The wise designer will add diodes to clamp the pads to V_{CC} because rubber shoes on nylon carpets can produce some horrifying voltages—as high as 10 kv for a man, and 20 kv for a woman—that can easily destroy the emitter junction of a gate. These diodes, included in Fig. 1, protect against positive voltage spikes. The internal ground-clamping diodes provide protection against negative spikes. □

Opto-isolators couple
CRT terminals to printer lines

by Andrew Longacre, Jr.
University of New Orleans, New Orleans, La..

When a terminal with a cathode-ray-tube display replaces a teleprinter terminal at the end of a full-duplex 20-milliampere current loop, the new interface is often complicated by the fact that the current loop must not be grounded at the terminal end. The University of New Orleans ran into this problem recently. It wanted to plug new CRT terminals into existing teleprinter hookups in its university-wide time-shared computer network in which the current loops are grounded at the computer. It succeeded with a simple and direct interface—receiving and sending circuits that are built round a pair of opto-isolators and take full advantage of the current driven in the loops.

Each circuit uses the 20-mA loop current to power one side of its opto-isolator. In the receiving circuit, which carries signals going to the screen of the terminal, the loop current directly drives the isolator's light-emitting diode, and the emitted light drives the integral photo-Darlington pair into saturation. ASCII-encoded signals occur as momentary interruptions in the 20-mA current, which in turn cause the photo-Darlington to cut off. The operational amplifier senses this condition and generates positive pulses corresponding to the interruptions.

The sending circuit, which carries signals coming from the keyboard, employs an analog comparator to sense the sign of the terminal's output and drive the opto-isolator LED on for the normally negative output. Once again, the light emitted from the LED saturates the photo-Darlington pair, which in turn drives the 2N4401 npn transistor into saturation so that it easily passes the 20-mA loop current. ASCII-encoded symbols occur here as positive pulses leaving the terminal, causing the LED to be turned off, the transistors to be cut off, and thus

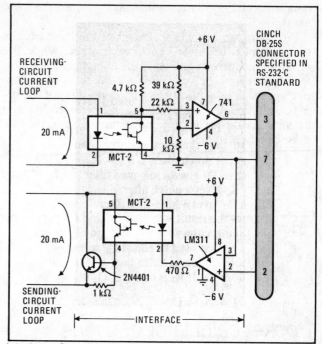

Interface. Opto-isolator couples CRT-display terminal to current loops used for electromechanical teleprinters, in arrangement where loops are not grounded at the terminals. Output of the graphic terminal is compatible with RS-232-C standard, which specifies signal levels and connector types for a modem/teleprinter interface.

the loop current to be interrupted periodically.

Two device characteristics primarily determine the maximum speed of the interface. In the receiving circuit, the output slew rate of the 741 proves the limiting factor, and the relatively low ±6-volt supplies were chosen to minimize its effect. In the sending circuit, the slowest part—indeed, the slowest link in the entire interface—is the phototransistor, which, however, would take even longer to turn off completely if it weren't for the 1-kilohm resistor.

In a closed-loop mode over more than 200 feet of cable, these interface circuits have run reliably and without errors at speeds up to 4,800 baud (480 characters per second). □

IC timer can function
as low-cost line receiver

by John G. Pate
Orbitec Corp., Carmel Valley, Calif.

Sometimes the operating speed of TTL or DTL circuits can be a handicap, rather than an advantage. This is especially true in many control circuits where system speed is limited by electromechanical devices. Furthermore, these electromechanical devices can generate cur-

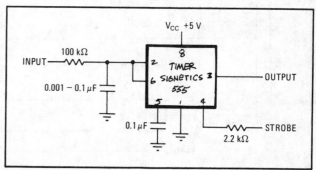

Interface circuit. Timer makes excellent line receiver for control applications involving relatively slow electromechanical devices. It can work without special drivers over single unshielded lines.

rent and voltage transients that may get into the logic paths.

Problems can become severe when the logic circuits to be coupled are not close to each other. While the standard line drivers and receivers offer a good solution to this problem, they are often not the most cost-effective approach in applications where speed is not important. Additionally, these drivers and receivers require an interface device at each end of the line; and the line must be a twisted pair.

However, the 555-type timer IC can be employed as a level-sensing device. When preceded by an RC integrator, the timer makes a noise-immune line receiver that has a high input impedance and requires no special driver at the sending end. Moreover, besides providing an output that is directly TTL-compatible, the timer can operate from a 5-volt supply. Only one signal conductor is required, and it can be unshielded.

The timing capacitance used should be as large as possible, consistent with the system's operating speed. A low signal on the strobe line holds the output low. □

Pocket calculator converts to keyboard entry station

by Fred W. Etcheverry
SWRL Educational Research & Development, Los Alamitos, Calif.

A low-cost data-entry device can be built from a pocket calculator, without disturbing its calculator functions, by connecting a few wires from easily located internal points to a few simple logic circuits.

In a typical calculator, the keyboard is a matrix switch. When power is on, the rows of the keyboard are rapidly and continuously scanned in sequence. Depressing any key makes a connection from one row circuit to one column circuit; the particular combination of row and column identifies the key and, in the calculator, initiates a function such as entering a digit into a register or executing an arithmetic operation on previously entered numbers.

Bringing the row and column signals outside the calculator to similar external logic circuits permits the key to be similarly identified and can initiate another function.

As shown in Fig. 1, two 1-out-of-N encoders convert the row and column signals into unique combinations of bits. All column signals go through an OR or NOR gate, then through a delay, and finally to a retriggerable one-shot circuit. The delay insures that the column signal is neither a legitimate key depression that has just caught the trailing edge of a scanning pulse, nor a spurious noise pulse. As long as any key is held down, the one-shot is repeatedly retriggered, providing an n-key rollover function to protect against accidental

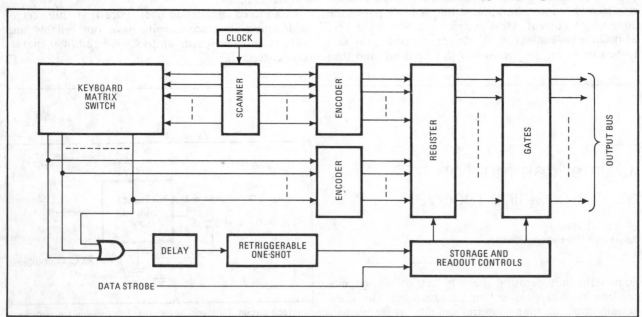

1. Keyboard functions. Standard row-and-column signals from a calculator keyboard can be encoded into a data word and stored in a register for gating onto a bus to any kind of digital system. All added components are standard integrated circuits.

multiple key depressions. The rise of the one-shot's output stores the encoded data corresponding to the key depressed—the first, if more than one—into a set of flip-flops. From these the data is available for use in any system requiring the keyboard entry.

A specific interface based on a Bowmar MX-50 calculator is shown in Fig. 2. The keyboard on this calculator has 18 keys in a 5-by-4 matrix, requiring a total of nine external connections to bring out the row and column signals. These are numbered P1 through P9, left to right as seen on the keyboard with the display facing up, after the calculator's cover is removed.

Each of the nine lines is connected to a voltage divider and a transistor to convert the calculator's MOS signal level to TTL. The new levels are inverted and encoded by five NAND gates in two ICs—all of a triple

3-input and half of a quadruple 2-input—and stored by five D-type flip-flops (two per IC package) in such a way that every key turns on at least one flip-flop, as shown by the encoder output listings in Fig. 2.

Meanwhile the four column lines are delayed by an RC network that filters out any spurious or trailing-edge pulses and triggers the one-shot. Its rise stores the data in the five flip-flops, and turns on a sixth flip-flop to indicate that the data word has been stored. An external-data strobe signal repeatedly attempts to set a seventh flip-flop, but is unable to do so until the latter has been conditioned by the sixth one. The seventh flip-flop transfers the data onto an external bus through a set of open-collector gates, and indirectly clears the whole register and, via another one-shot, prepares the data entry station for another key signal. □

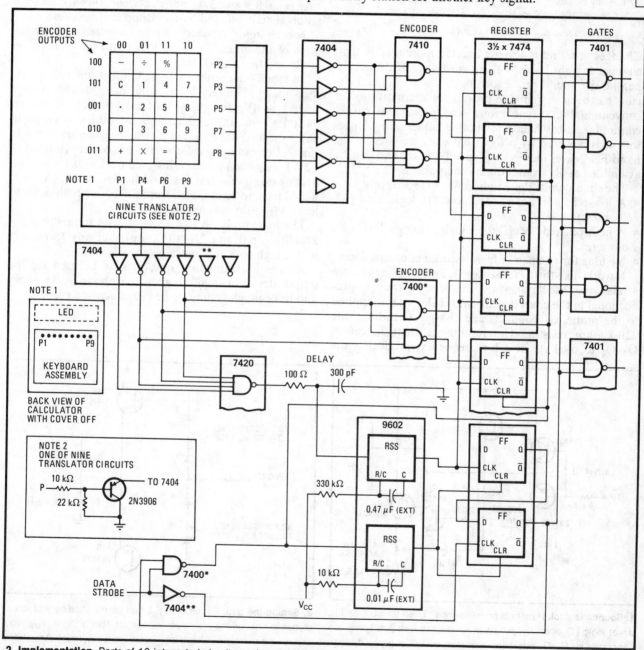

2. Implementation. Parts of 12 integrated circuits packages, plus a few discrete components, bring keyboard signals out to external bus. Only one external signal—the data strobe—is required; it sets the data on the bus and clears the register.

Low-priced logic probe indicates levels with tones

by T. Kelly Butler
Applied Research Laboratories, University of Texas, Austin, Texas

Changes in sound tones are detected more readily than changes in light levels. Taking advantage of this fact, a penlite-size sound probe for troubleshooting digital circuits has been designed to provide an alternative to the conventional LED-type probe. The probe also checks continuity and is handy for testing cables and connectors. It is powered by two AA batteries mounted in the hand-held case, requires no on/off switch, and can be assembled easily from ordinary components.

The circuit emits these indications of logic levels:
- A low-pitched "boop" for a low TTL-logic level (0.8 volt or less).
- A high-pitched "beep" for a high TTL-logic level (3.0 V or more).
- No tone for an open or high-impedance connection.

It works like this: Transistors Q_4 and Q_5 (Fig. 1) form a relaxation oscillator whose frequency is roughly proportional to the charging current I. If logic LO is applied to the probe, Q_1 conducts and charges C through the 220-kilohm resistor. The resulting current I_L causes Q_4–Q_5 to oscillate at a low frequency, producing the "boop" sound. Logic HI will turn on Q_2 and Q_3, causing I_H to flow through the 15-kΩ resistor. Since I_H is larger than I_L, Q_4–Q_5 oscillates faster, producing the "beep" sound. A dead-band effect occurs if the probe tip is left open or if the applied voltage falls between the maximum value of V_{LO} and the minimum value of V_{HI} (i.e., between 0.8 V and 3.0 V for the circuit shown); all transistors remain off, and battery drain is almost zero.

The charging resistors can be adjusted to vary the pitch of the tones. The logic probe in Fig. 1 has f_{LO} = 60 Hz and f_{HI} = 2,000 Hz.

To modify the probe for logic families other than TTL, the voltage of battery B_1 must be changed. This voltage should be $[V_{LO}(max) + V_{HI}(min)]/2$, but, of course, batteries come in standard sizes, so values of $V_{HI}(min)$ and $V_{LO}(max)$ are adjusted by use of diodes as shown in Fig. 2. For example, if B_1 were a 2-v battery (instead of 1.5-v), $V_{LO}(max)$ could be lowered back to 0.8 v by connecting one diode in series with the base of Q_1. (A diode would have to be removed from the base circuit of Q_2 to leave $V_{HI}(min)$ unchanged.)

The logic probe in Fig. 1 uses silicon transistor types 2N4401 (npn) and 2N4403 (pnp), but any transistors with a high gain and low leakage will serve.

Although a miniature speaker may be used for the output device, a small magnetic earphone works nicely and has enough volume to be heard across a room. □

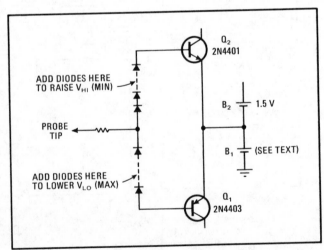

1. Sounds logical. Handheld probe "boops" when tip touches TTL pin at logic LO, and "beeps" when tip touches a HI pin. Tones are generated by Q_4–Q_5 relaxation oscillator, with C charged through 220 kΩ if LO voltage is applied, or through 15 kΩ if HI voltage is applied. Voltages between $V_{LO}(max)$ and $V_{HI}(min)$ produce no output.

2. Setting the gap. Circuit of Fig. 1 can be modified by addition of diodes to change the maximum voltage for "boop" tone, $V_{LO}(max)$, and/or the minimum voltage for "beep" tone, $V_{HI}(min)$. Any silicon diodes can be used; the voltage drop is about 0.5 volt per diode at the low diode currents.

TTL level tester identifies logic levels by audible tone

by John M. Jamieson
Technical Analysis Corp., Atlanta, Ga.

When checking a large number of test points for static TTL levels, turning one's attention from a probe to an oscilloscope or voltmeter is inconvenient and time-consuming at best, and disastrous if the probe should slip off the pin to contact a nearby high-voltage bus. This circuit was designed to simplify such checking.

The circuit produces one of two tones in an earphone or loudspeaker: low-pitched when the probe is in contact with a pin at less than 0.8 volt, and higher-pitched when the voltage is between 2.0 and 5.0 v. If the voltage is between 0.8 and 2.0 v, or if the test point is an open circuit, no tone is produced. The circuit uses a single quad operational amplifier such as the National Semiconductor LM324; two amplifiers serve as comparators and the other two generate the tones.

As shown in the diagram, the comparators test the voltage on the probe for one of the two TTL levels. Pin 3, the non-inverting input of one comparator, is held at 0.8 v by a 100-kilohm resistor R in series with two forward-biased diodes. When the probe is on an open circuit, the inverting input of the same comparator (pin 2) is held at about 1.5 v by a voltage divider R_2-R_3. Because the inverting input is at a higher level than the non-inverting input, the output (pin 1) of this comparator is near ground; but if a voltage less than 0.8 v is applied to the probe, the output goes to about 5 v.

Likewise, pin 13, the inverting input of the other comparator, is held at 2.0 v by another voltage divider, R_4-R_5. Here again, when the probe is on an open circuit, the inverting input is higher and the output (pin 14) is near ground; but if a voltage higher than 2.0 v is applied, the output goes to about 5 v.

When both pins 1 and 14 are near ground, pin 6 is also near ground, held there by the 1-megohm resistor, R_6; pin 7, the output of the tone generator, is near the supply voltage, 5 v. From this the 0.01-microfarad capacitor, C_1, is charged through resistor R_7.

When pin 1 rises to its higher level, the 0.33-μF capacitor, C_2, charges through the 10-kilohm resistor, R_8. Likewise, when pin 14 is high, C_2 charges, more quickly this time, through the 2.2-kilohm resistor, R_9. Either way, when it exceeds the 2.0-v level on pin 5, the output of the tone generator drops to ground, and C_1 discharges. Eventually its level drops below that same 2.0 v, also on pin 9, dropping the output of the fourth amplifier, pin 8, to ground. That discharges C_2 and the cycle begins again.

Thus the signal on pin 7 is a square wave, the frequency of which is determined by the rate at which C_2 charges—through either R_8 or R_9. At either frequency, the square wave is approximately symmetrical, because C_1 both charges and discharges at all times through R_7.

The output on pin 7 is sufficient to drive most earphones. Additional loading affects the absolute values of the two frequencies, but not their relative values. If the earphones are unsatisfactory for any reason, the 10-kilohm resistor R_{10} and a pnp emitter follower Q_1 can drive a small loudspeaker. □

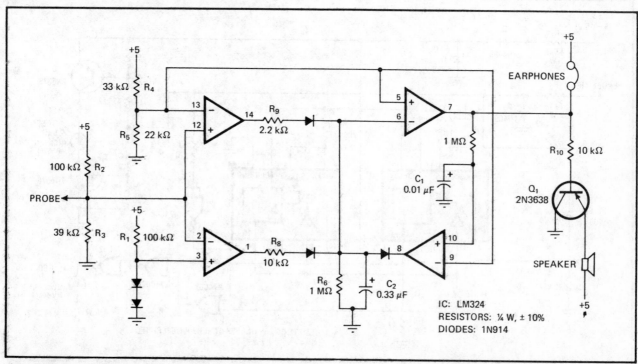

Beep-beep, boop-boop. Checking for static TTL levels is simplified when the voltage level is indicated by one of two audible tones in an earphone or loudspeaker. This circuit does the trick with only one quad op amp for level-comparing and tone-generating.

Versatile logic probe displays four modes

by Gordon W. Martin
Bendix Environmental and Process Instruments Division, Lewisburg, W. Va.

In addition to indicating static states—high and low logic levels as well as open-circuited nodes—an inexpensive logic probe can be built to indicate a pulse train by flashing. Packaged in a pen-type flashlight or similar enclosure, the probe performs as well as commercial models at a fraction of their cost, and it is compatible with both complementary-metal-oxide-semiconductor and transistor-transistor-logic voltage levels.

A pair of light-emitting diodes—red and green—indicates the various states in accordance with the truth table shown below. As evident from the schematic, the green LED glows only when the input is connected to a high impedance or open-circuited logic node; because neither situation affects the quiescent on state of Q_1 or Q_2, current flows through the LED. Application of a logic-1 or logic-0 level to the probe input turns off Q_1 or Q_2 respectively, and, in either event, the green LED goes off. The NOR gates turn on the red LED when a logic-1 input is applied through current-limiting resistor R_6. Note that the red LED will also glow when the 1Q output

of the dual monostable multivibrator goes high. The monostable is employed solely for the fourth condition in the truth table—the dynamic input of a pulse train to the probe.

The 74C221 C-MOS dual monostable has both positive- and negative-transition-triggering inputs, either of which can be used to inhibit the other—the output Q remains low whenever input A is high or input B is low. Firing the monostable generates a positive pulse at Q that has its duration determined by an external RC time constant. A pulse-train input to the probe is ac-coupled and shaped through C_1 and R_3 to the positive-transition input of the first monostable, 1B. The 1Q output then goes high for $T = R_4 \times C_2 = 200$ kilohms $\times$ 1.0 microfarad = 200 milliseconds. Upon returning to the low state, the 1Q output triggers the second monostable through negative-transition input 2A, and its 2Q output goes high, inhibiting the first monostable through input 1A for an additional $T = R_5 \times C_3 = 200$ kΩ $\times$ 1.0μF = 200 ms. After this 400-ms period, the monostables are ready for triggering by the next positive transition at 1B, and hence the system exhibits a characteristic frequency of 2.5 hertz or $(400 \text{ ms})^{-1}$, regardless of the input-pulse frequency. The 2.5-Hz signal at 1Q is coupled through the NOR gates to flash the red LED at this rate.

The OR gate consisting of D_3, D_4, and R_7 ensures positive indication of pulse-train inputs, irrespective of symmetry or duty cycle. Waveforms with very low or very high duty cycles, which could not otherwise be

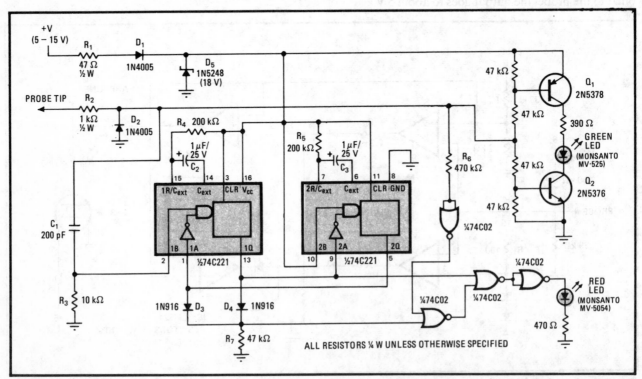

Discriminating probe. A 74C221 dual monostable and a 74C02 quad NOR gate enable this logic probe to indicate pulse trains as well as static inputs. Housed in a pen-type case with clip leads for ground and supply connections, the unit simplifies digital troubleshooting.

RESPONSES OF LOGIC PROBE		
Input condition	Output indication	
	Red LED	Green LED
Open circuit (Hi-Z)	Off	On
Logic 0	Off	Off
Logic 1	On	Off
Pulse train	Flashes at 2.5 Hz	Off

distinguished from constant-dc levels, will therefore flash the red LED at the 2.5-Hz rate.

The probe input is protected from negative-polarity signals by R_2 and D_2. The unit, which will operate from any 5-v to 15-v source, is protected against overvoltage by D_5 and R_1 and against the wrong supply-voltage polarity by D_1. Logic-level thresholds are about 20% and 80% of the supply voltage, and the probe draws only about 10 milliamperes from a 5-v source. □

Two-color LED pair is digital status indicator

by Bill Schweber
GTE Sylvania, Needham, Mass.

A red-and-green LED pair in a single package, such as the Monsanto MV 5491, can serve as a status indicator for digital levels with a single supply-voltage circuit. The polarity across the LED is reversed by changing the relative potentials at the two LED terminals, rather than by having one of its terminals at ground and putting positive and negative voltages on the other.

An on/off line enables the entire indicator. Transistors Q_1 and Q_2 serve as LED drivers. When the red/green control line is high (and the enable line is high), the output of gate A is low, turning Q_1 off, while gate C's output is high, so Q_2 is on. Current goes through limiting resistor R_1, and the LED glows red.

When the control line is low, the situation reverses, as does the difference of potential across the LED, which

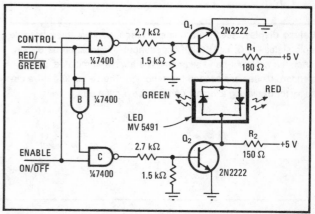

Logic probe. A red-and-green LED packaged pair, such as the Monsanto MV 5491, can serve as a status indicator for digital levels.

glows green with R_2 limiting current. Note that R_1 and R_2 are of different values because of the different forward drop across the LED, depending on which way it is biased. Pulling the enable line low causes the outputs of gates A and C to go high, so Q_1 and Q_2 turn on, putting both ends of the LED at the same potential; therefore the LED stays off. □

Adding numeric readout to logic probe displays

by Kai Lanz
Stanford University, Stanford, Calif.

Not too long ago, logic probes were little more than a light bulb, plus the necessary driver circuitry. Nowadays, however, they are more likely to consist of three light-emitting diodes, indicating the three possible logic states—logic 1, logic 0, and high impedance. And with

three flashing displays crowded into the narrow probe body, it is not uncommon to have to pause and check which legend is actually illuminated. A simple way to build a compact probe readout that is unambiguous and easy to decipher is to substitute a solid-state numeric readout for the three discrete LEDs.

The figure shows a seven-segment readout connected to display 0, 1, and H (for high impedance). The two right-hand segments are on at all times since they are tied directly to the 5-volt supply. A pair of diodes serves as a simple decoding network to prevent undesired segments from lighting. Any good general-purpose silicon diodes should be adequate, but devices having a low forward voltage drop will help to equalize segment brightness.

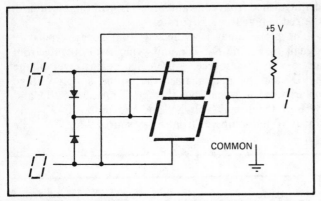

Deluxe display. Solid-state numeric readout shows three possible logic states—1, 0, or H (high impedance)—for logic-probe display. Since the two right-hand segments are always illuminated, only two standard diodes are needed for decoding. The sense and drive circuitry for displaying a logic 1 can then be eliminated.

The cost of building a logic probe this way is less than the cost of building one with three discrete LEDs. With the numeric readout connected as shown, the sense and drive circuitry for displaying a logic 1 can be eliminated because the 1 is always lit.

The readout's power requirement averages about 10 milliamperes per segment. Miniature readouts, such as Monsanto's MAN-3A, are slim enough to mount without difficulty in the end of the probe body, where they will be readily visible. □

TTL logic tester displays H or L

by Andrzej Gorajek
Polish Radio and TV Research Department, Warsaw, Poland

One of the world's simplest logic testers for integrated circuits can be built of a single transistor-transistor-logic package and a seven-segment light-emitting diode. The setup displays an H when the probe of the tester is floating or touching a pin at high logic level. When the probe touches a pin at the low logic level, the LED displays an L. As shown in the figure, gates G_1 and G_2, together with resistors R_1 and R_2, form a simple voltage monitor that has a trip point of 1.4 volts. Gate G_3 is simply an inverter.

The display section of the tester consists of the common-anode alphanumeric LED and current-limiting resistors R_3, R_4, and R_5. At TTL-voltage levels, the resistors limit the current through each segment to about 10 milliamperes. And since segments e and f are grounded through R_5, they are always lighted.

When the input voltage at the probe is less than the

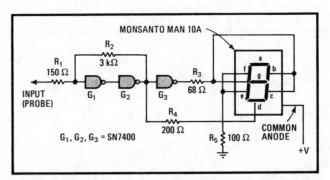

IC logic tester for TTL. Voltage monitor, which indicates whether input voltage is above or below 1.4 volts, displays an H or an L (for high or low logic-level) respectively. For high-impedance state or floating input, an H is displayed.

1.4-v trip point, the output of G_2 is low, and segment d lights up. Then segments d, e, and f are on, and the LED appears as an L. When the input level is greater than 1.4 V, the output of G_3 is low. Segments b, c, and g light up and, along with e and f, form an H. If the clock signal is applied to the tester, the LED displays a superposition of L and H—an H.

This complete tester can be mounted in a small plastic package, and its power supply can be taken from the circuit under test. □

26. Offbeat measurement techniques

Diode or transistor makes fully linear thermometer

by Cameron J. Koch
Ontario Cancer Foundation, London, Ont., Canada

An electronic thermometer circuit that uses a semiconductor diode or a transistor as its sensor can produce an output voltage that varies linearly with temperature. The voltage across the diode or the base-to-emitter junction of the transistor changes at –2.2 millivolts per degree celsius if the current through the junction is held constant. Previous circuits with such sensors have been nonlinear at low temperatures [*Electronics*, March 20, 1975], but this difficulty is easy to overcome.

The trick is to use a bipolar power supply so that the sensor's amplifier is not forced to operate near its V– supply voltage. The thermometers described here use this kind of supply, and both are linear and accurate to within 0.05°C. Self-heating of the sensors is extremely small, because they operate at about 50-microwatt power levels.

In the transistor-sensor circuit (Fig. 1a), the potential of the noninverting input of the op amp is set by resistor divider R_4 and R_5 between ground and B–. The output of the amplifier then drives the R_1-R_2 divider and the base of the sensing transistor via R_6. As a result, enough current flows through emitter resistor R_3 to make the potential at the emitter (and hence at the inverting input of the amplifier) the same as the potential at the noninverting input.

The operation of the circuit depends on the necessity for the emitter current I_E to remain constant in order to provide a constant potential at the inverting input of the amplifier. The base current I_B is just $I_E/(1+h_{FE})$; since I_B is constant, the base-to-emitter voltage depends only on the temperature of the transistor. Hence the output, which is proportional to the base-emitter voltage, is in turn proportional to the absolute temperature.

Neither the temperature variation of h_{FE} nor the collector-to-base leakage current affects the operation of the thermometer circuit significantly. The value of h_{FE} varies very slowly with temperature, and I_{CBO} is much smaller than the forward base-emitter current. The Analog Devices AD811 transistor used for the sensor has extremely low leakage.

The zero point is set by potentiometer R_4 and the gain by potentiometer R_6. Since the two adjustments interact somewhat, two or three iterations of the calibration are necessary. At the slight expense of an increased output impedance, it's possible to remove the interdependence of zero and gain controls by using a fixed feedback resistor for R_6 and connecting a 10-kilohm potentiometer between the output of the amplifier and ground. Then the overall circuit output becomes the wiper and ground terminals of the pot.

Figure 1b shows the output voltage as a function of ambient temperature at the transistor. The calibration adjustments were set for an output of –1 volt at 50°C. The line connecting the experimental points was drawn with a straight edge.

The sensor is fabricated by sealing the transistor—preferably along with a little dessicant—into thin stainless steel tubing with silicone rubber. Both the tubing and the collector are grounded. The unit operates satis-

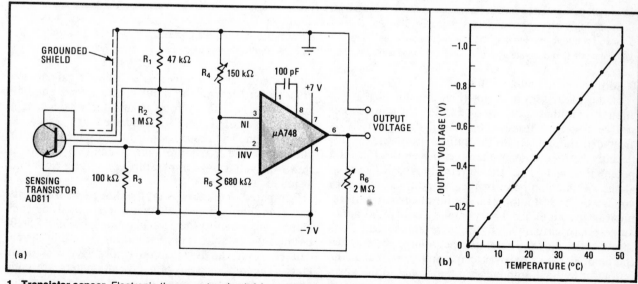

1. Transistor sensor. Electronic thermometer circuit (a) uses a low-leakage transistor to produce an output voltage that varies linearly with temperature. The fixed voltage applied to the noninverting input of op amp is matched by the constant emitter-current drop through R_3. Output voltage varies with temperature-dependent junction voltage to hold emitter current constant. Zero point is set by R_4 and gain by R_6. Response curve (b) is linear to within the 0.05°C accuracy of calibrating thermometers.

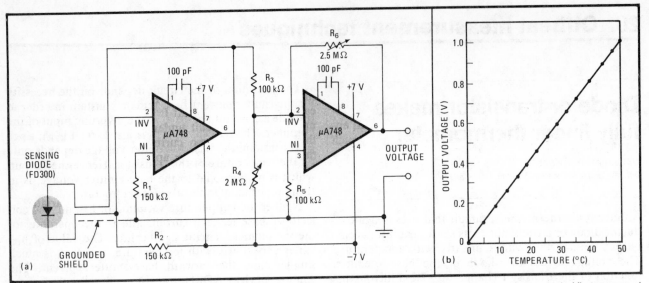

2. Diode sensor. In thermometer circuit with diode (a), constant diode-junction current through R_2 keeps inverting terminal of first op amp at same potential as grounded noninverting terminal. Output voltage varies with temperature-dependent diode drop to hold current constant. Second op amp allows zero adjustment through R_4 and gain control through R_6. Response curve (b) is linear within measurement accuracy.

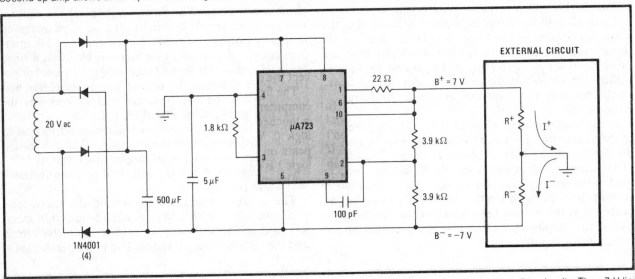

3. Supplying power. Precision voltage regulator IC is heart of this ±7-V power supply for low-current instrumentation circuits. The −7-V line is a stable reference for the thermometer circuits because it is just the reference voltage of the integrated circuit, with no temperature-dependent elements to reduce stability; the + 7-V stability is limited by the temperature dependence of the output transistor in the device.

factorily, even in boiling water.

In the diode-sensor circuit (Fig. 2a), the first operational amplifier acts as a simple constant-current source for the diode. The noninverting input is grounded through R_1, so the output always moves sufficiently positive to keep the inverting input at ground potential as well. Thus the current through R_2 is set at about −50 microamperes by the ground-to-B^- reference voltage (−7 v/150 kilohms). The input current requirement of the amplifier is very small (less than 50 nanoamperes), so virtually all of this (constant) current flows through the diode. Therefore, the voltage drop across the diode depends only on temperature, and hence the output of the first amplifier is proportional to the absolute temperature.

Since most temperature measurements are made in the range of 270 to 370 K (0–100°C), a second amplifier is used to offset the diode voltage to whatever tempera-

ture range is desired and also to provide gain. Potentiometer R_4 between the input of the second amplifier and ground sets the output at zero for whatever temperature is chosen (i.e. 0°C), and feedback resistor R_6 sets the gain. The input resistor to this stage, R_3, is 100 kilohms, so the maximum gain is about 25. Figure 2b shows the voltage-vs-temperature curve for a circuit adjusted to give 1 V at 50°C.

Compared to the transistor, the diode sensor is a little harder to fabricate and shield effectively by using commercial high-quality devices like the Fairchild FD300 because the cathode is only at virtual ground in the circuit. However, the diode circuitry does have two advantages. The zeroing and gain potentiometers are completely independent, resulting in a simple calibration procedure, and since both the diode input current and zeroing current are set by the −7-v reference voltage, any slight changes in these currents caused by reference voltage changes tend to cancel. Thus the overall circuit is about half as sensitive to reference changes as the transistor-sensor circuit.

If the diode is sealed entirely within a thin piece of grounded tubing, the shielding becomes just as effective as in the transistor sensor. However, the time constant of the sensor is several times larger because of the reduced heat flow between the diode and the external environment. Even so, this time constant is not much greater than that of a typical mercury thermometer.

In both of these electronic temperature-sensing circuits, the current requirements of the outputs are very low because the operational amplifiers need only drive a high-impedance readout device such as a recorder, digital voltmeter, or microammeter. Therefore a bipolar power supply and extremely stable reference can be achieved inexpensively with a single μA723 (Fig. 3).

With this type of power supply, two conditions must be satisfied. The external circuit resistances (labeled R+ and R−) must be such that the current always flows out of the reference (i.e., I− − I+ must be positive). Also, to comply with the specifications of the integrated circuit, this current must be less than 5 milliamperes. The easiest way to ensure that I− is greater than I+ is to set up the external circuit under maximum I+ conditions, then measure the two currents and make I− greater than I+ by connecting an appropriate resistor between ground and B−.

The second condition can be met wherever the total change in I− − I+ (caused by output current variations) is less than 5 mA, as in these circuits. □

Low-cost field-strength unit uses simple buffer

by M. J. Salvati
Sony Corp. of America, Long Island City, N.Y.

Field strength at frequencies from 150 kilohertz to 30 megahertz is measured by feeding the output of a standard flat-frequency-response antenna into a tuned voltmeter. Commercially available broadband antenna-and-amplifier units suitable for this task cost about $500; however, a setup identical in function and performance can be built for about $5.

In the field-strength measurement, a vertical antenna

1. Field-strength unit. Unity-gain FET buffer amplifier is heart of this inexpensive device for measuring field strength at frequencies from 150 kHz to 30 MHz.

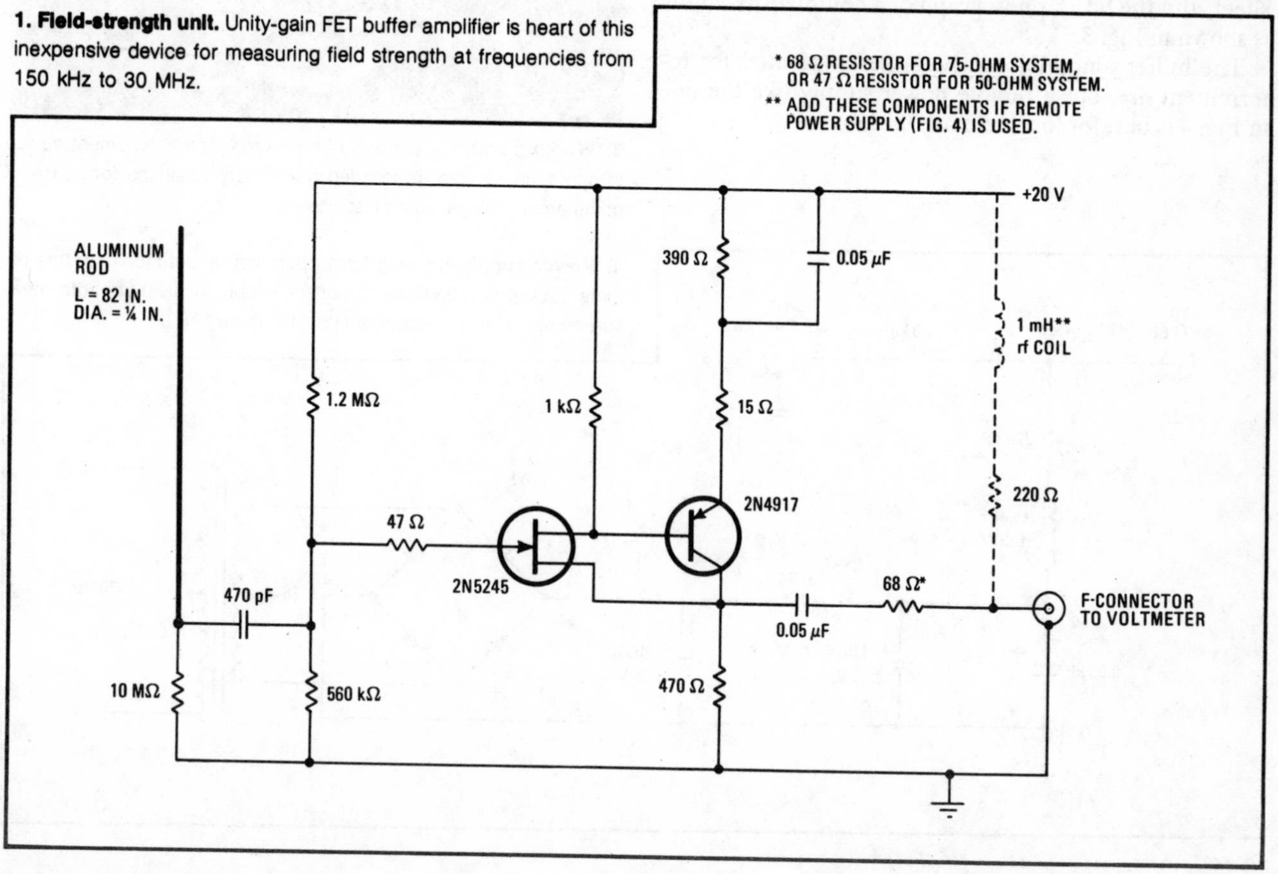

* 68 Ω RESISTOR FOR 75-OHM SYSTEM, OR 47 Ω RESISTOR FOR 50-OHM SYSTEM.
** ADD THESE COMPONENTS IF REMOTE POWER SUPPLY (FIG. 4) IS USED.

that is effectively two meters long provides an output, measured in microvolts, numerically equal to twice the ambient field strength (measured in microvolts per meter). This voltage cannot be applied directly to the tuned voltmeter because of the very high source impedance of the antenna at low frequencies. Instead, an impedance converter is used between the antenna and the tuned voltmeter (50-ohm or 75-ohm rfi receiver or spectrum analyzer). The 6-decibel loss resulting from the converter-to-voltmeter impedance match cancels the 6-dB gain produced by using an antenna two meters long; therefore, the voltage applied to the tuned voltmeter is numerically equal to the field strength, permitting direct measurement without any corrections for frequency or for antenna gain.

The heart of the device is a unity-gain buffer amplifier (shown in Fig. 1). The buffer uses a field-effect transistor and a pnp transistor connected to provide 100% negative feedback; the resulting stage has high input resistance, low input capacitance (about 4 pF), low output impedance, near-unity gain, and a frequency response that is flat to 85 MHz.

A biscuit tin about 9 inches in diameter supports the rod antenna and provides a no-cost, watertight enclosure for the buffer amplifier. At frequencies greater than 150 kHz, the loading on the antenna is determined primarily by the input capacitance—not the input resistance—of the buffer; therefore the construction technique must minimize capacitance in both the buffer amplifier and the antenna support. A suggested mechanical arrangement is shown in Fig. 2. For permanent outdoor installations, rubberized sealant should be used around the antenna-entrance hole, the Lucite sheet, and the lid. A photograph of a complete assembly is shown in Fig. 3.

The buffer amplifier can be battery-operated for intermittent use, but a remote power supply like the one in Fig. 4 is best for long-term or outdoor use. □

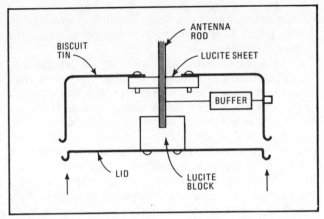

2. Assembly. Biscuit tin supports rod antenna and provides no-cost, weathertight enclosure for buffer amplifier. (In photograph below, the biscuit tin lid is screwed to a wooden board so the device won't tip over in high winds.)

3. Working unit. Photograph of field-strength measurement device in operation. Simple device described here equals performance of commercial units, at vastly less cost.

4. Power supply. For long-term operation or outdoor use, this remote source is preferable to battery supply for field-strength measurements. It increases system cost by about $10.

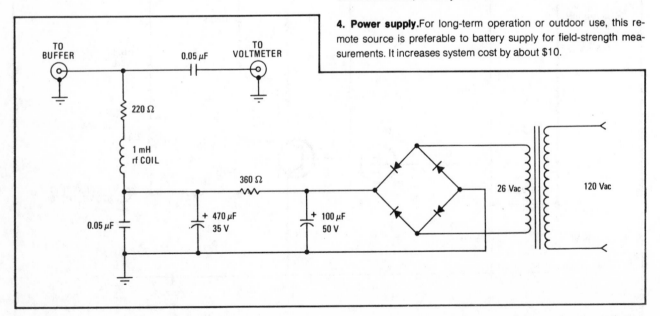

Low-cost optical sensor overcomes ambient light

by Helge H. Mortensen
National Semiconductor Corp., Santa Clara, Calif.

A low-cost solid-state optical system can be useful for measurements of light transmission or reflection in medical applications, in the manufacture of paper, textiles, and paint, and in smoke detection. This optical measurement system, which uses the conventional light-chopping technique to overcome ambient light and electrical noise, can be built for about $13.

The system (Fig. 1) consists of a light-emitting-diode source, a photodiode sensor, operational amplifier A_1, driven by the sensor, integrator operational amplifier A_2, which is connected to the output from A_1 only when the LED is off, and op amp A_3, which is connected to the output from A_1 when the LED is on. A clock drives transistor Q to turn the LED on and off, and also drives field-effect-transistor switches S_1 and S_2 to connect either A_2 or A_3 to the A_1 output.

The waveforms in Fig. 2 illustrate the operation of the system. When the LED is on, the material being tested transmits some light to the sensor. The transmitted light, plus ambient light, produces a photosensor current that is converted and amplified in A_1. Electrical noise also contributes to the output from A_1.

To make the system insensitive to the ambient light and electrical pickup, the output from A_1 when the LED is off is fed to the integrator, consisting of A_2 and C_1. The integrator output is applied to the non-inverting terminal of A_1 as an offset voltage to cancel the unwanted output, reducing the voltage from A_1 to zero when the LED is off.

When the clock turns the LED on again, it also opens S_1 to disconnect the integrator from the A_1 output. However, capacitor C_1 holds the offset voltage on the noninverting terminal, so that the net voltage from A_1 results only from the LED light.

The effect of the integrator is to measure the magnitude of the ambient light and noise while the LED is off, remember this magnitude, and subtract it from the incoming signal when the LED is on. The output from A_2 is a measure of the ambient light and noise.

While the LED is on, FET switch S_2 is closed, so the output from A_1 is applied to capacitor C_2. The capacitor holds this voltage during the off period, while S_2 is open. Thus S_2 and C_2 constitute a sample-and-hold cir-

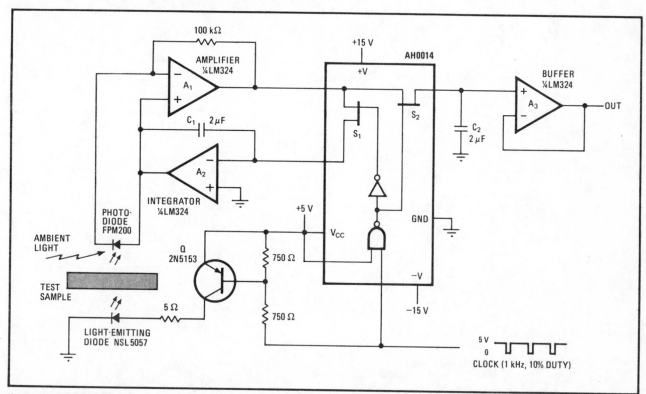

1. Keeping it light. Despite presence of ambient light, optoelectronic measurement system accurately indicates optical absorption or reflection by test sample. (For reflection measurement, geometry is changed so that LED light bounces from sample to sensor, instead of passing through sample.) Effects of stray light and electrical noise generate offset voltage that is subtracted from total voltage when LED is on.

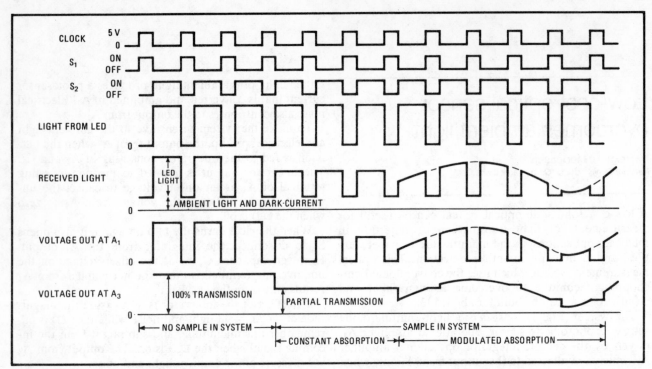

2. Chopping it right. Timing diagrams and waveforms illustrate operation of optoelectronic sensing and measurement system. Amplifier output is connected to integrator while LED is off, and integrator generates offset voltage to cancel outputs caused by ambient light and spurious voltages. When LED is on, amplifier output is connected to sample-and-hold and buffer, but offset still cancels background signals. (Proportions of timing diagrams are distorted for clarity. To avoid excessive dissipation, actual duty cycle of LED is 0.1.)

cuit. Amplifier A_3 serves as a simple output buffer, delivering the over-all output signal to whatever indicating meter or control circuit is to be driven by the optoelectronic measurement system. □

Automatic test setup checks thermal resistance

by Robert W. Bolvin
Signetics Corp., Digital Products, Sunnyvale, Calif.

Measuring the thermal resistance of microelectronic devices is usually a tedious one-device-at-a-time operation—it takes a long time to calibrate temperature-sensitive elements, to apply power to individual devices for long stabilization periods, and to calculate the thermal resistance. But with the technique described here, testing time can be cut significantly so that the thermal resistance of 40 devices can be determined in the time it previously took to measure just one device.

The equipment primarily includes an automatic dc digital IC tester, a special sequencer circuit, a modified oven setup, a liquid bath, and a high-current power supply.

The sequencer allows the thermal resistance of a large number of devices to be measured almost simultaneously. As noted in the block diagram (a), three 4-line-to-16-line decoder/demultiplexers interpret the program inputs from the automatic IC tester. These decoders provide a total of 40 output lines, one for each device being tested. Each output feeds a NAND inverter gate, a relay driver transistor, and a double-pole single-throw relay.

The circuit of (b) shows the hookup between the relay and the device under test, which, in this case, is a simple resistor/diode die. When a relay is activated by a program input, its contacts switch from their normally closed position to a normally open one. The test sequence here is designed to find diode slope with changing temperature, as well as forward voltage drop both before and after a power soak period.

Forward voltage drop is measured at six temperatures covering the expected operating temperature range, and diode slope is measured without any supply voltage applied. The dies are then brought to a specified test temperature for initial forward-voltage readings, before being exposed to a power soak period of 15 minutes. (This is long enough to allow the devices to stabilize at a constant junction temperature.) At the end of the soak period, each device is sequentially removed from the external "soak" supply and re-energized by an internal supply to determine what forward voltage it has because of power dissipation.

All the information needed to compute the slope and thermal resistance of each device is now available: the forward voltage at six temperatures, the initial forward voltage at a specified test temperature, the power applied, and the final forward voltage due to heating from the power applied.

The photos show the special door used for mounting the dies and their holders; it fits the oven and the tub employed for the liquid bath. To find the thermal resistance between a device's junction and ambient temperature, the door is placed in the oven. To measure thermal resistance between junction and case temperatures, the door is placed upside down in the liquid bath. The sequencer circuit is also mounted on the door, but can be removed by disconnecting the edge connectors on the front of the door.

The bath is made up of a stainless-steel tub that rests on two hot plates. Cooling is achieved by forcing carbon dioxide through copper tubing at the bottom of the tub. To obtain high temperatures, from 25°C to 125°C, the liquid used is ethylene glycol; for cold temperatures, from 25°C to –55°C, the liquid is Freon.

Only the extreme tips of the leads to the devices un-

Mounting. Devices to be tested are mounted on modified door (left photo), which fits an oven (right photo) as well as a heating/cooling bath.

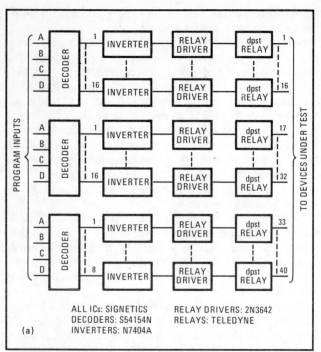

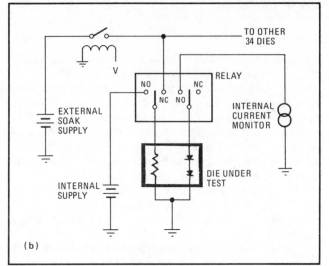

der test should be soldered, so that little or no heat sinking is provided by the solder joints. Also, it is a good idea to put cutouts in the pc board around the holder for each test device, to improve the flow of air and liquid around it. □

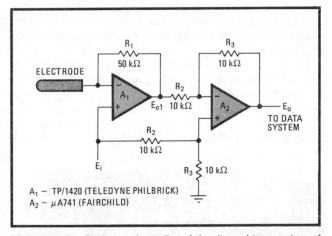

Sequencing circuitry. Sequencer (a) enables the thermal resistance of 40 devices to be determined at the same time in response to program commands from an automatic tester. In this case, resistor/diode dies (b) are measured for slope and forward voltage drop.

Op amp improves plasma probe's sensitivity

by P.J. Cherian and P.R.M. Panicker
Vikram Sarabhai Space Center, Trivandrum, India

In measuring extremely small currents, a probe electrode must have its voltage supply isolated from the current amplifier if leakage of the supply currents is not to limit the accuracy of the measurements. The need for such isolation vanishes, however, if the voltage is applied to the probe through an operational amplifier, as shown in the figure.

One use for this technique is in the measurement of the electron density and temperature of a plasma. An alternating voltage is applied to the electrode in contact with the plasma, and currents ranging from milliamperes to picoamperes are collected [*Electronics*, May 25, 1962, pp. 18–19]. The circuit shown here was developed for use in the ionosphere, with the probe projecting from the body of a rocket into the atmospheric plasma.

Voltage E_i is applied at the noninverting input terminal of operational amplifier A_1 and, because of the enormously high open-loop gain of the operational amplifier, appears at the inverting input terminal. This inverting input terminal is connected directly to the electrode without any series resistance so that currents drawn by the probe will not change the probe's voltage level. Operational amplifier A_1 has a field-effect-transistor input with a bias current of only a few picoamperes. Therefore, if I is the current drawn from the plasma, the output of A_1 is given by:

Plasma probe. Rocketsonde studies of density and temperature of electrons in the ionosphere may be achieved by measuring the current drawn to an electrode that projects out and is well insulated from the rocket body. The circuit shown here applies potential to the electrode through an op amp, thus avoiding voltage-supply-insulation problems and leakage errors in current measurement. Circuit measures currents from 10^{-3} amperes down to 5×10^{-11} A.

$$E_{o1} = E_i + IR_1$$

The second operational amplifier, A_2, is used as a differential amplifier to prevent applied voltage E_i from appearing at the output. The final output voltage is:

$$E_o = (R_3/R_2)IR_1$$

so the current drawn by the probe is given by:

$$I = R_2E_o/R_1R_3$$

The output voltage can be recorded on board the rocket

or telemetered to a ground station.

To permit measurements over a large dynamic range—a necessity in most plasma-probe measurements—feedback resistor R_1 may be replaced by a network with a logarithmic response.

The circuit has measured currents from 1 milliampere to 0.1 nanoampere. The bias current of A_1 is only 15 picoamperes, so currents as small as 50 pA can be measured.

Inductive proximity detector uses little power

by Matthew L. Fichtenbaum
General Radio Co., Concord, Mass.

A contactless limit switch and a tachometer pickup are two possible applications for the inductive proximity detector described here. This detector changes its output level from high (9 volts) to low (0 V) whenever a conducting object is close by. It uses less power than a photocell pickup and is immune to environmental dust and dirt.

The sensing element is an unshielded high-Q inductor coil wound on a ferrite core. When a metallic object is brought close to the inductor, eddy currents that are induced in the metal absorb energy from the rf field of the coil and thus reduce its Q.

The active elements in the detector circuit are four of the C-MOS MOSFETs in a CD4007A package, and two 1N3604 diodes are included. FET Q_1 and its associated components, together with the inductor, constitute an oscillator that operates at about 100 kilohertz. The two diodes develop a dc voltage proportional to the peak-to-peak value of the oscillator signal. This voltage is applied to a Schmitt trigger composed of Q_2, Q_3, and Q_4 and holds this circuit in the "on" state.

A conductive object near the coil absorbs energy from the magnetic field of the coil, so that the oscillator amplitude drops. The rectified voltage therefore drops, and the Schmitt trigger turns off. The variable resistor adjusts the oscillator's operating level and hence its sensitivity to metal objects.

The inductor used in this circuit consists of 150 turns of #34 enameled wire inside half of a Ferroxcube 1811-PL00-3B7 pot core set, as shown in the figure. The inductance is approximately 2 millihenries. The circuit can detect the presence of metal objects at distances up to a centimeter from the open end of the coil.

This circuit draws about 250 microamperes at 9 v. It may be used to drive C-MOS logic directly or to drive a buffer that in turn drives TTL.

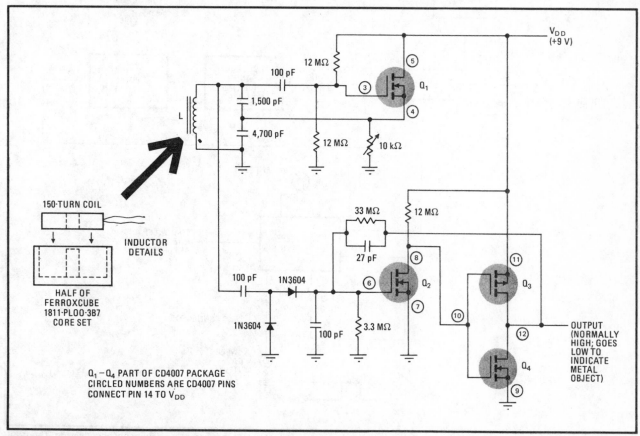

Detects metal. Proximity detector consists of modified Colpitts oscillator, amplitude detector, and Schmitt trigger. Output signal is normally high; but when oscillator coil is loaded by presence of metal object, amplitude decreases and output from Schmitt trigger goes low. Detail drawing shows construction of the oscillator coil in a proximity detector that serves as the noncontacting pickup for a tachometer.

27. Novel measurements with a scope

Scope detects narrow pulses with its triggering system

by Peter T. Uhler
Tinker Air Force Base, Midwest City, Okla.

The presence of single narrow pulses can be easily detected by an average oscilloscope without the need for special probes or adapters. By simply operating the instrument in its external-trigger mode, the scope can be made to display short-duration pulses, troubleshoot logic ICs, store a one-time transient permanently, or record transient hits. The scope's own triggering system and front-panel lamps detect the pulses.

Usually, special probes are required to detect the presence of short-duration pulses in complex logic-IC systems. These narrow pulses generally have very low repetition rates or even occur singly, making them difficult to observe on even the fastest storage scope.

What has been overlooked, however, is that the triggering system of the average scope can readily duplicate the function of these special probes while providing much more flexibility. Most modern scopes employ solid-state amplifiers coupled to tunnel-diode trigger-pulse generators, enabling them to respond to very-short-duration pulses. Such triggering systems are essential to allow triggering out to and beyond the stated bandwidth of the instrument.

Good triggering systems are designed so that if the signal can be displayed at all, the trigger generator will initiate the sweep. For example, the triggering system in the Tektronix 453A-series oscilloscope, which has a rated bandwidth of 60 megahertz, will trigger to beyond 200 MHz when signals are fed directly into its external-trigger input.

Although the measurement techniques described here apply mainly to the 453-series dual-trace scope, they should be suitable for most high-quality lab scopes with bandwidths of 50 MHz or greater. For the most part, the triggering system in these scopes can be considered to function like the one shown in the figure.

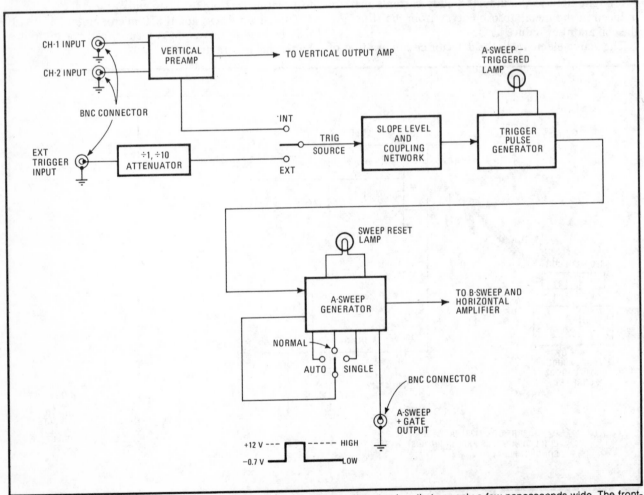

Scope triggering system. In its external trigger mode, an oscilloscope can detect pulses that are only a few nanoseconds wide. The front-panel A-sweep-triggered lamp acts as a visual monitor, lighting when the trigger pulse generator responds to a trigger signal input. Because the lamp stays lit for awhile, it acts as a pulse stretcher, enabling the operator to detect the narrow trigger signal.

Trigger signals can be either routed through the vertical preamplifier or applied directly to the external-trigger input. The latter approach bypasses the relatively bandwidth-limited preamplifier and allows the triggering system to operate to full bandwidth. All trigger signals then pass through the slope and level comparator into the tunnel-diode trigger-pulse generator, which starts the main (A) sweep.

The front-panel A-sweep-triggered lamp, along with its associated sensing and driving circuitry, monitors the trigger-pulse generator, lighting for about 100 milliseconds each time the generator recognizes a trigger signal. This one-shot characteristic of the lamp monitor effectively stretches out short-duration trigger signals so that the operator can easily detect their presence.

Just by observing this lamp, therefore, single-event pulses (that are coupled directly into the external trigger input) with amplitudes of under 250 millivolts and durations on the order of a few nanoseconds can be detected. Transistor-transistor-logic signals can also easily be coupled into the external-trigger input with a standard 10× probe. (If the Tektronix type P-6061 miniature 10× probe is equipped with a type 015-0201-00 DIP IC probe-tip adapter, the scope/probe combination becomes a compact and effective logic-IC troubleshooting tool.) The setting of the trigger-slope and level controls determines whether triggering occurs on the leading or trailing edges of the logic pulses.

The scope can also be made to store single-shot transient pulses for as long as desired by simply switching the A-sweep to its SINGLE sweep mode. When the scope's sweep reset button is momentarily depressed, the reset lamp goes on, and the A-sweep circuit becomes armed, awaiting a trigger pulse. Upon being triggered, the reset lamp is extinguished at the completion of the A-sweep and stays off until the reset button is depressed again.

The operator, therefore, can arm the A-sweep, and leave the scope unattended. The reset lamp will go off only when triggered, and it will stay off until it is manually reset. This feature is especially useful for detecting "once-in-a-lifetime" transient pulses.

Additionally, the scope can be transformed into a recording transient-hit monitor by connecting a chart recorder or suitable event counter to the A-sweep gate output and setting the A-sweep mode to its NORMAL position. While the A-sweep is not sweeping, the gate output rests in its low state. Upon initiation of the A-sweep, this output goes high and remains there for the duration of the sweep. The gate output returns to its low state as the A-sweep resets itself, and the cycle is completed.

The duration of the positive-going gate pulse equals the sweep time per division times the sweep length, plus any inherent time delays. A sweep time of 10 milliseconds per division over a sweep length of 10 divisions will cause a positive output pulse of approximately 100 ms at the gate output. This is ample time to produce a sharp time-mark on most slow-moving chart recorders—such a time-mark will be produced each time a transient triggers the A-sweep.

The transient-recognition threshold of the scope can be set initially by using an auxiliary pulse generator or power supply and adjusting the scope's trigger slope and level controls appropriately. If necessary, a buffer can be connected to the A-sweep gate output for driving TTL loads.

Dc logic levels can also be detected by the scope. As can be seen from the figure, the trigger-pulse generator and its indicator lamp operate independently of the A-sweep. This allows the A-sweep to be left in the AUTO position and a baseline to be displayed on the scope face. If logic signals are now routed through the vertical preamplifier, their dc logic levels can be determined by the baseline position, and otherwise undetectable single-shot pulses can be monitored with the A-sweep-triggered lamp at the same time. □

Picking the right film for better oscilloscope pictures

by Robert D. Anwyl
Eastman Kodak Co., Rochester, New York

There's no need to settle for less than top-quality photographs from CRT displays. Eastman Kodak's new exposure index for recording films helps the engineer select the proper film.

The index is based on simulated CRT exposures calibrated in radiometric units for three commonly used phosphor types: P-11 (blue), P-16 (near-ultraviolet), and P-24 (green). But the difficulty in determining the precise transient output of a CRT prevents the new index values from being applicable in an absolute manner. However, they are useful for comparing the merits of several films that could be used.

In the initial film selection, it's best to match spectral sensitivity of the film as closely as possible to the spectral output of the phosphor, and to choose a resolving power higher than that indicated by spot diameter or number of scan lines. Remember that resolving power determinations must be related to the size of the display *at the film*, as reduced or magnified by the camera lens.

It's practical to design around a film, phosphor, and lens combination that results in a density of 1.0 with a typical scan rate, but that is also capable of at least a 0.1 density for capturing fast-moving transients. (Density is the log of the reciprocal of transmission.)

The resolving power of photographic materials, rated in lines/millimeter, assumes spaces between the lines equal to the line width. However, in video displays such as TV pictures, where the scan lines are usually unspaced, the number of scan lines is halved. Dividing the resultant number of "line pairs" by the picture height in millimeters yields the minimum usable resolving power. For practical considerations, the resolving power of film should be two or three times greater than the calculated value.

For oscilloscope recording of reoccuring patterns, the minimum exposure duration is the reciprocal of the sweep rate. For example, a shutter setting of 1/500 second would be required to record one complete trace, using a sweep rate of 500 hertz. Because the sweep rate may not be known exactly and the calibration of shutters is rarely precise, it is generally advisable to optimize exposure over five or ten consecutive sweeps. In this case, five sweeps of a 500-Hz display would require a shutter speed of 1/100 s.

Recording of changing or transient patterns is a bit more complicated. Generally a pulse generator is used to trigger a "brightening gate" for a single-trace cycle. All other traces are suppressed in intensity below the recording threshold of the film.

Regardless of the type of CRT display, three important steps must be taken:
- Keep ambient light away from the CRT face by shielding it with a cone of black construction paper or other suitable shroud.

- Acquaint yourself with the focus, astigmatism, and intensity controls of the scope. Make a series of trial exposures with several combinations of focus and astigmatism settings at the lowest intensity level which is readily recorded in order to produce the sharpest image. These trials should be made at the sweep rate you intend to use.
- Expose several frames of film at different intensity settings, and process the film as recommended. □

BIBLIOGRAPHY
For more detailed information, "Kodak's films for CRT recording" (P-37) is available, free of charge, from the Eastman Kodak Company, 343 State Street, Rochester, N.Y., 14650

Helpful hints

If you're having trouble getting a good picture, check out these points before readjusting equipment settings or changing the film type:
- Remove any graticules or colored filters—either may seriously modify or attenuate phosphor output.
- Check the ultraviolet transmittance characteristics of all optics in the system when photographing a phosphor in the ultraviolet or near-ultraviolet region.
- Remember the phosphorescence of phosphors. If the film is generally foggy, the CRT phosphor was probably still phosphorescent from exposure to light.
- Avoid panchromatic films except when red sensitivity is required. Otherwise cathode glow may be recorded as an out-of-focus image of the cathode. Cathode glow can be eliminated either by switching to another type of film or by using a blue or green filter with high transmittance at the phosphor's output wavelengths.

CRT EXPOSURE INDEXES FOR VARIOUS INSTRUMENTATION FILMS

Kodak Film Product	Kodak developer and development	Resolving power (lines/mm)	Spectral sensitivity	P-11 CRT E.I. at net density of 0.10	1.0	P-16 CRT E.I. at net density of 0.10	1.0	P-24 CRT E.I. at net density of 0.10	1.0
Linagraph Shellburst 2474*	8 min. D-19, 68°F	125	Ext. red	64	10	125	16	50	8
Linagraph Shellburst 2476	8 min. D-19, 68°F	125	Ext. red	50	8	100	10	40	60
2475 recording film	8 min. DK-50, 68°F	60	Ext. red	400	20	650	25	250	20
2479 RAR film	1 min. D-19, 95°F	90	Ext. red	200	20	400	32	100	10
2484 pan film	4 min. D-19, 68°F	70	Pan	320	16	500	20	250	16
	1 min. D-19, 95°F			400	12	650	12	320	8
2485 high speed recording film	1½ min. MX-857, 95°F	50	Ext. red	400	12	650	25	200	8
	2½ min. MX-857, 95°F			800	125	1,250	200	400	64
	2½ min. D-19, 95°F			650	80	1,000	125	320	40
2490, 3490 RAR films	2 min. D-19, 95°F	160	Blue	32	8	80	12	25	6
2491 RAR film	2 min. D-19, 95°F	160	Blue	40	10	100	16	32	8
2495 RAR film	1½ min. D-19, 95°F	100	Ortho	200	40	400	64	160	32
2496 RAR film	1 min. D-19, 95°F	140	Ext. red	40	8	80	16	40	8
2498 RAR film	1½ min. D-19, 95°F	100	Pan	64	8	160	16	64	10
5498 RAR film	1½ min. D-19, 95°F	100	Pan	64	10	160	20	64	12
SO-200/201 recording films	2 min. D-19, 95°F	160	Blue	50	12	100	20	32	10
5374/7374**	4 min. D-19, 68°F	180	Blue	10	1.2	20	2.5	3	0.4

*Among these products, 2474 and 2490 are supplied on clear Estar base with dyed antihalation backing. Other products, which have identification numbers starting with 2 (as well as SO-200), are on Estar-AH base. 3490 and SO-201 are coated on Estar thin base. The TV recording films and 5498 use conventional triacetate supports.

**Eastman Television recording film 5374/7374 is included because it has been used as a reference product for relative CRT speeds in previous publication data.

Orthochromatic: blue and green sensitivity
Panchromatic: sensitivity to blue, green, yellow and some red
Extended red: same as panchromatic with greater red sensitivity

Exposure:	Simulated P-11, P-16 and P-24 phosphors (71 microseconds, Xenon lamp with suitable filter)
Development:	As indicated for exposure indexes listed
Densitometry:	Diffuse transmitted density
Exposure Index:	Reciprocal of the phosphor exposure in ergs/cm² required for net density specified

Oscilloscope probes
can do many jobs

by Arthur D. Delagrange
Naval Ordnance Laboratory, Silver Spring, Md.

If you walk into a design prototyping area and see oscilloscope probes sprouting not only from scopes but from oscillators, counters, meters, filters, and even power supplies, don't jump to the conclusion that either you or the engineer who works there is a bit daffy. On the contrary, when you are working with breadboarded circuits, especially the sloppy variety, scope probes are useful for getting signals both in and out of a circuit.

Scope probes are handy, shielded, insulated lines that have a built-in ground connection. They attach readily to component leads on one end and are equipped with BNC-type connectors on the other, as is most test equipment. An ordinary probe from one maker will work fine on equipment from another manufacturer.

For example, a Tektronix P6011 1× probe has a series resistance of about 300 ohms. This is insignificant when the probe is used with a measuring instrument providing an input resistance of 1 megohm, which is generally the case. A 1× probe is also usually acceptable for inserting signals into circuits that have an input impedance of 1 kilohm to 1 megohm. However, if the exact input signal amplitude or phase must be known, it may be necessary to measure the signal at the circuit, instead of at the driving source.

A Tektronix P6012 10× probe has a series resistance of 9 megohms; it operates into an input resistance of 1 megohm shunted by a capacitance of 15 to 47 picofarads. Many measuring instruments other than oscilloscopes have a similar input impedance, and the probe works equally well with them. At low frequencies (roughly those below 1 kilohertz), it is not even necessary to adjust the capacitance.

Sometimes when you're inserting a signal, you must either greatly attenuate the voltage (as for a preamplifier) or insert a current rather than a voltage (as for the virtual ground of an op-amp circuit). For these sorts of jobs, a series resistance is necessary, and the 10× probe with its 9-megohm resistance is handy.

If it is properly matched to the input impedance of a measuring instrument, a probe is accurate from dc to well up in the megahertz region. In fact, a probe can often improve the accuracy of your measurements, suffering from neither the noise picked up by unshielded test leads nor the loading caused by high-capacitance shielded cables.

When you insert a sine wave with a scope probe, there is no loss in accuracy provided that the signal's amplitude and phase are measured at the circuit. And if you are applying complex waveforms to your circuit, you must also check to see that distortion has not occurred because of attenuation and phase shift. □

Self-orienting probe tip eases
light pen use with CRTs

by E. V. Butera
IBM Corp., San Jose, Calif.

Accurate positioning of a conventional light pen to operate a cathode-ray tube display is inconvenient and soon becomes tiresome. The probe must be held nearly perpendicular to the surface of the CRT to establish accurate coordinates for each point being probed, or in some cases to respond to the CRT scan at all. This difficulty is compounded by the convex surfaces of many CRT screens.

However, a simple probe with a self-orienting tip capable of moving in any of three dimensions can help solve this problem. The tip has a ball mounting that swivels to position itself flat against the CRT screen. This always maintains the sensor or transducer in the perpendicular position, even when the probe itself may be far from perpendicular. The tip can be made slightly concave to match the convex surface of the screen.

Some probes contain photocells or other transducers in their tips. Outputs are electrical signals transmitted via wire or coaxial cable to controllers. Other probes simply transmit the light from the phosphor directly along optical fibers to photocells in the controllers. Any

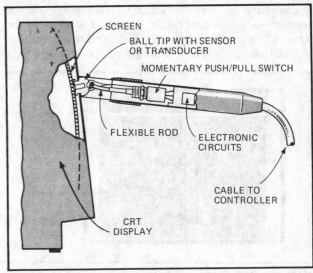

Versatile probe holds transducer or sensor perpendicular to CRT.

of these tips can be used in the self-orienting probe.

On the back of the ball mounting is a rectangular recess, which matches a self-centering flexible switch rod. This rectangular mate keeps the tip from rotating and thereby twisting, fouling, or breaking the wires or other connections between the tip and the body of the probe. As the ball mounting swivels, the rod flexes; when the tip is lifted from the screen, the rod's self-centering property centers the tip. The rod also actuates a switch that signals the probe's contact with the screen. □

Scope-face graticule highlights 3-dB signal points

by Donald F. DeKold
Santa Fe Community College, Gainesville, Fla.

A number of standard laboratory oscilloscopes have rectangular CRT graticules measuring 8 by 10 centimeters. A little-recognized feature of the 8-by-10 graticule is the ease with which it allows rapid and fairly accurate determination of the –3-decibel levels of ac signals.

Normally, the midfrequency voltage of a signal is displayed on the scope face at some convenient level. Then, the 70.7% level of the displayed signal amplitude is computed so that the signal's –3-dB point can be known. As signal amplitude drops, its level must be constantly monitored by repeatedly positioning the displayed trace against one of the horizontal graticule lines to measure the magnitude of its amplitude.

This approach is inconvenient because it involves a calculation and requires concentrated attention on the scope display to observe when the –3-dB level is reached. However, if the midfrequency level is adjusted to span exactly 7 cm peak to peak, then the –3-dB level will be indicated by a display trace that covers 4.95 units (70.7% of 7 cm) of vertical deflection. Now, the horizontal graticule lines can be put to convenient use.

A "band of light" can be made to fill the screen (using a slow sweep rate) between the 0- and 7-cm lines, as shown, by first adjusting the signal's midfrequency amplitude to be 7 cm peak to peak and then vertically positioning the display. When the amplitude of the displayed signal approaches –3 dB, the "band of light" will just fill the space between the 1- and 6-cm lines, as shown. Actually, this 5-cm-high display implies an attenuation of –2.92 dB, or a nominal attenuation of –3 dB.

With this method, only one vertical-positioning operation is needed, no calculations are required, and the signal's –3-dB point is easy to spot. □

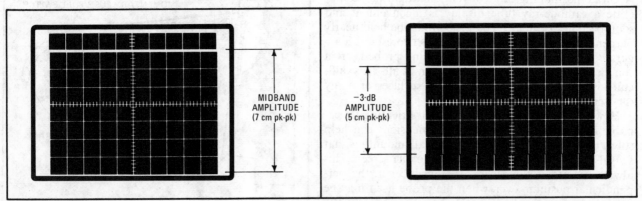

Measuring the midband. Graticule lines on scope face can aid in locating a signal's 3-decibel points. For 8-by-10-centimeter grid, adjust the displayed midband voltage to fill 7 cm. The signal is down by 3 dB when its display spans 5 cm, which represents 70.7% of 7 cm.

Isolator circuit permits scope to check ungrounded voltages

by Richard K. Dickey
California Polytechnic State University, San Luis Obispo, Calif.

Measuring low-level voltages in circuits that are not referenced to ground can be rather difficult. But a special oscilloscope isolator circuit allows a grounded scope to be used for observing small voltages—including their dc levels—in ungrounded circuits.

With this isolator, even common-mode potentials as high as 500 volts will have no effect on the measurement of differential potentials as low as 0.1 v. The circuit is particularly suitable for measuring SCR gate-to-cathode voltages and thyratron grid-to-cathode voltages in motor-control circuits, where the cathodes are typically removed from ground by 120 v ac.

The isolator circuit is divided into two sections, which are separated by the insulating barrier of an optical coupler. The input section consists of a precision decade step attenuator, limiting diodes, and an operational amplifier. The op amp employs current feedback so that the current supplied to the LED of the optical coupler is linearly proportional to the input voltage but offset by one-half of the full signal range. The circuit's output section contains the phototransistor of the optical coupler and a balancing network, which assures that the circuit's output voltage will be zero when the signal voltage is zero.

For maximum safety, the two sections should be assembled in a plastic box, with a plastic barrier separating the two, except for the connections to the optical coupler. The isolator's operating bandwidth is limited to the audio range by the 741-type op amp. A wider-bandwidth op amp will improve the frequency response. □

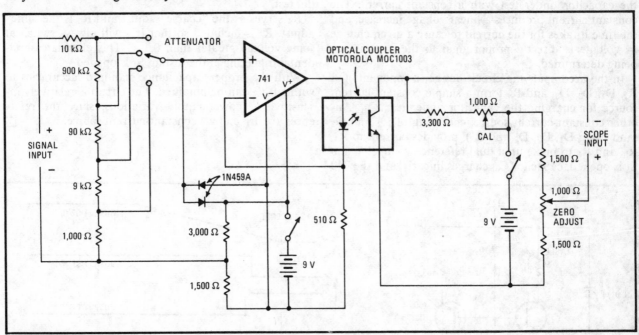

Floating Input. Oscilloscope isolator circuit is ideal for measuring small voltages in ungrounded circuits. Differential potentials as low as 0.1 volt can be discerned out of common-mode potentials as large as 500 V. An optical coupler separates signal and scope inputs.

Using a frequency counter to measure capacitance

by Thomas McGahee,
Don Bosco Technical High School, Boston, Mass.

Many frequency counters can be used to measure capacitances by exploiting their capability to measure time spans. Basically, the circuit described here charges the capacitor under test with a constant current. The constant current produces a linear voltage increase, and the time it takes for the current to cause a given change in voltage is directly proportional to the capacitance being determined.

In the accompanying circuit design, components Q_1, R_1, D_1, D_2, D_3, and R_3 form a simple constant-current source for charging the capacitor under test, C_{ut}. Another constant-current source, consisting of R_2 and Q_2 (and using D_1, D_2, D_3 and R_3), provides current to R_4, R_5, and R_6 to make up a dual reference voltage. When S_1 is opened, capacitor C_{ut} charges linearly, and the 740 operational amplifier buffers the voltage from the relatively low input impedances of IC_2 and IC_3. IC_2, whose output is normally at ground, switches to a positive output when the voltage from the op amp becomes greater than IC_2's reference voltage (at its inverting input).

A short time later, when the voltage from the buffer reaches the reference voltage of IC_3, the output of IC_3 switches from a positive level to ground. There is a small overlap where both outputs are positive. D_4 and D_5 detect this condition, and, when it occurs, R_7 causes the junction of the diodes to go positive, producing a pulse having a width proportional to the capacitor under test.

R_4 serves as the "coarse" adjust and R_5 is the "fine" adjust. R_6 is included so that IC_2 will always switch at some voltage greater than 0.1 V. This eliminates accidental triggering at the instant S_1 is opened.

With the proper capacitance standard, accuracies to within 0.1% can be obtained. The circuit is relatively insensitive to power-supply variations, since the references are driven by a constant-current source. □

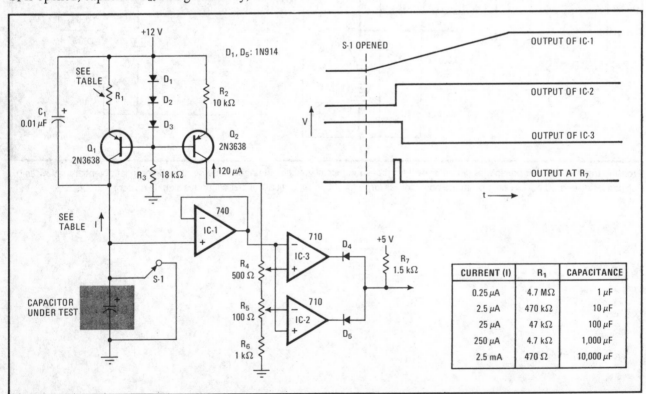

CURRENT (I)	R_1	CAPACITANCE
0.25 µA	4.7 MΩ	1 µF
2.5 µA	470 kΩ	10 µF
25 µA	47 kΩ	100 µF
250 µA	4.7 kΩ	1,000 µF
2.5 mA	470 Ω	10,000 µF

Counting capacitance. Two adjacent points on a voltage ramp (a), created by charging a capacitor, C_{ut}, are detected by comparators IC_3 and IC_2. These two voltages are compared in an AND gate, producing a pulse having a width proportional to capacitance.

Test circuit enables voltmeter to check electrolytic capacitors

by Mark Anglin
Novar Electronics Corp., Barberton, Ohio

Aluminum electrolytic capacitors are excellent low-cost components for noncritical timing applications. But, before they can be inserted in a timing network, their actual values must be checked because they typically have capacitance tolerances like +100% and −20%.

Though a capacitance bridge can be used to make these checks, it is sensitive to hum, requires attention to capacitor polarity, and is too slow for high-volume selection. The simple capacitance checker drawn in the figure overcomes these problems, permitting fast and efficient determination of capacitance value. Furthermore, it is accurate to within ±2% for capacitors having tolerances of +80% and −20%, it costs only around $5 to build, and it works in conjunction with a standard analog or digital ac voltmeter.

Circuit operation is based on capacitive reactance. If two capacitors are connected in series across a 1.2-volt ac source, the voltage across the lower capacitor (C_1) can be written as:

$$V_{C1} = \frac{(1/\omega C_1)1.2}{(1/\omega C_1) + (1/\omega C_2)}$$

where ω is the frequency of the ac source, and C_2 is the upper capacitor. If the reactance of C_2 is much greater than the reactance of C_1, this equation reduces to:

$$V_{C1} = (1.2/C_1)C_2$$

And, if the values of the applied voltage and capacitor C_1 are kept constant during the measurement, then:

$$K = 1.2/C_1$$

So that the voltage across C_1 can be regarded as being directly proportional to the value of capacitor C_2:

$$V_{C1} = K C_2$$

In the test circuit, transformers T_1 and T_2 are used to derive the 1.2-v ac source voltage. Such a low driving voltage permits aluminum electrolytics and most solid-tantalum electrolytics to be measured without regard to their circuit polarity. The low impedance of the voltage source and the large 4,000-microfarad capacitor make the test capacitor virtually immune to hum.

Variations in the constant K, which here equals (1.2 v)/(4,000 μF), can be adjusted for by using the 50-kilohm potentiometer. This trimmer also allows the circuit's output voltage to be scaled so that the test capacitor's value can be read directly from the voltmeter's display.

The circuit, as shown, is set up for selecting 150-μF capacitors, but other component values can be substituted to select other capacitor values. To calibrate the circuit, the switch is flipped to its CALIBRATE position, and the potentiometer is adjusted until the ac voltmeter reads 15 millivolts, which corresponds to the 150-μF value of the standard capacitor. With the switch in its TEST position, the voltmeter will read 21.8 mv if the test capacitor's value is 218 μF.

□

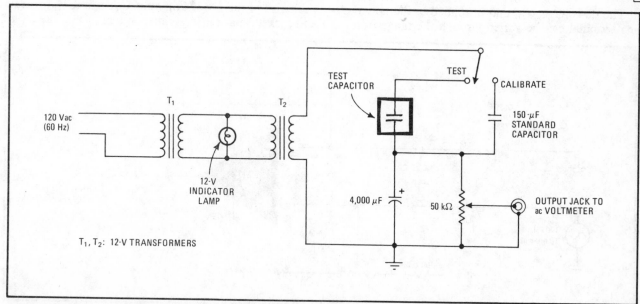

Fast and easy. The value of an electrolytic capacitor can be determined rapidly with this capacitance checker working in conjunction with an ordinary ac voltmeter. The capacitance value is read directly from the voltmeter's display. Because a low 1.2-V ac driving source is used, the test capacitor can be inserted without regard to its polarity. This particular circuit measures a capacitance of 150 microfarads.

Op-amp circuit measures diode-junction capacitance

by D. Monticelli and T. Frederiksen
National Semiconductor Corp., Santa Clara, Calif.

For measuring the small-signal junction capacitance of a semiconductor diode, this simple circuit has two advantages over conventional capacitance bridges or meters. The ac test voltage is low enough to avoid excessive modulation of the diode's depletion layer. (Many conventional capacitance meters use such high ac voltages that their readings do not accurately represent the small-signal characteristics of the diode.) And a variable dc bias voltage can be applied to the diode, making the circuit more flexible.

As shown in Fig. 1, the diode is connected to the inverting input terminal of an LM324 operational amplifier, and ac and dc voltages are applied to the noninverting input terminal. The values of the input and output voltages, v_i and v_o, are read on high-impedance voltmeters. The diode junction capacitance, C_J, is then

$$C_J = C_F (v_o - v_i)/v_i$$

where C_F is the known value of the capacitance in the op-amp feedback loop. In the circuit shown here C_F and v_i have been made numerically equal (10 picofarads and 10 millivolts, respectively), so

$$C_J = (v_o - v_i)\, pF/mV$$

The dc voltage, V_D, that is applied to the noninverting terminal can be varied through the range from 13 volts to –1 v by means of potentiometer R_1. As a result of the feedback, this voltage appears at the inverting input and is impressed across the diode to provide any value of reverse bias from –13 v to the verge of conduction. The ac input voltage, v_i, is made small to avoid excessive modulation of the junction's depletion layer; 10 millivolts rms is a good value. Voltage v_i is also impressed across the diode through the action of the op amp. C_F and C_J then make up a simple ac voltage divider so that $C_J = C_F (v_o - v_i)/v_i$.

Feedback resistor R_F provides a path for the input-bias current of the LM324 (typically 45 nanoamperes), which allows the amplifier to impress V_D across the diode. In doing so, it offsets the dc-output voltage slightly, but does not affect operation. The actual dc-output voltage is given by $V_O = V_D - I_b R_F$. R_F must be chosen carefully; too large a value offsets V_O excessively, and too small a value (relative to the reactance of C_F at the operating frequency) introduces phase shift.

When i_F is out of phase with i_X, the simple capacitive divider relation does not hold, and phasor relationships must be considered. A value of 10 megohms for R_F is practical if the frequency is about 100 kilohertz because the reactance of even a 10-picofarad C_F is only 160 kilohms and gives a phase error of only 1°. Furthermore, the real part of the 324's input impedance shunts C_J slightly and phase-shifts the diode current i_X in the direction of i_F, thereby minimizing the phase difference between the two currents.

To achieve good results in measuring small values of capacitance, the parasitic capacitance C_P that shunts C_J must be accurately known. The parasitic capacitance consists of stray capacitance C_{STRAY} and the input capacitance of the LM324 op amp C_{IN}. The C_{STRAY}, lead and socket capacitance, is independent of V_D. The input

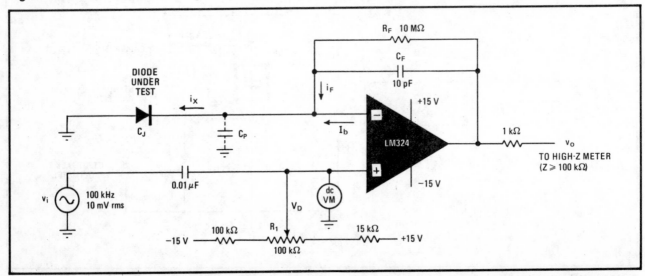

1. Measuring capacitance. Junction capacitance of a semiconductor diode is measured as a function of dc-bias voltage in this circuit. Diode is connected to inverting input terminal of LM324 operational amplifier, and dc-bias and ac-test voltages are applied to noninverting input terminal. Low ac test voltage avoids excessive modulation of depletion layer, for accurate measure of small-signal junction capacitance.

capacitance of the 324 is dependent on V_D (C_{IN} typically is 0.85 to 0.75 pF for common-mode voltages of 5 to 20 v). Fortunately C_{STRAY} usually dominates. Operating the 324 with positive and negative supplies while simultaneously restricting the input voltage to –1 V on the low end of the V_D range reduces the voltage dependence of C_{IN}. In the authors' circuit, C_P measured 3.55 pF with V_D = –1 V and 3.45 pF with V_D = 13 V. A differential measuring technique, first measuring C_P with the diode out of the circuit and then measuring (C_P + C_J) with the diode in, gives the best results. C_F should be a low-tolerance capacitor (a good silver-mica was used by the authors). The pin-to-pin parasitic capacitance of the LM324 that shunts C_F is negligible if the board layout minimizes adjacent lead length between the inverting and output pins.

Figure 2 shows a plot of junction capacitance in relation to reverse bias for a 1N914 diode as measured by the circuit in Fig. 1.

Those who want a self-contained unit can use the remaining three op amps in the quad LM324 package plus two additional amps from the dual LM358; both will operate from +9-V and –9-V batteries because of their small current drain. One amplifier can be wired as a Wien-bridge oscillator to supply v_i, while two others can peak-detect voltages v_i and v_o. These peak-detected voltages can then be differenced by a fourth amplifier, and a fifth amplifier can be used to drive a 1-mA meter for a direct reading of capacitance in picofarads. A pot in the noninverting leg of the difference amplifier can be used to offset-null the C_{STRAY} of the circuit. □

2. Result. Junction capacitance of 1N914 diode as a function of reverse bias is measured with circuit shown in Fig. 1. Data sheets do not provide all the information on C_J that is sometimes needed. Conventional capacitance meters use ac voltages that are too high for small-signal measurements and do not provide adjustable dc bias.

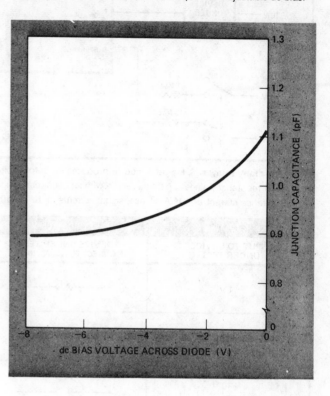

Log-ratio module measures high resistances

by Bucky Crowley
Butler Automatic Inc., Newton, Mass.

It doesn't take a voltmeter with a range switch to provide full-range measurement of low-level currents or high resistances. All it takes is a log-ratio module coupled with a voltmeter.

The module compares an unknown current to a reference current, producing an output voltage proportional to the ratio of the logarithm of the two currents. This proportionality allows accurate measurements over large ranges of input current. The inexpensive log-ratio module is a standard product from such firms as Analog Devices, Teledyne Philbrick, Intronics, and others.

The current-input terminals of the module are internally connected to inverting terminals of operational amplifiers, so they are at virtual ground. Therefore the driving voltage is applied to just one end of the device under test, as shown in the circuit diagram.

Reference currents of either 10^{-6} ampere or 10^{-8} A are provided. The output voltage is equal to k × log(I_{SIG}/I_{REF}), but here the module has been connected so that k is 1 volt per decade. The bias current into the op amps is less than 10^{-11} A, so resistance measurements can be accurate within 1% to 10^{10} ohms (10 V and 1 nanoampere) and have resolution of 10^{12} ohms (10 V and 10 picoamperes).

The table shows how this measurement technique is used for the production testing of different components. For example, to test the leakage in diodes, the reference input is set to a current that represents an acceptable level; screening for leakage current greater than 10 nA

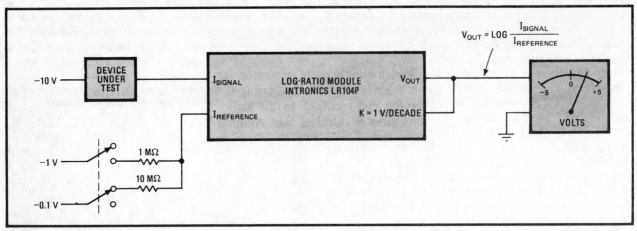

$$V_{OUT} = LOG \frac{I_{SIGNAL}}{I_{REFERENCE}}$$

Covering many ranges. A log-ratio module produces an output voltage proportional to the logarithm of the ratio of currents at inputs, so currents or resistance values can be measured without need for a range switch. Connections shown here give 1 V per decade of current ratio, and a reference current of 10^{-8} A. Hence, signal currents of 10^{-3} to 10^{-8} A (or test resistors of 10^4 Ω to 10^9 Ω) yield outputs of 0 to +5 V.

TYPICAL LOW-CURRENT MEASUREMENTS		
INPUT TO DEVICE UNDER TEST	**DEVICE UNDER TEST** (CONNECT TO I_{SIGNAL} INPUT)	**MEASUREMENT**
−1 V	⎓⎓⎓	Incoming sorting of resistors without range switching, over 6 decades (1 kΩ to 1 × 10^9 Ω).
−10 V	⟋	Switch leakage.
−10 V	⟩⟩ ⟩⟩	Connector leakage.
−10 V	〰	Printed-circuit board process leakage.
Voltage per specification	▷⊢	Diode leakage.
Voltage per specification	R_{LARGE} ⊣⊢ 10 kΩ Open to read	Capacitor leakage.
−10 V	🫙	Potting materials, insulating oils, etc.

requires a reference current of 10 nA (0.1 v and 10 megohms). Acceptable diodes will produce negative output voltages, and rejects will yield positive numbers, the exact values on the voltmeter being expressed in logarithms. For instance, if the meter reads + 2.00 v, the device fails (because the sign is positive), and the leakage current is 100 times worse than specification because the antilog of 2 is 10^2 or 100.

In measuring the leakage current of a capacitor, a few extra components are used, as shown in the test arrange-

ment in the table. The capacitor is charged to the desired voltage through the 10-kilohm resistor, and the switch is opened to take the reading of leakage. The other resistor, R_{Large}, prevents noise from being coupled from the supply into the input. This resistor should be as large as possible, but not large enough to cause a significant dc drop at the expected leakage current. ☐

Single time measurement determines capacitor R and L

by Carlo Venditti
Charles Stack Draper Laboratory, MIT, Cambridge, Mass.

The quality of a practical capacitor can usually be judged from its dissipation factor figure, unless the capacitor is to be used at frequencies above 1 megahertz. Then the capacitor's internal inductance must be taken into consideration, and a measurement that complements the dissipation factor test must be made.

A time measurement technique that employs two commonly available laboratory instruments—the pulse generator and the oscilloscope—permits internal capacitor inductance, as well as internal capacitor resistance, to be evaluated directly from scope voltage readings. Both polarized and nonpolarized units can be tested.

The equivalent circuit of a capacitor is shown in Fig. 1. Conductance G, which represents the losses in the dielectric, and resistance R can be found by measuring the dissipation factor at a specific frequency:

$$D.F. = \omega CR + G/\omega C$$

where C is the capacitance, and ω the radian frequency. To determine both effective capacitor resistance R and inductance L with a single time measurement, the associated test circuit of Fig. 1 is used.

Capacitor voltage response to an excitation pulse is monitored with the scope. The dc offset of this response allows the effective capacitor resistance to be computed, while the overshoot above the dc offset, which is due to the turn-on transient excursion, allows the effective inductance to be computed. The transient excursion occurs during the rise time of the input pulse because of the inductance. Input-pulse rise time must be at least as

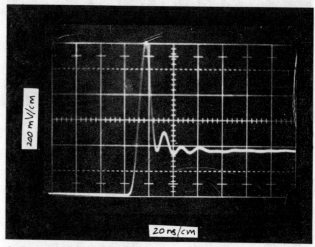

2. Evaluating the response. Capacitor transient response registers effective capacitor resistance by amount of dc offset voltage and effective inductance by height of peak overshoot above dc offset level.

fast as 15 to 30 nanoseconds to produce a measurable transient response.

Input-pulse voltage V_i can be approximated by two ramp functions: one is a positive-going ramp that starts at t_{0+} and rises to amplitude A in α seconds; the second is a ramp with the same, but negative, slope that begins at $t - \alpha$ seconds and has an amplitude of A. The slope of the ramps can be labeled K ($K = A/\alpha$), allowing the Laplace transform of V_i to be written as:

$$V_i(s) = K/s^2 - K\exp(-\alpha s)/s^2$$

And the Laplace transform of capacitor voltage is:

$$V_o(s) = [(R + sL)/(R_1 + R + sL)]V_i(s)$$

By using partial-fraction expansion and then taking the inverse Laplace transform of the terms, the capacitor voltage can be written as:

$$\begin{aligned} V_o(t) = &\; K(R/R_1)tU(t) + KL[(R_1 - R)/R_1^2]U(t) \\ &- K(R/R_1)(t - \alpha)U(t - \alpha) \\ &- KL[(R_1 - R)/R_1^2]U(t - \alpha) \\ &- KL[(R_1 - R)/R_1^2]\exp(-R_1 t/L) \\ &+ KL[(R_1 - R)/R_1^2]\exp[-R_1(t - \alpha)/L] \end{aligned}$$

This equation can be considerably simplified to compute the effective R and L from the voltage information on the scope display. For example, Fig. 2 shows the response of a 4.7-microfarad capacitor. The input pulse has an amplitude of 5 volts (A = 5) and a rise time of 16 nanoseconds ($\alpha = 16 \times 10^{-9}$). Thus, the positive ramp approximation has a slope of:

$$K = A/\alpha = 5/(16 \times 10^{-9}) = 3.12 \times 10^8$$

The dc offset voltage of 0.36 v can be read from the scope face, and resistance R computed from the first term of the equation for $V_o(t)$:

$$R = 0.36R_1Kt = 0.36(100)/(3.12 \times 10^8)(16 \times 10^{-9})$$
$$R = 7.2 \text{ ohms}$$

To find inductance L, the other five terms that make up the $V_o(t)$ expression can be factored and equated to the peak voltage excursion of 1.2 v:

$$KL(R_1 - R)/R_1^2 + K(R/R_1)t = 1.2 \text{ v}$$

Subtracting the dc offset contribution from the total

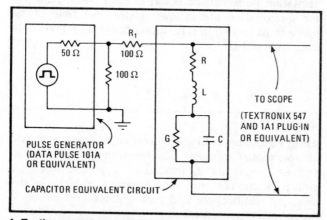

1. Testing capacitor quality. Internal inductance and resistance of capacitor are measured by applying fast-rise-time pulse to voltage divider network and displaying capacitor transient voltage response on scope. Conductance G in capacitor-equivalent circuit represents losses in the capacitor dielectric.

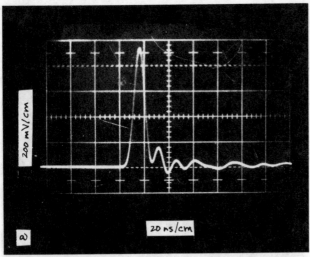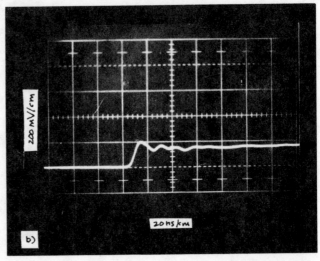

3. Dissipation factor is not enough. Capacitor with low dissipation factor (a) exhibits low effective resistance, but has high effective inductance. Although dissipation factor of another capacitor (b) is higher because of higher resistance, its inductance is almost negligible.

voltage leaves the voltage contribution due to L:

$$KL(R_1 - R)/R_1^2 = 1.2 - 0.36 = 0.84 \text{ v}$$

Solving for L yields:

$$L = 0.84R_1^2/K(R_1 - R) = 0.84(100)^2/$$
$$(3.12 \times 10^8)(100 - 7.2)$$
$$L = 0.29 \text{ microhenries}$$

These simplified computations for R and L are valid because the RC time constant of the test circuit is extremely long, while the L-R_1 time constant is short, compared to the duration of the transient condition.

In addition to quantitative evaluations, the test circuit can be used to make qualitative judgements as to what capacitor is best for a given application. The responses of two different 1-μF capacitors illustrate this point.

Figure 3a shows the scope display for a capacitor that has a dissipation factor of only 0.005 because its effective resistance is low. Its effective inductance, however, is quite high. On the other hand, the display (Fig. 3b) for a second capacitor, one that has a dissipation factor of 0.05, indicates that its effective resistance is higher than that of the first capacitor, but its effective inductance is considerably lower. If a low dissipation factor were the criterion for determining a capacitor's high-frequency (above 1 MHz) performance, the capacitor with the higher effective inductance—a detriment at high frequencies—would be chosen.

As with most critical measurements, care must be taken to minimize extraneous signal pickup within the test circuit. Every lead must be shielded, and the circuit must be calibrated with noninductive resistors.

Caution must also be observed when capacitance values are 0.01 μF or less, because the test circuit's time constant becomes too small for meaningful results to be obtained. A small RC time constant allows the capacitor to begin charging too soon. By increasing the value of test-circuit resistor R_1 to about 1 kilohm and speeding up the rise time of the excitation pulse to around 10 ns, the response of a 500-pF capacitor can be measured.

Minimum width for the excitation pulse is 0.2 microseconds, and its period should be at least 10 times larger than the test circuit's RC time constant. As already mentioned, nominal pulse amplitude is 5 v, and pulse rise time can generally vary between 15 and 30 ns. The pulse generator itself must be properly terminated.

Since transient conditions are being observed, the response time of the scope should be good. The one used here has a 7-ns rise time capability. If only qualitative testing is to be done, the rise time of the scope and the excitation pulse can be equal to each other. However, for quantitative measurements, the rise time of the scope must be two to three times faster than that of the excitation pulse. □

Simple a-d converter circuit measures resistance digitally

by Jerry Whitmore
Analog Devices Microsystems, Santa Clara, Calif.

An unknown resistance can be measured as a fraction of the value of a larger known reference resistance by use of an analog-to-digital converter, a comparator, and an operational amplifier. The measuring circuit is accurate and inexpensive. Instead of a precise reference voltage or current, with the associated problems of design, test, calibration, and repair, it requires merely a precise reference resistor.

The complete circuit for digital resistance measurement is shown in Fig. 1. It consists of an AD7570 10-bit monolithic a-d converter, an AD741 general-purpose operational amplifier used as an inverting amplifier, and an AD311 comparator. A voltage V_{REF} delivers current to the AD7570 and also to reference resistor R_S. The 75-kilohertz clock signal steps the converter through ten successive approximations, in the course of which the circuit reaches balance (i.e., zero voltage at pin 2 of the AD311). The circuit uses two ground busses—one for analog signals, and one for digital—kept separate to minimize pickup in the analog circuitry. Digital ground is tied back to the low side of the V_{CC} supply, and analog ground is run back to the low side of V_{REF}. Analog and digital grounds are tied together at the power supplies—that is, the low sides of the V_{CC} and V_{REF} supplies are tied together and grounded.

The digital output from the AD7570, D, is a 10-bit word that, after conversion, indicates the ratio of unknown resistance R_X to R_S. The bits represent successive powers of ½ selected by the converter in comparing R_X to R_S; that is,

D = 1000000000 represents ½
D = 1100000000 represents ½ + ¼
D = 1110000000 represents ½ + ¼ + ⅛

and so forth. Because the smallest fraction is $\frac{1}{2}^{10}$, or 1/1,024, R_X is measured to within 0.1% of R_S.

Operation of the circuit is most easily understood by referring to the functional equivalent in Fig. 2. Once the known and unknown resistors are connected to the circuit, the operator starts the conversion cycle by applying a positive pulse to the START pin. The converter assumes an initial value of D (i.e., 1000000000), and the voltage V_{REF} that is applied to pin 2 of the a-d converter emerges from the 741 op amp as $-DV_{REF}$ (i.e., $-½$ V_{REF}). This voltage is applied to the comparator through R_X, and V_{REF} is applied to the comparator

through R_S. The net voltage at the comparator input is V_C, and currents $I_S = -(V_{REF} - V_C)/R_S$ and $I_X = -(V_C + DV_{REF})/R_X$ flow through resistors R_S and R_X, respectively. These currents are always equal, no matter what value V_C has.

If the comparator input voltage V_C is greater than zero, the comparator output is high, the trial bit remains in the logic 1 state, and the next least significant bit is tried on the next clock pulse. If the comparator input is less than zero, the output from the comparator is low, the trial bit is reset to zero, and the next trial is initiated by the successive-approximation logic. When all 10 bits have been tried and either set or reset to their proper values, the $\overline{BUSY}$ pin goes high, indicating that conversion is complete. Eventually this action of the comparator and internal d-a converter servos the 741 output to a value $-D_0 V_{REF}$ that makes V_C approximately equal to zero.

For this condition,

$$I_X = -D_0 V_{REF}/R_X \text{ and } I_S = -V_{REF}/R_S$$

Since I_X is always equal to I_S, these expressions yield

$$D_0 V_{REF}/R_X = V_{REF}/R_S, \text{ or } D_0 = R_X/R_S$$

This result does not depend on the value of V_{REF}. In fact, the appellation V_{REF} is somewhat of a misnomer here, because the voltage V_{REF} can have any value between 5 volts and 10 V and can be either positive or negative; if it is negative, however, the negative input to the comparator must be used.

The interpretation of the digital output, D_0, is:

If D_0 is 0000000000, $R_X = 0$

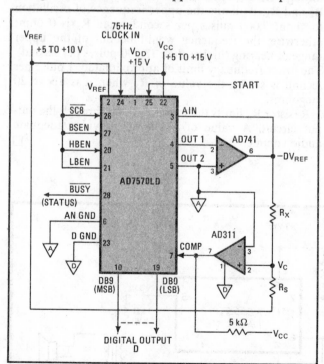

1. Measures resistance. A-d converter circuit measures value of unknown resistance R_X as a fraction D_0 of known resistance R_S. D_0, the digital output from the converter when conversion is complete, gives accuracy to 1/1,024 of R_S with 10-bit converter. No precise reference voltages or currents are required.

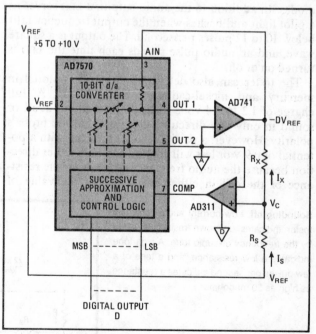

2. How it works. This functional equivalent of Fig. 1 shows that AD741 op amp is output amplifier of AD7570's internal d-a converter. Feedback loop is closed through AIN terminal (Analog INput) of the AD7570. When conversion is started, AD741 output is servoed (via AD311 comparator and internal d-a converter action) to a voltage that makes comparator input voltage zero. Digital output word is then D_0, and D_0 is digital binary fraction equal to ratio R_X/R_S.

If D_0 is 1000000000, $R_X = 0.5\ R_S$
If D_0 is 1010000000, $R_X = 0.625\ R_S$
If D_0 is 1111111111, R_X is equal to or greater than R_S

The ambiguity of the last condition could be removed by some extra circuits, but it is simpler just to use a larger R_S so that D_0 is less than 1111111111.

The circuit can also be used for temperature measurements if R_X is a thermistor. With the ready availability of programable read-only memories, thermistor nonlinearity can easily be compensated to provide a linear temperature-to-binary-readout converter. □

Audio continuity tester indicates resistance values

by Calvin R. Graf
San Antonio, Texas

A continuity tester built around a 555 timer audibly and visually indicates a wide range of resistance values. The unit, which can be assembled for less than $10, is especially handy for testing devices without having to glance from test probe to meter and back again. However, by merely changing the value of one resistor, the tester can function as a multivibrator.

The meter can indicate by tones over a loudspeaker or a headset forward and reverse continuity conditions from 0 to more than 30 megohms for such devices as resistors, diodes, transistors, capacitors, and light-emitting diodes. In addition to the audio output, a LED serves as a pilot light and flashes when the output frequency falls below 10 to 12 pulses per second. The output is a square wave, and an audio pulse sounds each time the LED is turned on or off.

The tester can also determine the charges stored in mercury and nickel-cadmium battery cells. A full charge of 1.2 to 1.4 volts will either not sound at all or sound in only one direction, depending on the probe's polarity. However, a partially discharged cell with a potential of 0.9 v or less will create a sound in either direction because the audio frequency depends on the resistance of the cell in either direction. For the value of resistors used an on-to-off duty cycle of about 60% is obtained. The circuit draws about 7 milliamperes from a standard 9-v battery.

The schematic shows where unknown resistor R_X is connected into the multivibrator circuit. The unknown can have any resistance value from zero ohms to more than 30 megohms. At 0 ohm, which is a short circuit across the test probes, the audio output frequency is about 7,000 pulses per second. This frequency sounds like a tone (sine wave) to the ear. At 30 megohms, the frequency from the speaker is about 1 pulse per second.

Very low current flows through the test probes. When R_X is 0 ohm, the current level through the probes is about 270 microamperes, and when R_X is 1 megohm, the current is about 9 μA.

The 555 timer is operated in the astable-oscillator mode. The free-running frequency and duty cycle are both accurately controlled with three external resistors and one capacitor. The external capacitor, C, charges through R_1, R_2, and R_X, but it discharges only through R_2 and R_X. R_2 limits the upper frequency of oscillation to about 7,000 pulses per second when R_X is 0 ohm; otherwise, the frequency would be out of the upper range of hearing (higher than 18,000 pulses per second). The lower frequency limit of approximately 1 pulse per second is set by the value of R_X when it is above 20 megohms.

Resistor R_3 limits the current drawn through the output circuit. A value of 1 kilohm provides adequate audio volume. □

Sounding off. Low-current audio continuity tester indicates unknown resistance value by the frequency of audio tone. A high tone indicates a low resistance, and a tone of a few pulses per second indicates a resistance as high as 30 megohms.

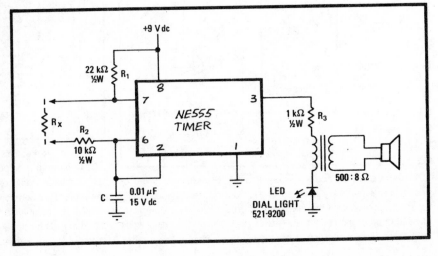

Measuring inductances below 100 nanohenries

by Gunther Dabrowski
Rohde·Schwarz, Munich, West Germany

You can measure very small inductance values by taking advantage of the fine resolution your existing inductance meter has when operating on its most sensitive range setting. For example, the instrument's most sensitive range setting may be only 0.1 microhenry. But, with the help of a special jig, this same meter can be used to determine inductances to within approximately 1 nanohenry.

The photographs show a typical inductance meter and the special low-inductance adapter jig. The jig consists of a single copper band loop, wound on a Teflon disk (50-millimeter diameter) and mounted on supports with banana plugs that can be plugged directly into the meter's measuring terminals.

The copper loop is cut and provided with two small holes. If a short piece of wire is plugged into these holes, the loop is closed and will have an inductance of just about 100 nH. The exact inductance value can be read with the meter.

By pushing the jig more or less deeply into the terminals of the inductance meter, you can change slightly the inductance of the jig so that you can adjust the inductance value exactly to one of the calibration lines on the meter scale. (The insulated knurled knobs on the instrument's front panel can be used as mechanical stops.)

After the meter has been properly peaked for a loop inductance of 100 nH, the short circuit is removed, and the unknown inductance plugged in as shown. The meter is now peaked again; it will indicate a somewhat larger inductance reading. The value of the unknown inductance is the difference between the two meter readings. This technique generally provides a measurement accuracy to within 1 nH. □

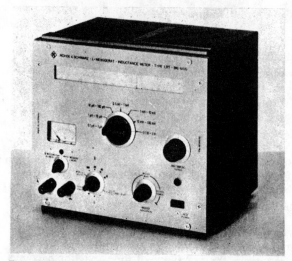

Extending meter range. With a special jig, small inductances can be measured with a standard inductance meter. The technique exploits the instrument's resolution at its most sensitive range setting. Measurements are made by taking the difference between two readings.

Charting capacitor frequency and temperature performance

by John Kropp
Mepco/Electra Inc., a North American Philips Co., Morristown, N.J.

In demanding applications, particularly those involving high frequencies or high temperatures, the specifications of the common capacitor, like capacitance value, cannot be assumed to remain constant. At times, even capacitor lead length must be accounted for, since lead length can significantly shift a capacitor's self-resonant frequency [*Electronics,* Sept. 25, 1972, p. 123].

Capacitance is a function of frequency. Figure 1a shows the equivalent lumped-parameter circuit that is realistic for electrolytic capacitors up to about 20 megahertz, for film capacitors up to about 30 MHz, and for ceramic capacitors up to about 200 MHz. Above these "realistic" frequencies, lumped-parameter representations break down, because the capacitor begins to behave somewhat like a distributed-parameter device—for example, a very short unterminated transmission line.

The distributed configuration, shown in Fig. 1b, is a valid representation when the frequency is high enough—when the longest dimension from the point of lead connection to the edge of the capacitor electrode is about 10% of the wavelength of the operating frequency. This is not as simple a constraint as it seems to be, since the velocity of propagation along a transmission line is inversely proportional to the square root of the dielectric constant of the material separating the capacitor conductors.

Consequently, in capacitors with high dielectric constants, the wavelength at a given frequency may be as much as 100 times shorter than it is in an air capacitor. And the frequency at which the distributed-parameter effect begins may then be 100 times lower than it is for an air capacitor.

The series inductance of the lumped-parameter case, as well as the transmission-line nature of the distributed-parameter case, cause a reduction of the effective capacitance with increasing frequency. For ceramic capacitors, the loss in capacitance is negligible up to about 50 MHz. Above this frequency, the loss gradually increases until the dimensions of the capacitor and the dielectric constant of its ceramic plate introduce the transmission-line effect. The capacitance then begins to drop sharply, approaching zero in the next octave or so.

Figure 2 contains curves that illustrate the variation of capacitance (impedance, in the case of electrolytics) with frequency for four popular types of capacitors. The plots are for typical capacitances and voltage ratings.

As the frequency of the applied signal is increased, some capacitors reach self-resonance before distributed-parameter effects become apparent. Above this resonant frequency, the reactance of the capacitor becomes inductive, with gradually increasing impedance.

Another important consideration is the effect of temperature on insulation resistance and dissipation factor, which is the ratio of the capacitor's equivalent series resistance to its capacitive reactance at a specific frequency and temperature. Insulation resistance is

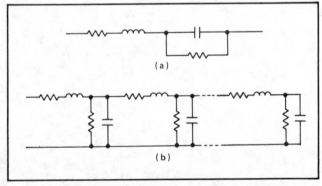

1. A look inside. Lumped-parameter equivalent circuit (a) can be used to model the capacitor at very high frequencies. But in the microwave region, a distributed-parameter configuration (b) must be used instead. Capacitance increases with rising frequency.

frequently confused with the equivalent capacitor shunt resistance. The two are only equal at dc. For ac operation, the equivalent shunt resistance is lower to account for dielectric and series losses.

Insulation resistance is the ratio of a specific dc test voltage that is impressed across the capacitor to the current flowing through it at a specified capacitor temperature. The current is measured after the capacitor charges up to the test voltage. A time interval is often specified before the resistance is measured to allow ca-

pacitor stabilization. In film capacitors, this interval is normally 2 minutes. Insulation resistance is usually given in megohms for small capacitors and as a time constant (megohm-microfarads) for large units.

The curves of Fig. 3 show the broad variation of insulation resistance and dissipation factor with temperature for two types of film capacitors. □

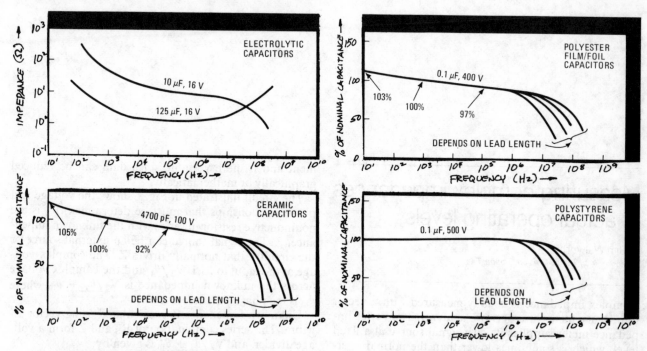

2. High-frequency behavior. Curves for four widely used types of capacitors show how effective capacitance changes with frequency.

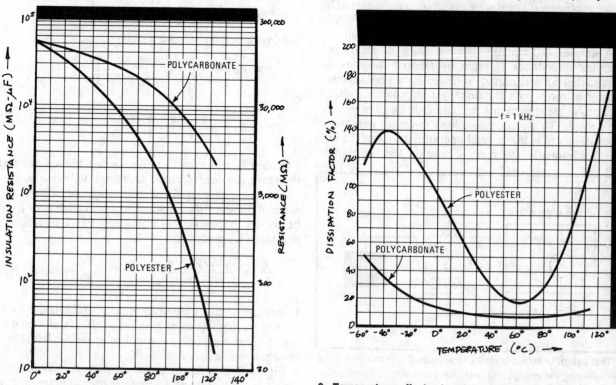

3. Temperature effects. Increasing temperature produces wide variations in capacitor insulation resistance and dissipation factor.

215

Measuring complex impedances at actual operating levels

by Jim Walworth
Honeywell Inc., Tampa Division, Tampa, Fla.

Complex impedance is usually measured with a vector impedance meter or a network analyzer. The vector impedance meter supplies its own signal source at a fixed level, which is sometimes lower than the normal operating level of the device under test. This approach can cause problems if the device involved is nonlinear. The network analyzer uses a dual directional coupler and measures the impedance relative to a 50-ohm system.

A simpler and equally effective means of measuring complex impedance is often overlooked as a useful data-gathering technique. By inserting a noninductive resistor in series with the unknown impedance, voltage and phase measurements can be made on each side of the resistor. This procedure allows in-circuit parameter measurements at the normal operating levels of the circuit. Additionally, the method requires less test equip-

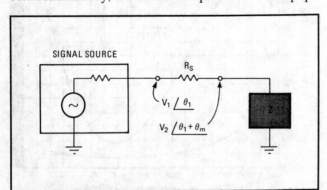

1. Test setup. Unknown complex impedance Z can be determined by measuring the voltage drop and phase shift across noninductive resistor R_s. Complex impedance Z can then be found graphically with a modified Smith chart or mathematically with a calculator.

ment and is more versatile since data can be reduced graphically or mathematically.

The circuit illustrated in Fig. 1 shows the voltage and phase relationships that must be determined. R_S is the noninductive resistor in series with the unknown impedance, Z. The signal source can be an external source or the circuitry that normally drives Z. The complex voltage at the input to R_S is $V_1 \underline{/\theta_1}$; and the complex voltage across the unknown impedance is $V_2 \underline{/\theta_1 + \theta_m}$, where θ_m is the phase shift across R_S.

Unknown impedance Z is calculated using vector algebra. The series combination of R_S and Z form a voltage divider, and $V_2 \underline{/\theta_1 + \theta_m}$ is given by:

$$V_2 \underline{/\theta_1} + \theta_m = V_1 \underline{/\theta_1} \left[\frac{Z}{R_S + Z} \right]$$

Solving this equation for Z yields:

$$Z = R_S \left[\frac{V_2 \underline{/\theta} + \theta_m}{V_1 \underline{/\theta_1} - V_2 \underline{/\theta_1 + \theta_m}} \right]$$

or:

$$Z = R_S \left[\frac{V_2 \underline{/\theta_m}}{V_1 - V_2 \underline{/\theta_m}} \right] \qquad (1)$$

The term θ_m is the relative phase across the resistor and, therefore, the desired phase parameter to measure.

The last equation for Z can easily be solved with some of the scientific calculators now available, or it can be solved graphically. Normalizing Eq. 1 in terms of resistance R_S produces:

$$\frac{Z}{R_S} = \frac{(V_2/V_1) \underline{/\theta_m}}{1 - (V_2/V_1)\underline{/\theta_m}} \qquad (2)$$

If this equation is plotted in polar coordinates, it forms a circle having its center point at –1. If it is plotted on a Smith chart, the circle's center lies at the far left side of the chart with a radius of V_2/V_1 and an angle of θ_m.

Figure 2 is a Smith chart showing the contours of Eq. 2. It now becomes a simple matter to determine an unknown impedance quickly by measuring the voltage

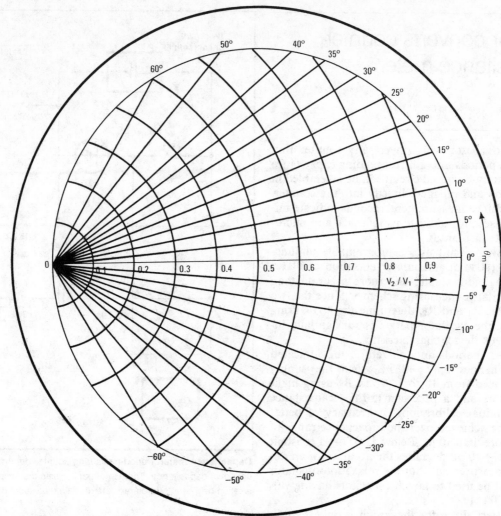

2. Graphical solution. The value of complex impedance Z, normalized with respect to noninductive resistor R_S, can be found graphically from this modified Smith chart. The chart establishes the coordinates for the voltage ratio of V_2/V_1 and the relative phase shift of θ_m.

ratio of V_2/V_1 and its relative phase, θ_m.

Suppose an unknown complex impedance is to be measured. The first step is to estimate the relative impedance magnitude and choose a noninductive resistor having such a value—511 ohms, for this example. (Optimum accuracy is obtained when R_S approximately equals the absolute value of Z.) By using the test setup of Fig. 1, the following data is then taken:

$$V_1 = 1.0\,V$$
$$V_2 = 0.6\,V$$
$$\theta_m = -10°$$

and:

$$(V_2/V_1)\;\underline{/\theta_m} = 0.6\;\underline{/-10°}$$

The point, $0.6\;\underline{/-10°}$, is next plotted on the modified Smith chart of Fig. 2, and the impedance, Z_n, which is normalized to 511 ohms, can be read off the chart in the conventional manner:

$$Z_n = 1.28 - j0.58$$
$$Z = (511\ ohms) \times (1.28 - j0.58)$$
$$Z = 654 - j296 = 718\;\underline{/-24.5°}$$

This procedure should be repeated until the computed magnitude of impedance Z is the same order of magni-

tude as the estimated value for resistor R_S.

The same equation—Eq. 2—can be solved mathematically on a scientific calculator. For this example, the measured data can be reduced to:

$$Z = 726\;\underline{/-24.29°} = 661.7 - j298.6$$

The mathematical solution is more accurate than the graphical one, but the graphical technique is quicker. The accuracy of the results depends on the tolerance and quality of the resistor used, the accuracy of the test equipment, and the accuracy of the data-reduction technique.

A modified Smith chart can also be a powerful analysis aid when VSWR measurements are to be made at low frequencies. A series resistor is chosen equal to the characteristic impedance, Z_o, of the system, and voltages V_1 and V_2, as well as phase θ_m, are measured. The maximum acceptable VSWR circle is drawn on the chart, and $(V_2/V_1)\;\underline{/\theta_m}$ is plotted at each frequency of interest. Since the chart is normalized to Z_o, all points of $(V_2/V_1)\;\underline{/\theta_m}$ falling outside of the circle are out of specification. ☐

Oscillator converts counter to capacitance meter

by M.J. Salvati
Sony Corp. of America, Long Island City, N.Y.

A relaxation oscillator will convert any counter that measures time periods into a direct-reading capacitance meter. The battery-operated circuit can be assembled in a small minibox and plugged directly into the counter. For the capacitance measurement, seconds indicate microfarads, milliseconds indicate nanofarads, and microseconds indicate picofarads.

The conversion circuit uses a programable unijunction transistor (PUT) in a standard relaxation oscillator that is simpler, more stable, and more accurate than previous capacitance-measuring schemes. Since the two biasing resistors, R_1 and R_2, determine the PUT's firing characteristics, the oscillator period is substantially independent of PUT device characteristics.

The oscillator period—and, therefore, the indicated capacitance—changes only +0.5% when the supply voltage is reduced from 18 to 14 volts. By using high-stability resistors and a precision (±0.1%) capacitance standard for initial calibration, an accuracy of better than 1% can be achieved over the capacitance range of 5,000 pF to more than 10 μF. Below 5,000 pF, a constant error of about +40 pF degrades the accuracy of an absolute-value measurement, but the relaxation-oscillator circuit can still be used to match capacitors having values as low as 100 pF.

Because battery drain for the circuit is only 0.5 milliampere, the two standard 9-v radio batteries that are used to power the circuit will last a long time. ☐

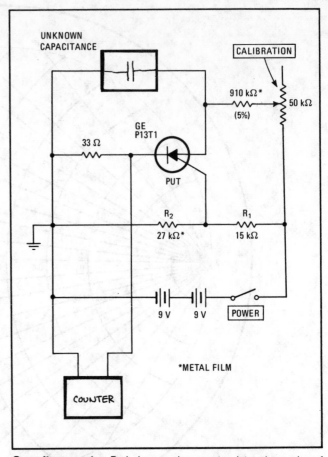

Capacitance meter. Period-measuring counter determines value of unknown capacitance. The test capacitor sets the timing of PUT relaxation oscillator. Microfarads are displayed as seconds.

Direct-reading ohmmeter needs no calibration

by V. Ramprakash
Electronic Systems Research, Madurai, India

A direct-reading ohmmeter with a linear scale can be made by connecting an operational amplifier, a milliammeter, a zener diode, and some resistors as shown in the circuit diagram. This ohmmeter does not require calibration, is self-zeroing, and is insensitive to the supply voltage.

The value of an unknown resistor is measured by connecting it as R_x. The reading on the milliammeter, I_m, is then R_x/R_c, where R_c is the resistance of a known standard resistor in the circuit. The current through the meter equals $(V_o - V_z)/R_m$, where V_o is the voltage at the output of the op amp, V_z is the drop across the zener diode (3 v), and R_m is the resistance in the meter circuit; here R_m is (2.9 + 0.1) kilohms. Since the voltages at the inverting and noninverting input terminals of the op amp must be equal, $V_oR_c/(R_c + R_x)$ must equal V_z. Therefore: $V_o = V_z(R_c + R_x)/R_c$, or $I_m = (V_z/R_m)(R_x/R_c)$ The values of V_z and R_m shown yield:

$$R_x = (R_c)(I_m)$$

if I_m is the meter reading in milliamperes.

For an R_c of 100 kilohms, the 1-mA meter deflects full scale when R_x is 100 kilohms. Similarly, full scale can be made to indicate 10 kilohms or 1 kilohm by selecting these values for R_c. A range switch can be included in the circuit to set these values.

The current through the unknown resistor, I_x, is independent of the value of R_x. The equality of the op-amp input voltages makes V_z equal to I_xR_c, so $I_x = V_z/R_c$.

The meter has automatic zeroing because, if the measuring leads are short-circuited, V_o rises to exactly 3 v, sending no current into the meter. No calibration is necessary because the meter deflection has direct correspondence to the value of resistance being measured.

The germanium diode limits the voltage across the meter, and thus protects it from over-current when the measuring leads are left open. □

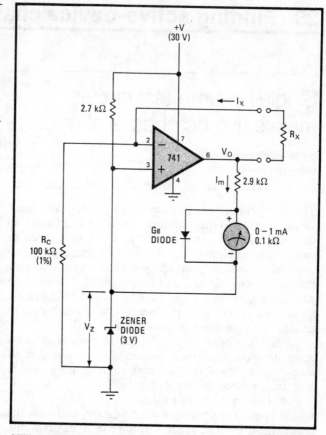

Milliamperes indicate resistance. The meter reading in mA is the value of the ratio R_x/R_c, so full-scale meter deflection indicates an R_x of 100 kilohms. An open circuit pins the meter, but does no damage because the germanium diode clamps the meter voltage. Since a short circuit produces no deflection, the circuit is self-zeroing.

Single op-amp test circuit makes five dc checks at once

by Jerald Graeme
Burr-Brown Research Corp., Tucson, Ariz.

The five primary dc characteristics of an operational amplifier can be tested simultaneously by one circuit, so that multiple tests are avoided as well as the need to switch the test circuit. The test circuit permits measurement of open-loop gain, offset voltage, input bias current, quiescent current, and output-voltage swing. The various output signals generated by the circuit can be monitored separately or processed and combined to produce a single pass/fail indication.

To find the open-loop gain, the ac portion of summing junction signal e_j is measured. This signal is an amplified replica of the op amp's input signal, e_i, which is, in turn, related to output signal e_o by:

$$e_j = 100e_i = 100(V_{OS} + e_s/A)$$

where V_{OS} is the op amp's offset voltage, and e_s is the input signal voltage. With a peak-to-peak detector, the ac portion of e_j can be converted to a gain-related dc voltage suitable for pass/fail examination by a voltage comparator. (A square-wave test signal is used here because it is simple to generate with a single op amp, but a sinusoidal test signal could be used instead.)

Input offset voltage V_{OS} is measured from the dc portion of output signal e_j. As with the open-loop gain measurement, a comparator can be used to provide a pass/fail indication. If e_j is not filtered for this type of monitoring, the amplitude of its ac component may introduce some error. Generally, however, the high gain and moderate offset-voltage levels of most general-purpose op amps produce an ac component that is an order of magnitude smaller than the dc component, allowing filtering to be eliminated to speed up testing.

Op-amp input bias current, I_B, can be determined through the simple current-to-voltage converter formed by amplifier A_1. The flow of input bias current through resistor R_1 creates a dc voltage at the output of A_1 for comparison against a specified related level. To avoid measurement errors due to A_1, this amplifier's offset voltage should be nulled and its input bias current should be much less than that to be measured.

Although this bias-current test checks only one of the two input bias currents, it is generally adequate as long as an extremely low input-offset current is not a requirement. Moreover, if a transistor mismatch at the input of the op amp being tested is severe enough to create an excessive input-offput current, then the mismatch would very likely also create a high offset voltage that would be detected by the V_{OS} monitor.

In a manner similar to the way bias current I_B is measured, quiescent current I_Q is monitored by amplifier A_2, which develops a voltage from the positive supply current drain of the amplifier under test. This voltage is due partly to feedback current i_f, as well as to I_Q. However, since i_f is known for a given feedback resistor and output voltage swing, its effect can be corrected by offsetting the monitor limit.

Output voltage swing can be checked against the level of the input signal since the amplifier under test is basically a unity-gain inverter. If the output voltage cannot swing over the full range of the input signal, a large error signal will be produced at the e_j output, and the gain monitor can detect this failure. If comparator monitors with OR gating are used, a single pass/fail output indication can be implemented. ☐

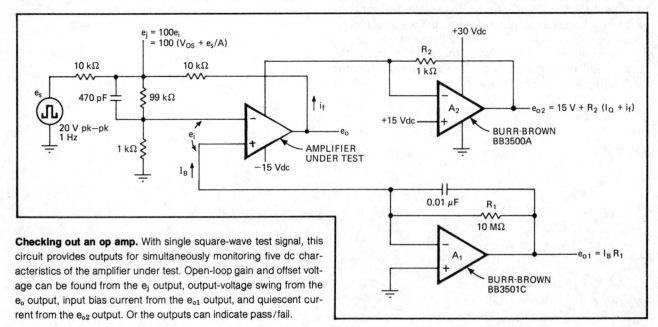

Checking out an op amp. With single square-wave test signal, this circuit provides outputs for simultaneously monitoring five dc characteristics of the amplifier under test. Open-loop gain and offset voltage can be found from the e_j output, output-voltage swing from the e_o output, input bias current from the e_{o1} output, and quiescent current from the e_{o2} output. Or the outputs can indicate pass/fail.

Finding MOSFET threshold with one measurement

by Amos Wilnai
Monolithic Memories Inc., Sunnyvale, Calif.

Measuring the threshold voltage of a MOS field-effect transistor is not simply a matter of finding the gate-to-source voltage that results in a certain drain current. Although direct, this method only approximates the threshold voltage and depends on both MOSFET geometry and test-current value.

At least two readings must be taken at two different current levels to determine the actual threshold voltage. Here's a technique that accomplishes this automatically and finds the threshold voltage directly, with no need for graphic extrapolation.

Usually, when two V_{GS}–I_D data readings are taken, they are plotted on a graph of V_{GS} versus $I_D^{1/2}$. The threshold voltage (V_T) is then extrapolated by determining the point at which the straight line connecting the two readings intersects the V_{GS} axis, where $I_D = 0$. This method is time-consuming and requires experience.

The test circuit in the diagram, however, offers an easy way to measure the threshold voltage automatically. To understand the principle on which the measurement is based, first consider the MOSFET's transfer characteristic in the saturation region:

$$I_D = k(V_{GS} - V_T)^2$$

where k is a constant. This equation can be rewritten as:

$$I_D^{1/2} = k^{1/2}(V_{GS} - V_T)$$

For two data readings:

$$(I_{D1}/I_{D2})^{1/2} = (V_{GS1} - V_T)/(V_{GS2} - V_T)$$

Solving for the threshold voltage yields:

$$V_T = [V_{GS2}(I_{D1}/I_{D2})^{1/2} - V_{GS1}]/[(I_{D1}/I_{D2})^{1/2} - 1]$$

Selecting levels of $I_{D1} = 4I_{D2}$ reduces this equation to:

$$V_T = 2V_{GS2} - V_{GS1}$$

Now the threshold voltage can be found from two data readings by a simple subtraction.

In the test circuit, currents I and 4I are alternately supplied by separate current sources to the MOSFET under test. The device's drain-source voltage drop is sampled and held on capacitor C_1 and C_2. Voltage-followers A_1 and A_2 isolate the capacitors and provide a low-impedance output for driving subtractor A_3. The output voltage of A_3 is the extrapolated threshold voltage and can be measured with any voltmeter. □

Circuit alternately drives test MOSFET with different currents so that output threshold voltage reading is based on different data points.

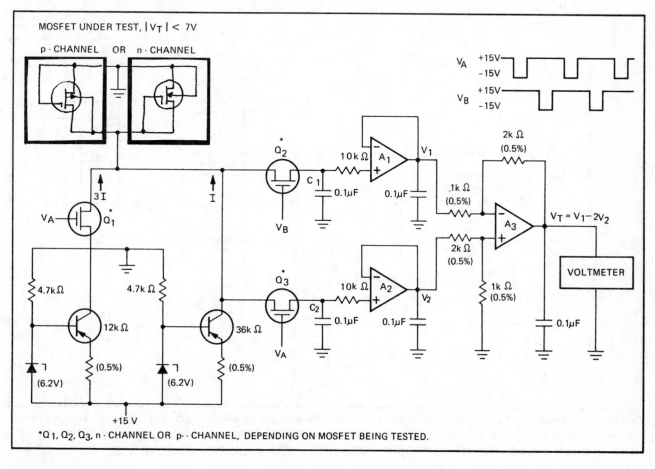

*Q1, Q2, Q3, n - CHANNEL OR p - CHANNEL, DEPENDING ON MOSFET BEING TESTED.

Test circuit checks optical isolators

by D. Bruce Johnson
Tullahoma, Tenn.

When you add your own voltmeter to this test circuit, you can accurately measure the current-transfer efficiency of an optically coupled isolator that has a phototransistor output. The test circuit also enables you to evaluate the current gain (h_{FE}) of the coupler's phototransistor. Both parameters, which are measured to within ±3%, can be read directly from the voltmeter's display over the useful current range of most couplers.

The test circuit employs an operational amplifier (A_1) as a voltage-to-current converter to supply a maximum drive current of 10 milliamperes for the coupler's input light-emitting diode for the transfer-efficiency test. A pnp transistor is also wired as a voltage-to-current converter for providing a maximum base current of 10 microamperes to the coupler's phototransistor for the h_{FE} measurement. Another op amp (A_2) acts as a current-to-voltage converter during both tests.

The coupler's transfer efficiency can be defined as:

$$efficiency = \left| (I_C/I_D) \times 100\% \right|_{I_B = 0}$$

where I_C is the phototransistor's collector current, and I_D is the LED's forward current. The transfer function of the voltage-to-current converter is expressed by:

$$I_D = E_i/100$$

and the transfer function of the current-to-voltage converter is:

$$E_o = I_C R_{FB}$$

The coupler's transfer efficiency can now be written as:

$$efficiency = (100 E_o / E_i R_{FB}) \times 100\%$$

For the circuit to provide direct reading, a ganged switch is used to control both voltage E_i and resistance R_{FB}. The product of E_i and R_{FB} is always 100, regardless of switch position. The transfer efficiency, therefore, simply becomes $E_o \times 100\%$—so that a 1-volt output indicates an efficiency of 100%.

A similar relationship exists for phototransistor h_{FE}, which is defined as:

$$h_{FE} = \left| I_C/I_B \right|_{I_D = 0}$$

where I_B is the phototransistor's base current. In terms of the transfer functions of the test circuit, phototransistor h_{FE} can be written as:

$$h_{FE} = E_o(10^5)/E_i R_{FB}$$

Since the product of E_i and R_{FB} is 100, then h_{FE} equals $1,000 E_i$—so that a 1-v output corresponds to an h_{FE} of 1,000.

If you use general-purpose 741-type op amps in the test circuit, you will be able to measure transfer efficiency to about 300% and h_{FE} to about 3,000. □

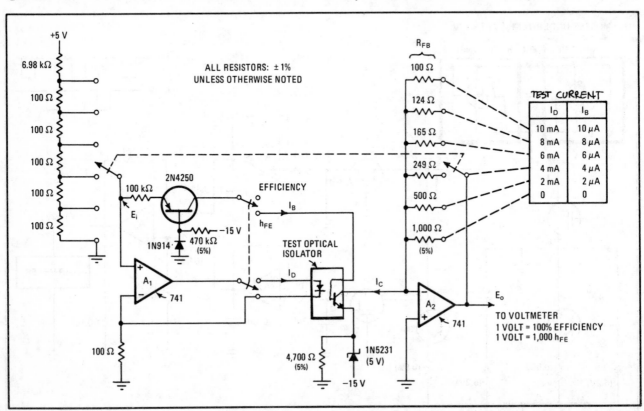

Optical coupler checkout. This test circuit, together with a voltmeter, provides a direct readout of the current-transfer efficiency of an optical coupler. The h_{FE} of the coupler's phototransistor can also be measured. Amplifier A_1 and the transistor operate as voltage-to-current converters, while amplifier A_2 is a current-to-voltage converter. A ganged switch acts as a range control for the test current.

Pulsed transistor test simulates linear operation

by Glenn Filler
Westinghouse Semiconductor Division, Youngwood, Pa.

Linear operation of high-power output transistors in audio systems may subject them to heat failure. Yet most reliability tests pulse the transistors into saturation, rather than subjecting them to the sudden, simultaneous high current and high voltage they will actually experience. The solution is simulation of operating conditions by pulsing the transistor in the unsaturated mode with the circuit used by audio manufacturers.

The circuit (Fig. 1) simulates the pulses of high power that elevate junction temperatures, particularly when the amplifier must produce high outputs at high frequencies. Prolonged high junction temperatures often cause collector-to-emitter shorts, and the transistors fail.

The transistor under test is pulsed at a low repetition rate. Capacitor C is charged to a preset voltage through resistor R_1 with switch S in position 1. When the switch is moved to position 2, C discharges through R_2 and D_1 to turn on the driving transistor Q. Resistor R_3 is in-

cluded in the circuit to allow C to discharge fully (instead of down to the sum of forward drops in D_1 and the base-to-emitter junction of Q); R_4 furnishes a path for the turn-off current of Q, and diode D_1 prevents R_3 from serving as a low-resistance shunt of R_4 for collector-to-base leakage currents.

The duration of the discharge pulse in the drive circuit is on the order of half a second; it can be varied by changing the values of C, R_2, and R_3. The long pulse of collector current from Q drives the base of the transistor under test.

The collector of the transistor under test is pulsed at a 60-hertz rate by a half-wave supply that consists of the Variac output and diode D_2. The peak collector voltage can be as high as 75 volts, and the current as high as 10 amperes (depending on the values of R_7 and R_8). The duration of the base drive covers many cycles of the collector voltage; therefore the transistor is subjected to extended pulsing that tests its high-power operating capability.

The self-triggered X-Y oscilloscope is set to a vertical range of 0.1 volt per division (corresponding to an emitter current of 1 A/div) and a horizontal range of 10 V/div (which measures the collector-to-emitter voltage). The base drive and the collector supply are first adjusted to provide a low-current, low-voltage display. When the transistor turns on, the base and collector

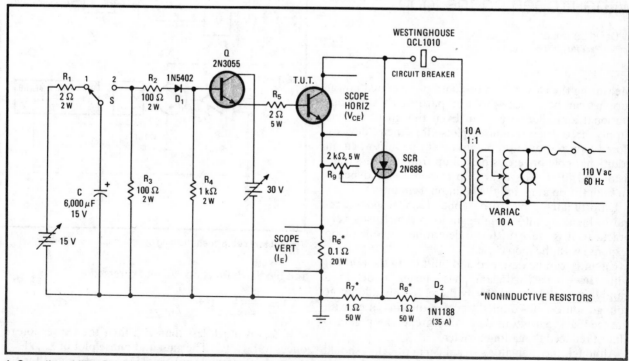

1. Operating ability. Circuit tests high-power audio output transistors for ability to perform at the high current and high voltage levels they'll meet in linear operation. Transistor under test is pulsed with collector voltage at 60 Hz; base drive is applied from 2N3055 for a duration determined by discharge of C. Failure mode is most likely to be second breakdown caused by heat dissipation at junctions.

2. Here's the picture. Audio transistor performance in circuit of Fig. 1 is monitored by oscilloscope display. Here transistor shows satisfactory behavior. If second breakdown causes collector-to-emitter short circuit, oscilloscope trace drops back to zero.

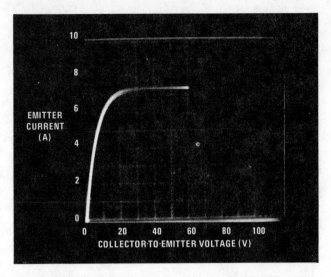

supplies are readjusted to the test levels of V_{CE} and I_E.

If the transistor can meet the test conditions, the scope display looks like Fig. 2. But if second breakdown causes a collector-to-emitter short circuit, the voltage falls to zero. When V_{CE} drops, the current through the transistor exceeds the test level; this triggers the silicon controlled rectifier, which puts a short across the line and opens the circuit breaker.

The triggering level of the SCR is set before base drive is applied. With the transistor under test shorted out, potentiometer R_9 is adjusted to let the SCR fire at the desired current level. ☐

Finding open-loop gain without opening the loop

by David Luttropp
Hewlett-Packard Co., Loveland, Colo.

Measuring the closed-loop response of regulated power supplies can be a tricky problem, particularly when operational amplifiers are used. Even though IC makers supply frequency-response plots for their devices, closed-loop response problems always pop up when an additional pole or zero is picked up from the pass transistor and filter. The total loop response now depends on both the op amp and the additional circuitry.

Unfortunately, measuring open-loop response requires breaking into a high-gain loop, which isn't very practical. It is much better to determine the open-loop response with the loop closed.

Circuitry can be designed and built to do the job, but with Hewlett-Packard gain phase meter model 3575 handy, you're already halfway there. Simply add an ac voltage source, dc-coupled and floating in series with the feedback path, and determining open-loop gain is almost reduced to reading a meter.

Although the oscillator's signal isn't critical, it should be low enough for the amplifier to remain linear. An oscilloscope can be used to monitor the signal.

The open-loop response of an amplifier with gain A

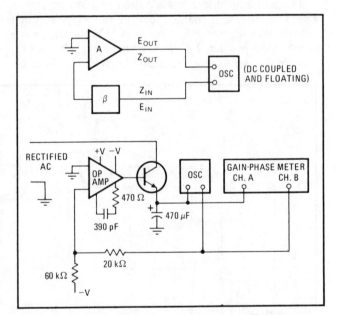

Typical test setup needs floating direct-coupled oscillator

and feedback function can be expressed as:

$$A\beta = \frac{E_{OUT}}{E_{IN}} \left(1 + \frac{Z_{OUT}}{Z_{IN}} \right)$$

If Z_{out} is much less than Z_{in}, then the expression reduces to E_{out}/E_{in}. The gain and phase plot of E_{out}/E_{in} is a simple Bode plot, but the 3575 is well suited for this role because it measures the log ratio of E_{out} and E_{in} and the phase between them. ☐

Curve tracer can check optoisolator performance

by Ken Lindsay
Tektronix Inc., Beaverton, Ore.

A conventional transistor curve tracer can be used to check the performance of optoisolators against the manufacturer's specifications. These tests, performed before the component is installed, can save many costly hours of troubleshooting in the prototype, production, and test stages of manufacturing.

An optoisolator consists of a light-emitting diode and a phototransistor in a single package, as shown in Fig. 1. The characteristics of the diode and the characteristics of the transistor can be measured in the same way as for any other diode or transistor. The two optical-coupling characteristics—ratios of transistor collector current and base current to diode forward current—and the isolation can be checked by three procedures.

In the examples, the MCT-2 optoisolator is used as the device under test because it is probably the most widely used isolator. A Tektronix 577 curve tracer was used to perform the tests; however, other instruments can be used in a similar manner.

The isolator may be connected to the curve tracer in the same way as a standard diode or transistor. Since many optoisolators are packaged in a six-pin mini-DIP flatpack, a dual in-line socket and adapter allows easy connection of the device to the curve-tracer terminals. As an alternative, a standard dual in-line IC socket, with banana plugs wired to the terminals, can be used.

The first coupling test is a measurement of the dc collector current-transfer ratio, which is the ratio of dc collector current, I_C, to diode forward current, I_F. The manufacturer specifies a value for this ratio under conditions of I_F of 10 milliamperes and collector-to-emitter voltage V_{CE} of 10 volts. To check this value, connect pin 5 of the device to the collector terminal of the curve tra-

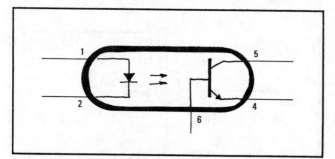

1. Optoisolator. Characteristics of the input diode and the output transistor can be checked with a curve tracer, and so can isolation and signal-coupling between the diode and transistor. (Some optoisolators do not provide access to the transistor base lead.)

cer, pins 2 and 4 to the emitter terminal, and pin 1 to the base terminal of the curve tracer so that the step generator drives current through the diode. With no voltage at the terminals, set the controls of the curve tracer as follows:

Collector supply

Max peak voltage	25 v
Max peak power	0.6 w
Variable collector	0%
Collector-supply polarity	+ (not +dc)

Step generator

Step offset amplitude	5 mA
Offset multiplier	000 (fully ccw)
Number of steps	Midrange
Any other adjustments	Set for conventional operation
Horizontal volts/division	2 v
Vertical current/division	2 mA
Intensity, Focus, and Position	Set for well-defined spot in the lower left corner of the CRT graticule.

Switch on the voltages at the curve-tracer terminals and set the VARIABLE COLLECTOR % between 60% and 80%. The display obtained should be similar to that shown in Fig. 2. The number of curves displayed depends on the setting of the NUMBER OF STEPS control on the curve tracer.

Rotate the control for VARIABLE COLLECTOR % until the end of the second curve lies at the horizontal center of the screen, as in Fig 2 (disregard the bottom curve representing zero drive current). This display represents a V_{CE} of 10 v (5 divisions × 2 v/division) and an I_F of 10 mA (5mA/step × 2 steps). In the example shown, the I_C is approximately 7.7 mA, so I_C/I_F is 7.7/10 or 77%. The manufacturer's specifications guarantee a minimum of 20%, with a typical value of 50%.

For the second test, which measures the base-current-transfer ratio, the setup must be changed slightly. Remove the cable connected to the emitter of the isolator, (pin 4) and connect it to the base (pin 6). This change grounds the base and opens the emitter, which allows the collector-base current to be measured. Change the VERTICAL CURRENT/DIV control to 5 µA and check that the display is similar to the one in Fig. 3.

According to the manufacturer's specifications, the typical value for dc-base-current transfer ratio is 0.2% with a voltage between collector and base (V_{CB}) of 10 v, and a diode forward current (I_F) of 10 mA. The second step displayed (again, disregard the baseline) represents an I_F of 10 mA, and center screen horizontally represents V_{CB} of 10 v. The base current, I_B, is 9.8 µA, so the base current transfer ratio I_B/I_F is about 0.1%.

The third and last test must be made with caution. Isolation voltage should be tested only up to the guaranteed minimum rating. If the devices are tested to their maximum, their isolation voltage would have to be

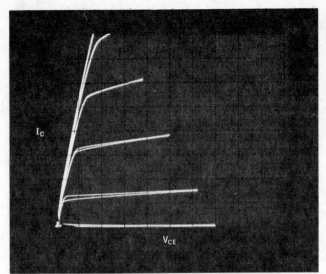

2. Tracer display. Collector current is displayed as function of collector-to-emitter voltage for diode forward currents of 0, 5, . . . 25 mA. Horizontal scale is 2 volts/division; vertical scale is 2 mA/division. Manufacturer rates I_C/I_F ratio at specified I_F and V_{CE}.

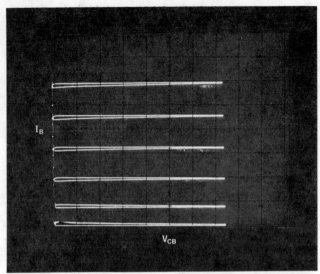

3. Base current. If optoisolator has base lead, base-current-transfer ratio I_B/I_F can be checked as in this curve-tracer pattern. I_F steps are 0, 5, . . . 25 mA; horizontal scale is 2 volts/division; and vertical scale is 5 μA/division.

exceeded, and it would destroy the device.

To test the isolation voltage of the optoisolator, simply connect the curve-tracer COLLECTOR SUPPLY terminal to any one point on an element of the optoisolator, such as the diode, and ground one point on the transistor. Then apply the specified voltage and check for any leakage current, which will cause an upward shift of the base line from the zero-current position. ☐

A simple way of measuring high-frequency transistor gain

by Glen Coers
Texas Instruments, Dallas, Texas

Accurately measuring transistor high-frequency gain requires the collector-to-emitter voltage to remain constant—and in some test setups this is difficult to accomplish. Using a tuned transmission line makes life much easier, since it lets dynamic collector current be measured without any change in V_{CE}. The test method, useful up to several hundred megahertz, gives consistent results and requires no critical collector bypassing.

Usually, the value of h_{fe} is obtained by reading the rf voltage developed across a small sampling resistor (R_1) of about 1 to 3 ohms as shown in Fig. 1. Since this voltage can be as low as 10 microvolts, an amplifier providing a gain of about 50 decibels is generally required. Also, noise voltage must be minimized because the amplitude of the desired signal is extremely small. The rf base current is multiplied by the transistor's gain, which becomes proportional to the rf voltmeter reading.

This method, although straightforward and easy to implement, has some problems. Perhaps the worst is the need to bypass the sampling resistor at high frequencies, since the impedance of the bypass capacitor may be several ohms, sufficient to cause a large error.

A better approach, which also reduces the problems caused by ground loops and stray capacitances, uses a one-quarter-wavelength transmission line (Fig. 2). A section of coaxial cable, slightly less than λ/4, is tuned by C_2, so that the collector of the transistor under test looks like a short circuit and V_{CE} remains constant. The tuned line also steps up the voltage, eliminating the

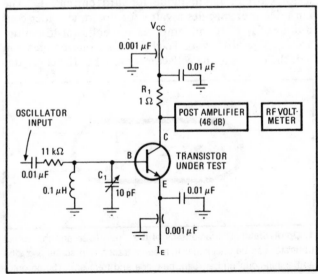

1. Measuring h_{fe} with sampling resistor requires extra amplification.

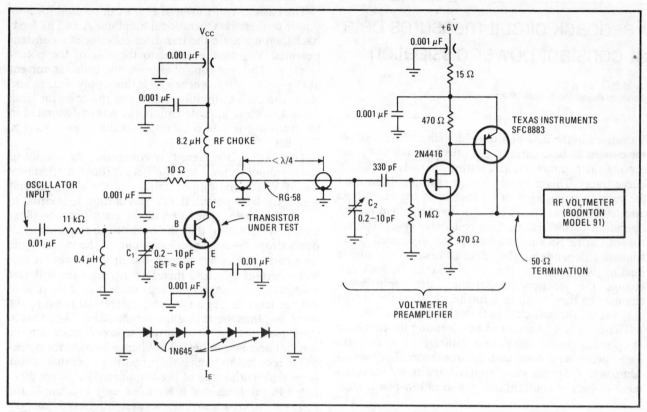

2. Tuned transmission line uses a foreshortened quarter-wavelength line to simulate good short-circuit condition at transistor collector.

TUNED·LINE CHARACTERISTIC AT 100 MHz

Resonant frequency: f_o = 100 MHz
Cable velocity propagation constant: v_p = 0.66 for type RG-58 cable
Cable attenuation: dB loss = 5.2 dB/100 ft for RG-58
Cable characteristic impedance: Z_o = 52 ohms for RG-58
Wavelength: λ = 300 v_p/f_o = 1.98 meters
Line length: $\ell = \lambda/4$ = 0.495 m
Line attenuation constant: α = 0.378 (dB loss/ft) = 0.0197
Line phase constant: $\beta = 2\pi f_o/3(10^8) v_p$ = 3.18
Line impedance: $Z_r = Z_o/\alpha\ell$ = 5.33 kilohms
Line Q: $Q = \beta/2\alpha$ = 80.5
Impedance at collector: $Z_s = Z_o^2/Z_r$ = 0.511 ohms
Line voltage transformation ratio: $V_r/V_s = (Z_r/Z_s)^{1/2}$ = 102

FREQUENCY (MHz)	LINE LENGTH (INCHES)
50	39.4
100	19.7
200	9.8
400	4.9

need for a high-gain amplifier.

At low frequencies, however, there are limitations. The cable has to be very long, and the impedance at the transistor's collector becomes prohibitively large.

To calculate line resonant impedance and Q, at least three cable parameters must be considered. These are: characteristic impedance, Z_o, velocity factor, v_p, and line attenuation, which is usually specified in decibels per 100 feet. At 100 MHz, type RG-58 coaxial cable is described by: Z_o = 52 ohms, v_p = 0.66, and attenuation = 5.2 dB/100 ft. Wavelength at 100 MHz:

$$\lambda = 300 v_p/f_o = 1.98 \text{ meters}$$

A measurement of the tuned line at 100 MHz will yield an impedance of 0.511 ohms at the generator end. Even at higher frequencies, good short-circuit conditions can be obtained because the low impedance at the collector is transformed to a higher value, resulting in a higher voltage at the open end. The small voltage across the 0.511-ohm resistance is stepped up by a ratio of 102. The voltage at the open (meter) end of the transmission line is typically 1 mV, a significant improvement in sig-nal-to-noise performance over the sampling resistor method.

A voltmeter preamplifier assures that the open end of the line is terminated by a high impedance. A bootstrap source-follower is used to minimize loading of the resonant circuit. Because of the small amount of capacitance at the input of the source-follower, the transmission line should be physically less than a quarter of a wavelength long when resonated with C_2.

The test procedure is straightforward. A 68-kilohm resistor is inserted between the transistor's base and collector socket pins, and C_1 is adjusted for a peak reading on the voltmeter. Then the resistor is removed. Next, a 0.01-microfarad capacitor is placed between the base and collector pins, and the oscillator input level adjusted for a voltmeter reading of 1 mV. The capacitor is removed, and the transistor to be tested inserted in the socket. The collector-emitter voltage (V_{CE}) and emitter current (I_E) are adjusted to the desired operating conditions, and h_{fe} can be read directly from the voltmeter (a meter reading of 5 mV corresponds to an h_{fe} of 5).

To reduce ground loops, the shield of the transmission line should be connected as closely as possible to the transistor's emitter. Any general-purpose signal generator can be used, as long as it can deliver 0.5 Vrms into a 50-ohm load.

□

Feedback circuit measures beta at constant power dissipation

by H.P.D. Lanyon
Worcester Polytechnic Institute, Worcester, Mass.

Variations in the beta of a transistor (the ratio of collector current to base current) are often monitored by observing the common-emitter output characteristics on a curve tracer. This method has, for example, been used for routine monitoring of transistors of the same type and to determine the effect of a magnetic field on the operation of transistors. Unfortunately, systematic errors can arise, because the total power dissipated in the transistor depends on the value of beta. When ohmic heating is significant, the initial change in beta can change the junction temperature; this temperature change can then result in a further change in beta that may exceed the beta change from the original effect.

The error can be removed by operating the transistor at constant power dissipation, rather than at constant base current as is done with a curve tracer. The two accompanying figures show simple circuits for measurement of beta at constant dissipation in low-power transistors and in high-power transistors, respectively.

The basic circuit shown in Fig. 1 can be used for low-power transistors. Operational amplifier A and its feedback loop maintain the transistor collector at a constant potential V_{CE} that is equal to the V_{set} of the potentiometer. This one control also sets the collector current at $(V_{CC} - V_{set})/R_C$, where V_{CC} is the supply voltage and R_C is the current-limiting resistor in the collector lead. Thus, to a close approximation, the power dissipated in the transistor is held constant at a value $(V_{CC} - V_{set}) \times V_{set}/R_C$.

The control is achieved by connecting the output of the amplifier to the transistor base through a resistance R_B. If V_{out} is the output voltage of the amplifier and V_{BE} is the base potential, the base current I_B is equal to $V_{out} - V_{BE})/R_B$. Operation of the circuit can be illustrated by assuming that the beta of the transistor suddenly drops from its previous value. If the value of the base current does not change, this drop reduces the collector current, βI_B, and therefore increases the collector potential V_{CE} from its previous value V_{set}. This shift in voltage level causes a non-zero differential input to the amplifier, thus increasing the magnitude of V_{out}. This in turn increases the base current to compensate for the original decrease in beta. The change in collector potential is reduced to negligible proportions because of the large differential gain of the amplifier. The power dissipated in the transistor is modified only because of the increase in base current. A straightforward analysis shows that the change is lower in the ratio $V_{BE}/\beta V_{CE}$ than it would have been in the absence of the feedback loop. In a typical silicon transistor with $V_{CE} = 12$ volts, $V_{BE} = 0.6$ v and $\beta = 100$, the power change with the feedback loop is only 1/2,000 of the power change with constant base drive.

The value of beta is found by measuring the voltages, and changes in beta are reflected in the value of V_{out} (β is inversely proportional to $V_{out} - V_{BE}$). If the value of R_B is chosen to give a V_{out} of approximately 10 v, changes in V_{BE} can be neglected. Thus

$$\beta = (R_B/R_C)(V_{CC} - V_{set})/V_{out}$$

The useful range of operation of the circuit of Fig. 1 is limited by the input common-mode range of the op amp. For a op amp operating with a ±15-v power supply, the differential gain becomes smaller when the

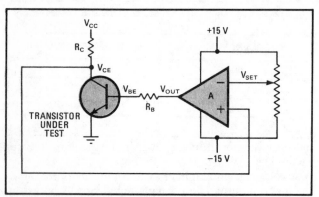

1. Constant dissipation. Basic circuit for measurement of beta with constant power dissipation in transistor uses op amp and feedback loop to hold V_{CE} at V_{set} and I_C at $(V_{CC} - V_{set})/R_C$, so dissipation is fixed. Base drive changes if beta is changed by variation of test parameter, such as magnetic field.

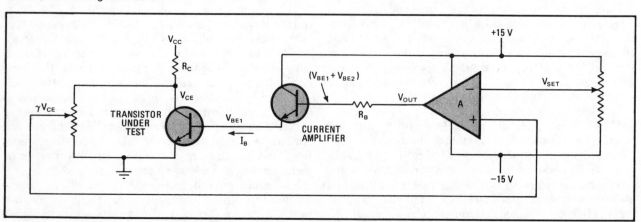

2. Modified circuit. For high-power transistors, feedback loop maintains a fraction of V_{CE}, γV_{CE}, at V_{set}, allowing the operational amplifier to stay in its input common-mode range for large values of transistor voltage. The current amplifier can provide several amperes of base drive.

common-mode voltage exceeds approximately 8 V. With a 40J op amp, common-mode voltage as high as 12 V can be tolerated. In the circuit of Fig. 1, the maximum permissible value of V_{CE} can be extended to 27 V by referencing the emitter to the negative side of the amplifier power supply rather than the common ground. In this case, $V_{CE} = V_{set} + 15$ V. This modification also allows larger values of R_B for a given base current and increases the system sensitivity to changes in beta. It cannot be used in power transistors when V_{CE} may be several hundred volts and a base drive of several hundred milliamperes may be required—far in excess of the current-handling capabilities of most op amps.

The circuit in Fig. 2 shows how the original circuit may be modified to maintain constant power in such cases. Instead of the direct connection of V_{CE} to the noninverting input of the operational amplifier, a fraction, γV_{CE}, of this potential is tapped from a voltage divider chain to ground. The impedance level of this chain is kept high to minimize the current drain from the current flowing through R_C. A current amplifier is used in the base-drive circuit. In Fig. 2, an emitter follower is shown; the base current is given by the relationship $I_B = (V_{out} - V_{BE1} - V_{BE2}) \times A_I/R_B$, where A_I is the current gain of the emitter follower and V_{BE1} and V_{BE2} are the base-emitter-junction voltages of the transistor under test and the current amplifier, respectively. Thus changes in beta are reflected in changes of V_{out}, as in the original circuit. □

Adjustable active load maintains constant dc power dissipation

by Norm Bernstein
Analog Devices Inc., Norwood, Massachusetts

An active load that dissipates constant power despite variations in supply voltages is useful for calibrating a dc power meter and for several thermal-control applications. Such a load may consist of one or more transistors, like the Darlington pair shown in the circuit diagram. The value of reference voltage V_{ref} and the accompanying control components determine how much power the load can dissipate. For the circuit arrangement shown, the transistors dissipate 1 watt when V_{ref} is 1 volt and proportionally less for lower reference voltages at any value of input voltage from 1 v to 10 v. The dissipation is constant to within 1% over this whole range of V_{in}.

The operation of the circuit is simple. Amplifier A_2 references the dissipating element to ground and produces a signal proportional to the load current. This signal is inverted by amplifier A_3 and then is multiplied by V_{in} in the AD435 multiplier. The output from the multiplier is therefore a voltage that is proportional to power dissipation. This voltage is compared to V_{ref} and integrated to produce a bias voltage for the Darlington pair.

If the load voltage changes, the integrator adjusts the Darlington bias until the multiplier output equals V_{ref}, thereby maintaining constant power. The power dissipation can be adjusted by simply changing V_{ref}.

This circuit arrangement can be used for almost any power range by applying appropriate biasing current to the transistors and scaling the multiplier inputs. To minimize errors from multiplier offset and drift, and thus optimize accuracy over dynamic range, the multiplier should be operated with an output of at least 100 millivolts. Therefore, the input voltage range for each multiplier input should be between 1 and 10 V. The color-tinted components in the diagram represent all of the power-dissipation elements and may be easily isolated from the rest of the circuit.

The constant-power property of this circuit has several interesting applications. For example, placing the power-dissipating elements within an environment of constant thermal transfer results in constant temperature. Measurement of temperature rise will give the thermal resistance of that environment. Or, if the power-dissipating elements are used as a heater for an environmental chamber, constant temperature can be achieved without the limit-cycling usually associated with thermostat-type controllers. □

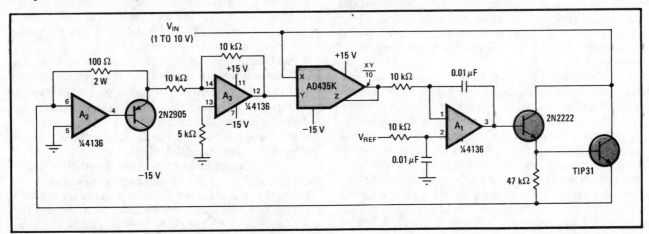

Constant dissipation. Darlington pair dissipates constant power for fixed V_{ref}, even though V_{in} varies. Maximum dissipation in load for circuit shown is 1 watt when V_{ref} is 1 V. Different load transistors and different biasing arrangements permit higher power dissipation.

ROMs in microprocessors can test themselves

by John B. Peatman,* David G. Dack, and David A. Warren
Hewlett-Packard Ltd., South Queensferry, Scotland

Read-only memories that contain the programs and constants needed in a microprocessor-based system can be given self-test capability by reserving one word of the ROM for a bit-for-bit parity check on all the other words. The approach can detect any of several possible ROM malfunctions.

As illustrated in the diagram, the check word can be, but need not be, the last word in the memory. Each of its bits is selected to force an odd number of 1s (odd parity) in the corresponding column of the ROM. Even parity won't work.

To check the contents of the ROM, the microprocessor reads out every word in the ROM and performs a cumulative parity check—an exclusive-OR operation on each bit. At the end, the result should be a 1 in every bit position of the accumulating register.

If the specific microprocessor's instruction set doesn't include an exclusive-OR instruction, it can execute the equivalent operation in a subroutine.

This self-test always detects single errors, whole-word errors, data output lines stuck at 1 or 0, and address input lines stuck at 1 or 0. It sometimes detects address lines short-circuited to each other, output lines short-circuited to each other, and multiple random errors. Each of these has its own effect on the test.

Single errors occur at random as a result of flaws in the chip, or occasionally when a bit in a programable ROM reverts to its unprogramed state—unlikely in recent versions of programable ROMs. Any single error changes the parity of its column from odd to even.

Multiple errors in a single word change the parity of every column involved. They occur only rarely.

If a data output line is stuck at 1 or 0, there may be a short circuit to ground or to a power line from wiring connected to that output, or the output driver circuit may be dead. Since most ROMs have a total capacity equal to a power of 2, the number of words is even, and the stuck output line looks like an even number of 1s or an even number of 0s—thus creating an even parity. (This is one reason why even parity in the check word won't work.)

If an address input line is stuck at 1 or 0, it may similarly indicate a short circuit somewhere in or near the ROM, or a dead bit position in the address input buffer. This fault renders exactly half of the words inaccessible; an attempt to read all the words in the memory will read the other half twice, necessarily generating even parity. (Even if a user perversely loads a whole ROM with two identical groups of words, contents of the one location reserved for a check word must necessarily be different from its image in the other half of the memory.) Likewise, if two address lines are stuck, a sweep of the ROM reads one quarter of the words four times, again giving even parity.

*Now at Georgia Institute of Technology, Atlanta, Ga.

Self test. Reserving one location in a read-only memory for a check word enables a variety of faults in the ROM to be detected.

Of the kinds of fault detected with uncertainty, short circuits in address and data lines can occur either on the chip or in associated wiring. A short circuit between two address lines causes the lines always to have the same logic state. They correctly address one quarter of the words in the ROM when they both should be 0, and another quarter when they both should be 1; but when they are supposed to be different, for access to the remaining half of the ROM, they address one of the same-state quarters instead. Which quarter is addressed depends on the circuit family and the definition of the 1 and 0 states; in some cases a short-circuited 0 pulls a 1 down, while in others a 1 pulls a 0 up. This may or may not cause a parity error; if the inaccessible words themselves have even parity in all columns, the remaining words generate odd parity and thus don't upset the check-word parity. Assuming the distribution of 1s and 0s in the ROM to be random—an assumption that's not necessarily justified—the probability of an error in any one column is 0.5, and the probability of an error somewhere in n columns is $1 - (0.5)^n$. If $n = 8$, this probability is 0.996, which is close to certainty.

If two output lines are short-circuited, those two lines always present the same bit pair, either 00 or 11, regardless of the true contents of the addressed word. Which pair is presented again depends on the circuit family and the logic state definition. With a random distribution of 1s and 0s, half the words will present an incorrect bit in one column or the other.

For multiple random errors in the ROM, even parity results if any column has an odd number of errors.

The self-test is intended to be performed on individual ROM chips, each with its own check word, even if the system contains multiple chips. This pins down the location of detected errors to particular chips, which a single check word over a whole system can't do. □

Test circuit measures optical coupler's speed

by John R. Torok
National Semiconductor Corp., Santa Clara, Calif.

Although the performance of optical couplers has improved considerably in the last year or so, the method of measuring their switching times has not. Data sheets for most optical couplers still specify switching time at some unknown LED drive current, making it difficult, to say the least, for a designer to know what the actual switching time is.

Generally, the forward current applied to the coupler's input LED is increased until the collector current of the coupler's output phototransistor reaches some specified value. (This current limit is typically 1 or 2 milliamperes.) Then, the rise and fall times of the collector current are measured at the 10% and 90% points of the specified value.

However, this type of measurement does not accurately define the coupler's switching speed because the output rise and fall times are not referenced to the input current applied to the LED. For example, a 1-microsecond rise time for the output collector current is meaningless if the LED input current must flow for 2 μs before there is any output current at all.

A far better indication of coupler speed is device on time, which includes the input-to-output delay time, as well as the rise time of the output current. Likewise, device off time, which accounts for the phototransistor's storage time and the fall time of the output current, should also be determined. These two measurements can be referenced directly to the input current.

Since most couplers having a phototransistor output are driven from TTL signals, the input current to the LED is constant—that is, the input drive can be considered to be fixed and constant with respect to pulse width, pulse amplitude, and duty cycle.

The test circuit for determining a coupler's on and off times is shown in the figure. For this measurement, the base terminal of the phototransistor must be defined electrically, rather than leaving it open, as is usually done. Therefore, a high-value resistor (R_2) is placed between the phototransistor's base and emitter terminals. This resistor has only a negligible effect on the coupler's speed and current-transfer ratio.

The input driving-pulse waveform has a peak amplitude of 10 mA, constant to within +10% and –0%, a duration of 8 μs, and a maximum duty cycle of 10%. The phototransistor's collector-emitter voltage must also be kept as constant as possible. Here, it is held to 4 V between +10% and –0%.

The apparent load seen by the phototransistor is approximately 25 ohms with the components shown. This load impedance is established by the base-emitter junction of transistor Q_1. If desired, the load-impedance value can be increased by inserting a resistor in series with the base terminal of transistor Q_1.

The coupler's true switching speed can be measured by comparing the input pulse drive voltage with the output voltage at transistor Q_1. The on time will be the delay between the application of the leading edge of the input pulse and the time when the phototransistor's collector current exceeds 1 mA. The off time will be the delay between the trailing edge of the input pulse and the time when the collector current drops below 1 mA.

The magnitude of the LED drive current, which is set at 10 mA here, can be increased or decreased by simply changing the value of series resistor R_1. If more drive current is needed, be certain that the input TTL circuitry can sink it.

Resistor R_3 determines the test level of the phototransistor's collector current. The size of this current is computed by dividing the base-emitter (on) voltage (about 0.75 V) of transistor Q_1 by the value of resistor R_3. Therefore, if the collector current is to be doubled, then the value of R_3 must be halved. Or, in contrast, if the collector current is to be halved, then the value of R_3 must be doubled. In this way, collector-current values can be varied from about 100 μA to around 100 mA. (To assure a logic 1 output level at transistor Q_1, the value of resistor R_4 must be the same as that of resistor R_3.)

Besides checking the switching time of an optical coupler, the test circuit is also useful as an interface to a TTL buffer amplifier. $\square$

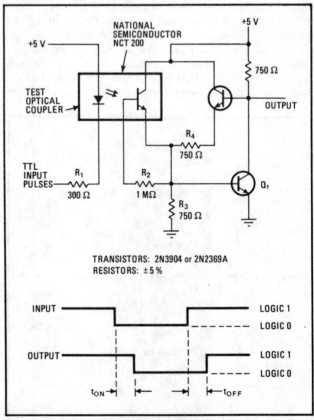

Speed check. Test circuit permits the true switching time of an optical coupler to be measured with reference to the input driving current to the coupler's LED. The circuit determines device on time (t_{ON}) and device off time (t_{OFF}), both of which take the inherent device turn-on and turn-off delay times into account, as well as the rise and fall times of the coupler's phototransistor output current.

Multimeter measurements yield device-model parameters

by Martin A. Green
University of New South Wales, Kensington, Australia

In computer analysis of electronic circuits, the most frequently used bipolar-transistor models for dc conditions are derived from the well-known Ebers-Moll equations:

$$I_E = -I_{ES}[\exp(qV_{BE}/kT) - 1]$$
$$+ \alpha_R I_{CS}[\exp(qV_{BC}/kT) - 1]$$
$$I_C = \alpha_F I_{ES}[\exp(qV_{BE}/kT) - 1]$$
$$- I_{CS}[\exp(qV_{BC}/kT) - 1]$$
$$I_B = -(I_E + I_C)$$

where I_E, I_C, and I_B are the terminal currents, V_{BE} and V_{BC} are the voltages between these terminals, q is the electron charge, k is Boltzmann's constant, and T is the absolute temperature. A positive value of current flows into the transistor; a negative value flows out of the transistor. Values of the Ebers-Moll parameters I_{ES}, I_{CS}, α_F, and α_R are usually required as program inputs [see "Modeling the bipolar transistor, part 1," *Electronics*, Sept. 19, 1974, p. 114]. These parameters, as well as the device beta, can be determined for any given transistor

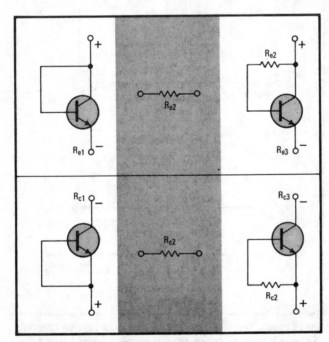

Just measure ohms. These six resistance measurements, made with a digital multimeter, yield the parameters for the Ebers-Moll model of a transistor. The open circles represent the terminals between which the measurements are made, while the + and − signs indicate the bias the DMM must establish on the junctions.

by measuring six resistances with a digital multimeter.

The method exploits the measurement technique commonly used on the resistance ranges of a DMM, which is, essentially, to pass a known constant current through the unknown resistance and measure the resulting voltage developed across it. The current passed, I_M, depends on the resistance range selected and, typically, may vary from 100 nanoamperes on high-resistance ranges to 10 milliamperes on low ranges.

Preliminaries consist of determining the current through the unknown on the different ranges of the DMM and selecting the range where the current, I_M, is reasonably near the probable operating current of the transistor. I_M, multiplied by the full-range reading in ohms must equal a voltage large enough to forward-bias the transistor junctions (about 0.7 V for silicon devices).

All measurements described (except those of R_{e2} and R_{c2}) must then be made on this range. After experimenting to find which direction of the probe connections forward-biases the transistor junctions, the following measurements are performed (see the diagram):

- Measure R_{e1}, the forward-biased resistance of the emitter-to-base junction with collector shorted to base.
- Select a resistor with its nominal resistance near the value $\beta_F R_{e1}$, where β_F is the estimated beta of the transistor in the normal forward mode of operation. Measure the exact resistance, R_{e2}, of this resistor.
- Measure the resistance between the emitter and collector while the emitter-to-base junction is forward-biased and R_{e2} is connected between the base and the collector. Call this value R_{e3}.
- Repeat the above procedure with the transistor in its inverse connection, i.e., with the collector and emitter exchanged in the above description. Record the corresponding resistances R_{c1}, R_{c2}, and R_{c3}.

From the Ebers-Moll equations, it is not difficult to show that the required transistor parameters can be calculated by the expressions:

$$\alpha_F = 1 - (R_{e3} - R_{e1})/R_{e2}$$
$$\beta_F = [R_{e2}/(R_{e3} - R_{e1})] - 1$$
$$I_{ES} = I_M/\exp(R_{e1}/r_e)$$
$$\alpha_R = 1 - (R_{c3} - R_{c1})/R_{c2}$$
$$\beta_R = [R_{c2}/(R_{c3} - R_{c1})] - 1$$
$$I_{CS} = \alpha_F I_{ES}/\alpha_R$$
$$[\text{or } I_M/\exp(R_{c1}/r_e)]$$

where r_e is equal to $(kT/q)/I_M$ and has a value in ohms of $25/I_M$ at temperatures around 17°C if I_M is expressed in milliamperes.

As an example, the following measurements were made upon a 2N3693 transistor using the 20-kΩ range of a Fluke 8000A DMM (except for the measurement of R_{e2}). The current through the unknown in this range was 0.1 mA, giving a value of r_e of about 250 Ω. The measured resistances were:

$$R_{e1} = 6,080 \ \Omega$$

$R_{e2} = 216,000 \ \Omega$
$R_{e3} = 10,630 \ \Omega$
$R_{c1} = 5,620 \ \Omega$
$R_{c2} = 4,770 \ \Omega$
$R_{c3} = 9,760 \ \Omega$

These readings yield the following values for the transistor parameters:

$\alpha_F = 0.979$
$\beta_F = 46.5$
$I_{ES} = 3 \times 10^{-15} \ A$
$\alpha_R = 0.132$
$\beta_R = 0.152$
$I_{CS} = 2 \times 10^{-14} \ A$

Inserted into the Ebers-Moll equations, these values allow the transistor performance to be predicted over a wide range of operating conditions.

At moderate to high current levels, parasitic resistances can influence the transistor performance [see "Modeling the bipolar transistor; part 2," *Electronics*, Oct. 31, 1974, p. 71]. This method of calculating α_F, α_R, β_F, and β_R continues to give accurate results. The value calculated for I_{ES} also will usually be accurate for values of meter current, I_M, up to the likely maximum of 10 mA. However, the first expression given for I_{CS} is preferable to the alternative one that is given in brackets, because the high series resistances associated with the base and collector can cause the bracketed expression to be inaccurate. □

Digital logic circuit
reads phase difference

by Demetrios K. Kostopoulos
Dalmo Victor Co., Belmont, Calif.

The phase difference between two sinusoidal waves of the same frequency can be measured digitally if the phase difference is converted into a time difference and the time difference is converted into a number of pulses. A count of these pulses then serves as a numerical representation of the phase difference between the two input wave forms.

The basic outline for this simple and inexpensive digital phase meter is shown in the diagram. Signal A is the reference sinusoidal waveform, while signal B is the sinusoidal waveform whose phase (relative to signal A) is to be determined. Both signals must have the same frequency, but they may differ in amplitude. The waveforms are converted into square waves by means of the voltage comparators, and two square waves are then ANDed together.

The output of comparator COMP$_A$ is low when signal A is positive and high when signal A is negative. The opposite is true for the output of comparator COMP$_B$. This makes it possible to detect any phase difference between the two waveforms. When they do not overlap, both comparator outputs are high for a length of time that is proportional to the phase difference between signal A and signal B.

The function of the AND gate is to clear and enable the binary-coded-decimal counter. When both gate inputs are high, the gate output is also high, and the counter is enabled. The counter is cleared when the gate output goes low. The number of gate-output pulses logged by the counter is directly proportional to the time that the gate output is high. Therefore, the final number in the counter is directly proportional to the phase difference between input wave form A and input waveform B.

During the high-to-low transition of the gate output, the counter output is stored in the register. This storage register drives a set of numerical readouts that display the phase difference. The phase weight of the least-significant digit in the display is:

$$\Delta\phi = 360°(f_s/f_c)$$

where f_s is the signal frequency, and f_c is the clock frequency. If $f_c = 360 f_s$, then the units of the displayed number are whole degrees; and if $f_c = 3,600 f_s$, the units become tenths of a degree. ☐

Determining phase digitally. Straightforward approach permits standard logic ICs to be used for measuring phase—the phase difference between sinusoidal inputs A and B is converted into a time difference. When the square-wave outputs from the comparators overlap, a phase difference exists, and the AND-gate output goes high, enabling the counter. The final count is stored in the register for display.

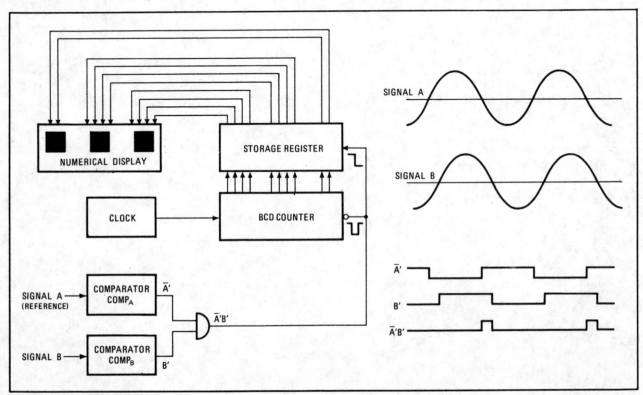

Edge-triggered flip-flops make 360° phase meter

by James C. Hager Jr.
Columbia Gas System Service Corp., Columbus, Ohio

Many phase detectors measure the amount of overlap of two waves to determine the phase difference between the waves. Often designed around some form of AND gate, they can measure a maximum phase difference of 180°, because, for example, they cannot distinguish between a phase difference of 20° and a phase difference of 340°. To measure differences up to 360°, a detector must use circuit elements that respond to the sequence

in which the waves arrive. A pair of edge-triggered flip-flops provides this capability.

A representative AND-type circuit by D. K. Kostopoulos appeared on page 119, in the Dec. 20, 1973, issue of *Electronics*. In this circuit, two signals are applied as inputs to comparators. The resulting square-wave outputs become the inputs to an AND gate, with one comparator output inverted with respect to the other. The AND-gate output is a pulse produced by the positive coincidence of the two signals. This pulse has a width proportional to the phase difference between the two input signals; maximum width occurs for a phase difference of 180°, as shown in Fig 2(a). The output pulse can enable a counter for a digital phase measurement, or it can be filtered with an RC network to give an analog signal proportional to the phase difference.

The Kostopoulos circuit can be modified to provide a

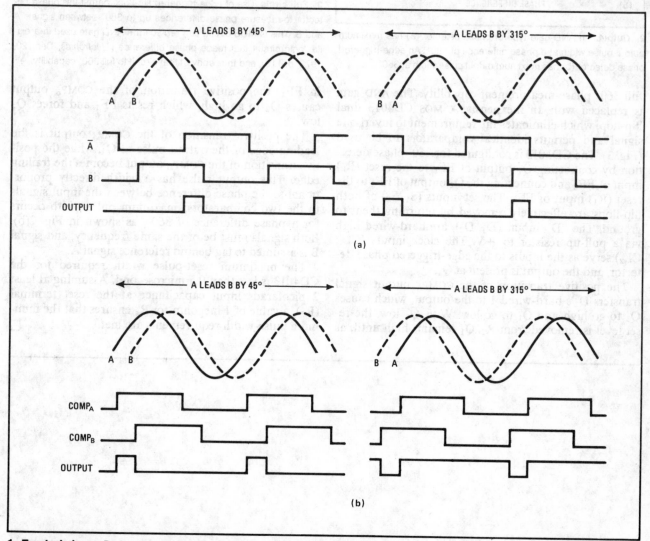

(a)

(b)

1. Two techniques. Performance of phase detector that operates on basis of overlap of two waves is shown in (a). Output is high only while both Ā and B are high. Performance of phase-detector circuit that operates on basis of sequence of leading edges is shown in (b). Output goes high when A goes high, and output does not go low again until B goes high.

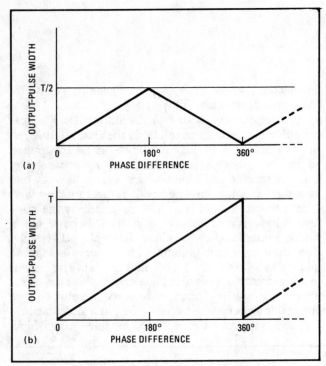

(a)

OUTPUT-PULSE WIDTH

T/2

0   180°   360°

PHASE DIFFERENCE

(b)

OUTPUT-PULSE WIDTH

T

0   180°   360°

PHASE DIFFERENCE

2. Output. An AND-gate type of phase detector (a) has maximum output-pulse width at a phase difference of 180°. An edge-triggered phase detector (b) has maximum output pulse width at 360°.

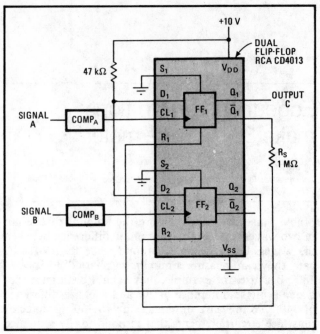

3. Full circle. Use of edge-triggered flip-flops permit this phase detector to measure phase differences up to 360° between signals A and B. This C-MOS circuit can replace the AND gate used in a digital-logic circuit that reads phase difference [*Electronics*, Dec. 20, 1973, p. 119], and thus convert that circuit to full 360° capability.

full 360° phase-measurement capability. The AND gate is replaced with an inexpensive C-MOS CD4013 dual flip-flop, which eliminates the requirement to invert one signal and permits identical comparators to be used (Fig. 3). The CD4013 is configured for 360° phase detection by connecting $\bar{Q}_1$ output of FF_1 to the reset (R_2) input of FF_2 and connecting the Q_2 output of FF_2 to the reset (R_1) input of FF_1. The set inputs (S_1, S_2) of both flip-flops are effectively removed by returning them to ground. The "D" inputs (D_1, D_2), are hard-wired high via a pull-up resistor to +V. The clock inputs (CL_1, CL_2) serve as the inputs to the edge-triggered phase detector, and the output is present at Q_1.

The positive transition of the COMP$_A$ output signal transfers D_1's hard-wired 1 to the output, which causes Q_1 to go high and $\bar{Q}_1$ to go low. With $\bar{Q}_1$ low, the reset level is removed from R_2. Q_1 remains high until, as

in FF_1, the positive transition of the COMP$_B$ output causes Q_2 to go high, which resets FF_1 and forces Q_1 low.

The positive transition of the COMP$_A$ output is the leading edge of the output pulse at Q_1, while the positive transition of the COMP$_B$ output becomes the trailing edge. This output pulse has a width directly proportional to the phase difference between the input signals to the two comparators; maximum pulse width occurs for a phase difference of 360°, as shown in Fig. 2(b). Both signals must be of the same frequency, and signal B is assumed to lag behind reference signal A.

The maximum reset-pulse width required for the CD4013 is less than 0.5 microsecond. Assuming at least 2 picofarads input capacitance at the reset terminal (R_2), a value of 1 megohm for R_s ensures that the minimum pulse-width requirements are met.   □

Spectrum analyzer aids fm deviation measurement

by Glenn Darilek
Southwest Research Institute, San Antonio, Texas

The ordinary technique for measuring the frequency deviation of a frequency-modulation signal is the carrier-null method. The level of the modulating voltage is increased, or the modulation frequency f_{mod} is decreased, until the carrier level goes to zero—disappears from the screen of the spectrum analyzer. At that point, the modulation index, β, equals 2.405, so the frequency deviation Δf equals $2.405 \times f_{mod}$.

But sometimes it may be necessary to determine the frequency deviation of an fm signal when the amount of deviation is not sufficient to use the carrier-null method. Also it may not be possible to vary the frequency or amplitude of the modulating signal in order to get a carrier null. In either of these situations, the modulation index, the frequency of modulation, and hence the frequency deviation can be easily determined by the technique described here.

The frequency deviation of a narrow-band fm signal can be determined quickly by observing the voltage ratio between the first sideband and the carrier, together with their frequency separation. These measurements can be made directly from a spectrum-analyzer display.

The amplitude-ratio measurement gives the modulation index, β of the signal. This index is defined as

$$\beta = \text{(frequency deviation)}/\text{(modulation frequency)} = (\Delta f)/f_{mod}$$

For narrow-deviation fm signals such as those in telemetry and communications links, β is equal to twice the ratio of the first sideband to the carrier. This relationship is accurate within 10% for β values below 0.8 (i.e., for the first sideband below the carrier by 8 decibels or more).

The amplitude of the carrier of any fm signal is proportional to the Bessel function $J_0(\beta)$, and the amplitude of the first sideband is proportional to $J_1(\beta)$. For small values of β, however, $J_0(\beta)$ is nearly equal to unity, and $J_1(\beta)$ is nearly equal to $\beta/2$. Therefore,

$$\text{(first sideband)}/\text{(carrier)} = J_1(\beta)/J_0(\beta) = (\beta/2)/1$$

or

$$\beta = 2\text{(first sideband)}/\text{(carrier)}$$

As an example, assume that the carrier of a particular fm signal is set at an arbitrary level of 1.0. If the first sideband is at a level of 0.2, the modulation index is:

$$\beta = 2 \times (0.2)/(1.0) = 0.4$$

If a decibel scale is used, one simply adds 6 dB to the ratio and converts this sum to an amplitude ratio. For example, in the illustration, the ratio of the first sideband amplitude to the carrier amplitude is measured to be -16 dB, so

$$\beta \text{ (dB)} = -16 \text{ dB} + 6 \text{ dB} = -10 \text{ dB}$$

Conversion of -10 dB to a ratio gives $\beta = 0.32$.

To find the actual frequency deviation, Δf, one must multiply the modulation index by the frequency of modulation. If the modulation frequency is not known, it also may be determined from the spectrum-analyzer display because the frequency separation between the carrier and the first sideband is equal to the modulating frequency. In the illustration, since the modulation frequency is 10 kilohertz, the frequency deviation is 10 kHz $\times$ 0.32 or 3.2 kHz. ☐

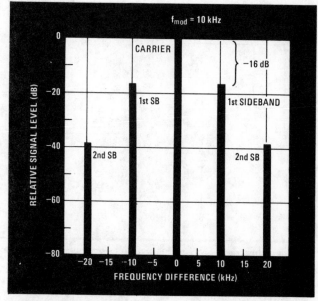

Analyzer display. Frequency spacing and relative amplitudes of carrier and sidebands in an fm signal can be read off directly from spectrum analyzer. The modulation frequency, f_{mod}, is given by the difference in frequency between adjacent components, and for small values of modulation index β, the numerical ratio of first sideband to carrier amplitude is $\beta/2$. Frequency deviation Δf of the fm signal is then found from $\Delta f = \beta \times f_{mod}$.

Pre-emphasizer speeds fm-tuner measurements

by M. J. Salvati
Sony Corp. of America, Long Island City, N.Y.

An fm tuner has a nonlinear frequency response because it contains a de-emphasis network to cancel the high-frequency boost added at the transmitter. Performing frequency-response measurements on such tuners is tedious; measured voltage must be recorded and correction factors added at each of the test frequencies to arrive at the "true" frequency response.

The pre-emphasizer circuit shown in Fig. 1 eliminates the extra notation, the need to look up correction factors, and the arithmetic, by altering the output of the modulation oscillator in the same manner as the frequency shaping performed at the transmitter. This unit is connected into the test setup between the audio oscillator and the audio-input terminal of the fm-signal generator, as shown in Fig. 2. With the pre-emphasizer compensating for the de-emphasis in the tuner, the tuner output should ideally be a constant voltage at all audio-frequencies from 30 hertz up through 15 kilohertz. Any variation from uniform output indicates imperfect frequency response in the tuner.

The pre-emphasizer circuit operates by means of a frequency-selective network in the feedback to the inverting input of a 741 operational amplifier. This configuration allows the network to be identical to the de-emphasis network used in the tuner under test. The 75-microsecond de-emphasis network used in fm tuners in the U.S. is shown installed; a switch can be added to select another network, such as the 50-μs standard used in European receivers, or the National Association of Broadcasters compensation for tape or for phonograph.

Battery operation (with economical 9-volt transistor-radio batteries) makes the unit independent and eliminates the possibility of ground-loop-induced hum in the measurement system. □

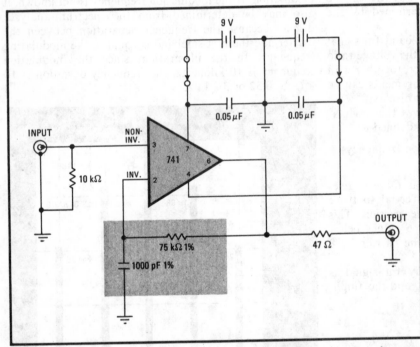

1. Pre-emphasizer. Feedback network to inverting input of op amp has same frequency characteristic as the de-emphasizer in fm tuner; this results in a frequency response alteration complementary to that of the tuner. Circuit shown here has the 75-μs network that is standard in American fm broadcasting.

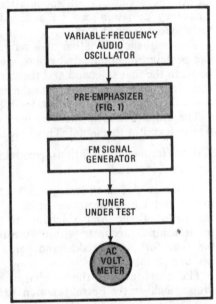

2. Flat-out testing. With pre-emphasizer that uses same frequency-selective network as tuner, this test circuit gives a flat audio output for a good tuner. The pre-emphasizer could be put between the tuner and the voltmeter, but the arrangement shown gives a better signal-to-noise ratio.

C-MOS phasemeter can be built in lab

by M. G. Fishel
Free University of Brussels, Belgium

Since most electronic laboratories need a phasemeter only once in a while, here is a cheap alternative to buying one. All it needs is three identical C-MOS 4011 integrated circuits, some discrete components, and a good voltmeter to measure the output, and all of this should cost less than $10.

The phasemeter accepts both analog and digital signals as inputs. Its usable frequency range starts at less than 5 hertz and goes up to several megahertz, depending on power-supply voltage.

The input signals are amplified by self-biased inverting ac amplifiers and then are shaped to obtain square waves. The square waves are then fed to two separate circuits, each of which is built around a single IC.

The first of the two circuits is the actual phasemeter; it is in fact a simple EXCLUSIVE-OR gate. The phase comparator's output (at twice the input frequency) is filtered through an RC network to remove the ac ripple. The output voltage is proportional to the phase difference between the input signals. If they are in phase, the meter reading will be zero. A phase difference of 90° yields an output of $(V_{DD} - V_{SS})/2$, and the full supply voltage will appear at the output when the phase difference is 180°. The output can be adjusted to any full-scale value that is convenient by means of the calibration potentiometer.

The second circuit, which is an edge-triggered memory cell, indicates which input signal leads the other. This information is displayed by light-emitting diodes. If the phase at input 1 leads the phase at input 2, D_1 lights, and if the phase at input 2 leads, D_2 lights.

The impedance seen at the inputs is on the order of 10^6 ohms. Both inputs are protected against overvoltage by 1N914 diodes. Power-supply voltage is not critical; V_{DD} can be anywhere between 3 and 15 volts. □

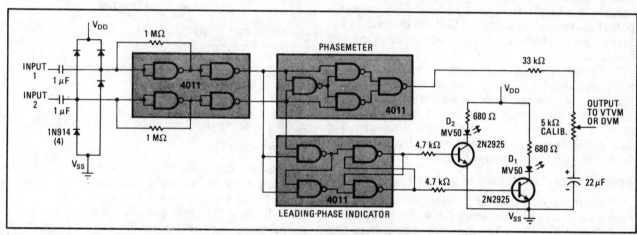

Phasemeter. Incoming digital or analog signals are shaped into square waves in first IC. Then phase difference is measured and displayed as an output voltage that is directly proportional to Δφ. Light-emitting diodes indicate which signal has leading phase. Supply voltage can be anywhere in 3-to-15-volt range. Meter can be built for less than $10 and operates at frequencies up to 5 MHz with V_{DD} of 12 volts.

31. Pulse effects and measurements

Evaluating high-energy pulse effects on materials

by J. F. Burgess, C. A. Neugebauer, and R. A. Sigsbee
R&D Center, General Electric Co., Schenectady, N. Y.

If your circuits may encounter high-energy pulse environments, the choice of material, as well as its thickness, becomes quite important. Some materials are much more tolerant to such environments than others. Gold, for instance, is unsatisfactory because of its high rate of absorption of incident pulse energy, which can cause failures from excessive heating.

On the other hand, aluminum conductors and aluminum-germanium chip-bonding solders behave more favorably. But before any choice is made, the high-energy pulse behavior of the materials likely to be used for hybrid-circuit conductors, resistors, and substrates must be considered.

The following charts and summary detail the thermal and mechanical effects of various amounts of short high-intensity energy pulses on aluminum-oxide substrates with gold, copper, aluminum, and nickel-chromium films, as well as a solder alloy of aluminum and 30% germanium, and beryllium oxide. Here are guidelines that span several energy ranges.

Energy range A (highest energy level)

When the energy absorption coefficients of all materials used in a particular circuit are within a factor of 2 or 3, failure usually occurs when the temperature rises to the melting point of the material having the lowest

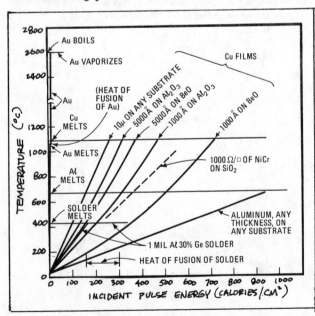

Chart 1: Temperature versus absorbed energy

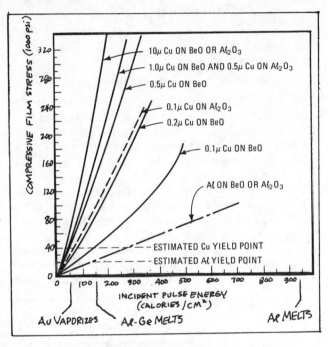

Chart 2: Stress induced by absorbed energy

melting temperature, such as chip-attachment solder.

Energy range B

When the difference in absorption between various materials is great, naturally low-absorption materials are preferred. For this energy region:

■ Al, Be, Si, Al_2O_3, BeO, and SiO_2 all experience similar temperature increases. Also the temperature rise in aluminum films does not depend on film thickness.

■ For similar energy dosages, transient temperature rise for copper films on Al_2O_3 or BeO substrates is less than 2% that of gold films.

■ The transient-temperature rise for copper films depends strongly on its thickness and the thermal conductivity of the substrate, in addition to the pulse duration. The thinnest copper film on the highest-conductivity substrate is optimum. Nevertheless, even 1,000 Angstroms of Cu on BeO experiences twice the temperature rise of aluminum films for similar energy levels.

■ If a solder containing appreciable quantities of medium-absorption elements is used, an incident pulse energy of 160 calories per square centimeter may cause melting.

To take full advantage of either an aluminum or a thin (5,000 Å) copper conductor, only aluminum or lower-absorption materials should be used in the die attachment. There is, however, no thickness limitation on these materials. Similarly, nickel-chromium resistors on the chip must be replaced by lower-absorption materials, or a better heat sink than SiO_2 must be used. Since stress-induced failures can be caused by shear stresses generated during heating, the interfacial bond strength is critical. Film thickness, as well as temperature increases, should always be minimized to reduce interfacial shear stresses, even if yielding occurs.

Energy range C

The energy absorption of aluminum and silicon is approximately 33% that of gold, whereas copper and nickel-chromium absorb about 20% that of gold. The transient-temperature rise for medium-absorption materials is greater than for range A, but may be acceptable for medium-energy-density environments.

Energy range D

The absorption by aluminum and silicon is about 10% that of gold, and copper absorption is about 25% that of gold. Also, the absorption by beryllium and beryllium oxide is significantly lower than it is for aluminum or aluminum oxide, which makes BeO substrates better heat sinks in this energy range. This may be particularly important when the pulse is repetitive. □

ICs replace memory scope for pulse measurements

by Daniel A. Swihart and Robert W. Thompson
DeWild Grant Reckert and Associates Co., Rock Rapids, Iowa

A 10-megahertz crystal oscillator is the secret ingredient in a circuit for reading out the time interval between two nonrecurring logic pulses or the duration of a single pulse. The circuit is an inexpensive alternative to a memory oscilloscope or a commercial frequency counter for examining the nonrecurring pulses.

By counting oscillator cycles, the circuit provides a digital readout of the nonperiodic time intervals—for example, with proper interfacing circuitry, it can measure the cycle time of a microprocessor function or calibrate test equipment such as a pulse generator. Parts for the complete circuit cost about $50.

As the figure shows, two-input exclusive-OR gates

FUNCTION TABLE FOR EXCLUSIVE-OR GATE (7486)			
Pulse edge to be detected	Inputs		Output
	Control	Probe	
Rising	Low	Low	Low
	Low	High	High
Falling	High	High	Low
	High	Low	High

(7486s) are the first stage in the pulse detection. The output of such a gate provides a high only when the logic levels on its inputs are different (see table). By using one input as a control (switching it to either the supply voltage, V_{cc}, or ground), the user can make the output go high, no matter whether a low or a high logic level is applied to the other input, which is connected to a test probe.

The gates' outputs are connected to a dual monostable multivibrator (74123). When a gate's output goes high, the multivibrator triggers on the rising edge, and an output pulse goes to a set-reset ($\overline{S}$-$\overline{R}$) latch (74279). The latch output, Q, controls a NAND gate, which passes the 10-MHz signal to a series of decade counters when Q is high. Each 10-MHz pulse corresponds to a time interval of 0.1 microsecond.

When a nonrecurring logic pulse occurs at probe input A, a pulse is applied to the $\overline{S}$ input of the latch, setting the latch's output to a high logic level. Probe input B causes a pulse to be applied to the $\overline{R}$ input of the latch, thereby resetting the latch's output to a low level.

The oscillator signal is counted only during the time interval between the set and reset pulses to the latch. The data displayed is the time interval between the rising (or falling) edge at probe input A and the rising (or falling) edge at probe input B. Of course, the input to probe A must always precede the input to probe B.

To measure the time interval between two nonrecurring pulses, connect probe inputs A and B to the circuit under test and switch control inputs A and B to the desired positions, whichever are necessary to detect rising or falling edges.

The duration of a single nonrecurring pulse is measured by connecting probe inputs A and B to the same place in the circuit under test, and setting the control inputs to the proper positions. For example, to measure the duration of a positive pulse, position switch A to ground and switch B to V_{cc}. The rising edge of the pulse will set a high on the latch's output, and the falling edge will reset the output to a low. The system's accuracy depends on the accuracy of the 10-MHz oscillator.

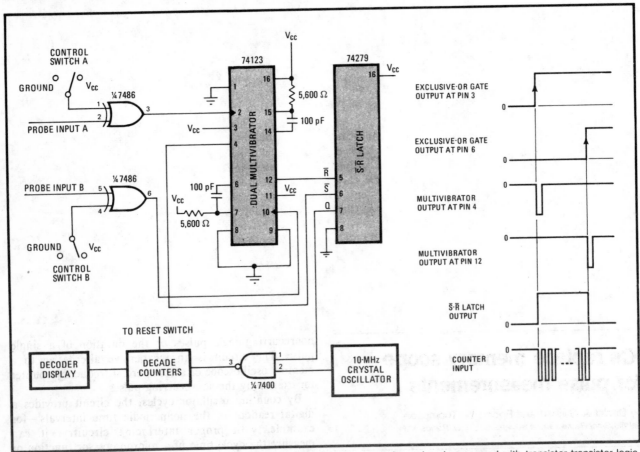

Alternative to memory scope. In this circuit, the spacing or duration of nonrecurring pulses is measured with transistor-transistor-logic detection circuitry that counts cycles of a 10-MHz oscillator. Seven digits can be displayed, giving readings from 0.1 microsecond to 0.9999999 second. This technique can be used in lieu of a memory scope for preserving nonrecurring pulses in digital circuits.

32. Frequency and time measurements

Overrange indicator can enhance frequency meter

by F. E. Hinkle
The Applied Research Laboratories, University of Texas, Austin, Texas

By making use of a 556 integrated circuit, which is composed of two 555 timers in a single package, an overrange indicator can be economically added to an analog frequency meter. A 555 can be used alone as a monostable multivibrator that is triggered by the frequency to be measured. To provide unambiguous measurements, however, the meter described here uses a second timer to flash a warning light whenever the input exceeds the maximum frequency setting. Although the technique of using monostables in analog frequency meters is not new, the use of new circuit developments makes the design economical and easy to implement.

When the range switch on this meter is set to the 50-hertz range, any input frequency from near dc to 50 Hz causes a panel meter to read correctly; e.g., a frequency of 42 Hz produces a meter reading of 42 microamperes. However, the meter reading is incorrect when the input frequency exceeds 50 Hz, and therefore a light-emitting-diode overrange indicator flashes. If the range switch is then moved to a setting higher than the frequency, the LED stops flashing and the meter again indicates correctly. For example, a 300-Hz signal would be measured on the 500-Hz range, and the meter would show 30 microamperes.

In the meter diagramed here, the upper portion of the circuit measures the frequency and has the 50-μA panel meter as its readout. The lower portion provides the overrange indication and has the LED as its warning light. These two portions of the circuit are driven by a common input.

The input signal is a rectangular pulse train; the pulses are differentiated to produce the negative spikes that are needed to trigger the timer. For a sine-wave or sawtooth input signal, a Schmitt trigger might be used to generate the negative impulses.

When pin 6 of the frequency-measurement monostable is triggered, pin 5 goes high. It stays high and delivers current for a time equal to $1.1R_1C_1$. This positive output pulse appears once for every cycle of the input frequency (unless the trigger impulse arrives while the output at pin 5 is already high). The current pulses, smoothed by the 10-microfarad capacitor, provide an average value that is shown on the microammeter.

At low frequencies, the output pulses are well separated, so the average current is low. At higher frequencies, however, they are closely spaced and approach a duty factor of about 95% at the upper frequency limit set by the range switch. Average current thus increases as the frequency increases. Resistors in the output circuit are chosen so that the average current is 50 μA at the maximum frequency in each range.

If the input frequency exceeds the meter range, a trigger spike arrives while the output is already high. As a result, that input cycle is not counted, so the frequency meter indication is erroneous.

To warn that trigger impulses are arriving while pin 5 is high, pin 5 is also connected to the base of pnp transistor Q_2. When pin 5 is low, Q_2 conducts and holds pin 8 high, thus preventing the warning-indicator monostable from being triggered. But when pin 5 is high, Q_2 is turned off; a negative input spike that reaches pin 8 therefore can trigger an output from pin 9 that flashes the LED. The duration of the flash is $1.1R_2C_2$. □

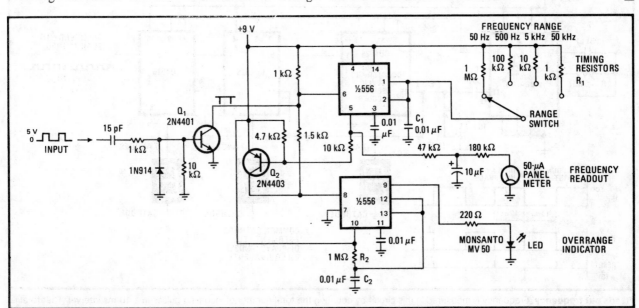

Unambiguous. Addition of overrange indicator to analog frequency meter warns when switch is set to wrong frequency range. Transistor Q_2 allows input signal to trigger LED monostable whenever input frequency is greater than meter range. Inexpensive and reliable circuit shown is useful from near dc to well over 20 kHz.

Frequency-counter design minimizes number of parts

by Lloyd F. Botway
University of Missouri, Columbia, Mo.

A handful of commonly available complementary-MOS integrated circuits can be made into a simple digital frequency counter capable of 100-hertz accuracy at 5 megahertz. The circuit uses only $(N+1)$ IC packages for an N-digit display. It dispenses with display latches, extra logic for generating a count-reset pulse, and current-limiting resistors for the seven-segment light-emitting-diode display.

As the diagram shows, the frequency to be measured is applied to a series of cascaded CD4026 decade counter/decoders. The counters count incoming cycles for 10 milliseconds and then drive LEDs to display the count for another 10 ms. Thus the display is updated every 20 ms and appears to be continuously on.

The element that controls the alternate counting and displaying is a CD4047 astable multivibrator, which generates a square wave with 20-ms periodicity. When the multivibrator's output, Q, is low, the clock inputs of the counter/decoders are enabled, their displays are disabled, but the counters count. When Q goes high, the clock inputs are disabled, and the count is displayed.

The counters are reset at the end of each 10-ms display interval by the positive pulse obtained by differentiating the rising $\overline{Q}$ output from the CD4047. The negative pulses are clamped to ground by diode D.

With values of C_1 and R_1 chosen to give a counting interval of 10 ms, the least significant digit in the display indicates hundreds of hertz because 100 pulses per second × 10 ms gives one pulse. Thus, a display of 246 indicates a frequency of 24,600 Hz, or 24.6 kilohertz. The counter is calibrated by adjusting R_1 for proper reading with an input signal of known frequency.

Supply voltage V_{DD} may have any value from 3 to 15 volts. The higher the supply voltage, the greater is the range of input voltages and the faster the counting—and the brighter but more current-consuming the display. The values of C_2 and R_2 should be chosen to give a reset-pulse duration of at least 250 nanoseconds. Diode D can be any general-purpose diode with a peak reverse voltage of at least $2V_{DD}$.

The same circuit can be used with a counting time of 100 ms to obtain frequency resolution to 10 Hz, but at such a long multivibrator periodicity, the display's 50% on/off duty cycle causes objectionable blinking. □

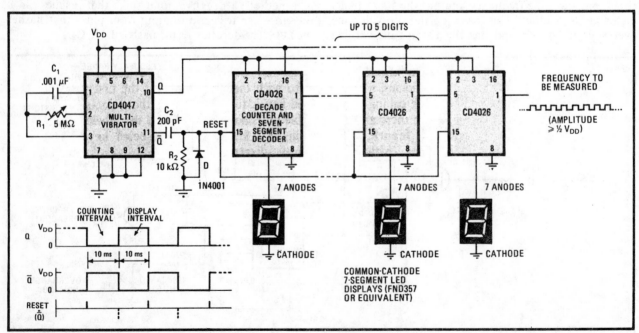

Reads out frequency. Frequency is measured in this circuit by counting the total number of incoming pulses in a 10-ms interval. That total is then displayed for the next 10 ms. This cycle, repeated every 20 ms, produces a flicker-free display. The multivibrator output determines the timing intervals and supplies reset signals to erase the counters every period. The C-MOS devices shown are RCA types or equivalents.

Color-TV set calibrates standard oscillators

by Carl F. Buhrer
GTE Laboratories Inc., Waltham, Mass.

A 3,375-kilohertz crystal oscillator is a good laboratory frequency standard because it is easily calibrated with great precision against a commercial TV network color signal, and because its frequency can be divided to provide many useful substandards. Several other frequencies also possess these characteristics to greater or lesser extent, and therefore are also discussed here.

Use of the television color subcarrier for adjusting local frequency standards to high accuracy has been recommended by the National Bureau of Standards [*Electronics,* May 10, 1971, p. 96, and March 20, 1975, p. 107]. The frequencies suggested here don't need phase-locked-loop synthesis and display-generating circuitry in the frequency comparison. The calibration can be made with just a color-TV receiver.

The method is based on the formation of steady color-stripe patterns on the TV screen when certain frequencies are substituted for the set's chroma signal. A succession of these stripes, each having a red, green, and blue component, will intersect vertically m times and horizontally n times per full video frame for an input frequency f_k given by:

$$f_k = f_c + nf_h + mf_v$$

Here n and m are positive or negative integers, and f_c, f_h, and f_v are the color-subcarrier, horizontal-scan, and vertical-scan frequencies, respectively. All three are nonintegral, but they are related as follows:

$$f_c = 5 \text{ MHz} \times 63/88 = 3.5795454\ldots \text{ MHz}$$
$$f_h = f_c \times 2/455 = 15.734265\ldots \text{ kHz}$$
$$f_v = f_h \times 2/525 = 59.940057\ldots \text{ Hz}$$

However, their combination, f_k, can be an integer. If n and m are chosen in relation to an integral index k such that:

$$n = -13 + 21 k$$

and:

$$m = -7 k$$

then f_k becomes an integral multiple of 15 kHz, given by:

$$f_k = (225 + 22 k) \times 15 \text{ kHz}$$

The table shows suggested standard frequencies that correspond to k of -1, 0, 1, and 2. For the non-0 values of k, m is not 0, and the result is diagonal stripe patterns on the TV screen. Therefore 3,375 kHz is the most useful as a standard frequency; since m = 0, that frequency

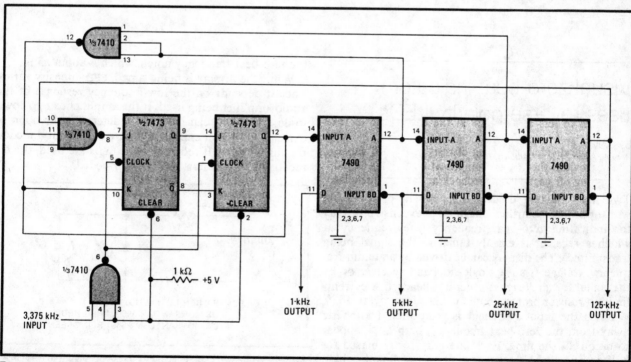

Frequency divider. This circuit uses a dual flip-flop and three divide-by-2 stages with feedback to divide the input frequency by 27. Three divide-by-5 stages then give further reductions. The input frequency of 3,375 kHz is convenient for use as a laboratory standard oscillator frequency because it has many useful submultiples and, besides, can be calibrated with great precision simply with a color-TV set.

gives a vertical stripe pattern easily distinguished from the associated m = ±1 frequencies, which are 59.94 hertz away. Moreover, all of its prime factors are small; 3,375 kHz = $2^3 \times 3^3 \times 5^6$ Hz, so a variety of lower frequencies such as 50, 60, 500 Hz, 1, 3, 5, 15, 25 . . . kHz can be obtained directly by division.

Calibration of the oscillator against the TV networks' rubidium standard for color video transmission requires selection of a broadcast originating live in New York or Los Angeles, where the standards are located. A sample of the 3,375-kHz frequency is injected into the chroma input of the demodulator circuit after the program color is turned off with the color-level control. About 1 to 2 volts fed into a 15-picofarad capacitor connected to the chroma input pin of the color-demodulator integrated circuit is sufficient to give vivid color stripes. (Since most TV chassis are not grounded, care is necessary to avoid electrical shock in this operation.)

When the crystal oscillator is tuned about 60 Hz higher than 3,375 kHz, the pattern with n = −13, m = +1 appears, with stripes tilting to the left. As the oscillator frequency is lowered, this tilted pattern drifts faster and faster to the left until the drift is too fast to be observed. As 3,375 kHz is approached, the desired vertical stripe pattern appears drifting to the right. As the frequency is further reduced through 3,375 kHz the vertical stripe pattern stops and then starts drifting to the left. At about 60 Hz below 3,375 kHz, the m = −1 stripe pattern, tilted to the right, appears to stop.

Because of an offset of approximately −300 × 10⁻¹⁰

USEFUL STANDARD FREQUENCIES				
k	n	m	f_k	Factors
−1	−34	+7	3,045 kHz	7 x 29 x 15 kHz
0	−13	0	3,375 kHz	3^2 x 5^2 x 15 kHz
+1	+8	−7	3,705 kHz	13 x 19 x 15 kHz
+2	+29	−14	4,035 kHz	269 x 15 kHz

in the network frequency relative to the National Bureau of Standards value, the crystal oscillator should be tuned to a frequency slightly higher than the network signal. This is done by adjusting the oscillator such that the vertical stripe pattern drifts to the right one stripe width in about 9.31 seconds. Exact offsets of the network standards are published regularly by NBS.

When 3,705 kHz is used as the standard frequency, the directions of tilt and drift are reversed, because n is positive. This frequency is a desirable standard if its prime factors 13 or 19 are needed.

As an example of use of the 3,375-kHz standard to produce precision submultiples, a simple divider chain useful as a counter time base or frequency synthesizer reference is shown in the figure. It consists of a 7473 dual flip-flop predivider followed by three binary stages with feedback to give a divide-by-27 output of 125 kHz and then three divide-by-5 stages with outputs at 25 kHz, 5 kHz, and 1 kHz. Harmonics of 125 kHz also permit comparison of this standard with all of the high-frequency transmissions of WWV. □

Visual zero-beat indicator uses reverse-polarity LEDs

by Calvin R. Graf
Kelly Air Force Base, San Antonio, Texas

Two light-emitting diodes connected in parallel, but with opposing polarities, make an inexpensive display for indicating zero-beat frequency (the frequency at which a receiver is exactly tuned to the signal being transmitted). The display can be driven by an audio-frequency voltage from a single-sideband receiver or by the signal for an rf signal-generator headset. A current-limiting resistor protects both the LEDs from overload.

When the input frequency is more than 1 kilohertz away from the zero-beat frequency, both LEDs appear to be on all the time. Each one is correctly biased for half a cycle of the input and shut off for the other half. As the input frequency comes within about 20 hertz of zero beat, the LEDs will flicker until zero beat is reached. Both LEDs then go out and remain out over the width of

the zero-beat-frequency notch, which is about ±5 Hz.

While the display is being tuned, LED intensity varies, since it depends on the low-frequency response of the audio amplifier being used. If the amplifier can go down to dc, the circuit can be used to detect the direction of current flow—each LED can indicate a different direction for current flow. If red and green LEDs are used, the direction of current flow can be color-coded. □

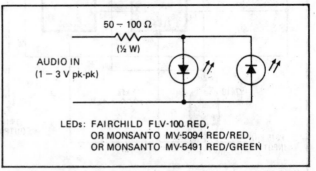

Zero-beat display. Light-emitting diodes connected with reverse polarity provide visual indication of zero-beat frequency. Each LED is on for only half a cycle of the input. Both LEDs glow or flicker until zero beat is reached, when they go out. The zero-beat notch is ±5 hertz.

Induction pickup drives elapsed-time indicators

by Edmund Osterland
Boonton Township, N.J.

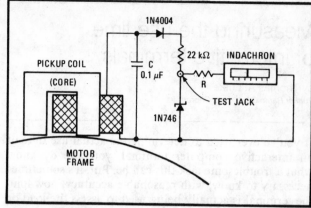

1. Counts the hours. Operating time of ac equipment is measured by wireless pickup, rectification, and integration of total dc charge transfer. Zener diode sets dc voltage, and resistor R sets current level through current-integrating module such as the Indachron shown. Capacitor resonates pickup coil for maximum induced voltage, which can be monitored at jack.

Maintenance intervals for alternating-current machines like pumps, fans, and transformer-operated equipment can be monitored without hard-wiring to these units. By simple inductive pickup through the frame of a motor, for example, it is possible to operate such integrating modules as the Curtis Indachron, the Philips 49800 electrochemical elapsed-time indicator, or the Plessey E-cell device. These units function on microampere levels of current to record operating times of 100 to 10,000 hours, depending upon their specific dc input.

Figure 1 shows a pickup unit clamped (either mechanically or magnetically) to a motor frame. The location is not critical, but proper orientation can be aided by measuring the voltage at a test jack. Capacitor C in parallel with the pickup coil resonates the coil for maximum output voltage. The induced ac is rectified and applied through a current-limiting resistor to a zener diode. The zener diode regulates the rectified voltage input to the timing cell, and series resistor R determines the operating span.

A satisfactory pickup coil may be made from a small commercial choke such as the Stancor C-1003 by removing the strap mounting and the "I" portion, and sawing off one leg of the "E" laminations to provide a single-gap "U" configuration. This pickup delivers up to 10 volts ac when applied to the frames of ¼-horsepower to 1-hp motors and adjusted for optimum coupling.

A resistor of 22 kilohms is shown in Fig. 1 followed by a zener diode (1N746) nominally rated at 3.3 v. However, in the low-current application described here, the regulated voltage drops below 2 v. In the event that

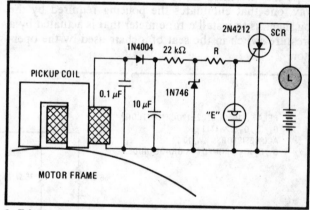

2. Triggers a signal. The rectified current from the pickup coil deplates the working electrode of a Plessey E-cell device. When the electrode is completely deplated the device changes from a low impedance to high impedance, triggering the SCR to activate a battery-powered warning.

RESISTANCE VALUES FOR INTERVALOMETER USING CP3 INDACHRON		
TEST-POINT VOLTAGE	R (OHMS)	TIME SCALE (HOURS)
3.3	1.03 M	1,000
2.0	630 k	1,000
2.0	63 k	100
1.0	315 k	1,000

the source voltage is insufficient for regulation by the zener, the system may still be used in the unregulated state by appropriate choice of calibrating resistor R. The table at left represents typical parameters for a circuit that uses a CP3 Indachron. Intermediate hourly spans may be observed on the calibrated scale of the Indachron unit.

If a signal is desired at the end of a prescribed time interval, a Plessey E-cell device can be used. Instead of having a scale readout, the E-cell abruptly increases in resistance at the expiration of its time cycle. In the circuit of Fig. 2, the bias change on the silicon controlled rectifier triggers an indicating light or a sound source such as the Mallory Sonalert, powered by the battery.

In addition to simplicity of connection, the pickups have the advantage of isolation in sealed systems such as, for example, cooling fluids in nuclear power plants or tightly sealed corrosive pumping systems. Also, it is possible to sample ON intervals of various machines without interrupting the power flow. □

Measuring the use time of interactive terminals

by Thomas A. Lutke
Bunker Ramo Corp., Falls Church, Va.

If you've ever tried to determine the actual use time of an interactive computer terminal, you already know what a troublesome task this can be. But, it's sometimes necessary to know, with reasonable accuracy, how long the terminal is actually being used to assess the load or amount of traffic on the terminal.

Generally, the terminal's use time is greater than the time recorded by the computer's central processing unit, but smaller than the total time that the terminal in on-line with the computer. One way for you to determine this figure is to keep a log sheet by the terminal and hope that it's filled in, rather than forgotten. Another way, one that eliminates the policing required by the log sheet, is to install a time meter that is actuated by a pressure switch in the seat of a chair used by the operator.

An even better method is to use the circuit in the diagram to drive a running-time meter. This circuit is conveniently activated by a 1-millisecond communications pulse or pulse train, which can be taken from the computer's interrupt line.

There is a delay between the time the input to the circuit resets and the time the meter is deactivated. This delay lets the meter run continuously all the while the operator is using the terminal, provided that he interrupts the computer often enough to keep the circuit from resetting.

An input pulse at either diode D_1, D_2, or D_3 turns on transistor Q_1, which in turn charges the timing capacitor. Now transistors Q_2 and Q_3 also conduct so that current is supplied to the relay coil, energizing the relay and running the meter.

When the input resets, transistor Q_1 turns off, and the timing capacitor discharges through the base of transistor Q_2. This reduces the base current to transistor Q_3 so that the relay is eventually de-energized. The circuit's timing, which can be varied from 1 to 50 seconds, is controlled by the 2-kilohm potentiometer. □

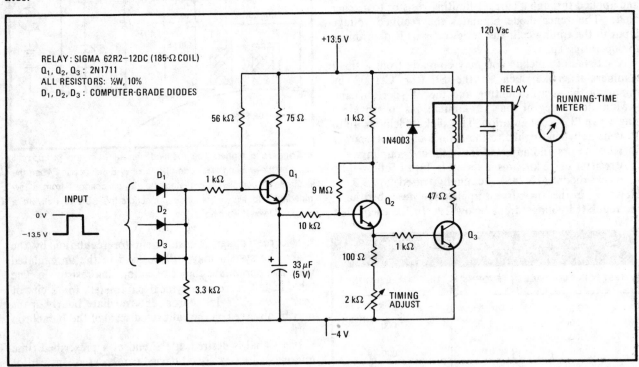

Making an accurate record. Circuit employs running-time meter to determine the actual use time of an interactive computer terminal. A pulse from the computer's interrupt line activates the circuit, so that the reading on the meter is reasonably accurate.

C-MOS gate package forms adjustable divider

by David Newton
Abbott Transistor Laboratories Inc., Los Angeles, Calif.

A single complementary-MOS package—like RCA's type CD4001 quad two-input NOR gate—is readily connected as an even-order digital frequency divider circuit. The division modulo, N, is easily varied by adjusting an external potentiometer.

The circuit accepts pulses at frequency f_1 and generates complementary square waves at frequency f_2:

$$f_1/f_2 = N$$

where N is an even number. Two of the four gates in the IC package, G_1 and G_2, are cross-connected in a simple bistable latch configuration.

The feedback resistors (R) permit the capacitor (C) at the input of the gate that is enabled to charge to the supply voltage. Input pulses are then steered to the inhibited gate, causing the latch to change state, in the simplest case, on every pulse (modulo 2).

For higher division ratios, the 5-picofarad capacitance inherent at the input of each MOS gate is put to work. The potentiometer decreases input pulse amplitude so that the pulses can be integrated by the inherent capacitance of the inhibited gate. The latch, therefore, will change state only every four, six, eight, or more pulses. (The limit is determined by the allowable system noise margin.)

Naturally, the value of modulo N is a function of input pulse amplitude, operating voltage, and discrete component values. For the circuit shown, N can be varied between 2 and 30 with the potentiometer. Gates G_3 and G_4 are used to correct for the signal droop that occurs at the outputs of gates G_1 and G_2 as N approaches its maximum value. □

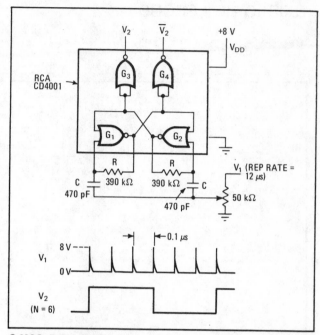

C-MOS digital divider. Even-order frequency divider consists of two C-MOS NOR gates, G_1 and G_2, which are connected as a simple latch. Division modulo N can be varied from 2 to 30 by adjusting the potentiometer. For high values of N, inherent capacitance of MOS gate is used to integrate input pulses and keep latch from changing state. Gates G_3 and G_4 act as output pulse shapers.

Circuit adds diagonal axis to any scope

by Kai Lanz
Stanford University, Stanford, Calif.

True three-axis displays can be generated in place of the usual X-Y plot on any oscilloscope with a circuit that provides a diagonal-deflection channel independent of the existing vertical and horizontal channels. The resulting X-Y-Z display can create three-dimensional effects of striking depth without any modification to the scope. Its uses include three-parameter curve tracing, three-frequency Lissajous figure studies, and

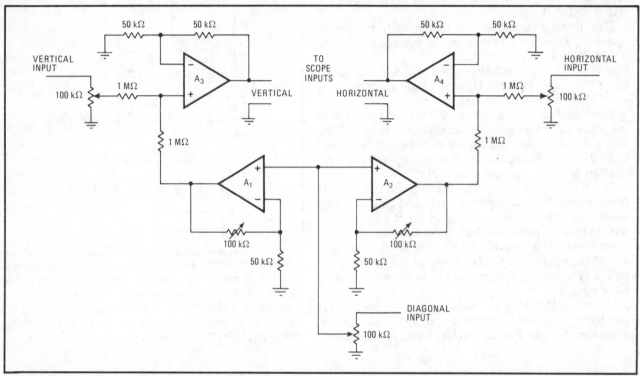

3-d circuit. Four operational amplifiers generate diagonal deflection to create illusion of depth on ordinary scope screen. Two op amps isolate the diagonal and the conventional inputs, and two more add these components to control the deflection.

Three axes, various perspectives. Triple exposure (left) shows the three deflection axes, vertical, horizontal, and diagonal. Multiple exposure (right) shows different angles of perspective, obtained by varying the ratio of the gains of the isolating amplifiers.

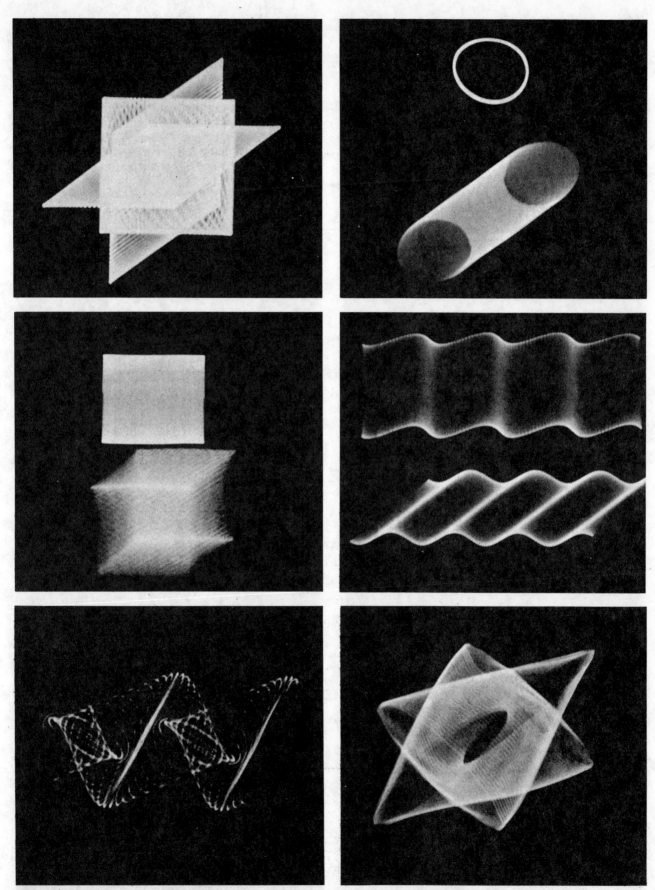

3-d displays. Triple exposure (top left) illustrates three deflection planes, X-Y, Y-Z, and X-Z. At top right is a 2-d Lissajous circle, also shown expanded into a cylinder. A square raster expanded diagonally into a cube is at center left. Two sine waves expanded vertically create wavy surfaces in X-Z and X-Y planes, respectively. At the bottom are two complex shapes produced from Lissajous figures.

three-dimensional character generation—to say nothing of many eye-catching and fascinating visual displays of all sorts.

For diagonal deflection, the diagonal input signal is applied simultaneously to both the vertical and horizontal amplifier inputs. This produces the familiar in-phase Lissajous pattern, a simple 45° line. Operational amplifiers A_1 and A_2 isolate the diagonal input from the vertical and horizontal inputs, while A_3 and A_4 add the diagonal signal components and the vertical and horizontal inputs respectively. The gains through A_1 and A_2 are adjustable, to vary the angle of the diagonal axis, which is proportional to the ratio of these gains. Adjustments on the three inputs provide noninteractive control of the sensitivities of the three channels.

The four op amps should be identical and identically compensated, especially for work at high frequencies. Otherwise, for example, if the phase-shifts through the two legs of the diagonal channel are not equal, the diagonal deflection line expands into an ellipse. Obviously a quad op amp is the best way to obtain these identical characteristics. Also, since the circuit uses the scope's external horizontal input, the internal horizontal sweep, if it is desired, must be connected from the scope's sweep-output jack to the new horizontal input. □

Optical trigger for scope reduces rf interference

by R.J. Prochazka
Harry Diamond Laboratories, Washington, D.C.

Oscilloscopes are usually designed to accept an externally generated trigger signal through coaxial cable. In most cases, this approach is adequate, but it does not suffice in an electromagnetic environment. However a simple, inexpensive modification of the external input triggering-circuit solves this problem, thus making the oscilloscope more useful for testing chores where there is electromagnetic interference. The modification doesn't interfere with any of the scope's other triggering abilities, and the instrument can be restored easily to

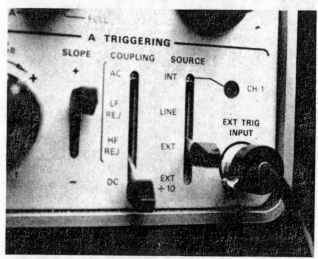

1. Modified. Optic trigger input in standard oscilloscope achieves high isolation in an electromagnetic environment.

the conventional external triggering when desired.

The modification consists mainly of substituting a fiber-optic cable for the conventional coaxial cable and terminating it at a photodetector inside the scope. This provides a light-activated, electrically isolated trigger. In addition to an easily constructed assembly to hold the photodiode and provide a receptacle for the fiber-

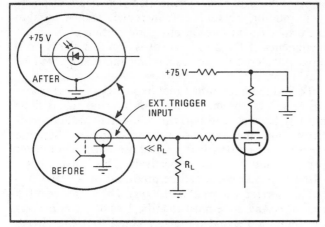

2. Small change. A single photodiode is the only electrical component to convert an external trigger input to an optical trigger.

optic cable, a couple of minor wiring changes are all the modifications that are necessary in the instrument. No external components or voltages are required, since both bias voltage and load resistor R_L for the photodiode are available inside the oscilloscope. Either p-i-n silicon or Schottky barrier-type photodetectors can be used, depending on the supply voltages available in the oscilloscope (this determines the junction capacitance, C_j of the diode) and the load resistance (R_L) of the trigger input of the scope.

The $R_L C_j$ combination determines the rise time of the trigger signal, however the full amplitude of this signal isn't needed for proper triggering. R_L is fixed by scope design; it can vary from as low as 50 ohms to about 1 megohm. C_j is a diode parameter that depends on bias voltage.

Optical external trigger conversion was tried and tested at Harry Diamond Laboratories, using a Motorola MRD-500 photodetector mounted in a Tektronix scope with a 1-megohm trigger input impedance. This combination produces a trigger response time of about 10 nanoseconds. The diode assembly and fiber-optic receptacle is fabricated from a bulkhead BNC connector, type UG-657/U (see drawing). Each end of the connector is cut off to remove the conventional bayonet cou-

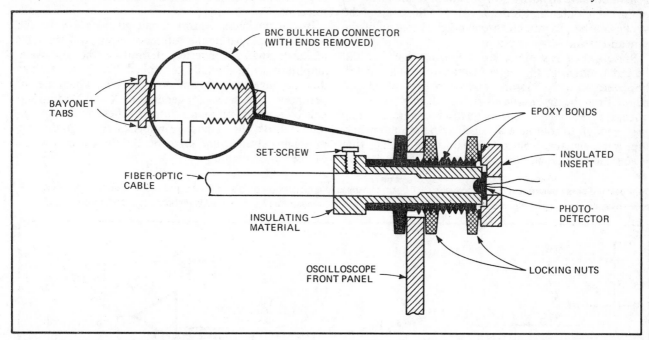

3. New fixture. A modified bulkhead-type BNC connector (UG-657/U) provides the foundation for an easily constructed assembly, which serves as a diode mount and optic cable receptacle.

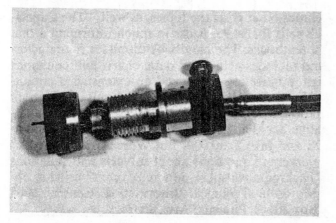

pling mechanism and to allow removal of the coaxial inner conductor and dielectric.

A nonmetallic insert is then placed inside the connector shell and secured with epoxy. A hole is drilled and tapped in the insert and a set-screw clamps the fiber-optic cable in place. The photodiode is secured at the opposite end of the insert by a locknut, backed by insulating material. □

Varying beam thickness in CRT display systems

by P.V.H.M.L. Narasimham
Indian Institute of Technology, Kanpur, India

Though computer-driven CRT displays have many programable parameters, including intensity, blinking, and dashed- or dotted-line generation, beam thickness is not among them, except indirectly through the display's brightness control. Thickness variability can, however, be provided if the control circuit shown is inserted in the display's stroke vector generator. The circuit superimposes equal-amplitude sine and cosine waves on the generator's X- and Y-deflection ramp signals.

When the CRT beam is stationary, the sine and cosine waves produce a circle. As this circle is moved by the generator ramp signals, a straight line with the thickness of the circle's diameter is displayed. The thickness of the stroke can be programed through digital control of the sine and cosine wave amplitudes.

Since a circle is symmetrical, the stroke thickness will be independent of the slope of the stroke. The circles, however, must be closely spaced to prevent ragged edges from being produced in the display. The frequency of the sine and cosine waves, therefore, must be high enough to complete a full circle before the generator ramp signals displace the beam by a distance that is equal to the diameter of the cathode-ray spot.

The stroke vector generator must be the constant-rate type, so that the velocity at which the beam moves over the CRT screen is constant, no matter the length and slope of the stroke being generated. The beam displacement rate for only an X or Y increment is then equal to the displacement rate for any combination of X and Y increments. If the displacement is in either the X or Y direction alone, the corresponding ramp slope will be maximum.

To find the minimum signal frequency of the sine and cosine waves, the maximum X or Y ramp signal slope must be known, as well as the X and Y deflection sensitivity, and the cathode-ray-spot diameter. Suppose these values are 0.01 volt per microsecond, 1 centimeter per volt, and 0.01 cm, respectively. This means that a 0.01-cm displacement can be produced by a 0.01-v signal in 1 μs (for a slope of 0.01 V/μs). The period of a full sine or cosine cycle must then be 1 μs at most, making the minimum signal frequency equal to 1 megahertz. For this case, the maximum stroke thickness is limited to 2.5 millimeters; beyond this, the circles become conspicuous.

In the thickness control circuit given, a 1-MHz sine wave is employed as the reference input to a three-bit digital-to-analog converter, permitting the sine-wave amplitude to be digitally controlled. The phase splitter then produces the sine and cosine waves, which are superimposed on the vector generator's X and Y ramp signals by a pair of op-amp summers. These summing amplifiers drive the X and Y inputs of the CRT display, producing straight-line segments the thickness of which can be varied digitally. □

Controlling display thickness. Circuit converts CRT beam thickness to a digitally programable display parameter. Beam thickness is controlled by superimposing sine and cosine waves to create a circle with a diameter that can be varied in response to a digital input.

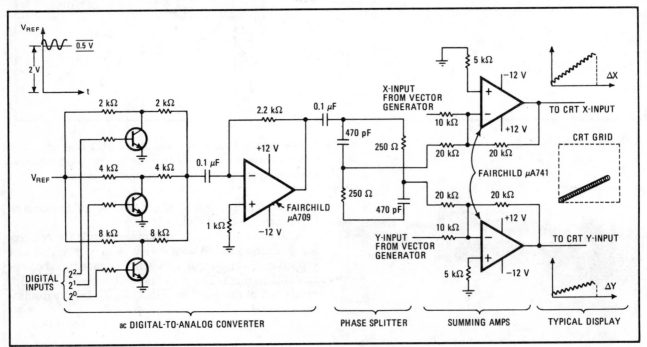

Displaying gray-scale images on bistable storage tubes

by J. Karman and N. Kroese
Delft University of Technology, Delft, The Netherlands

With relative ease, the bistable storage cathode-ray tube can be adapted to display halftone photograph-like images. Although it is reliable, rugged, and inexpensive, the bistable storage CRT cannot normally produce the varying intensity levels needed for gray-scale information. This is because its phosphor can be in only two states—either written or unwritten.

However, an intensity-varying signal can be simulated by the halftone generator shown in the diagram.

Taking pictures. Halftone generator circuitry enables bistable storage display units to produce gray-scale images. The generator provides a duty-cycle-modulated square-wave output that effectively varies CRT beam intensity, storing a picture on the tube face. The photograph of a satellite weather picture made with this technique shows that resolution is fairly good although the beam dot structure is visible.

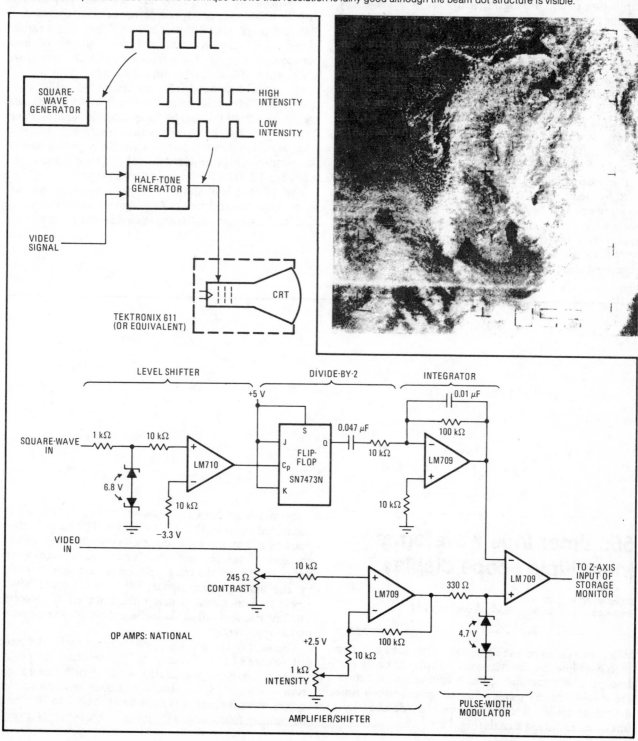

255

This circuit enables the many oscillosopes and monitors containing a bistable CRT to be easily adapted for displaying gray-scale images. Also, new applications, such as facsimile and long-term display of X-ray pictures, become feasible.

The circuitry for the halftone generator in the figure is intended to store and display satellite weather pictures, which are transmitted line by line at a rate of four lines per second. The intensity level of each portion of a line is controlled by the video signal.

Since the only control that can be exercised over the storage monitor is to turn the CRT beam on and off, the impression of a changing intensity can be achieved by varying the time that the beam is on as the video level varies. In this way, a halftone display can be produced. The inputs to the halftone generator are a symmetrical square wave and the video signal. The generator output is a nonsymmetrical square wave with a duty cycle that varies with the video level.

The square-wave input to the generator first passes through a level-shifter stage so that the signal logic levels are correct for the rest of the circuit. The divide-by-2 stage is included for added stability. Its output is converted to a triangular wave by the integrator.

The video signal is processed for intensity and contrast by being put through the level-shifter/amplifier stage, which is followed by the pulse-width modulator containing an open-loop amplifier. Each time the triangular wave from the integrator crosses zero, this amplifier's output jumps to its maximum positive or negative level (depending on the triangle's level), producing a square wave at the output of the circuit.

The video level signal, which is applied to the non-inverting amplifier input, determines the symmetry of this output square wave. When the video level is minimum, the square-wave duty cycle is also at its minimum; likewise, when the video level is maximum, the duty cycle is maximum. This duty-cycle-modulated square-wave output is applied to the storage monitor's Z-axis input.

To get the best picture resolution, each line displayed on the CRT must contain as many dots as possible. Maximum resolution is controlled by the specifications of the storage display unit. For the Tektronix 611 storage display used here, the specified horizontal resolution is 300 line pairs or 300 dots per line. Since the weather pictures are being broadcast at a rate of 4 hertz (4 lines per second), a square-wave frequency of 1,200 Hz allows a resolution of 300 dots per line to be achieved.

The signal broadcast from the weather satellite contains a 2,400-Hz reference; the line and frame signals are derived from this signal. Increasing the square-wave frequency to 2,400 Hz permits the line, frame, and dot rates to be synchronized so that interference patterns in the picture can be eliminated. (The square wave is returned to 1,200 Hz by the divide-by-2 stage.)

The photograph shows a typical weather picture made using this technique. Although the dot structure is visible, the weather patterns are clearly recognizable. □

---

555 timer tags waveforms in multiple scope display

by Howard M. Berlin
Edgewood Arsenal, Aberdeen Proving Ground, Md.

When two or more analog signals referenced to a common base line are simultaneously displayed on an oscilloscope, it is sometimes difficult to distinguish between the waveforms. By using a 555 integrated-circuit timer, dotted or dashed line markers can be added easily to one or more analog signals (Fig. 1).

By means of the circuit shown in Fig. 2, the 555 is connected as an astable multivibrator. The scope's trace position at any instant is determined by the sum of the voltages across R_4 and R_5. When the square wave across R_4 is zero, the trace position is determined solely by the analog input signal. When the square wave across R_4 is not zero, it drives the trace off the screen. The fast rise and fall of the pulse cannot be seen at normal scope intensity.

The supply voltage V_{CC}, and, consequently, the output voltage of the 555, must be greater than the peak-to-peak voltage of the analog signal, which can range from 4.5 V to 16 V. Also, for proper operation, the square-wave frequency should be at least 5 to 10 times the analog frequency. The timer's frequency is easily

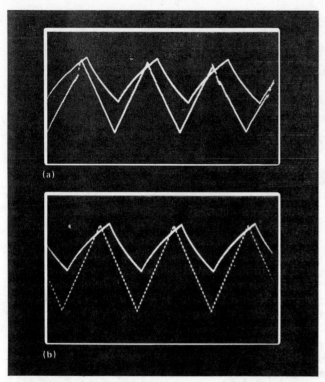

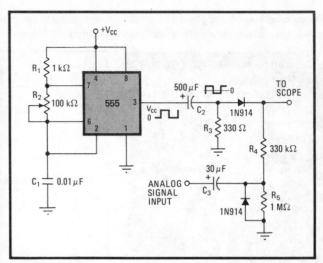

2. Dots all, folks. A 555 integrated-circuit timer generates pulses that drive the scope trace off scale with fast rise times and fall times, to produce a dotted or dashed display of a waveform. The timer frequency, set by R_2, determines the appearance of the trace.

1. Tagging. When two or more waveforms are displayed on a single scope (a), identifying markers can be added to the analog input signals to display them as dotted or dashed traces (b).

adjusted by varying R_2. The value of the frequency in hertz is $1.44/(R_1 + 2R_2)C_1$, where resistance and capacitance values are in ohms and farads, respectively. With the components shown, the circuit can handle without distortion input signals having a peak-to-peak voltage of 1 v. □

Adding automatic erasure to storage oscilloscopes

by T. Richardson and Alan R. Freeman
Indiana University, School of Medicine, Indianapolis, Ind.

When you are inspecting a slow event in detail with a storage oscilloscope, it's often convenient to have the trace automatically erased at the end of each sweep. As a matter of fact, automatic erasure is now a standard feature on the later models of many storage scopes. But a model with only manual erasure can frequently be modified without much trouble to include this desirable feature.

The circuit diagram shows a simple and inexpensive way to add automatic erasure to the popular model 564B Tektronix storage oscilloscope. With this modification, the scope's screen is automatically erased at the end of each sweep. Single-sweep information of slow events can then be easily observed without mechanically clearing the screen. The circuit is stable and costs less than $10 to build.

The model 564B scope is particularly easy to modify because its manual erasure is accomplished by grounding a single charged capacitor. The modification circuit samples the scope's horizontal sawtooth at one of the CRT horizontal-deflection plates. This potential triggers

a one-shot that then closes two transistor switches, each one in parallel with an existing erase switch. A toggle switch in series with the transistor switches allows the automatic erasure to be overridden so that the advantages of the manual erasure can be retained.

In greater detail, the sawtooth potential at the left horizontal plate is sampled. The voltage divider made up of resistors R_1, R_2, and R_3 establishes a potential offset, placing the wiper of R_2 at 5.5 volts. When the sawtooth drops to around 80 v, potentiometer R_2 permits this triggering point to be adjusted through the last 2 centimeters (on the screen) of the sweep.

Diode D_1 protects transistor Q_1 from large reverse potentials. Since Q_1's base terminal is isolated by the $R_1R_2R_3$ resistor network, Q_1's base voltage varies only between 6 and 5 v, changing potential as the one-shot is triggered at the end of the sweep. When the base of Q_1 shifts from 5 to 6 v, this device turns on. The base of Q_1, therefore, varies by ±0.5 v from a nominal voltage of 5.5 v, which is the power-supply potential determined by resistors R_4 and R_5.

Transistors Q_1 and Q_2 make up the one-shot. The collector current of Q_1 forward-biases the base of transistor Q_2, turning Q_2 on and decreasing Q_2's collector resistance so that the potential of point H (the model 564B junction of R_{305} and R_{313}) drops from about 12 v to zero.

Capacitor C_1 discharges through the base of transistor Q_1 and holds both Q_1 and Q_2 on long enough for Q_2 to trigger the erase cycle of the upper beam of the

Scope modification. For under $10, simple circuit adds automatic erasure to Tektronix model 564B storage scope. The modification allows slow events to be observed conveniently with a single sweep. Photo shows actual installation, including a front-panel mode selection switch.

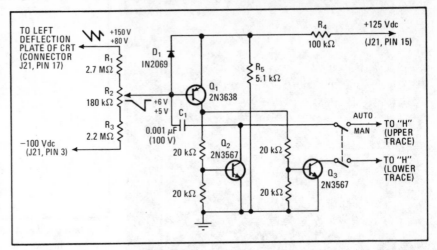

scope. In the same manner, transistor Q_3, which is also in the collector loop of transistor Q_1, triggers the erase cycle of the scope's lower trace.

The scope can be switched between automatic and manual erasure modes with the double-pole double-throw toggle switch. Once the circuit is installed and the scope has warmed up for 15 to 20 minutes, potentiometer R_2 can be adjusted to have erasure occur at the desired point on the scope face.

The modification circuit allows the model 564B to operate with automatic erasure at sweep speeds as fast as 50 milliseconds per centimeter. It may be necessary to reduce the scope's erase-cycle duration slightly to display the first centimeter of the overall sweep setting. However, the erase cycle should not be made so short

that the screen's background is brightened (a condition that may vary with age).

The nominal supply voltage of 5.5 v derived by resistors R_4 and R_5 is not a critical value. The resistance tolerances of R_4 and R_5, therefore, are also not critical, provided that potentiometer R_2 can be adjusted to trigger transistor Q_1 properly and Q_1's collector-emitter breakdown voltage is not exceeded.

The photo shows an actual installation of the modification circuit. The mode-selection switch is mounted on the front panel, and the rest of the circuitry is located inside the scope. □

Scanning only bright spots generates CRT characters fast

by P.V.H.M.L. Narasimham
Indian Institute of Technology, Kanpur, India

Generating dot-matrix characters on cathode-ray-tube screens wastes more than 50% of display time when, as is usually the case, the beam scans every point of the dot matrix, whether bright or dark. But if the beam scans only the bright spots of the matrix for each character, the flicker-free display capacity of the CRT is more than doubled, with no increase in bandwidth and without substantially increasing the memory and control logic requirements.

In the conventional approach, the entire 5-by-7 dot matrix is generated from a read-only memory that stores 35 bits per character, or a total of 2,240 bits for the standard Ascii font of 64 characters. This approach requires a bandwidth in the associated circuits of about 2 megahertz, well within the 2.5 MHz maximum of television-type CRTs.

Providing that the refresh rate and bandwidth are fixed, reducing the number of dots per character has the effect of proportionately increasing the number of characters per frame without introducing flicker. One way to reduce the number of dots per character is to scan only the bright spots.

To scan the bright spots directly, a position code must be supplied for every bright spot. For the dot matrix's 35 possible positions, the position code must have six bits, which can be divided into two three-bit fields for row and column codes, corresponding to the three-bit counters in the point-to-point scanning method. If this six-bit code were stored independently for each character in a font of 64, which contains about 800 bright spots, it would require a ROM of 4,800 bits. But the order of scanning the bright spots is immaterial; exploiting this fact facilitates packing bright-spot data in fewer than 2,400 bits—a slightly larger number of bits but a much faster scan.

Several bright spots are common to many characters, which therefore can share common storage. These characters can be grouped; one such group, for example, is B, C, D, E, F, the letter O, and the numeral 0 (printed here with a slash, as computer output printers often show it, because the standard dot-matrix representation

1. Common spots. Many alphanumeric characters generated within a 5-by-7-dot matrix overlap at certain matrix points, which can therefore share memory space. At bottom left, overlapping representations of B, D, and F are shown.

2. Coordinates. Every point in a 5-by-7 matrix can be represented by a two-digit number (bottom middle) that designates the row and column of that point.

3. Seven characters. The eight coordinates in color (right) are common to B, C, D, E, F, the letter O, and the numeral Ø. Other listed coordinates are the remainder for these characters when the control logic enters and leaves the list as shown.

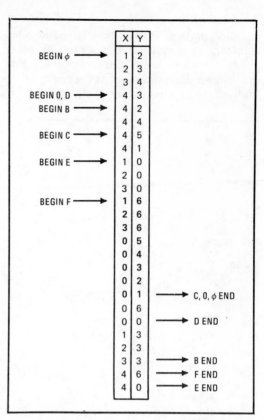

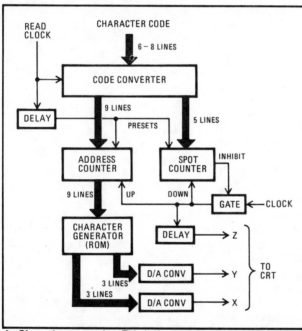

4. Character generator. This logic produces beam deflection and blanking information for a CRT to generate alphanumeric characters without wasting time at matrix points that remain dark.

acters mentioned previously. The other coordinates in that list represent every bright spot of all seven characters when scanning begins and ends at the points shown. The spots need not be scanned in sequence.

In general, such close packing isn't possible for all characters; but the standard Ascii font can be represented by as few as 380 coordinate pairs of six bits each, overlapping for points common to many characters. This list may be reduced still further by about 10 locations by carefully matching patterns. Space does not permit the entire list to be reproduced here.

Character generation from this overlapped memory requires a starting address, the number of bright spots per character and control logic (Fig. 4). The list's words call for a nine-bit starting address code, which points to the location just before the actual starting address. In this font, the maximum number of bright spots for one character is 20 (for B, @, and #), requiring another five bits. This 14-bit character-generating code requires a converter driven by the character code, which is seven bits in Ascii, six or eight bits in certain other codes. This converter's output presets two counters; clock pulses increment the nine-bit address counter and decrement the five-bit spot counter. When the latter reaches 0, the preset number of steps have been applied to the address counter, producing that many bright-spot coordinates of the character. Each clock pulse, delayed, also unblanks the CRT beam to produce a bright spot on the screen after the beam has moved to the position specified by the coordinates.

The character generator for the new method doesn't differ appreciably in cost from the conventional type, especially in view of the shrinking costs of MOS memories. The two- to three-fold increase in the flicker-free display capacity warrants pattern matching to pack

also has a slash to distinguish Ø from O). All of these seven characters have bright spots in the middle three of the top row of five, and in all but the top and bottom of the left-most column of seven. Commonality for B, D, and F is illustrated in Fig. 1.

The coordinates of the 5-by-7 dot matrix can be represented by a two-digit number representing the X and Y coordinates, respectively (Fig. 2). A list of these coordinates, in any order, can be scanned to obtain the common parts of many characters; and often the non-common parts can be represented by other lists appended above or below the common list. For example, the list of eight coordinates at the center of Fig. 3 represents all the common points of the group of seven char-bright-spot data as densely as possible. For the 5-by-7 matrix on the average, 35% to 40% of the dots are bright, but for larger matrixes, the percentage drops—to perhaps 20% for 16-by-16 and larger—and the increased capacity of the new method becomes more apparent. □

34. Checking binary data with a scope

Oscilloscope displays contents of RAMs and ROMs

by James A. Blackburn
Wilfrid Laurier University, Waterloo, Ont., Canada

The contents of random-access and read-only memories can be represented graphically on any oscilloscope that has an X-Y mode and a Z-axis control input. And the cost of parts for the system that produces this useful display is less than $50.

The scope photograph in Fig. 1 displays the storage in a RAM that is configured as 256 4-bit words. Each word appears as a square in a 16-by-16 checkerboard on the CRT, and each square consists of 16 dots; all 16 of the dots shine with a single intensity that corresponds to the magnitude of the word. That is, the intensity of the CRT beam is modulated so that (in this case) the maximum possible brightness represents a 1111 word and minimum brightness represents a 0000 word. This makes it possible to assess the memory contents at a glance.

The system can also be used as a pattern generator merely by loading the RAM with appropriate data. The gray scale provided by intensity variation lets you shade in pictures, though full-contrast alphanumerics can, of course, also be displayed. And by viewing the display of a RAM that has been loaded through the filter, you can evaluate digital filter designs.

The digital graphic display circuit is shown in Fig. 2. A clock circuit feeds a 6-bit binary counter whose output in turn drives a second 6-bit counter. The outputs of these 12 flip-flops are connected to Motorola MC1406 digital-to-analog converters that use Analog Devices' AD580 reference-voltage sources. The d-a converters feed MC1741 op amps that function as current-to-voltage converters to drive the X and Y deflection amplifiers of the oscilloscope. As the CRT beam is sequentially stepped along a series of horizontal lines, 64-by-64 beam coordinates are defined. Final over-all image size is directly adjustable by means of the oscilloscope vernier controls (channel A and time).

The 64-by-64 array is subdivided so that each memory word occupies a 4-by-4 submatrix on the display. The scan circuitry thus must deliver the same read address to the RAM for groups of four points along a given horizontal line, and in addition, must repeat each line four times before incrementing the corresponding address bits. The logic shown in Fig. 2 performs this indexing sequence.

The Signetics 2606 n-channel static RAM outputs are fed to the d-a converter that generates the appropriate beam-modulation voltage to drive the Z input of the scope. The two lowest-order bits of this converter are held high because the memory delivers only a 4-bit word. Because the MC1406 responds to $\bar{w}$, where w is the input 6-bit word, a memory word of 0000 results in maximum output voltage, whereas 1111 yields zero volts. Fourteen intermediate equally spaced voltages are also possible, depending on the value of w. High levels at the Z input produce low beam intensity, and therefore spot brightness is directly proportional to the magnitude of the memory contents at the selected address.

The Z voltage may be set to the required value for full blanking of empty memory cells by adjustment of the 10-kilohm trim resistor that is in series with the reference voltage of the Z d-a converter. On the Hewlett-Packard 1220A oscilloscope that was used in these studies, a Z input of about 5 volts blanks a trace of any in-

1. Word picture. The 16-by-16 array of intensity-modulated squares in this scope photo represent the 256 words stored in a random-access memory. Each square consists of 4-by-4 dots with equal brightness that is proportional to the magnitude of the word. Shown here is a random bit pattern that occurred at turn-on of the RAM.

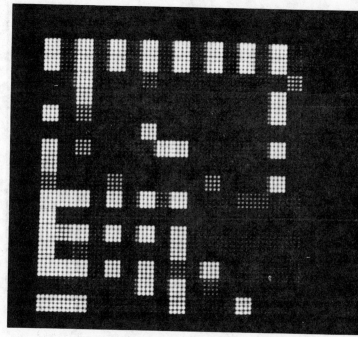

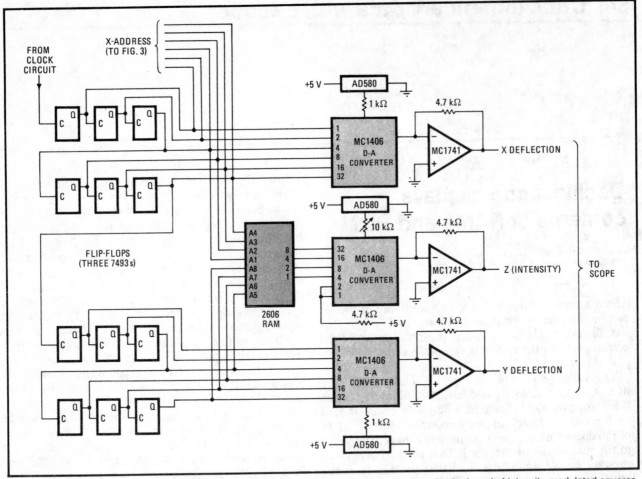

2. The inside story. Circuit displays RAM contents on laboratory oscilloscope by generating checkerboard of intensity-modulated squares. Each square represents a stored word, and its brightness is proportional to magnitude of word: 0000 is represented by fully-blanked square, 1111 by maximum brightness, and 14 intermediate magnitudes by proportionate intensities. Power supply, reset, chip-enable, and read/write connections are omitted for clarity. The digital-to-analog converters require 20-pF and 1-kilohm compensation.

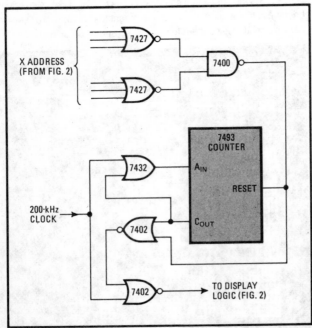

3. Clock circuit. Counter and logic elements insert a "wait" at beginning of each horizontal line of raster to prevent distortion and/or loss of display. Delay has negligible effect on raster timing.

tensity. Thus, the combination of the scope beam-intensity control and the trim resistor makes it possible to set the display contrast to a suitable level.

In the interests of low cost, the widely available type 741 op amp is used throughout. However, the relatively slow speed of this device causes some display loss and distortion when switchback to the beginning of the next line occurs. The circuit shown in Fig. 3 compensates for this speed limitation by inserting a "wait" at the beginning of each line. To create this pause, the binary counter (7493) is enabled whenever an X address of 000000 is generated, while at the same time, the output NOR gate is disabled with a high input. When the output from the counter goes high, the clock stream is again passed through the final NOR gate. For the oscilloscope and ICs chosen, a four-cycle delay is optimal. With a clock frequency of 200 kilohertz, the added time per raster is essentially negligible.

The typical display shown in Fig. 1 represents a random bit pattern created when the RAM is powered up. Since the refresh rate in this example was 46 hertz, a flicker-free display was obtained. □

Circuit lets regular scope monitor eight logic inputs

by P.V.H.M.L. Narasimham
Indian Institute of Technology, Kanpur, India

Checking the logic levels of digital circuits can be greatly simplified if both their inputs and outputs can be observed simultaneously. Here is a multiplexing circuit that allows an ordinary oscilloscope to accept up to eight logic inputs at the same time, thereby considerably easing digital-circuit testing. Furthermore, with this scope-input expander, actual signal-voltage levels, instead of just their logic states, can be observed, or any one of the signal waveforms can be displayed for some time.

The logic levels to be checked are applied to the eight-channel analog multiplexer, which also contains a three-line-to-eight-line decoder. The multiplexer's output goes directly to the Y-input of the scope. The three-bit counter drives the three channel-selector inputs of the multiplexer. The counter determines which of the logic inputs is displayed on the scope screen. Its output also drives the three-bit digital-to-analog converter that produces eight discrete voltage levels corresponding (in ascending order) to the eight input channels.

For example, when the state of the channel counter is 110, the logic input on channel 7 is connected to the Y-input of the scope. And the converter's output for this operating condition will be at its level 7 (assuming that the level corresponding to 000 of the channel counter is taken as level 1).

The circuit has two switch-selectable operating modes. In the MULTIPLEX mode, the channel counter logs clock pulses continuously. In the MANUAL mode, the counter can be set to any one of eight binary counts (from 000 to 111) with the thumbwheel switch (or with a set of three individual switches).

In the MULTIPLEX mode, there is a continuous clock input, and the signals on input channels 1 through 8 are sequentially applied to the scope's Y-input. Since the converter's output drives the scope's X-input, the scope sweep is disabled. When the signal on channel n is applied to the Y-input, the converter's output, which is at level n, horizontally displaces the scope beam by (n – 1) steps to the nth position. Therefore, the actual signal voltage levels, not merely the logic states, of all eight channels can be read directly from the scope screen. Clock frequency can be 1 to 5 kilohertz so that the display remains stable.

For dynamic testing, when a single signal must be studied, the circuit is operated in its MANUAL mode. The desired input is selected by loading the channel counter with the appropriate channel number. The signal waveform can then be observed at length—an advantage that many logic testing devices do not offer.

This scope input-expander circuit can be easily extended to cover 16 inputs by using a 16-channel multiplexer, a four-bit counter, and a four-bit converter. For convenient handling, the 16 signal wires can be terminated with a dual in-line clip. □

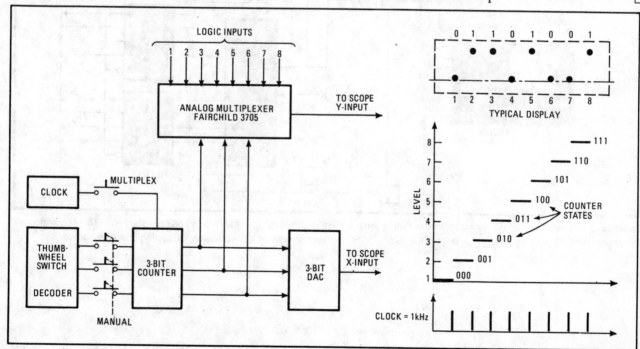

Scope input expander. Multiplexing circuit speeds up digital-circuit monitoring by enabling any scope to display up to eight logic inputs at the same time. With the circuit in its MULTIPLEX mode, the scope displays the actual signal-voltage levels, rather than only the logic levels, of all eight logic inputs. In the MANUAL mode, a single signal waveform can be selected with the thumbwheel switch and studied at length.

Scope-triggered register freezes serial data

by Matthew L. Fichtenbaum
GenRad Inc., Concord, Mass.

The technique that uses the trigger and delay functions of an oscilloscope to latch a data bus at a particular time [*Electronics*, April 1, p. 103] may be extended to systems where data is transmitted or processed serially. Data from such systems as calculators and serial microprocessors may be easily captured and displayed under the control of a scope such as the Tektronix 465 or 475.

As shown in the figure, the hardware requires relatively few components. A serial-to-parallel shift register converts the serial data for display and serves also to count the bits that comprise a serial word. A second register stores the resulting parallel data and drives the light-emitting diodes that show the data. The circuit shown is for 8-bit serial words, but may be adapted for any word length by changing the number of bits in the two registers.

The scope should be operated in its A-intensified-by-B mode, with the A (main) sweep set to trigger on an event before occurrence of the data (any timing signal in the program). The B (delayed) sweep should be externally triggered by the same clock signal that shifts the serial

data. The B sweep's starting time, indicated by the start of the trace's intensified section, advances one clock pulse at a time as the delay-time control is advanced. Since this time is the start of the displayed serial word, data at successive system cycle times may be displayed by advancing the delay-time control to make the intensified trace begin at these times.

Before the triggering event occurs, the A-gate scope output is low, and the serial register is preset with a 1 in the first bit and 0s in the remaining bits. When the scope triggers, the A gate goes high, removing the clear signal, but the register remains in the preset state.

When the delay-time interval is complete, the B sweep is armed to be triggered, and it triggers synchronously with the clock in the system. When B triggering occurs, the B-gate output enables the system clock to shift the serial register, shifting in the serial data.

After the proper number of shift pulses (in this case, eight), the 1 that was preset into the first bit reaches the last bit of the serial register (the Q_H output of the 74LS164). This inhibits further shift pulses and forces the register to hold the 8 bits of data just gathered.

At the end of the scope sweep, the A-gate output goes low again. This loads the data from the serial register into the display register to drive the LEDs and sets the serial register to its initial state again. The cycle may then repeat when the next trigger event occurs. □

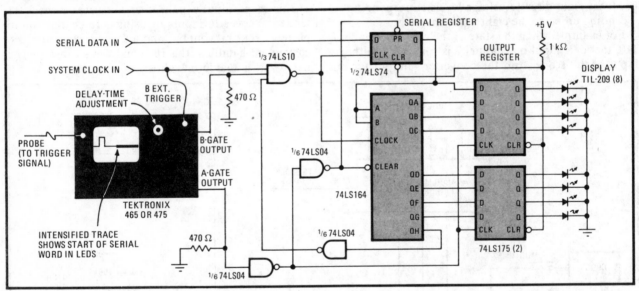

Serial-data catcher. Data from a microprocessor or other serial system is converted to parallel form and displayed on LEDs. Acquisition and conversion are controlled by timing signals from the oscilloscope; the convenience of delayed-sweep triggering is used to advantage.

Scope-triggered register freezes data for display

by Matthew L. Fichtenbaum
General Radio Co., Concord, Mass.

As an aid in logic analysis and program debugging, a standard delaying-sweep oscilloscope, such as the Tektronix 465 or 475, may be augmented with some logic circuitry, to capture and display the data present on a data bus.

The two time bases of the scope perform trigger and trigger-delay functions, the delayed trigger clocks a register to store the data, and light-emitting diodes display the stored levels. The data is not displayed on the face of the scope, which merely shows the timing of operations including a visual indication of the point at which the data state is stored for display by the LEDs.

The scope is operated in a repetitive or nonrepetitive mode, as appropriate. Generally the technique is used to study a repetitive process such as a program loop.

The figure shows a register of two 74175 quad D flip-flops, used to "freeze" the state of a multibit bus, such as a microprocessor's data bus, for examination. The scope trace is triggered by some major timing signal in the program, e.g., an input or output pulse, and its length corresponds to the program's duration.

The scope is operated in its A-intensified-by-B mode. Using the delay-time control of the scope, the brightened area of the trace that represents the delayed sweep is positioned to begin at the time point of interest.

When the B gate output goes high at the start of the delayed sweep interval, it loads and latches the register, which allows the LEDs to display the data levels that were on the bus at the instant of loading. As the delay time is advanced, the display lights show successive data values.

A 74LS08 AND gate is used as a buffer between the scope and the clock terminals of the quad D flip-flops.

The register, which in this example is eight bits wide, should be as wide as the bus being examined. The ordered array of LED's is easier to interpret as a number than multiple scope traces, and the storage of the register makes it possible to examine nonrepetitive events.

If desired, the LEDs may be replaced by decoders and numeric readouts to present a binary-coded-decimal, octal, or hexadecimal interpretation of the data. □

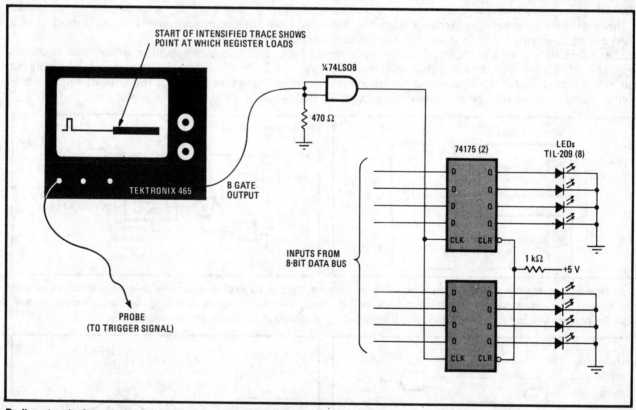

Rudimentary logic analyzer. A lit light-emitting diode shows a logic 1 on the microprocessor data bus and a dark LED shows a logic 0—both at the moment that is determined by the setting of the delay-time knob on the oscilloscope. Scope trace indicates duration of program loop; the trace becomes brighter at the point where the data sample is loaded into the register to light the LEDs.

35. A potpourri of controls

Counter keeps track of microprocessor interrupts

by Douglas M. Risch
Woodward Governor Co., Fort Collins, Colo.

A counter for keeping track of the number of times a microprocessor executes its interrupt-enable and interrupt-disable instructions permits the use of nested interrupts. With nesting, a routine that interrupts another program can itself be interrupted by a subroutine, which may be subject to still another interrupt, and so on to almost any desired depth. By this means, the power of the microprocessor to implement complex logic designs can be greatly extended.

A single microprocessor can often be assigned several related tasks, which it executes in rotation, either with a fixed amount of time devoted to each task, or to interrupt on a demand basis. A program yields when the interrupting program requires service.

However some programs may contain segments that must not be interrupted. For instance, if a routine that fetches information from a multiplexed analog interface (Fig. 1) is interrupted after the input channel is selected, but before that channel's signal moves to the analog-to-digital converter, erroneous information could be transmitted. Or, when a multiple precision operation is under way (Fig. 2), an interrupt after the first word is loaded into the register, but before the second, may generate an incorrect output for a period much longer than normal in this period.

These examples show why the newer microprocessors include interrupt-enable and interrupt-disable instructions with their interrupt capabilities. Simpler microprocessors can implement these instructions with hardware (Fig. 3). But a simple enable/disable capability would be insufficient when a program that would disable the interrupt called a subroutine that would also disable the interrupt. The subroutine, when finished, would enable the interrupt before the program could tolerate enablement.

The solution is to remember how may interrupt-disable instructions were given and to prevent interrupts until each disable instruction has been matched with an enable instruction. A hardware implementation (Fig. 4) is just a modification of the simple enable/disable logic, including an up/down counter to remember the number of disable signals. A corollary software solution is also possible; it merely implements the up/down counter in a memory location instead of in a separate register.

Interrupt-disable commands can be nested as deeply as $2^n - 2$ for the hardware implementation, using an n-stage counter, or $2^n - 1$ for the software implementation, where n is the number of bits in a word. □

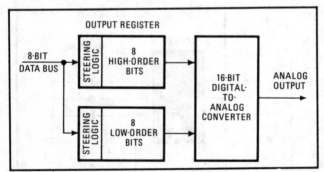

1. Multiple precision. When desired precision requires more than one word, all bits must be loaded before an interrupt can be tolerated. This prevents an incorrect level from appearing at the output.

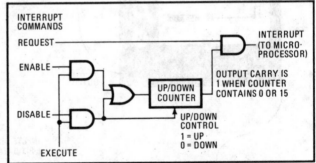

3. Counter for nesting. Successive disable and enable instructions step the counter respectively up and down. Only when enables have canceled previous disables can interrupts pass.

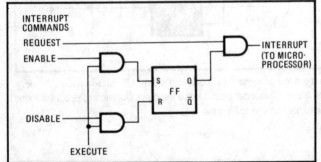

2. Interrupt gate. An enable instruction, stored in the flip-flop at execution time, permits subsequent interrupts to pass. A disable resets the flip-flop and blocks following interrupts.

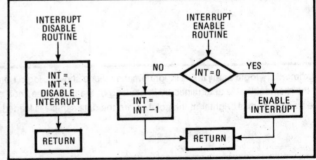

4. Software counter. These routines count the enables and disables as does the counter in Fig. 3, but the count is stored in a memory location called INT, rather than in a separate register.

Optical isolator circuit shows phone-line status

by Matthew L. Fichtenbaum
General Radio Co., Concord, Mass.

OPERATION OF PHONE-STATUS-DISPLAY CIRCUIT			
Phone condition	Line voltage (V)	Isolator output level	LED condition
On hook	50 dc	Low	Off
Ringing	100 ac	Pulses	Flashing
Off hook	6 – 8 dc	High	On
Dialing	6 – 50 dc	Pulses	On

The status of a telephone line can be indicated at a remote location, such as the key unit on a secretary's desk, by a light-emitting diode connected in the circuit shown here. The LED is dark if the phone line is not in use, flashes on and off once every second if the phone is ringing, and stays on if the phone is off the hook.

The circuit includes an oscillator that operates continuously, some logic elements, and an optical coupler that senses the voltage on the phone line. If this voltage is ac, the logic circuit connects the oscillator to the LED, producing the flashing light. Low dc voltages, either steady

or pulsed, hold the LED on, and high dc voltages leave it off. The table summarizes circuit performance.

As can be seen from the schematic diagram, the isolator output signal is applied to two RC networks—an integrator and a differentiator. The integrator filters out the ring and dial pulses, giving an output dependent on the steady state of the phone line. The differentiator extracts the pulses.

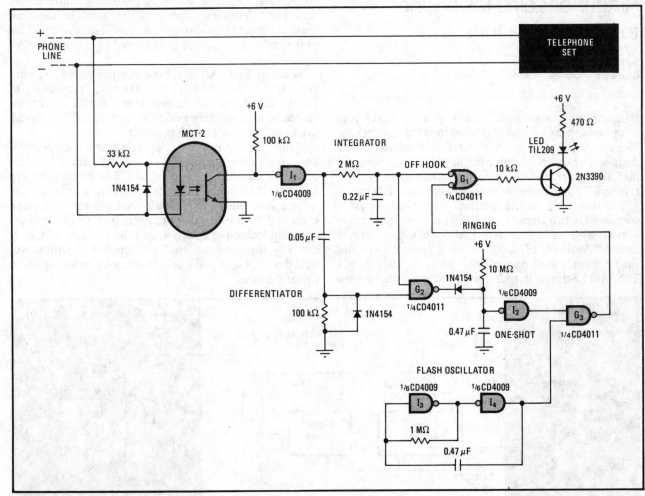

Secretary's helper. LED indicates status of a remote telephone. Light is off if phone is hung up, shines steadily if phone is off hook, and flashes on and off while phone rings and for 5 seconds after ringing stops. The flashing oscillator operates continuously, but can drive LED only when a ringing signal discharges the one-shot capacitor to enable NAND gate G₃. Thus, one oscillator handles several phone lines.

When the phone is on the hook, so that inverter I_1 has low input and high output, G_1 is deactivated and cannot turn the transistor or LED on.

When the phone rings, the high dc from I_1 and the high output from the differentiator combine to activate G_2, allowing the one-shot capacitor to discharge and enable G_3. Thus the output from the flash oscillator is applied to G_1, flashing the LED. Flashing continues during the slow charge-up of the 0.47-microfarad one-shot capacitor between rings and after ringing stops.

When the phone is off the hook, I_1 has high input and low output, so G_1 is able to turn on the transistor and let the LED light. The momentary high-voltage pulses that occur during dialing are suppressed by the integrator, so G_2 is not enabled.

The 100-V ac ringing signal might apply excessive reverse voltage to the light-emitting diode in the optical coupler. Therefore, the coupler input is shunted by a protecting 1N4154 diode.

Because the flash oscillator operates continuously, it can be connected to the NAND gates G_3 associated with a number of different phone lines and LEDs. In the author's office, one oscillator is used for 10 phones.

This circuit uses ordinary C-MOS ICs and operates from a noncritical supply voltage between 5 and 10 volts. The ac adapter from a pocket calculator is a convenient source. A single power supply can handle all of the phone lines.

The signals that are developed at the integrator and differentiator outputs can be used for other purposes than lighting a LED. Other areas of application include playing a recorded message when a phone rings, or running a timer while a phone is in use.

This circuit does not draw appreciable current from the phone line, feed back to the line, or reference any voltages to the line because the coupling is optical. Nonetheless, the telephone company should be consulted before the circuit is installed. □

Ringer enables telephone to play simple tune

by Kenneth Dugan
General Telephone and Electronics, Clearwater, Fla.

By combining two simple circuits, you can make your telephone play a simple signature tune—perhaps "Smoke gets in your eyes" if you're an electronic-circuit designer, while an educator might like "*Gaudeamus igitur*," or a journalist might prefer "Somewhere over the rainbow." The number of programable tunes is large.

The schematic for the interface circuit shows how to combine the two circuits, each of which has appeared in a past issue of *Electronics* ("Making music with IC timers," April 18, 1974, p. 106, and "Optically coupled ringer doesn't load phone line," Feb. 20, 1975 p. 92). The 74121 Schmitt trigger input produces a sharp pulse

from the sinusoidal telephone-system ringing generator signal. The negative pulse output of the monostable turns the 555 timer on for about 10 seconds to allow the musical ringer to go through its cycle. This cycle will repeat until the telephone is answered or until the caller hangs up.

You may find your telephone company uses a ringing generator frequency that's not 40 hertz. Frequencies of 20, 30, 42, 54, and 66 Hz are common, and a PABX installation in a building generally uses 30 Hz. The circuit can handle any of these frequencies.

If the idea of a musical telephone ringer sounds frivolous, that's because it is. It was used with amusing effect on one of the old-time radio shows. But the circuitry can be adapted to control other devices besides a ringer.

One last thing—you should consult the telephone company before installation, even though the optical-coupling technique does not load the line severely. Incidentally, the company itself will supply you with a musical device, but it plays only three notes—nothing like a signature tune. □

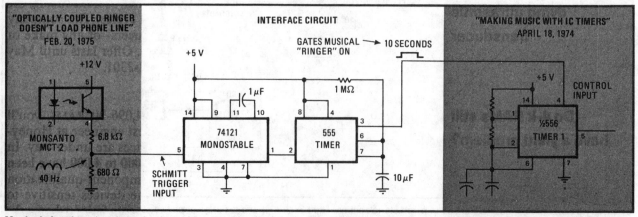

Musical signature. Interface circuit combines two circuits described in past issues of *Electronics*, as indicated. Optically coupled ringing detector triggers music synthesizer here; more generally, it allows control of other devices by dialing of a telephone number.

Power hybrid circuit
controls tape-recorder speed

by W.D. Harrington
University of Florida, Gainesville, Fla.

A hybrid power amplifier, the HC1000 from RCA, makes it possible to build, for only about $50, a speed control for line-operated tape recorders with ratings of up to 35 watts. The circuit is essentially a power converter, consisting of the hybrid amplifier and a power transformer. The amplifier is a multi-purpose plastic-packaged device that provides a 7-ampere peak output current at up to 100 W root-mean-square.

Most line-operated tape recorders employ synchronous drive motors, permitting the tape speed to be controlled by a change in the effective line frequency. Since the power converter's frequency is determined by the function generator, the line frequency effectively applied to the recorder can be varied by changing the frequency of the function generator.

The transformer may be any filament- or power-type unit having a 12-volt secondary rated for at least 5 A. (The secondary windings of several transformers can be paralleled to obtain this current rating.) The transformer is connected in reverse—that is, its secondary faces the amplifier and must be driven at close to 4 A peak at 12 v to deliver 35 w at 120 v to the primary.

The bias network for the hybrid amplifier cancels its dc offset voltage, which is typically 200 to 300 millivolts. This prevents the offset voltage from working into the fractional dc resistance of the secondary transformer winding and causing unneccessary power dissipation in the amplifier's internal output transistors.

When output power is at maximum—35 w at 120 v—and the effective line frequency is less than 60 hertz, some transformers become inductive and may activate the current protection circuitry of the HC1000 amplifier. This situation can be avoided by lowering the input level of the function generator's so that the circuit operates at an effective line voltage of less than 120 v. Voltages as low as 95 v may be used.

The dual ±24-v dc supply voltage can be provided by an array of motorcycle batteries, making the power converter attractive for field use. □

Tape control. This power converter varies tape speed by changing the frequency applied to a recorder's synchronous motor. The circuit's input function generator determines motor driving frequency and voltage. The heart of the converter is a hybrid amplifier that develops a 35-watt output at 5 amperes. The transformer secondary faces the amplifier so that the motor receives the correct drive voltage.

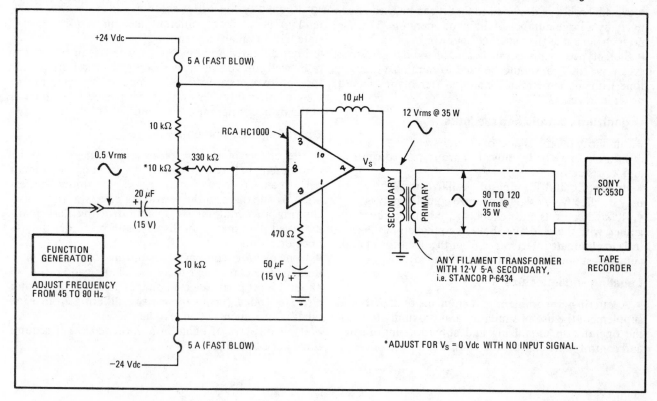

269

Guidelines for design of front panels

by Roy Udolf and Irving Gilbert
Litcom Division of Litton Systems Inc., Melville, N.Y.

Laying out a display/control panel so that an operator can function efficiently with little training requires more than just making sure that everything fits. In fact, many future problems can be avoided by spending time early in the project to plan the interface between internal components and front-panel controls and displays. Not only must the panel layout assure a good man/machine interface, but often the location of certain controls and displays determines the layout of many critical internal components.

The following guidelines can't cover all the considerations involved in designing effective control/display panels, but they should help the designer with this aspect of the project early in the design phase. Later, he can make mock-ups of the proposed man/machine interfaces for prototype use to detect any previously unpredicted problems.

General considerations

■ A panel must be designed so that it can be used effectively by a large number of different operators. There is no such person as the "average operator."
■ Stereotyped symbols, such as red = danger/stop; green = O.K./go, should be used to minimize training time with the panel. Such common stereotypes should never be reversed.

Organizing controls and readouts

■ Similarity of size, shape, or color, as well as proximity of location, may be employed to group related controls and/or readouts.
■ Bracketing and framing of similar control functions may be effectively used to organize complex panels.
■ Related controls and readouts should be grouped together, with the readouts above or to the left of the controls to eliminate interference from the operator's hands (since most operators will be right-handed).

Labeling and letter size

■ A lettering-size gradient in increments of 25% should supplement the use of similarity and proximity to assist the operator in organizing and subordinating display and control functions.

■ Clutter, unnecessary labeling, and abbreviations should be avoided to eliminate operator confusion due to sensory overload.
■ Labels need to be large enough for comfortable viewing under ambient illumination at a normal operating distance. This should never be less than 20 inches.
■ Unless the panel is to be viewed from below, labels should be consistently placed above the devices to which they refer to eliminate hand interference and ambiguity of reference.

Operator's field of view

■ Limitations of the operator's field of view must be considered. When the operator focuses on a fixed object, he has maximum acuity within ±1° of his center of vision, he can no longer see reds and greens at ±20°, and he loses both blue and yellow at ±40°. If readings are necessary beyond these limits, the operator's head must be free to turn.
■ Important color displays that must be placed beyond these limits of the fields of view require either flashing or auditory signals to gain attention. Auditory signals are frequently the better solution, since flashing lights tend to be assigned different meanings from steady-state lights in many systems.
■ Intermittently illuminated devices require refresh rates well above the viewer's critical flicker frequency for approximately 95% of the operator population to view comfortably. This critical frequency is a function of the display brightness, size, and duty cycle.

Operating environments

■ The effects of the operating environment must be considered, both for its direct degradation of human performance (such as visual degradation under acceleration or anoxia) and the restricting effects of protective clothing and equipment. Operation in the dark mandates red illumination of displays and precludes the use of color coding.
■ Controls for equipment requiring operation in a darkened environment may be shape-coded (up to about 15 properly selected shapes may be used) and also size-coded (up to three sizes, differing from each other in increments of no less than 50%).
■ Point displays of lights in a darkened room require some back-lighting. □

Microprocessor converts pot position to digits

by John M. Schulein
Aeronutronic Ford Corp., Palo Alto, Calif.

A few bytes of program in an 8008/8080 microprocessor, plus a 555 integrated-circuit timer, can convert the position of a potentiometer into a digital value. The arrangement is both economical and convenient when the position data is an input to a system already using the microprocessor, such as an industrial control system or a video game.

As the figure shows, a strobe pulse from the microprocessor triggers a 555 connected as a one-shot multivibrator. The output from the 555 stays high for a period of time that is proportional to the resistance of the pot. To measure this time period, the processor increments an internal register for as long as its input (D7) from the 555 remains high.

When data on the pot position is required, the microprocessor program calls up the POTPOS subroutine, which uses four flags, the accumulator, and the B register. In this subroutine, as the table shows, the processor:
1. Sets register B to 0.
2. Triggers the 555.
3. Increments register B.
4. Inputs the status of the 555 to bit D7 of the accumulator.
5. Sets a sign flag minus if status is high.
6. Jumps back to step 3 if flag is minus.
7. Returns to main program if flag is not minus.

Upon return to the main program, register B contains a number that measures the 555 output pulse duration and hence is a digital representation of the pot position.

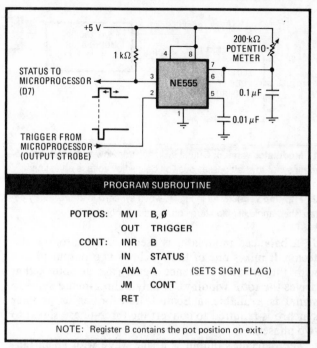

PROGRAM SUBROUTINE			
POTPOS:	MVI	B, Ø	
	OUT	TRIGGER	
CONT:	INR	B	
	IN	STATUS	
	ANA	A	(SETS SIGN FLAG)
	JM	CONT	
	RET		

NOTE: Register B contains the pot position on exit.

Where is the pot? Potentiometer position is digitized by one-shot multivibrator and subroutine for the 8008/8080 microprocessors. When program calls subroutine, processor triggers one-shot and measures output pulse duration (which is proportional to resistance of pot). Register B stores this value for use in computation of next step in a TV game, process control, etc.

When the hardware and software are used on an 8008 system with a 2.5-microsecond clock, the B register digital output varies from 2 to 65 Hex, i.e., has 100 different values, as the potentiometer is varied across its range. The values of the pot and the timing capacitor can be modified to suit the speed of the processor and the desired range of the digitized output. □

Two circuits indicate synchro shaft position

by W. Thomas Adams
University of Texas, Austin

The circuitry for either digital or analog indication of shaft positions need not cost much if it simply indicates the time at which a synchro system passes through a certain point. At any rate, the cost is much higher if shaft position itself is determined very accurately—to within 0.1% and 0.01%—as in so many commercial synchro-to-digital converters.

The two inexpensive circuits discussed here are for a standard synchro with a three-phase stator and one-phase rotor, always rotating in the same direction. It's the kind used, for example, in servo-controlled scanning switches.

In the first circuit for sensing synchro positions (Fig.

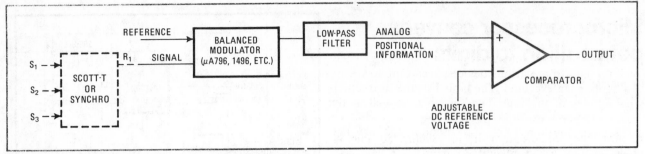

1. Modulator version. Output switches from low to high at the moment synchro shaft passes position defined by voltage adjustment.

2. Flip-flop version. As in Fig. 1, when synchro is at previously established angle, flip-flop turns on to indicate position.

1), a balanced modulator is used as a synchronous detector. It mixes one of the synchro's two output phases with the synchro reference signal (the ac source that drives the rotor winding). If only a three-phase synchro signal is available, a Scott-T transformer or another synchro is required to convert the three-phase signal to two phases.

The detector's output is a sine wave with an instantaneous value directly proportional to the synchro's position. This analog signal can be used directly, or it can be an input to a Schmitt trigger or comparator to provide a logic level that changes state at any desired point on the sine wave corresponding to an angle in the synchro system.

Another way to achieve the same result (Fig. 2) uses a zero-crossing detector to enable the D input of a flip-flop, plus a peak detector to clock the flip-flop. The circuit gives a transition corresponding to an angle in the synchro. It can be calibrated by manually turning the

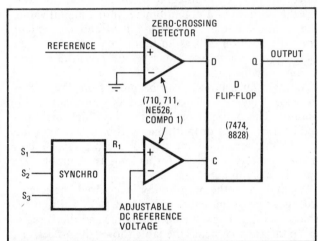

input shaft, or by adjusting the reference voltage on the peak-detector comparator.

For exactness, this circuit requires the modulation frequency (rotor speed) to be much less than the carrier (reference) frequency, because the flip-flop transition can be delayed by as much as one cycle of the carrier, depending on phase relationship of the two signals. ☐

Minicomputer controller is inexpensive

by Richard Hilton
U.S. Naval Weapons Laboratory, Dahlgren, Va.

Minicomputers are frequently used as controllers, but most commercially available models are much faster than needed and often cost more than a prospective customer can afford to spend. With the proper architecture, however, a minicomputer can be built easily. It is easy to debug, and costs hundreds, rather than thousands, of dollars. It features a 16-bit word length, 22 instructions, and provisions for up to 4,096 words of memory.

The minicomputer can be fabricated from small- and medium-scale TTL integrated circuits, including a memory array that is composed of 256-bit static random-access IC memories, like the Signetics type 2501. Package count can be minimized because the system employs a one-dimensional memory array, as well as serial data processing and routing.

parallel-set capabilities for input/output data and indicator lights. There is a two-part memory address register. The lower part (MARL), together with the four-bit operation register (OP), make up a 16-bit shift register that can receive the serial memory output and hold it as a 16-bit parallel word. The upper memory address register (MARU) is a 12-bit latch that can be cleared for sampling the contents of the lower memory address register when desired.

The arithmetic section is composed of a Boolean logic network (one AND gate and one OR gate), a full adder

The memory format requires the 16-bit references be made for each word reference. During each system memory cycle, which is made up of 16 phases, each memory module is first accessed and then optionally written into, permitting the contents of any memory location to be added to in a single cycle with only a few instructions.

The minicomputer's functional block diagram shows the accumulator to be a 16-bit right-shift register with (two exclusive-OR gates, four NAND gates, and one carry flip-flop, called the C register), and a half-adder or incrementer (one exclusive-OR, one NAND, and one flip-flop). The accumulator, the write-in port of the memory array, the full adder, and the half-adder are provided

Data selection. Minicomputer controller has four data selectors that pick up input data according to the instruction being executed. As shown in the block diagram, they are located at the accumulator, the memory's write-in port, the adder, and the incrementer.

with data selectors that are only one bit wide. These pick up data from various devices, according to the instruction being executed. The table lists the instructions and settings of the four data selectors, as well as the command that is executed.

Memory location $(000)_{16}$ is used as the program counter. Every instruction goes through three memory reference cycles—p, i, and x. The phase counter is a four-stage ripple counter that goes through 16 states for each memory reference cycle and feeds its four output lines to the lowest four bits of the memory-address port of the memory array.

As the memory cycle proceeds, the contents of the memory cell specified by the 12 bits of memory address register MARU appear at memory-array output M in serial. During the p cycle, MARU is cleared and the contents of memory location $(000)_{16}$ are directed serially to the OP and MARL registers, as well as to the incrementer. The output of the incrementer is selected by the write-in port of the memory array. When the p cycle is over, the contents of the program counter are increased by one, and the old contents of the program counter lie in OP and MARL.

Next the minicomputer enters the i cycle. At the out-

DATA SELECTOR INSTRUCTIONS

INSTRUCTION CODE (HEXA-DECIMAL)	ACTION	SELECT WTM	SELECT ACCUM	SELECT ADD	SELECT INCRE
0 yyy	ENTER ACCUM WITH [yyy]		M		
1 yyy	STORE ACCUM IN yyy	A	A		
2 yyy	ADD [yyy] TO ACCUM		S	M	
3 yyy	ADD ACCUM TO yyy	S	A	M	
4 yyy	COMPARE ACCUM WITH [yyy]		A	$\overline{M}$	
5 yyy	INCREMENT [yyy] AND COMPARE RESULT WITH ACCUM	I	A	$\overline{I}$	M
6 yyy	AND [yyy] WITH ACCUM		AND		
7 yyy	OR [yyy] INTO ACCUM		OR		
80 __	ONE'S COMPLEMENT ACCUM		$\overline{A}$		
81 __	TWO'S COMPLEMENT ACCUM		I		$\overline{A}$
82 __	INCREMENT ACCUM		I		A
83 __	INCREMENT ACCUM IF C = 1		I		A
84 dd	HALT FOR INPUT/OUTPUT ALERT DEVICE dd				
85 __	RIGHT SHIFT ACCUM INTO C			A	
86 __	CLEAR ACCUM				
9 yyy	INCREMENT [yyy]	I			M
A yyy	ONE'S COMPLEMENT [yyy]	$\overline{M}$			
B yyy	CLEAR [yyy]	ZERO			
C yyy	JUMP TO yyy IF Z = 1	MARL			
D yyy	JUMP TO yyy, [0] TO ACCUM	MARL	M		
E yyy	JUMP TO yyy IF C = 1	MARL			
F yyy	JUMP TO yyy	MARL			

[yyy] = CONTENTS OF LOCATION yyy; [0] = CONTENTS OF LOCATION ZERO

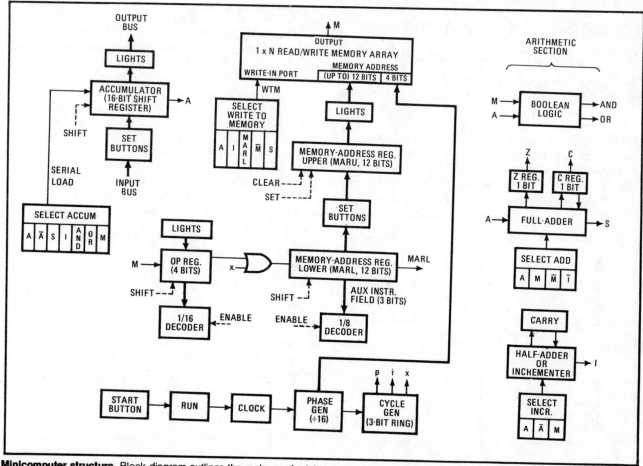

Minicomputer structure. Block diagram outlines the makeup of minicomputer intended for use as controller. The machine processes data serially and has one-dimensional memory array. Because it operates at a conservative speed, which is all that's needed for controller applications, it can be built for only several hundred dollars. The faster, commercially available minicomputers cost thousands.

set of this cycle, MARU samples MARL and uses that address to fetch an instruction that is placed in both OP and MARL. During the x cycle, data is routed serially, as it is needed to effect the desired instruction.

When jump instructions are executed, the contents of MARL are serially transferred to memory location $(000)_{16}$. During this transfer, the upper four bits of MARL's contents are ORed to logic 1s so that the contents of location $(000)_{16}$ are kept equal to those of the unconditional jump instruction.

The unconditional jump instruction in location $(000)_{16}$ is never used by the processor directly, but a jump-to-subroutine instruction causes the old contents of location $(000)_{16}$ to be loaded into the accumulator as the new contents are being placed into $(000)_{16}$. The programer then generates his subroutine exit by placing a store instruction into his exit location.

An index register for the minicomputer can be easily implemented with a suitable shift register—one that can be incremented during the i cycle while having its new contents added to the address that is being serially loaded into the MARL register. An interrupt structure could also be included.   □

Packaged power circuits satisfy control applications

by Larry Carver and Bryan Bixby
International Rectifier Corp., Semiconductor Division, Los Angeles, Calif.

Design engineers can now benefit from a new class of devices—power hybrid circuits—that blend the technologies of microcircuitry and power semiconductors. In many cases, these circuits do away with the need for special packaging, sophisticated heat sinking, and complicated isolation. Complete control circuits composed of diodes and thyristors are now available in a single convenient package.

As with integrated circuits, the designer is no longer selecting an individual component. Instead, he looks through a variety of standard packaged circuits to find the one that will meet his job requirement, and so takes advantage of the lower cost of a volume-produced item.

For example, a family of these power hybrid circuits, tradenamed Pace/Pak, is intended to perform a number of everyday control functions. There are three series of devices—PH400, P100, and P200—which can carry currents of up to 10, 25, and 50 amperes, respectively. In quantity, they cost approximately $5 to $50.

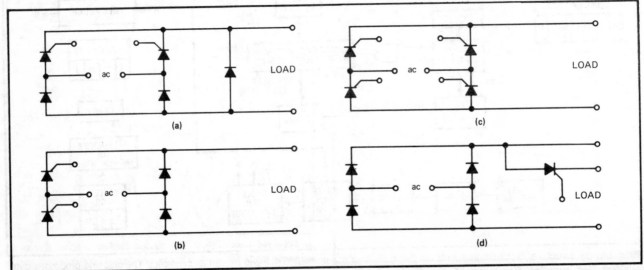

1. Power supply circuits. Packaged SCR/diode arrays satisfy a variety of power supply needs. Circuit (a) requires only one SCR gate drive source, while circuit (b) requires two. Circuit (c) is for motor control applications, and circuit (d) can provide crowbar protection.

Figure 1 shows several of these circuits intended for dc power supply applications. The circuit of Fig. 1a is available with or without the free-wheeling diode, which is required if the load will be inductive. Since the cathodes of the SCRs are common, only a single gate drive source is needed. The circuit of Fig. 1b provides the free-wheeling path for the load without employing an extra diode, but requires two isolated gate drives.

Although most appropriate for motor control applications, the circuit of Fig. 1c can be used to control an inductive current. The circuit of Fig. 1d places the SCR across the dc output for use as a crowbar to protect a load from short circuits or line transients. The SCR can interrupt the circuit or reduce output voltage to zero.

The circuits in Fig. 2 can be used as controlled power supplies—either a center-tapped (Fig. 2a) or a full-wave bridge (Fig. 2b) unit. With these, the lead (or filter) connected to the output of the bridge must appear to be resistive or capacitive. If the load appears to be inductive, the output SCR may lose control and switch to its fully on state.

These circuits can also be used as the switching device in controlled battery chargers. Even with an inductance in the circuit (for form factor improvement), they will work with a single SCR. The battery voltage forces the current to fall whenever the supply voltage falls below the battery voltage. This occurs every half cycle. After the current reaches zero, the battery voltage reverse-biases the SCR until the supply voltage again exceeds the battery voltage.

There are many applications where a solenoid must be energized rapidly, held in position, and then released rapidly to operate a mechanical device under controlled conditions in a very short period of time. The full SCR bridge shown in Fig. 3 is ideal for this application. When an energize demand signal is applied to the bridge, it turns fully on and produces the output waveform of Fig. 3a, applying full line voltage to the load.

With the right load characteristics, the energize demand signal can be an overdrive condition that forces the load current to rise rapidly and operate the mechanical output from the solenoid's magnet in a minimum amount of time. Once the mechanical change of state is achieved, it may be necessary to reduce the output current to some lower level to limit the power dissipated in the solenoid or to reach a hold level of current in preparation for a rapid release of the solenoid.

A reduced output level is easily achieved by phasing-back the firing angle of the SCRs to obtain the output voltage shown in Fig. 3b. The average output voltage varies with the phase-back angle as a cosine function—to halve the output voltage, for example, the phase-back angle is 30°.

When required, the solenoid can be released rapidly by phasing the firing of the SCRs fully back and using the line voltage to force the current to zero. Because of the inductive nature of the load, the output waveshape of Fig. 3c is obtained for this condition. The load generates a voltage sufficiently above the line voltage to force the load current through the supply. But, of course, the flux change required to generate this voltage results in the decay of solenoid current.

In this type of operation, the control circuits must have a sufficient end stop (turn-off time) so that the SCRs are reverse-biased long enough to regain their blocking capability. A turn-off time of 50 microseconds, which converts to a maximum phase-back angle of approximately 179°, is generally adequate.

With this type of power module, very precise control can be exercised over magnetic loads, including the instant that power is applied, the hold power, the timing, and the rate of discharge. □

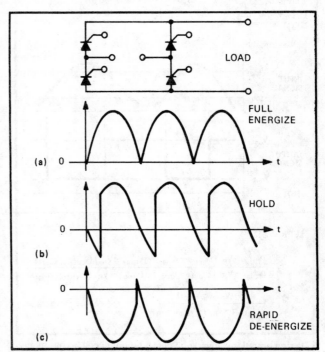

3. Solenoid control. Full SCR bridge permits precise control of magnetic loads. Output waveforms are shown for fully energizing a solenoid (a), maintaining a desired hold level (b), or quickly discharging the solenoid (c). Timing can also be precisely controlled.

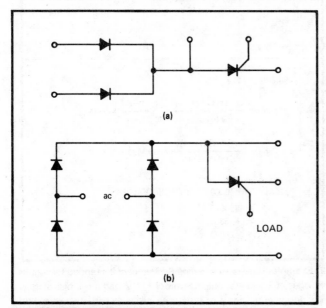

2. Controlled supplies. Center-tapped circuit (a) and full-wave bridge circuit (b) are intended for driving non-inductive loads.

36. Switching made easy

Comparator circuit makes versatile Schmitt trigger

by Phil Sherrod
Vanderbilt University Computer Center, Nashville, Tenn.

Just three resistors added to a monolithic comparator or operational amplifier are enough to build an inverting Schmitt trigger. What's more, the trigger voltages for switching the output state may easily be set at any values desired if the resistor values are chosen according to the formulas in Fig. 1.

The operation of the circuit is straightforward. When the input signal falls below the voltage at the comparator's noninverting input, the comparator switches on into the output-high state. The high output voltage is fed back through resistor R_3 to the voltage divider circuit R_1R_2, which is connected to the noninverting input. This positive feedback causes the trigger-voltage level to swing to a higher value (V_{trig+}). When the input signal rises to a level above this voltage, the output of the comparator goes to its low value (V_{out-}), pulling the trigger voltage to a lower value (V_{trig-}).

The relative values of resistors R_1, R_2, and R_3 set the trigger points; circuit operation is unaffected if all three are multiplied by a constant. Consequently the formulas yield values for R_2 and R_3 that are ratios of these resistances to the value of R_1, taken to be 1 ohm. Then all three values may be multiplied by a constant to scale them to reasonable resistances. Anything in the range of 1,000 to 50,000 ohms is usually acceptable. In general, each of the resistance values should be less than 1/10 the input resistance of the comparator.

The output voltages of the comparator (V_{out+} and V_{out-}) typically swing within 1 or 2 V of the comparator supply voltages (V_{s+} and V_{s-}). Thus, the desired output-voltage levels determine the supply voltages and hence the choice of comparator.

Figure 2 is an example. The Schmitt trigger in this

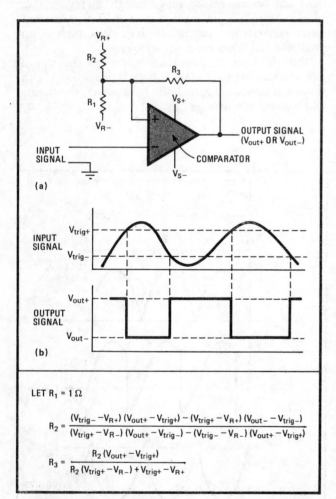

LET $R_1 = 1\ \Omega$

$$R_2 = \frac{(V_{trig-} - V_{R+})(V_{out+} - V_{trig+}) - (V_{trig+} - V_{R+})(V_{out-} - V_{trig-})}{(V_{trig+} - V_{R-})(V_{out+} - V_{trig-}) - (V_{trig-} - V_{R-})(V_{out-} - V_{trig+})}$$

$$R_3 = \frac{R_2(V_{out+} - V_{trig+})}{R_2(V_{trig+} - V_{R-}) + V_{trig+} - V_{R+}}$$

1. Design equations. Inverting Schmitt-trigger circuit (a) has triggering voltages and output levels as shown in (b). The circuit diagram and the waveforms illustrate the terms used in the design equations for resistors R_1, R_2, and R_3. The resistance values found from these equations are then scaled up to match the comparator.

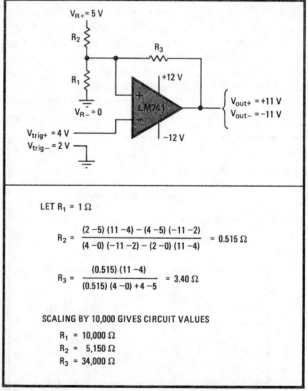

LET $R_1 = 1\ \Omega$

$$R_2 = \frac{(2-5)(11-4) - (4-5)(-11-2)}{(4-0)(-11-2) - (2-0)(11-4)} = 0.515\ \Omega$$

$$R_3 = \frac{(0.515)(11-4)}{(0.515)(4-0) + 4 - 5} = 3.40\ \Omega$$

SCALING BY 10,000 GIVES CIRCUIT VALUES

$R_1 = 10,000\ \Omega$
$R_2 = 5,150\ \Omega$
$R_3 = 34,000\ \Omega$

2. Example. Here is an inverting Schmitt circuit intended for trigger voltages of 2 and 4 V, output levels of ±11 V, and a 5-V bias supply. The design equations yield resistance values that are then scaled up by 10,000 to match the National LM741 op amp, chosen because its ±12-V supply voltages bracket the desired output levels.

design requires positive- and negative-going trigger voltages of 4 v and 2 v, respectively, bias voltages of +5 v and ground, and output levels of +11 v and -11 v. The formulas then supply values for R_1, R_2, and R_3 as shown. The supply voltages selected are +12 v and -12 v, making a National LM741 op amp appropriate. Resistor values are then scaled up by a factor of 10,000 to complete the design. □

Reed-relay switch turns on calculator chip fast

by Irwin Math
Great Neck, N.Y.

A reed-relay switch, used for fast application of the dc supply voltage, assures proper functioning of calculator chips in systems where supply voltage V_{CC} might otherwise rise slowly. In addition to their use in hand-held calculators, inexpensive calculator chips like the National Semiconductor MM5736 can be designed into logic systems to serve such functions as control devices, up/down counters, and arithmetic units.

In using these chips, however, it is necessary to apply their dc power quickly. If V_{CC} rises too slowly, the chip simply does not operate properly because the registers on the chip take on random initial values before the multiplexing oscillator gets started.

A battery supply with a single-pole, single-throw switch in the line provides the necessary fast-rise-time characteristic in calculator applications. When the chips are used in logic systems, however, slow-rise-time supplies are often all that are available. Two circuits that can provide fast turn-on of the chips in such systems are shown in the figure.

In a system that includes a dc-voltage source greater

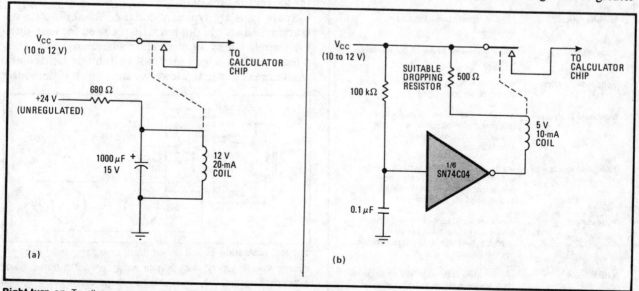

Right turn-on. To allow power supply to reach full voltage before V_{CC} is applied to calculator chip, an RC circuit delays relay closure. Relay in (a) requires a drive voltage greater than the V_{CC} for the chip, and the relay in (b) is driven directly from the V_{CC} line. The values of R and C depend on the V_{CC} level and the relay type. A time delay of 0.1 second is usually adequate for proper operation of the calculator chip.

than V_{CC}, such as the unregulated dc from the primary power supply, the arrangement in part (a) of the figure can be used. The higher voltage (24 v from the unregulated dc source) drives an inexpensive spst normally open reed relay in a simple time-delay configuration. The relay closes to apply the V_{CC} voltage to the calculator chip only after full supply voltage has been reached. The relay used in this arrangement can be one of the Magnecraft W102M series or a low-power equivalent.

When no voltage higher than V_{CC} is available, one section of a complementary-MOS hex inverter such as the SN74C04 can be used, as in (b). Here again, an RC circuit delays application of drive to the relay long enough for V_{CC} to reach full value after turn-on. The inverter easily drives a low-power reed relay such as the Magnecraft W101MX-35. □

Spark gaps can switch as well as protect

by Michael Distefano
General Instrument Corp. Sygnalite division, Neptune, N.J.

A spark gap, or surge arrester, not only protects circuits against sudden voltage overloads, but also acts as a high-energy, voltage-sensitive switch. In this role, it can be used to transfer pulses in such applications as exploding bridge wires or triggering flash tubes, and in capacitive-ignition discharge systems. When a triggering element is added to the two-element spark-gap device, the combination can be used where triggering energy is limited.

Spark gaps now available can operate with trip voltage ratings from 75 volts to as high as 25,000 v. They are cold-cathode discharge devices that operate as high-energy, short-duration, low-loss switches. Normal operation is in the arc mode, with tube drops (operating voltage during current conduction) on the order of tens of volts for currents of hundreds to thousands of amperes. They present a near-infinite impedance to a circuit while unfired, and a near short when fired.

When the applied voltage is sufficient to ionize the gas in the envelope, a discharge occurs from one electrode to the other. The degree of ionization is determined by the amount of current through the gap during operation—if excessive current flows, the gap will remain ionized even after the transient is removed. Since this current is proportional to the source impedance, the turn-off of the gap also depends on the source impedance—the higher the current level of the previous pulse, the longer the turn-off time.

Spark gaps are typically designed for short-term operation, and should not normally be used for long-duty-cycle applications. In a situation where voltage is reapplied quickly, the gap may not be fully de-ionized and would break down at a lower voltage level. If the source

GLOSSARY OF SPARK-GAP TERMS	
Dc breakdown:	voltage at which ionization occurs when subjected to a slowly rising dc voltage.
Impulse breakdown:	voltage at which ionization occurs when subjected to a fast-rising voltage.
Trip voltage:	voltage at which ionization occurs under any circumstance (also referred to as firing voltage).
Impulse ratio:	ratio of impulse breakdown to dc breakdown.
Tube drop:	operating voltage of device during current conduction.
Follow-on current:	current that flows through ionized arrester from a power source.
Maximum dissipation:	maximum average power device can dissipate during operation while still remaining within published life specifications.
Peak discharge energy:	maximum amount of energy device can withstand during operation without permanent change in breakdown ratings or published life specifications.
Peak current:	maximum amplitude of current ionized device can pass without permanent change in breakdown ratings or published life specifications.
Life:	number of ionizations before a change in dc breakdown rating, pulse breakdown rating, or both, exceeds the initial value by some specified amount.

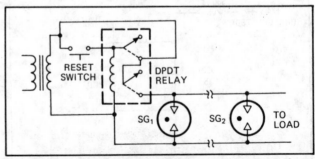

1. Load protection circuit is first reset, energizing relay and connecting load to supply; relay is held energized via its own contact. If transient occurs, SG₁ fires, and its voltage drops below voltage needed to hold relay, opening contacts and disconnecting load. Second spark gap is used if load is connected through long length of line, susceptible to transient pick-up.

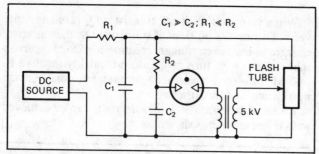

2. Two-terminal spark gap repetitively triggers flash tube when C_2 charges to the gaps breakdown voltage. Capacitor C_1 then releases its charge through the flash tube.

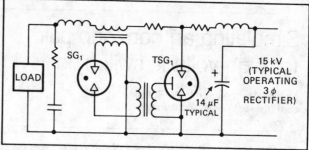

4. Crowbar protection against overcurrent surges is provided by STG_1, set to trigger from the secondary of the series transformer, T_1 and TSG_1, which absorbs overcurrent when triggered.

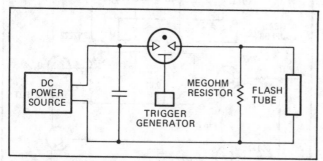

3. Three-terminal triggered spark gap fires flash tube when pulsed. Megohm resistor provides path for trigger pulse and also for initial rush of current through spark gap.

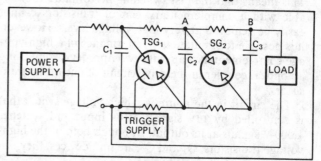

5. High voltage Marx generator uses triggered spark gap and two-terminal spark gap to place three capacitors in series providing high-voltage pulse to load.

impedance is low enough to maintain conduction through the gap, provision must be made for circuit interruption before excessive energy is dissipated in the gap, ultimately destroying the unit.

A term often used with spark gaps is "impulse ratio." A ratio of unity means that the device will trip at its rated breakdown voltage, regardless of the rate of rise of the wavefront of the transient (breakdown voltage, firing voltage, and trip voltage are synonymous). Impulse ratios greater than 1:1 define the amount of overshoot the gap will permit before tripping when the wavefront is very steep.

Impulse ratio is important when a gap is used to protect sensitive components. For some gaps it can be as damagingly high as 10:1. At that level, spikes with steep wavefronts would bypass the gap before it could go into operation.

Spark gaps can be simply paralleled across an expensive component for protection. Alternatively, two of them can be employed in a more elaborate circuit (see Fig. 1).

A typical circuit using a spark gap as an energy transfer switch is shown in Fig. 2. It repetitively fires a flash tube in a relaxation oscillator circuit. Voltage from the dc source charges capacitor C_1, which will supply the voltage across the flash tube, and also C_2, which fires the spark gap. C_1 charges much faster than C_2. When C_2 charges to the firing point of the spark gap, current flows through the transformer, providing a trigger pulse to the flash tube. C_1 then dumps its charge into the flash tube to fire it, recharges quickly, and holds its charge until the charge on C_2 again reaches the trip voltage of the spark gap.

The three-element triggered spark gap permits high levels of stored energy to be switched in fractions of a

microsecond by low-energy control pulses. Triggered gaps require no standby power, are relatively small, and are extremely rugged.

As with the two-element spark gap, the triggered gap presents a near-infinite impedance to the circuit before ionization. Triggering can be done by a transformer, capacitor discharge, or some similar means. When the trigger voltage reaches the gap's breakdown potential, a low-energy discharge occurs between trigger and adjacent electrode. This provokes the high-energy main discharge.

A circuit using the three-element spark gap for triggering flash tubes is shown in Fig. 3. Firing of the spark gap is controlled by the trigger generator, which then permits discharging of the capacitor to activate the flash tube.

When used in a crowbar circuit (Fig. 4), spark gaps can provide fast-acting protection from overcurrents. An arc fault occurring in the load causes excessive current to be drawn from the 14-microfarad supply capacitor, which could destroy the load. Transformer T_1 senses this overcurrent, and pulses the fast-acting triggered spark gap, TSG_1, which then "crowbars" the remaining energy in the capacitor. The two-element spark gap, SG_1, in this circuit acts as a regulator to prevent spurious firing of the triggered gap.

The circuit for a Marx generator, a source of high-voltage low-current pulses, is given in Fig. 5. In operation, all three capacitors are charged in parallel. Then, after switch S_1 is opened, a low-level pulse is applied to the trigger electrode in the triggered spark gap TSG_1. When this gap fires, C_1 and C_2 are placed in series, and the voltage at point A is doubled, providing an overvoltage pulse to the two-element gap SG_2, which then fires. Voltage at point B then is tripled. □

Simulating an npn/pnp pair for high-voltage switching

by P.G. Mitchell and K.W. Robbins
Sperry Research Center, Sudbury, Mass.

High-voltage transistors—those that have ratings on the order of 1,000 volts—are available only as npn devices. Pnp transistors generally have ratings of 400 v or less. This means that the fast switching performance obtainable with a complementary pair of transistors cannot easily be achieved at very high voltage levels. However, it is possible to simulate the performance of a high-voltage complementary pair with two npn devices by using an optical coupler in the drive circuit of one of the transistors.

The circuit in the figure is a high-voltage switch that is controlled by TTL signals at its input and switches 1,000-v signals at its output. Although both of the high-voltage transistors, Q_1 and Q_2, are npn devices, they operate as a complementary pair.

Transistor Q_1 is optoelectronically coupled to its drive voltage to simulate the operation of a pnp device. The optical coupler acts as a simple single-device voltage-level translator that also provides a voltage-polarity inversion. The base voltage of transistor Q_1 can then follow its emitter voltage during switching. The coupler avoids the low-frequency switching problems associated with capacitive circuitry.

When transistor Q_1 is off, transistor Q_2 is on, and vice versa. During the off time of transistor Q_1, the capacitor charges to the zener voltage, creating a voltage reservoir that allows Q_1 to turn on hard and quickly through its optical coupler. Transistor Q_2 operates normally as an npn switching transistor.

Rise and fall times of 2 microseconds can be achieved with the components shown. □

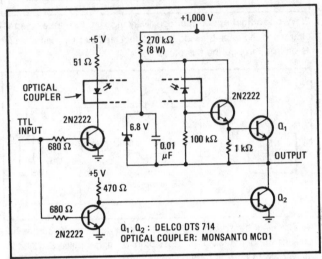

Optical helping hand. Complementary high-voltage switching transistors can be simulated with two npn devices by placing an optical coupler in the drive circuit of one of the transistors. The coupler translates and inverts the TTL-level input voltage so that transistors Q_1 and Q_2 conduct alternately. When Q_1 is off, a voltage reservoir is created across the capacitor for turning Q_1 on fast and hard.

Another way to build a two-gate flip-flop

by Donald P. Martin
Martin Research Ltd., Chicago, Ill.

Most logic designers know that a flip-flop may be built with two NAND gates or two NOR gates, but few seem to realize that one AND gate plus one OR gate may often do just as well. This simple substitution can be helpful in minimizing the IC package count for a complex design.

In general, a flip-flop is constructed by taking two two-input gates and connecting one of the inputs of each gate to the output of the other gate (Fig. 1). For proper flip-flop operation, each gate's exceptional input state must be the complement of the other gate's exceptional output state. (A gate's exceptional output state is the logic state that occurs with only one combination of inputs; the exceptional input state is the logic state at both inputs that creates the exceptional output state.)

Figure 2 illustrates the three ways to build a flip-flop—with NAND gates (2a), with NOR gates (2b), or with

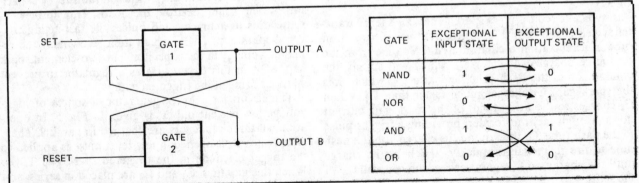

1. By definition. For the two-gate flip-flop, one gate's exceptional input state must be the complement of the other gate's exceptional output state. A gate's exceptional output state is that logic state produced by only a certain combination of (exceptional) inputs.

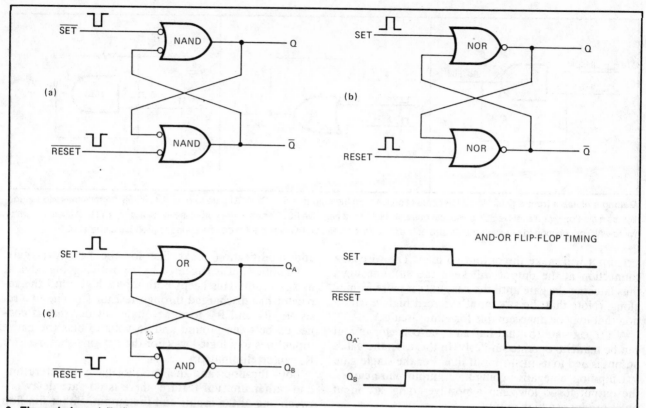

2. Three choices. A flip-flop can be made from two NAND gates, as in (a), or from two NOR gates, as in (b). A third alternative—one that is particularly handy if you're trying to use leftover gates—is to wire up an AND gate and an OR gate. The resulting flip-flop does not have complementary outputs, nor same-polarity set and reset inputs, but it can help avoid undesirable race-prone situations.

AND and OR gates (2c). (The AND gate is drawn here as an equivalent negative NOR gate so that the operation of the AND-OR flip-flop will be clearer.)

The NAND flip-flop requires negative set and reset inputs, while the NOR flip-flop needs positive set and reset inputs. Each of these flip-flops provides complementary (Q and $\bar{Q}$) outputs. Needless to say, the designer who is trying to use leftover gates can employ an AND gate, followed by an inverter to get a NAND gate, or he can put together an OR gate and an inverter for a NOR gate.

Unlike in the NAND and NOR flip-flops, the set and reset inputs of the AND-OR device have opposite polarities—often very conveniently—and the outputs of this flip-flop are not complementary—sometimes quite inconveniently. Of course, an inverter can be added at one of the outputs to change its polarity.

It should be noted that the AND-OR flip-flop can be particularly useful in race-prone applications. During the set pulse of this flip-flop, the Q_A output rises to logic 1 before the Q_B output even starts to rise. ☐

Operating a logic gate as a flip-flop

by William Wilke
University of Wisconsin, Madison, Wis.

Did you ever need just a single flip-flop, and find that all you have left on your circuit board is one unused gate? Or, perhaps space is your problem—you have room for one more gate, but can't fit a flip-flop.

Here's a way to make that unused gate behave as

though it were a flip-flop. The technique relies on the wired-AND capability of a TTL gate, and the wired-OR capability of an ECL gate.

If the outputs of two or more TTL gates are tied together, then the resulting wired-AND connection will go high only when the outputs of all the gates are high. Similarly, if the outputs of two or more ECL gates are joined together, the resulting wired-OR junction will become high when any one of the gate outputs go high.

An ECL AND gate (a), then, that has its output tied back to one of its inputs will act like a flip-flop. The gate's RESET input is normally high, and a negative-going pulse on this RESET input causes the gate's output to go low. On the other hand, a positive-going pulse at the

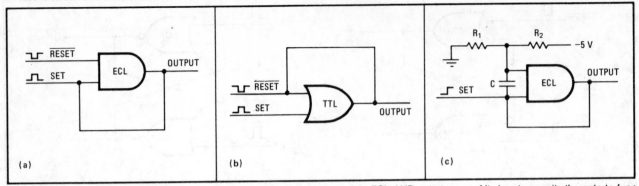

(a) (b) (c)

Getting a bistable from a gate. Wired-OR connection (a) from the output of an ECL AND gate to one of its inputs permits the gate to function as a flip-flop. For a positive SET pulse, the output is high; for a negative RESET pulse, the output is low. Similarly, a TTL OR gate (b) with a wired-AND connection to one of its inputs also acts as a flip-flop. A simple RC network (c) can be added to produce a one-shot.

SET input will make the output go high. The wired-OR connection at the output will keep the SET line high, thus latching the gate until the next RESET pulse comes along. (Note that the SET input is forced high, a condition that may be unacceptable for some circuits.)

A TTL OR gate (b) that has an open-collector output can be made to operate similarly. In this case, the gate's output is tied to its RESET input line. For the single-gate TTL flip-flop, a negative-going RESET input pulse causes the output to go low, and a positive-going SET input pulse produces a high output.

With a slight modification, the flip-flops can be operated as one-shots. The circuit of (c) shows what this easy-to-add modification looks like for the ECL AND gate.

The one-shot is triggered by a positive-going edge at its SET input. This keeps both inputs high until the capacitor has discharged through resistor R_1. The two resistors, R_1 and R_2, form a voltage divider that is connected between ground and –5 volts to bias the gate's input lines to a logic low. (For the TTL one-shot, resistor R_2 can be eliminated.)

Both flip-flops and the one-shot have an interesting and rather unusual feature—there is no gate delay between one of the inputs and the output. Either flip-flop does have one important limitation, however—one of its input lines is forced to follow the output. □

37. Regulating temperature on circuit boards

Digital ICs set temperature compensation for oscillators

by Jan Willem L. Prak and Ralph J. Peduto
Bulova Watch Co., Flushing, N.Y.

The availability of digital integrated circuits, along with a trend toward monolithic analog-to-digital and digital-to-analog circuits, demands that an engineer take a fresh look at his field to ascertain if digital techniques could do the job better then his present analog methods. In temperature-compensated crystal oscillators (TCXOs) where low power and compact circuitry are musts, digital methods can simplify the adjustments needed and remove many constraints imposed by purely analog methods of compensation.

Such a digital system therefore must be integrated to save space, while power consumption can be reduced by low-power IC technology such as low-power MOS or even complementary MOS. Another way is to use a low duty cycle; since the temperature response of the crystal is rather slow, conversion rates of one per second or less are quite acceptable.

The analog temperature-compensated crystal oscillator circuit (Fig. 1) contains a varactor as part of its load capacitance. With a fixed bias voltage, the oscillator frequency will vary with temperature. This frequency-versus-temperature curve can be used to determine the varactor bias voltage, as a function of temperature, needed to compensate for temperature changes. A network of resistors and thermistors can be used to generate the temperature-dependent bias voltage. The closeness with which the voltage can be approximated will determine the oscillator's over-all frequency stability.

There are several problems inherent in this analog compensation scheme. The number of elements and accuracy of the resistor-thermistor network depend on the parameters of the crystal curve to be compensated (such as the curve's steepness) and the level of accuracy required. Corrections may also have to be made to the network a number of times to trim it into final form. However, if the slope of the crystal frequency-versus-temperature curve is steep, and the supply voltage is limited, sufficient voltage change may be impossible to get from the resistor-thermistor network over some temperature intervals.

A digital temperature-compensation system will overcome some of these problems. In its simplest form (Fig. 2), the oscillator circuit also contains a varactor, but bias voltage is generated digitally. A simple temperature sensor (one thermistor-resistor voltage divider) generates the input voltage for an a-d converter. The converter output addresses a ROM, which stores the compensation data, and the ROM is in turn connected to a d-a converter. The required bias-voltage-versus-temperature curve is matched by the curve generated by the digital system. Thus, by adjusting the contents of the ROM, it's possible to accommodate most constraints on the analog system. A programable ROM that will have contents that can be determined after a temperature run of a complete system can be used to eliminate the need for any trimming and adjusting.

How well the ROM compensates depends on its capacity. If N is the number of output bits of the a-d converter (and thus the number of words in the ROM) and M the number of input bits to the d-a (M is thus the word size of the ROM), then the number of bits needed in the ROM can be expressed as $M \times 2^N$; thus N should be minimized before M.

For TCXOs of limited accuracy (about 1 part per million over the specified temperature range) the circuit used for the direct method (Fig. 2) is probably most cost-effective. However, there are ways of reducing the number of ROM bits from the $M \times 2^N$ needed for this "brute-force" approach. Figure 3 shows one alternative.

Assume a system with a resolution requiring N = 10 and M = 12, so that the direct method would require 12,288 bits in the ROM. Let the a-d converter consist of a clock generator, a 10-stage binary counter (not an up/

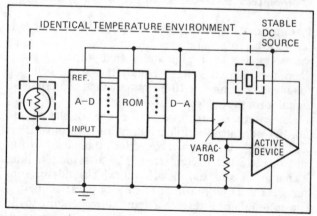

1. Analog way. Temperature compensation for crystal oscillator is obtained by providing temperature-variable voltage to varactor.

2. Digital way. Read-only memory stores correction-curve characteristics; a-d converter addresses ROM, which drives d-a converter.

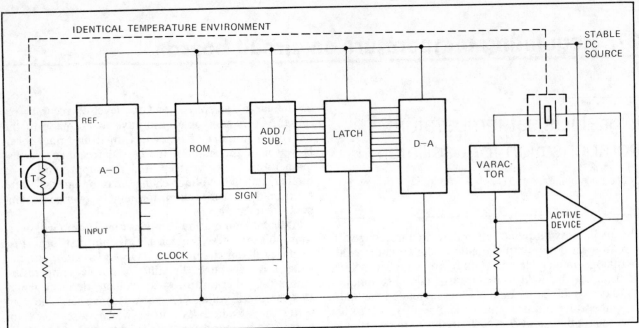

3. Small ROM. Capacity of ROM can be reduced by using adder-subtracter to effectively bias correction curve at base temperature.

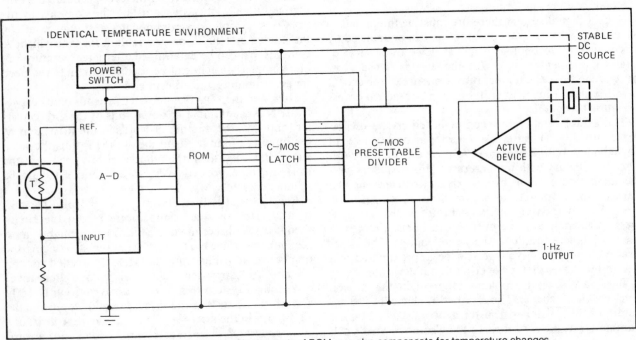

4. Divider control. A presettable divider, controlled by contents of ROM, can also compensate for temperature changes.

down counter) with current sources, and a resistor ladder network to generate an internal voltage. This voltage is applied to a comparator that stops the count when the internal voltage equals the applied analog voltage. The counter's 10-bit output then represents in digital form the analog input voltage.

The seven most significant bits of the counter are fed to a 128-word ROM with five output bits, one of which is used as a sign bit. The a-d converter's three least significant bits are left unconnected. The ROM output lines feed into an add/subtract circuit which adds or subtracts the ROM output to or from a 12-bit accumulator. The accumulator is reset to a value corresponding to the output voltage desired at the bottom of the temperature range. When the conversion starts, every clock pulse ap-

plied to the counter in the a-d converter simultaneously causes the ROM output from the previous conversion to be added to (or subtracted from) the contents of the accumulator. Since the three least significant bits are not connected, the contents of each ROM address will therefore be added eight times before a new number appears on the ROM output lines. In this way, the total curve is divided up into 128 linear segments, and each segment is broken down into 8 steps.

This is not a very fast system, but quartz crystals normally respond fairly slowly to changes in ambient temperature. One conversion per second or less is adequate. With such a system, the worst-case frequency error obviously becomes somewhat greater, but more than offsetting that, the number of ROM bits has been reduced nearly 20-fold—from a high of 12,288 to 640.

A digital temperature-compensation system, as it might be used in a watch or clock, is shown in Fig. 4. The a-d converter and the ROM are used in a low-duty-cycle mode. The output of the ROM is stored in a C-MOS latch that is permanently on. The d-a converter and the varactor have been eliminated by using the digital information to modify the operation of the divider, which divides the crystal frequency down to 1 hertz. This output drives either a stepping motor for a conventional time display or a counter/decoder-driver circuit for a digital display system. The divider also provides the signal that turns on the low duty cycle components.

There are many more ways of applying these ideas to an actual system (several patents have been applied for). Its application is not limited to quartz crystal oscillators but extends to all types of temperature-dependent systems. Moreover, the basic circuits can be easily modified to obtain an ultra-linear voltage-controlled crystal oscillator (VCXO) or any other functional dependence of frequency on voltage that the system designer may want. □

IC timer plus thermistor can control temperature

by Donald DeKold
Santa Fe Community College, Gainesville, Fla.

Although it is really intended for timing applications, the 555-type timer IC makes an economical and versatile solid-state thermostat when used with a negative-temperature-coefficient thermistor.

The timer's internal resistive divider establishes reference voltages at $(\frac{1}{3})V_{CC}$ and $(\frac{2}{3})V_{CC}$ for each of the timer's comparators. When an external voltage applied to the threshold input (pin 6) exceeds $(\frac{2}{3})V_{CC}$, an output is generated by the threshold comparator that toggles the flip-flop. This turns on the discharge transistor and results in a low output signal from the timer's driver-amplifier output stage.

In most applications, as in this one, the turn-on of the timer's discharge transistor lowers the voltage at the threshold input to less than $(\frac{2}{3})V_{CC}$. If the trigger input then drops below $(\frac{1}{3})V_{CC}$, the trigger comparator generates a pulse that retoggles the flip-flop, drives the discharge transistor off, and causes the output stage to return to its high output level.

This circuit action lends itself nicely to temperature-control applications, particularly those normally reserved for thermostats that must maintain an environment within a bounded temperature range. A voltage that is directly proportional to temperature will rise (along with temperature) until threshold voltage $(\frac{2}{3})V_{CC}$ is reached. The timer's output stage will then change state, so that a refrigeration unit can be turned on or an oven can be turned off. Temperature will then drop until $(\frac{1}{3})V_{CC}$ exists at the trigger input, causing the output stage to return to its first state—with the refrigerator off or the oven on.

For the thermostat in the diagram, thermistor/resistor divider networks produce the voltage that is directly proportional to temperature. When temperature is rising (high output state, discharge transistor off), the threshold input voltage is determined by the division between the combination of $(R_T + R_1)$ and R_2, and in-

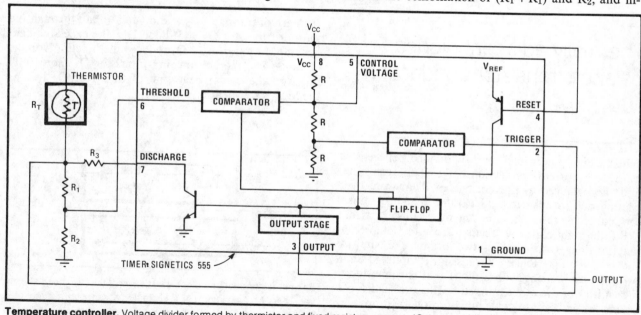

Temperature controller. Voltage divider formed by thermistor and fixed resistors converts IC timer to solid-state thermostat. Upper and lower temperature limits are set by the switching voltages of the threshold comparator and the trigger comparator, respectively.

creases as the value of R_T decreases.

When R_T is equal to the thermistor resistance at the hot setpoint temperature, R_{TH}, the divider relationship needed to establish $(\frac{2}{3})V_{CC}$ at the threshold input is:

$$(R_{TH} + R_1)/(R_{TH} + R_1 + R_2) = \frac{1}{2}$$

After an input to the threshold comparator reaches this level, the discharge transistor is switched on, effectively placing R_3 in parallel with $(R_1 + R_2)$.

As the temperature drops, R_T increases in value, and the division is between R_T and $[R_3 \parallel (R_1 + R_2)]$. When R_T is equal to the resistance at the cold setpoint temperature, R_{TC}, the divider must produce $(\frac{1}{3})V_{CC}$ at the trigger input. The divider relationship becomes:

$$[R_3 \parallel (R_1 + R_2)]/[R_{TC} + (R_3 \parallel (R_1 + R_2))] = \frac{1}{2}$$

Therefore, the impedance level of the thermistor/resistor dividers is effectively changed in different ways, depending on whether the thermostat is in the rising temperature portion of its operating cycle or the cooling portion. This is necessary since a thermistor's resistance varies quasi-exponentially with temperature and may exhibit a two- or three-fold change over a narrow temperature range. That is, the thermistor's cold setpoint resistance, R_{TC}, may be several times larger than its hot setpoint resistance, R_{TH}.

If a standard thermistor is used and its resistance as a function of temperature is known, a straightforward design approach applies. When R_{TC} exceeds R_{TH} by a factor of 2 or more, let $R_2 = R_{TC}$ and let $K = R_{TC}/R_{TH}$ where K is a constant. For proper divider ratios:

$$R_1 = (K/2 - 1)R_{TH}$$
$$R_2 = KR_{TH}$$
$$R_3 = [(3K^2 - 1)/(4K - 2)]R_{TH}$$

However, if the setpoint resistance ratio, R_{TC}/R_{TH}, is less than 2, then let $R_1 = 0$ and $R_2 = 2R_{TH}$, so that:

$$R_3 = 2R_{TH}R_{TC}/(2R_{TH} - R_{TC})$$

(For this analysis, it is assumed that the timer's trigger and threshold inputs do not load the dividers.)

Thermistor power dissipation must be kept as low as possible to maintain the accuracy of the thermostat's setpoints. By operating the timer from the lowest possible supply voltage—5 volts—thermistor self-heating can be minimized. But at high temperature setpoints, where thermistor resistance may be quite low (only a few hundred ohms), this approach may not be practical. On the other hand, at very cold temperatures, the thermistor/resistor divider impedance levels must be evaluated in terms of the timer's threshold and trigger input impedance levels.

To prevent noise signals from causing premature state changes, the timer's trigger and threshold inputs should be bypassed with capacitors. This is particularly important when divider impedance levels are high, the environment is noisy, or long leads are used to connect the thermistor to the circuit. □

Thermally adjacent diodes balance transistor conduction

by Oliver C. Stanley
San Diego, Calif.

When a high-power load must be divided between two transistors, current conduction between the transistors must be balanced to prevent one of them from overheating due to mismatch. Generally, matched transistors, balancing resistors, or balancing circuits are used.

But the right corrective feedback can be obtained by the judicious placement of two ordinary diodes. As shown in the diagram, each transistor is mounted on its own heat sink, along with a diode that is connected to the emitter of the other transistor. This provides a balancing action because diode junction voltage drops with increasing temperature.

For example, suppose more current passes through the path of transistor Q_1 and diode D_1 than through the path of transistor Q_2 and diode D_2. The excessive heat generated by transistor Q_1 reduces the junction voltage of diode D_2, thereby turning transistor Q_2 more fully on. And the cooler heat sink of transistor Q_2 lessens diode D_1's self-heating effects. □

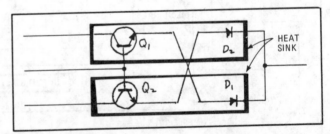

Balanced conduction. Diode location prevents two load-sharing transistors from overheating. A diode and a transistor are mounted on the same heat sink, but the diode is electrically connected to the other transistor. As temperature goes up, diode voltage goes down.

One transistor senses, heats in temperature regulator

by Neil Dvorak
Technical Equipment Corp., Denver, Colo.

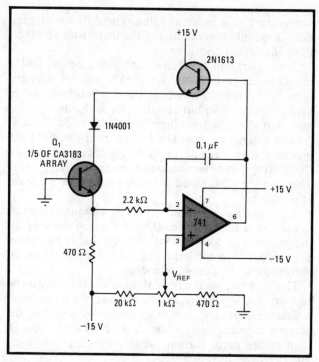

Most circuits for regulating the temperature of a substrate employ at least two transistors—one for sensing the temperature, and another for generating heat. But the designer can make a single transistor serve as a combination sensor and heater by exploiting the fact that the voltage drop across a silicon junction changes by –2 millivolts per °C change of temperature. As a result, he is free to use, for example, a matched dual transistor as a temperature-independent logging element or to use all but one of the transistors in an array for purposes other than temperature regulation.

In the accompanying circuit diagram, transistor Q_1 is connected as a current source. The grounded-base configuration permits the base-to-emitter junction voltage V_{BE} to be easily monitored by the operational amplifier. The op amp compares V_{BE} to a preset reference voltage, V_{ref}, that is equal to the junction voltage at the desired substrate temperature. Unbalanced voltage at the op-amp inputs causes it to drive more current through Q_1, thus changing the junction temperature and voltage.

To calibrate the regulator, the collector of Q_1 is initially grounded so that the emitter-to-collector voltage is essentially zero, and, therefore, power dissipation in the transistor is zero. The base-to-emitter voltage is then measured, preferably to the nearest millivolt. This reading, V_0, is the junction voltage at ambient temperature. If the ambient temperature is, for example, 23°C and the desired junction (substrate) temperature is 63°C, the V_{ref} must be set to $V_0 - [2 \text{ mv} \times (63 - 23)]$. When the op amp is then reconnected to the collector of Q_1, the

Double duty. Transistor Q_1 serves as both temperature sensor and heater element in this circuit for regulating substrate temperature. Reference voltage is set to the value that a base-emitter junction has at the desired substrate temperature. The op amp senses the difference between the reference level and the actual V_{BE} of Q_1, and it drives current through the transistor to bring it to that temperature.

servo action will maintain enough collector dissipation in Q_1 to keep its junction at 63°C.

Although a small-signal transistor in an array is shown as Q_1 here, this same principle can of course be applied to larger transistors, such as the 2N3055. To enable the op amp to source more current, an emitter follower can be added to the circuit, in the line connecting the emitter of the 2N1613 to the anode of the 1N4001 diode. □

Single thermistor can serve as simple temperature regulator

by Trevor Blogg
Kelowna General Hospital, Kelowna, B.C., Canada

It is often desirable to stabilize the temperature of a small device such as the differential input transistor for a high-gain dc amplifier. The device temperature can be held constant by placing it in thermal contact with a thermistor that is made to maintain its own internal

Temperature regulator. Thermistor maintains temperature at a constant value corresponding to value of its resistance R_T, given by the design equation. Components shown hold a small device at 55°C (±1°C) over wide range of ambient temperatures; the device is mounted on thermistor stud in a thermally insulated enclosure.

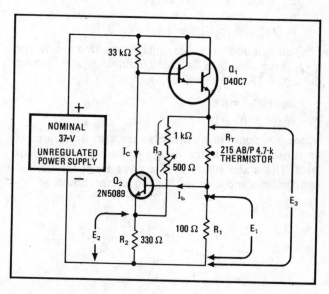

temperature at a constant value. The differential transistor is mounted on the stud of the thermistor in a thermally insulated enclosure.

General criteria for design are given below, and a practical design is shown for a 55°C control temperature; with proper insulation, the temperature can be held constant to within about 1° for ambient temperatures anywhere in the range from 20°C to 50°C. More precise designs are possible, but external thermal loading may then become of more significance than the thermistor-bead temperature changes. The stud-mounted thermistor used in this circuit is ideal for many applications.

An unregulated power supply is adequate because the circuit is primarily sensitive to the resistance of the thermistor. The power-supply voltage should be at least 50% higher than the expected voltage drop across the thermistor at the desired temperature.

The figure shows the regulator circuit. If the temperature drops below the equilibrium value, the thermistor's resistance increases; therefore, the voltage across R_1 decreases, reducing conduction through transistor Q_2. Q_1 then passes more current, which heats the thermistor and decreases its resistance.

The component values are derived by assuming the equilibrium-temperature value for thermistor resistance R_T. For small I_c,

$$E_3 = KE_2$$

where the constant K is $(R_3 + R_2)/R_2$. For a silicon device,

$$E_1 = E_2 + 0.6$$

Therefore,

$$E_3 = K(E_1 - 0.6)$$

For small I_b,

$$E_1 = I_T R_1$$

where I_T is the current that is needed to maintain temperature T.

Therefore,

$$E_3 = K(I_T R_1 - 0.6) \text{ or } E_3/I_T = KR_1 - 0.6 K/I_T,$$

but

$$E_3/I_T = (R_T + R_1)$$

Therefore, if $0.6K/I_T$ is very small compared to KR_1 (or if Q_2 is replaced by a differential amplifier to eliminate the term $0.6K/I_T$ altogether),

$$R_T + R_1 \approx KR_1$$
$$\text{or } R_T \approx R_1(K - 1)$$

which is a constant quantity, so the temperature must be constant. This is the design equation for the regulator. The manufacturer's data gives R_T at the desired temperature, and then R_1, R_2, and R_3 are chosen. □

38. Rf, microwave, and noise measurement

Choosing the right detector for rf power measurements

by Wallace F. White
Boonton Electronics Corp., Parsippany, N.J.

Thermal detectors are often thought to be the best means of making accurate power measurements at high frequencies. But this is not necessarily true—diode detectors also have their place in rf power measurement.

Actually, the user of an rf power meter is not concerned with what mechanism of conversion lies between his source of high-frequency energy and the instrument readout. What he does care about is the range of measurements possible, their accuracy, and their stability.

In a matched system, the power transmitted by a purely sinusoidal rf signal to a purely resistive load is the product of the equivalent dc voltage and current—$V_{rms}I_{rms}$. This power can be determined thermally by measuring the heat generated in the load with a calorimeter, a bolometer, or a thermoelectric power meter. The power can also be found by sensing the voltage across the load with a diode detector followed by a properly calibrated voltmeter.

Both methods will result in the same answer. However, it is often mistakenly believed that a diode detector will give a false reading if there is any harmonic distortion present or if the rf signal is modulated. This belief arises because a diode detector is thought to respond only to voltage peaks, while the instantaneous power is varying continuously with the modulation waveform. On the other hand, a thermal detector can always respond correctly since it averages out these variations, providing a true mean power indication.

This explanation tends to oversimplify the actual situation. First of all, only amplitude modulation is really being considered, and, secondly, a diode detector will be inaccurate only if the diode is driven out of its square-law region of operation. For power levels below approximately 20 microwatts, most diodes always perform as square-law devices, and a diode detector will give the same readings for amplitude-modulated or distorted signals as a thermal detector.

Moreover, for the broad range of applications involving frequency-modulated signals, a diode detector will always produce the same readings as a thermal detector. This is because the response of the meter used with a diode detector is shaped to indicate true average sine-wave power, regardless of the level of that power.

The so-called major limitation of diode detectors, then, really only applies for amplitude-modulated signals having a power level of above 20 μw. There are, of course, ways around this problem: for example, attenuators could be inserted ahead of the diode detector, or the power could be sampled with a directional coupler. Naturally, the convenience of either one of these techniques depends on the particular application.

Another common misconception is that thermal power meters are more accurate than diode power meters. Power-meter accuracy is a function of both instrumentation error and detector error. Instrumentation error, which is the dc error or the low-frequency-ac error of the measuring system following the detector head, is typically 0.5% for either thermal or diode power meters. This error is often the only advertised accuracy specification for an rf power meter.

Detector error is a measure of how efficiently the detector converts rf power to a dc signal or a low-fre-

A good combination. Rf power meter, with diode detector head provides high sensitivity, low zero drift, fast response, and good stability.

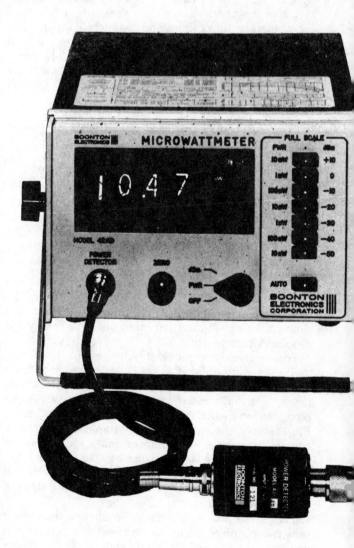

quency ac signal. It is frequency dependent, and may be specified as an over-all uncertainty, a calibration factor, or an effective efficiency. For both thermal and diode detectors, this error is typically 10% or less.

One other detector specification can lead to additional measurement inaccuracy—the detector's input VSWR. For many power measurements, detector VSWR, together with the source VSWR, creates an uncertainty that cannot be resolved without knowing the complex reflection coefficients of both the detector and the source. When the VSWR of both equals 1.3, this uncertainty, which is the same for thermal and diode detectors, is approximately ±3.5%.

. There may be one possible justification for the generalization that thermal detectors are more accurate than diode detectors. The error of a thermal power meter can be checked by applying a known dc power to the detector input. This conveniently links both detector and instrumentation errors for a thermal power meter to an accurate dc measurement.

However, diode power meters can be similarly calibrated with low-rf standardized sources. Therefore, when all the possible major sources of error in high-frequency power measurements are taken into consideration, no one type of detector has any inherent advantage over the other.

Some other things should be considered, though. For instance, diode detectors are inherently more efficient transducers than thermal detectors. Full-scale sensitivity is typically on the order of nanowatts for a diode power meter, as compared to microwatts for thermal power meters.

Additionally, diode power meters offer better zero drift, typically 0.01% for a full-scale range of 10 μW. For the same full-scale range, thermoelectric power detectors have typical zero drifts of approximately 1%, while bolometer detectors may have zero drifts as high as 15%. What's more, the temperature stability of diode detectors can be as high as 0.007 decibel/°C.

Because of their fast response, diode detectors can be used to measure the average power of pulsed sources. Unlike thermal detectors, they are not restricted to minimum pulse widths of 250 to 350 nanoseconds, and are even useful for measuring low-duty-cycle pulsed signals. For example, a diode power meter can detect 10-μW power bursts of 100-ns duration and with duty cycles down to 0.01%.

Furthermore, diode detectors offer a better low-frequency response. Both bolometer and thermoelectric power detectors usually can be employed only down to 10 megahertz because their VSWR becomes too large at lower frequencies. But diode detectors can be used (with one head) over the range of 200 kilohertz to 12.4 gigahertz. (Additional heads make it possible to operate up to 18 GHz.)

There is one last, but important, consideration—detector burnout. All detectors are susceptible to permanent damage or failure with overloads. Diode detectors generally can be exposed continuously to as much as 300 milliwatts, whereas many thermal detectors will fail at a continuous power level of only 30 mw.

The selection of a diode or thermal power detector should be based on over-all application requirements and not on misleading generalizations. □

Compensating couplers improve measurement accuracy

by John Zorzy
General Radio Co., Concord, Mass.

Broadband swept-frequency measurements in the microwave region are not renowned for extreme accuracy. One of the main reasons is that broadband directional couplers with good directivity tend not to have very flat coupling characteristics.

To overcome this problem, it is helpful to observe that, though it's difficult to get a single coupler with an extremely flat coupling response over a wide frequency range, it is much easier to get two couplers with coupling characteristics that track each other very closely. For example, the return-loss test setup shown uses one coupler to make a measurement and a second one to compensate for the lack of flatness in the first. The second coupler can be used to drive the reference channel of a network analyzer, or possibly to level the output of the microwave source.

The illustrated reflectometry configuration, which uses two couplers, improves measurement accuracy in two more ways: it reduces source pulling, and upgrades

the equivalent source match. *Source pulling* is the change in output amplitude and/or frequency that occurs when the immittance at the coupler test port is changed. (This can happen when the level is set with a standard mismatch or short circuit.) *Equivalent source match* is the return loss or SWR, looking back into the coupler test port. A poor match causes reflections that produce ripple in the coupler output as the frequency is swept. A source-match return loss of 20 decibels, for example, will cause a 10% error in the measurement of a 0.1 reflection coefficient.

With the setup illustrated, the test port is isolated

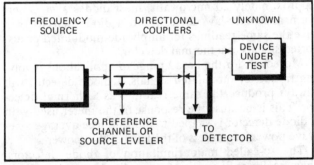

Auxiliary coupler flattens over-all measurement system response when used either to level the frequency source output or to drive the reference channel of a network analyzer. By isolating source from device under test, setup reduces source pulling.

from the source by an amount equal to the coupler's co-efficient of coupling. This is typically 15 to 20 dB. (Extra attenuation can be added at the output of the source if needed.) Furthermore, since most detectors provide a better match than do most sources, the equivalent source match is also improved. ☐

Probing system noise from hertz to megahertz

By Clarence Lundy
California Institute of Technology, Jet Propulsion Laboratory, Pasadena, Calif.

Since an electronic system is often an assembly of inter-connected subassemblies, unplanned noise-coupling paths that degrade the performance of the system are frequently created. The engineer who tries to trace these unwanted noise paths needs some way to measure un-balanced currents in signal cables.

Three probes make it easy to measure the wide fre-quency range of noise signals that may plague the oper-ation of an installation. One probe is useful from 30 hertz to about 400 kilohertz, another probe discrimi-nates against power frequencies and operates from a few kilohertz to about 400 kHz, and the last probe is sensitive in the megahertz region. None of these probes responds to balanced currents, which generally do not cause any noise.

The low-frequency probe is a modified clip-on amme-ter—in this case, the Amprobe RS-1, which is a direct-reading ammeter for measuring currents from about 2 to 100 amperes. Auxiliary scales enable the unit to read voltage when a pair of test leads is added, but these scales are not used after the modification. The modified ammeter gives a satisfactory oscilloscope dis-play of any current from 1 milliampere to 100 A, and its own current scales can still be used when the ammeter is employed for normal service.

Figure 1 shows the modified ammeter. First, remove the back of the unit by taking out the two deeply count-ersunk plastic screws. These may be removed by cutting a screwdriver slot in each or making a thin-walled deep socket wrench by forming a piece of tin around a quar-ter-inch Allen wrench, fastening it with a twist of wire, and sliding it down to project a quarter-inch beyond the end of the wrench.

Next, add a 100-ohm ⅛-watt resistor to the instru-ment's printed-circuit board. This resistor is used only as a fuse; it will burn out and save the instrument from damage if someone tries to use the meter to read volt-age. If this precaution is not considered necessary, a wire can be run directly from the upper right-hand pad of the pc board to the lower-left-hand pad on the pc board. Now, the cover can be put back on. But be sure to mark the instrument plainly to show that it can no longer be used to read voltage.

The ammeter comes with a pair of voltage-test leads that are terminated with connectors. Remove the fe-

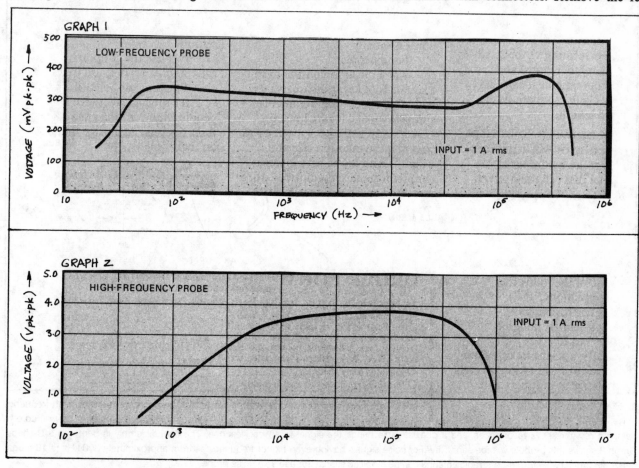

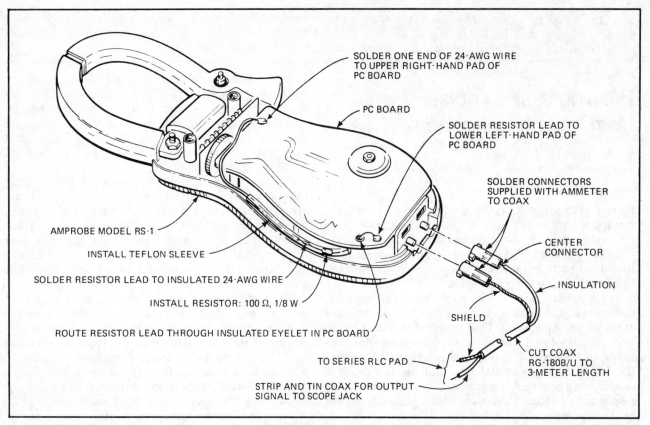

SOLDER ONE END OF 24-AWG WIRE
TO UPPER RIGHT-HAND PAD OF
PC BOARD

PC BOARD

SOLDER RESISTOR LEAD TO
LOWER LEFT-HAND PAD OF
PC BOARD

SOLDER CONNECTORS
SUPPLIED WITH AMMETER
TO COAX

CENTER
CONNECTOR

INSULATION

AMPROBE MODEL RS-1

INSTALL TEFLON SLEEVE

SOLDER RESISTOR LEAD TO INSULATED 24-AWG WIRE

INSTALL RESISTOR: 100 Ω, 1/8 W

ROUTE RESISTOR LEAD THROUGH INSULATED EYELET IN PC BOARD

SHIELD

TO SERIES RLC PAD

CUT COAX
RG-180B/U TO
3-METER LENGTH

STRIP AND TIN COAX FOR OUTPUT
SIGNAL TO SCOPE JACK

1. Low-frequency probe. When set on its voltage scale, a modified direct-reading ammeter makes an excellent probe for tracing noise signals occurring at frequencies from about 30 hertz to 400 kilohertz. The voltage response curve of this unit is shown in Graph 1.

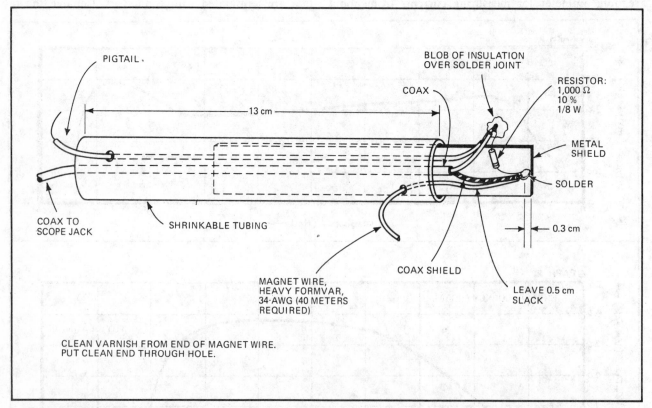

PIGTAIL

BLOB OF INSULATION
OVER SOLDER JOINT

COAX

RESISTOR:
1,000 Ω
10 %
1/8 W

METAL
SHIELD

13 cm

SOLDER

COAX TO
SCOPE JACK

SHRINKABLE TUBING

0.3 cm

COAX SHIELD

LEAVE 0.5 cm
SLACK

MAGNET WIRE,
HEAVY FORMVAR,
34-AWG (40 METERS
REQUIRED)

CLEAN VARNISH FROM END OF MAGNET WIRE.
PUT CLEAN END THROUGH HOLE.

2. High-frequency probe. Operating from a few kilohertz to around 400 kHz, this probe is particularly good for sensing high-frequency noise, even if it is buried amid large-level power frequencies. The probe consists of a long 1,000-turn coil wound on a thin soft-iron core. A damping resistor spoils resonances, and a coaxial cable brings the signal to an oscilloscope. The final assembly is bent into a U-shape. Graph 2 shows this probe's voltage sensitivity. For noise signals having even higher frequencies—from approximately 300 kHz to 10 megahertz—an ordinary flat ferrite-core radio antenna can be modified slightly for use as a noise probe.

292

male connectors and attach them to one end of about 3 meters of miniature coaxial cable. On the other end of the coax, attach a pad made up of a series RLC network—a 2.2-millihenry inductor coil (such as the J.W. Miller 70F223A1), a 470-ohm resistor, and a 4.7- or 5-microfarad capacitor.

One end of the coil goes to the coax's center conductor, and the free end of the capacitor is grounded to the coax's shield. (A miniature electrolytic capacitor is adequate.) The three parts used for the pad, along with an appropriate oscilloscope jack, can be conveniently placed in a separate compact box. The voltage response of the finished probe is shown in Graph 1.

The second probe is about 10 times as sensitive as the low-frequency probe, but only to higher-frequency signals. This probe is especially useful when a large-level power-line signal obscures a high-frequency signal.

Figure 2 shows the first stage of construction. A metal core measuring about 12 by 2 centimeters is cut from 0.15-cm-thick magnetic foil. The preferred stock is Hypernom, an alloy that is similar to Permalloy, but sustains less damage from bending. If handled gently, Permalloy can serve as well, or a piece of a tin can is equally good for measuring signals from 10 kHz to 400 kHz.

The next step is to solder to one end of the core a 1,000-ohm resistor, the shield of a piece of miniature coaxial cable about 3 meters long, and the start of approximately a 40-meter length of magnet wire. A pigtail of hookup wire (15 cm long) is laid beside the coax, and one end is soldered to the center conductor of the coax and to the free end of the resistor. This solder joint must be insulated from the core.

A piece of shrinkable tubing or a layer of vinyl tape is now used to form a cushion over the core. The free end of the pigtail of hookup wire must be left exposed. Then 1,000 turns of the magnet wire, one end of which is already grounded to the core, is bank-wound in one pass over the plastic. This can be done by hand. The other end of the magnet wire is soldered to the pigtail.

Finally, a plastic jacket is added, and the entire assembly is bent into a U-shape. The far end of the coax is provided with a connector that matches the input of the oscilloscope being used. When the core is Hypernom, the finished probe has the voltage-sensitivity characteristic shown in Graph 2. The curve droops more sharply on the left if the core is fabricated from part of a tin can.

The third probe, for tracing signals with frequencies from 300 kHz to 10 MHz, is simpler to build. It is an ordinary ferrite-core antenna, shunted by a 1,000-ohm resistor. A little flat antenna, like one for a pocket-size transistor radio and intended to be tuned with a 365-picofarad capacitor, is best (for example, J.W. Miller 2001 or 2004). The probe can be connected to either an oscilloscope or a high-frequency voltmeter by means of short open leads. To test for signal radiation, with this probe is simple—just hold the probe against the cable being checked. □

Microwave leakage monitor is economical but sensitive

T. Koryu Ishii and Thomas A. Panfil
Marquette University, Milwaukee, Wis.

You can build a simple and inexpensive microwave-leakage monitor that is as sensitive as its costly counterparts and can operate without a power source of any kind. This detector is completely passive, offers an inherent self-test capability, and is ready to operate at all times.

The potential radiation hazard[1] of microwave leakage from household microwave ovens[2], industrial microwave heating and drying equipment, and microwave communications and navigation systems has been widely publicized. Industrial consumers, as well as the general public, are concerned about the safety of their currently installed equipment. Needless to say, monitoring the almost unavoidable low-level microwave power leakage can greatly enhance the safety of operating microwave devices.

A variety of microwave-leakage detectors is available today, but most of them cost too much for household and industrial consumer use. In some models, an electrical discharge tube is used to indicate leakage power level. But since this type of detector does not give any indication at the low leakage levels achieved by well-designed equipment, it does not have any inherent self-test capability, and its failure can go undetected.

The photographs show the front and rear views of an economical yet highly sensitive microwave leakage monitor—it consists of a type 1N263 crystal detector and a milliammeter. The performance of the monitor is determined by the sensitivity of the meter and the crystal mounting configuration.

The milliammeter used here has a coil resistance of 730 ohms and a full-scale-deflection current of 1 milliampere. The crystal detector is soldered to the small lugs attached directly to the meter studs, which act as an antenna and an open-circuited transmission line. The inductance of the meter coil behaves as a radio-frequency choke.

The microwave monitor is calibrated with an approved standard device. The microwave radiation power density is measured at some point, the standard device is then removed, and the monitor is positioned at the same point. Since the monitor is direction-sensitive, its orientation must be adjusted to maximize its deflection. The deflection and power level are then recorded, and the procedure is repeated for other power levels until the meter is fully calibrated.

Graph 1 is a plot of the calibrated meter's response with respect to distance from a leakage source. (The meter is always oriented to maximize its deflection.) A full-scale deflection on the calibrated meter represents 2 milliwatts per square centimeter. As the plot indicates, this simple monitor is capable of detecting leakage levels in the neighborhood of 1 mw/cm², which is the

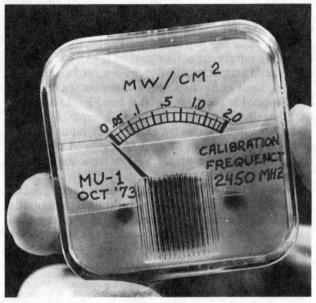

safety standard set by the U.S. Government Department of Health, Education, and Welfare for new domestic microwave ovens.

Graph 2 shows the monitor's directional sensitivity. In this case, the orientation angle of 0° means that the direction of the crystal detector is parallel to the microwave electric field. As the figure illustrates, the half-value orientation angle is only 50°, but the meter's sensitivity rapidly degrades to zero thereafter.

A more sensitive microwave-leakage monitor can be made by using a milliammeter that has a greater sensitivity. For example, if a meter with a coil resistance of 640 ohms and a 200-microampere full-scale deflection is used, the full-scale sensitivity of the leakage monitor increases to 0.05 mw/cm², which represents an improvement of a factor of 20. □

REFERENCES
1. W.H. Walter, K.C. Mitchell, P.O. Rustan, J.W. Frazer, and W.D. Hurt, "Cardiac Pulse Generators and Electromagnetic Interference," Journal of the American Medical Association, Vol. 224, Issue N12, pp. 1,628–1,631, 1973.
2. Richard Davis, "Microwave Oven Controversy Sizzles," Microwaves, Vol. 12, No. 5, pp. 9–19, May 1973.

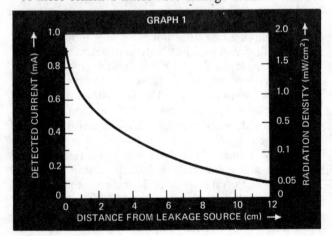

GRAPH 1

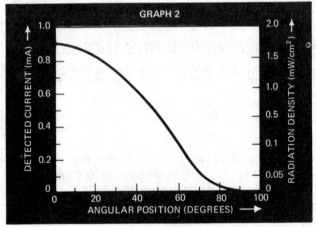

GRAPH 2

Compact rf wattmeter measures up to 50 watts

by Fred C. Gabriel
Perkin-Elmer Corp., Norwalk, Conn.

A direct-reading rf wattmeter that is accurate to within ±1% of full scale for power levels of up to 50 watts can be built around a single integrated balanced-mixer circuit. The design multiplies instantaneous voltage by instantaneous current and then averages the two to get a true power reading. It can be assembled either as a separate test instrument (with battery power, if desired) or as part of a larger instrument, such as a transmitter.

Unlike reflectometer-type instruments, which are generally used for in-line rf measurements, this wattmeter does not require the user to subtract two meter readings to find the power transferred to mismatched loads. Rf load power is read directly on a linear wattage scale. Rf line current and rf line voltage are sensed by a current transformer and a voltage divider, respectively, in a simple assembly that may be remotely located from the rest of the circuitry.

Signal voltages representing the load current and the load voltage appear across the 51-ohm terminating resistors at the far ends of each of the equal lengths of miniature coaxial cable. These signal voltages drive the inputs of the IC balanced mixer, which functions as a four-quadrant analog multiplier operating at rf.

The averaged product of the voltage and the current appears as a dc reading on the microammeter. The meter can be read directly in watts. It can be set to full scale (50 microamperes) when the circuit is driving a 50-ohm dummy load at an rf power level of 50 w (as read on a calorimetric wattmeter).

The other components of the input circuitry to the balanced mixer are included to trim the residual phase and amplitude errors of the current and voltage sensors. The variable capacitors are adjusted to produce a reading of zero when a short circuit, open circuit, or purely capacitive load is placed on the output.

The full-scale accuracy of the instrument is on the order of ±1%. Although the design shown is for operation at 27.12 megahertz, the basic circuit can probably be adapted for any frequency up to about 100 MHz.

As shown by the photograph, the entire circuit, except for its sensing components, can be built on a small circuit card and mounted directly on the back of the wattage-reading microammeter.

□

Snug fit. Excluding sensing components, rf wattmeter circuit can be mounted on single pc card and attached to its own microammeter.

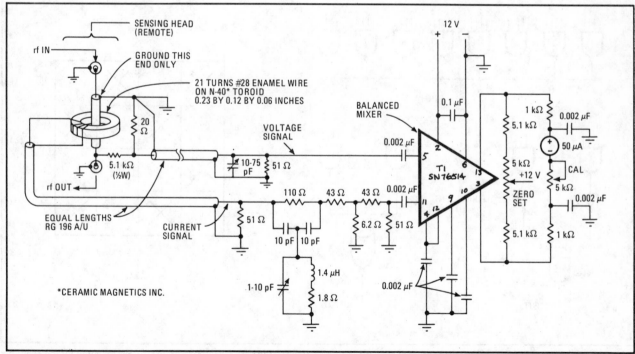

Small and accurate. For this rf wattmeter, an IC balanced mixer functions as an analog multiplier, generating a signal that represents the true average power. The meter can be read directly in watts. Rf power inputs as high as 50 watts can be measured within ±1% of full scale.

Checking wired-AND gates in just one test setup

by C.W. Moser, Jr.
Western Electric, Winston-Salem, N.C.

One of the most difficult types of circuits to test effectively is an array of wired-AND logic gates. But a standard design aid, the Mahoney map, can be used to determine the best waveform setup for completely testing such an array.

A typical wired-AND configuration is shown in (a). If only four different waveforms are to be used for testing, the circuit seemingly requires eight test setups and observations of the output to completely verify that it is operating properly. For each of these eight setups, seven of the gates must be disabled, and the gate being tested enabled with the four waveforms.

The wired-AND gates are functionally equivalent to the circuits of (b). The one highlighted in color is actually a circuit that sums logic minterms and has a negative true output. This means that if eight minterms that cannot be reduced through Boolean algebra can be found, the wired-AND circuit can be completely tested with only one setup of the four waveforms by applying all eight minterms to the circuit at once.

A four-variable (A, B, C, and D) Mahoney map (c) can be used to find the appropriate minterms. (The Mahoney map is identical to the Karnaugh map, with the exception of the minterm digits.) The map consists of 16 squares, each one containing a digit that represents the minterm equivalent of that square. Eight of the squares are marked with a colored X; none of these can be reduced with another X-marked square to form a simpler expression.

The logic equation derived from the minterms is:
$$X = m_0 + m_3 + m_5 + m_6 + m_9 + m_{10} + m_{12} + m_{15}$$

or:
$$X = \bar{A}\bar{B}\bar{C}\bar{D} + AB\bar{C}\bar{D} + A\bar{B}C\bar{D} + \bar{A}BC\bar{D} + A\bar{B}\bar{C}D + \bar{A}\bar{B}CD + \bar{A}BCD + ABCD$$

By applying this equation to the inputs of the eight wired-AND gates, every input and output of every gate can be tested with only one setup of four waveforms and only one observation of the output.

This mapping technique can also be applied to other forms of combinational logic. The only requirement is that the test waveforms be similar to straight binary or Gray-code waveforms.

Moreover, the method can be used to determine whether or not a logic circuit has been completely tested. To do this, the circuit's Boolean equation (or equations if the circuit is complex) is first written as a function of the applied waveforms. This equation is next mapped on the Mahoney map or any other device that will reduce Boolean expressions. If any input can be eliminated, the test is not complete. Then, either the waveforms must be reassigned, or additional setups made that will test the unchecked circuitry. □

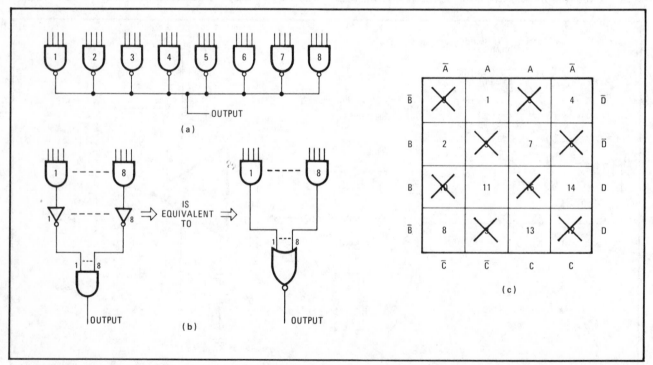

Logic testing. Wired-AND gates (a) are functionally equivalent to the circuits of (b). The one in color can be represented by the Mahoney map of (c). The eight X-marked minterms determine the inputs needed to test the gates with only one setup of four input waveforms.

How not to destroy beam leads in testing IC chips

by Allen Y. Chen
Univac Data Processing division, Roseville, Minn.

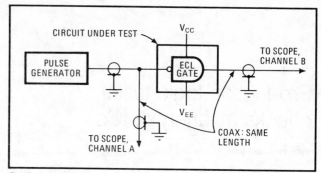

Basic test circuit uses rf techniques to check dynamic parameters.

Checking the dynamic performance of high-speed beam-lead integrated circuit chips cannot be done very efficiently with conventional chip-probing heads. The standard heads do not maintain the rf integrity that accurate testing of these circuits requires, unless the beams of the IC chip are bonded to large metal paths on a ceramic substrate—a process that usually destroys the beams before the chip can be reused.

A test fixture using a modified lead-bonding machine, however, will perform dynamic testing of beam-lead chips without any lead destruction. The accuracy is as good as if the chip were fully packaged. Moreover, the fixture can be used for static testing of all beam-lead ICs and, in addition, to insert a chip temporarily into a working system and hold it there to check performance.

Essentially the only modification needed is to replace the standard bonding head with an insulated head. During testing, this holds the chip's beams firmly against the metal pattern of a substrate. The pattern can be made part of the signal transmission-line system or fabricated separately, with a length of less than ⅛ inch to minimize transmission-line distortion. Since the beams of the chip are in pressure-contact with the metal pattern, signals to the chip and/or from it pass through a controlled-impedance transmission-line system. In the

basic test circuit, an internal scope-channel resistor (50 ohms) terminates the circuit output to eliminate ringing and assure accurate results.

Although the probing head was made of Plexiglas with a silicone rubber end to hold the chip, other materials can be used. A tunnel with a diameter of 20 mils is drilled through the head to serve as part of a vacuum system for picking up and holding the chip. (The tunnel opening at the silicone rubber end must be the exact size of the chip.) A metal shaft is then attached to the probing head for fixing the assembly to the bonder. This shaft also has a 20-mil-diameter tunnel that aligns with the opening in the probing head.

Thermal environmental testing can be accomplished by drilling a hole in the metal pattern of the substrate where the chip sits and putting a nozzle underneath the hole. An external temperature-controlled gas may then be fed through this nozzle to establish whatever environmental condition is wanted over the chip area. □

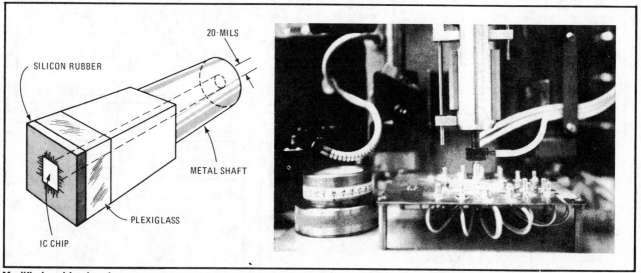

Modified probing head uses a vacuum system for picking up and holding the chip's beams firmly against the metal substrate pattern.

Production logic tester checks a variety of ICs

by T.K. Tawfiq
Allerod, Denmark

A complete stand-alone IC logic tester, which is ideal for small production lines, can be built at low cost by making use of Hewlett-Packard's model 10529A logic comparator. This production IC tester performs full functional testing of a logic circuit, yet is compact enough to fit on a small metal plate.

The performances of two identical circuits—that of the device being tested, and that of a reference device—are compared. All possible binary combinations are applied to the inputs of both devices, and the states of their outputs compared. A defective IC will light the display on the logic comparator.

The figure shows the schematic for the tester, and the photograph depicts an assembled tester (excluding the main body of the logic comparator). Three decade counters are connected in series; their outputs, which are designated A through M, are brought out to a row of jacks. The clock signal is applied to a BNC-type connector before it is gated to the counter chain.

To fix the duration of a test, a patch cord is run from the STOP jack to the counter output jack following the last-used counter output. This output goes high at the end of the test cycle, preventing the clock from reaching the counter input. When the test ends, the light-emitting diode on the top card turns on. The START push button manually clears the counters for a new test cycle.

The power-supply terminals labeled 7.5–30 volts dc and GND are for the counters, while the ones labeled 5 V and DEVICE GND are for the package being tested. Here, a 22-pin socket serves as the socket for the device to be checked, and a 16-pin dummy package receives the probe of the logic comparator.

The pins of the dummy package are connected in parallel to the pins of the IC test socket. These same pin connections are also brought out to two rows of jacks and numbered to correspond with the two sets of socket pins. Patch cords can be used to connect the pin jacks to the appropriate supply terminals and counter outputs.

To test a device, begin by inserting a reference circuit into the logic comparator and plugging the comparator's probe into the dummy package. Next connect the dc power supply to the tester's supply terminals, and then run patch cords from the 5-V and DEVICE GND jacks to the appropriate numbered jacks of the IC to be tested. The on-indicating LED in the logic-comparator's display will now light.

Using a data sheet as a guide, connect patch cords be-

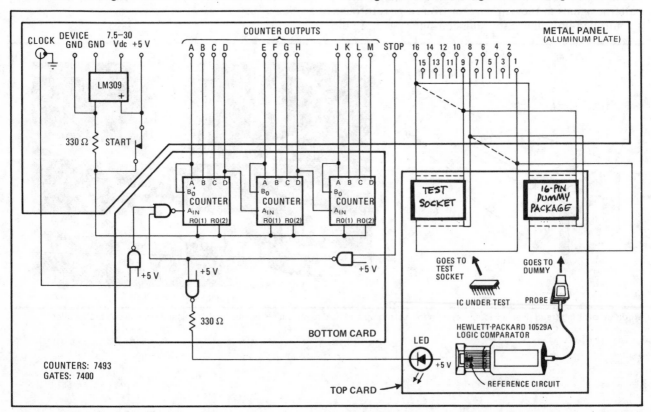

Functional checkout. Compact IC tester makes a complete functional check of many different logic circuits. The performance of the device under test is compared with that of a reference circuit. Series-connected decade counters provide the necessary binary inputs for the test device. A defective unit will light the display on the logic comparator. The assembled tester occupies a small metal panel (see photo).

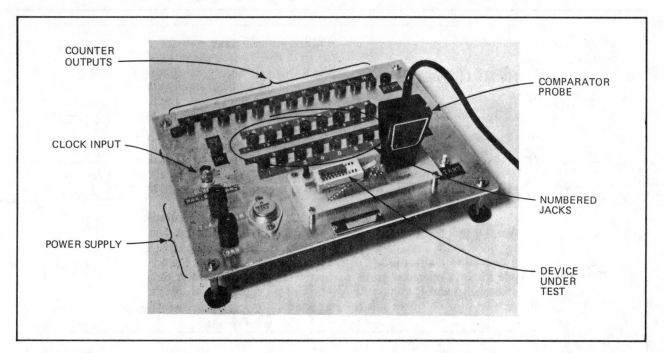

COUNTER
OUTPUTS

COMPARATOR
PROBE

CLOCK INPUT

NUMBERED
JACKS

POWER SUPPLY

DEVICE
UNDER
TEST

tween the counter output jacks and the numbered jacks to the inputs of the IC to be tested. Run another lead from the STOP jack to the jack following the last-used counter output. The clock signal generator can now be hooked up to the CLOCK jack. (The maximum clock amplitude should not exceed 5 V, nor the maximum clock frequency 10 megahertz.)

After inserting the test device, depress the START button and observe the LED display on the logic comparator. If any LED position in this display lights, the test device is defective. At the end of the test cycle, the LED on the top card lights.

To speed up the testing process, patch-cord connection charts can be prepared for various logic ICs. □

Precision comparator circuit satisfies LSI testing needs

by George Niu
Fairchild Systems Technology division, Palo Alto, Calif.

Testing large-scale integrated-logic arrays requires an analog comparator with characteristics that cannot be found in an off-the-shelf unit. To perform state-of-the-art LSI testing, you must build your own comparator.

The modern LSI functional-testing system needs low-cost comparators because many of them must be used in any test system. Generally, two comparators are required for each pin of the device under test. For example, in a 240-pin system, there must be 480 comparators.

Another consideration is miniaturization—a basic requirement for an LSI test-system comparator that allows it to be mounted as close as possible to the device under test. Short lead lengths are a must to minimize the capacitance on the output pins of the unit being tested. High capacitance will produce discharge currents, causing spikes or noise on the system ground and producing faulty readings.

For MOS-circuit testing, where output voltages may reach ±30 volts, the comparator must have a common-mode voltage range that is at least this high. The comparator must also provide high common-mode rejection over the entire range. To test circuits quickly, the comparator's response time must be low. Moreover, the comparator must have a high input impedance, a low input bias current, and an adjustable hysteresis loop to overcome unpredictable system noise.

The circuit shown in (a) satisfies these requirements and provides an accuracy to 0.01%. Its input stage contains two matched Darlington pairs (transistors Q_{1A}, Q_{1B}, Q_{2A}, and Q_{2B}). Because the input stage is perfectly balanced and has an extremely high resistance looking into its constant-current source (transistor Q_3), a high common-mode rejection ratio is obtained. The first and second stages (transistors Q_4 and Q_5) form a "negative

299

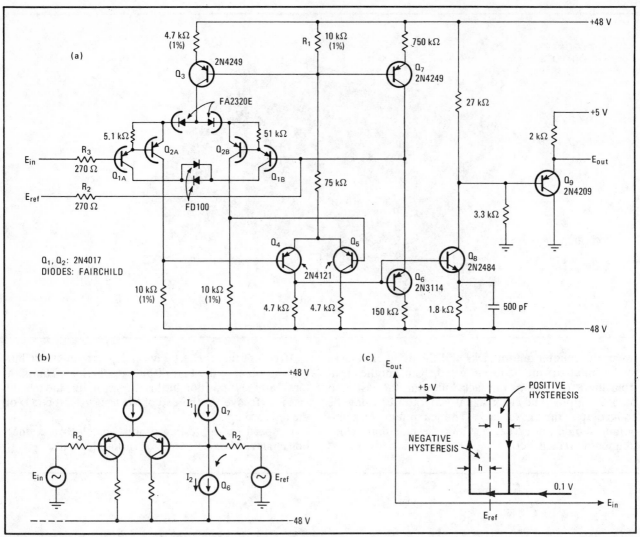

Designed for LSI systems. High-performance inexpensive comparator (a) meets the special requirements of testing LSI circuits. Besides a fast response and a high input impedance, the comparator has a wide common-mode voltage range, making it ideal for use with MOS circuits. It also provides (b) an adjustable hysteresis loop (c) to avoid false readings due to system noise.

common-mode feedback" circuit through resistor R_1, reducing the current drift in the first stage's constant-current source.

Transistor Q_6 provides positive feedback and supplies a current that enables the comparator's hysteresis to be adjusted with the current flowing through transistor Q_7. The hysteresis is controlled by the currents from transistor Q_6 and Q_7 and the value of resistor R_2, as shown by the equivalent circuit in (b). If the currents from Q_6 and Q_7 are kept fixed, the hysteresis loop can be adjusted by changing only the value of R_2. This resistor can be conveniently located away from the rest of the comparator circuit, permitting an adjustable hysteresis to be obtained easily.

The output stage (transistors Q_8 and Q_9) provides a level-shift for interfacing to DTL or TTL circuits. If the input voltage, E_{in}, is lower than the reference voltage, E_{ref}, a high (logic 1) output signal is obtained. When E_{in} is higher than E_{ref}, a low (logic 0) signal is present at the output.

Under quiescent conditions, both E_{in} and E_{ref} are shorted to ground, and transistor Q_6 is reversed-biased. Since Q_6 is off, current I_2 is zero, and the current (I_1)

from transistor Q_7 must flow through resistor R_2. The voltage drop across R_2 then produces the positive half of the hysteresis loop drawn in (c).

As input voltage E_{in} is increased, the positive half of the hysteresis must be overcome before the output can switch from high to low. When the hysteresis is overcome, transistor Q_6 turns on, and current I_2, which is twice the value of current I_1, flows through Q_6 to the negative supply voltage. At the same time, the current through resistor R_2 changes direction, reversing the polarity of R_2's voltage drop. This produces the negative half of the hysteresis loop. To switch the comparator output back to the high state, the negative hysteresis must be overcome in the same manner as the positive half is overcome.

Because of the action of the two differential pairs at the input, the real hysteresis experienced by input voltage E_{in} is half of the IR drop across resistor R_2. The total hysteresis, therefore, will be equal to the actual IR drop across R_2. ▫

Measuring the access time
of bipolar read-only memories

by Joseph J. McDowell
Monolithic Memories Inc., Sunnyvale, Calif.

The access time of a semiconductor memory, particularly that of a bipolar read-only memory, can be difficult and time-consuming to measure. But here's a tester that makes this measurement quickly and does not require the data pattern stored in the ROM to be known. There is one condition, however. The ROM must be tested first for its dc parameters.

Memory access time is considered to be the maximum address-to-output delay from any address to any output. For bipolar ROMs, access time typically ranges from 30 to 150 nanoseconds, and storage capacities can be as large as 8,192 bits. Conventional testing techniques require a single-shot time-interval measurement for each bit, since each address and output of the ROM

generally has a different delay time. The maximum delay measured in this way is recorded as the access time.

Single-shot time-interval measurements, however, have two major drawbacks. Each reading requires about a millisecond, which can add up if the memory is a large one. And the Schmitt-trigger discriminators, which are used to establish the start and stop times, rely on a specific transition direction (either high to low or low to high) through a voltage threshold to implement the start or stop.

This last condition is a problem because the transition direction cannot be predicted for a ROM, unless the data pattern in the ROM is stored in a random-access memory. The problem then becomes one of finding a RAM that is as large and as fast as the ROM being tested to tell the measurement system what to expect. Even if such a RAM can be found, spikes can appear prior to the access time and can trigger the discriminators.

Another measurement technique is to compare the ROM with a RAM that is loaded with ROM data. But again, there is the problem of finding a RAM as fast as the ROM to be tested.

The tester in the figure uses a totally different ap-

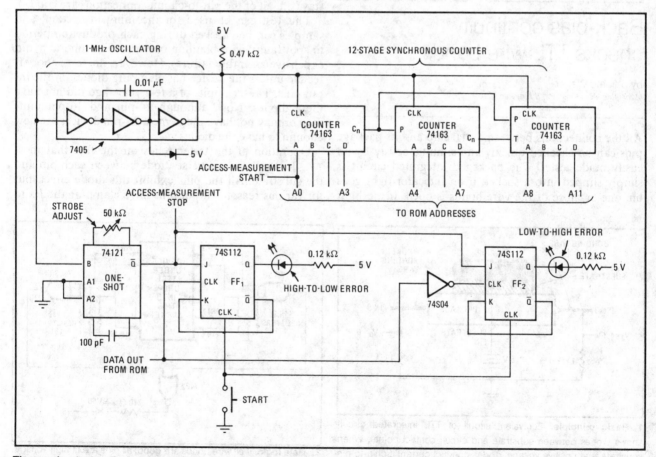

Time-saving tester. This circuit checks out the access time of a bipolar read-only memory by regarding any transition occurring at the memory output after the allowable access time as an error. The counter string changes all of the ROM's addresses at the same time. The one-shot acts as a strobe whose timing cycle is set to the allowable access time. A pair of Schottky-TTL flip-flops monitors each ROM output line. If a high-to-low transition error occurs, FF₁ lights its LED; if a low-to-high transition error occurs, FF₂ lights its LED.

proach. It looks for transitions after the expected access time, and defines any transition from this access time until the next address change as an error. This method takes advantage of the fact that the memory reaches a steady-state value before the access time, and the data outputs should not change again until the address is changed. Although the data pattern stored in the ROM does not have to be known, the unit must first be checked for dc parameters, since a package without a chip inside will pass the test.

In the test circuit, 4-bit totally synchronous counters are used to count through all the addresses of the ROM, guaranteeing that all the addresses change at the same time. These address transitions define the start of the access measurement. The counters are driven by a 1-megahertz oscillator, which is constructed with logic inverters. Two Schottky-TTL J-K flip-flops are employed to look for transitions after the access time—FF_1 looks for high-to-low transitions, while FF_2 looks for low-to-high transitions.

The one-shot stops the flip-flops from watching for transitions prior to the access time by holding each one's J input low until the access time is reached. This prevents the flip-flops from changing state. They remain in their initially cleared condition, with their Q outputs low and their $\bar{Q}$ outputs high.

After the one-shot completes it timing cycle, the J input of each flip-flop goes high. If a high-to-low transition now occurs on the memory output line, flip-flop FF_1 changes state—its $\bar{Q}$ output goes low, and its Q output goes high, turning on the error-indicating light-emitting diode. The flip-flop, and therefore the error, remain latched because the unit's $\bar{Q}$ output is tied to its K input. (Depressing the START button will clear the error.)

Flip-flop FF^2 operates identically, but turns on its error-indicating LED for a high-to-low transition on the memory output line. This scheme can be expanded to monitor n memory outputs by adding 2n flip-flops to the test circuit. (A pair of flip-flops is required for each memory output.)

The tester can be calibrated by attaching a pulse generator or delay line of known duration between the access-measurement start and stop inputs to the circuit. This simulates the memory access time, so that the one-shot strobe can be adjusted until a failure just occurs for a set GO/NO-GO limit. The tester can accurately measure an access time to within an accuracy of ±4 ns. □

Back-bias continuity checks TTL wire bonds

by Shlomo Waser
Monolithic Memories Inc., Sunnyvale, Calif.

All the connections between a TTL chip and its package pins can be checked quickly and simultaneously by an easily made tester. The packaged integrated circuit is simply slipped into a socket; if an indicator light goes on, one or more of the wire bonds is open. If the light stays off, all of the pin-to-circuit connections are good.

This test can be used for incoming inspection, and samples can be checked during each production period to spot faulty wire-bonding operations in time to avoid expensive assembly failures. However, the test is not effective unless the device has clamping diodes on the input pins. The TTL units of a few years ago did not have these diodes. Now, although 14-pin and 16-pin units may or may not have them, most 24-pin devices are new enough to have the diodes.

Operation of the tester relies on the fact that most TTL devices have a reverse diode between each pin and the substrate. All the pins exhibit this diode effect, but for various reasons. Input pins have clamping diodes to

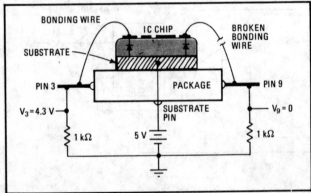

1. Basic principle. Equivalent circuit of TTL integrated circuit shows diodes between substrate and circuit contact points. When substrate is at positive voltage, diodes conduct current if chip-to-pin connections have continuity. Voltage drops across 1-kilohm pull-up resistors provide logic levels for simultaneous test of all bonding connections, as shown in Fig. 2.

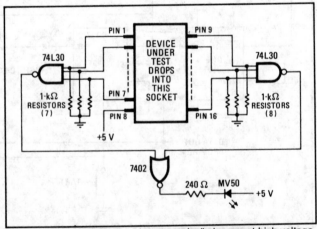

2. Gate logic. If all wire bonds are good, all pins are at high voltage, output of NOR gate is high, and LED remains dark. If any bonds are defective, LED glows red. This test, by monitoring performance of bonding operation, can prevent expensive assembly failures.

reduce transmission reflections. Output pins show diode action between collector and substrate if the substrate is made positive. Similarly, there is a diode action between the V_{CC} pin and the substrate.

Under these conditions, the continuity of the connections from the chip (or die) to the pins can be tested by connecting the substrate to the positive side of a 5-v supply and providing pull-up resistors from each pin to the negative side of the supply. Figure 1 shows two typical pins in this test arrangement.

Pin 3 has a good bond to the die; therefore the voltage at pin 3 is the substrate voltage minus the voltage drop across the diode (i.e., 5.0 – 0.7 = 4.3 v), which is a definite logic 1. However, since the bond between pin 9 and the chip is broken, the voltage at pin 9 is zero, which is a definite logic 0.

With the two distinct logic states, it is a simple matter to connect an OR gate to all pins so that a light-emitting diode will turn on if one or more pins has a defective bond. Figure 2 shows such a circuit for a 16-pin device. The terminals of the zero-force-insertion socket are connected to 74L30 NAND gates. The NAND-gate outputs go into a 7402 NOR gate. If the NOR output is low, the LED lights. Obviously this technique can be extended to devices with more than 16 pins.

The circuit of Fig. 2 uses the 74L30 low-power NAND gates because 1 kilohm is too much resistance to use with standard NAND gates (where the input current at low level is sometimes as much as 1.6 milliamperes). An apparent alternative is to use smaller resistors, but then the current through the substrate would be too large, especially for devices with 24 pins or more. □

DIP switch isolates faults in system

by Robert A. Dougherty
RAD Technical Consulting, Dunedin, Fla.

A time-honored technique for isolating faults in a digital system is to bend up a pin of a dual in-line package, thus breaking the circuit by removing that pin from its socket. Sometimes, however, the circuit is not the only thing that breaks, because DIP pins are delicate.

The new in-line DIP switches offer a better way to disconnect one pin from the circuit. Two 16-pin DIP switches, each with eight spst slide switches, plus a 16-pin DIP socket and a 16-pin DIP component carrier, form a neat package that allows selective removal of any or all pins from the circuit at will. The DIP device is plugged into the socket on top of this package, and then the package is plugged into the circuit.

The accompanying sketch and photo show the simple assembly. (A 12-pin switch was used in the unit that was photographed.) □

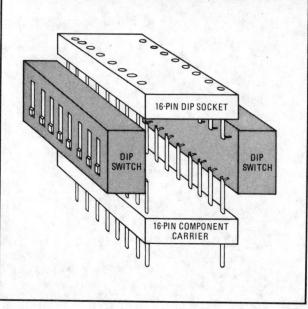

Test assembly. DIP switches are mounted between socket and carrier to provide handy unit for isolating faults in a digital system. When a DIP IC is plugged into the socket and the whole assembly is plugged into the system, any pin or pins of the IC can be disconnected and reconnected quickly and safely.

In-circuit IC tester checks TTL and C-MOS

by Ronald G. Ferrie
Communications & Controls Co., Pittsburgh, Pa.

An in-circuit IC logic tester, which can be built easily and inexpensively, can check ICs operating from supply voltages of 5 to 15 V. This means that the tester can be used for C-MOS devices, as well as TTL devices. The IC, however, must be powered from a single-polarity supply.

Although the test circuit draws its operating power from the IC being checked, it does not load the IC's logic points. Total operating current is usually less than 60 milliamperes for a typical 16-pin IC package.

Figure 1 shows what the test circuit looks like for checking three logic points. Light-emitting diodes are used to indicate whether the input signal is logic 0 or logic 1. As the truth table indicates, a logic 1 at an input causes the LED associated with that input to light. A pair of junction diodes and an inverting C-MOS buffer are used to gate each logic signal for driving the LED.

This simple arrangement can be easily extended to handle any number of logic inputs by simply adding more stages—an additional buffer, diode pair, LED, and current-limiting resistor for each new logic input to be checked.

To conserve power, the indicator LEDs are operated at 2 mA. Because of this, the LEDs will have a low luminous output, making it necessary to mount them so that they do not compete with ambient light. Recessing the lamps slightly and providing a dark background color is usually adequate. For this tester, the LEDs and their associated electronics were mounted in a small plastic box and connected to the IC under test by means of a cable terminated in a dual in-line test clip.

Figure 2 shows a complete test circuit for a 16-pin DIP. Resistor R_2 is included here at each input to prevent ambiguity when an IC with uncommitted terminals is being measured. The power supply formed by the zener diode and the transistor is poorly regulated—its main purpose is to limit the voltage driving the LEDs and thereby conserve current consumption. □

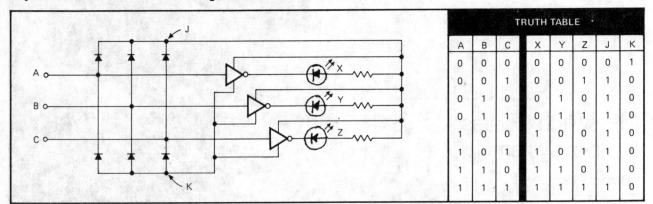

TRUTH TABLE							
A	B	C	X	Y	Z	J	K
0	0	0	0	0	0	0	1
0	0	1	0	0	1	1	0
0	1	0	0	1	0	1	0
0	1	1	0	1	1	1	0
1	0	0	1	0	0	1	0
1	0	1	1	0	1	1	0
1	1	0	1	1	0	1	0
1	1	1	1	1	1	1	0

1. Simple go/no-go check. The basic circuit employed by the in-circuit IC tester is illustrated here for three logic inputs. Light-emitting diodes indicate the presence of a logic 1 at the input. A C-MOS buffer and a pair of junction diodes gate each logic signal.

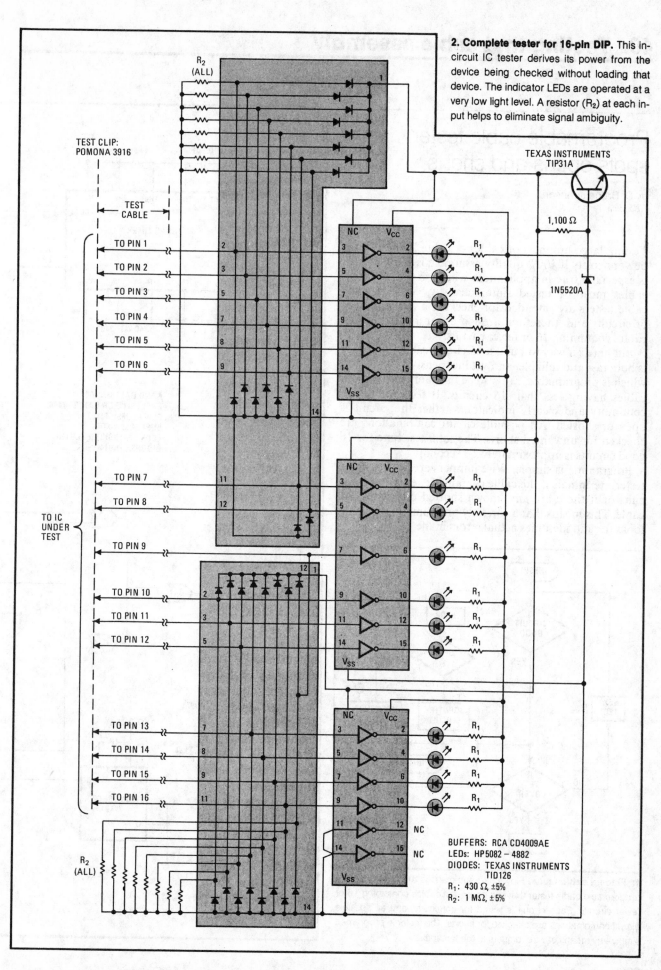

2. Complete tester for 16-pin DIP. This in-circuit IC tester derives its power from the device being checked without loading that device. The indicator LEDs are operated at a very low light level. A resistor (R_2) at each input helps to eliminate signal ambiguity.

BUFFERS: RCA CD4009AE
LEDs: HP5082–4882
DIODES: TEXAS INSTRUMENTS TID126
R_1: 430 Ω, ±5%
R_2: 1 MΩ, ±5%

Programable cable tester spots opens and shorts

by D. Bruce Johnson
Tullahoma, Tenn.

Testing large numbers of cables or cable harnesses can be very costly if 100% quality assurance is wanted. This is especially true in applications where several different cables must be tested simultaneously. Most existing cable testers are intended for checking a large number of circuits and, therefore, are too expensive for testing cables containing 16 or fewer circuits.

But here's a way to build a 16-circuit cable tester that is both fast and reliable, and yet inexpensive. The tester, which is programable, can also be used for checking out cables having less than 16 circuits. It tests for circuit continuity and clearly indicates whether the circuit is open or shorted. All possible circuit combinations are checked for unwanted shorts. The total test time for 16 good circuits is approximately 2½ seconds.

Programing is simple. Wire jumpers are added at the tester's terminals if the cable contains fewer than 16 circuits or if there are any known shorted circuits in the cable. This means that a correctly programed tester only looks for and identifies actual errors in the cable.

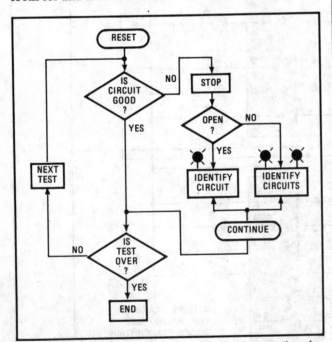

1. Finding cable faults. Flow chart summarizes the operation of a programable cable tester that can check out cables containing 16 or fewer circuits. Each circuit is tested for continuity, and all possible circuit combinations are checked for shorts. The tester is programed simply—by means of wire jumpers at the terminals.

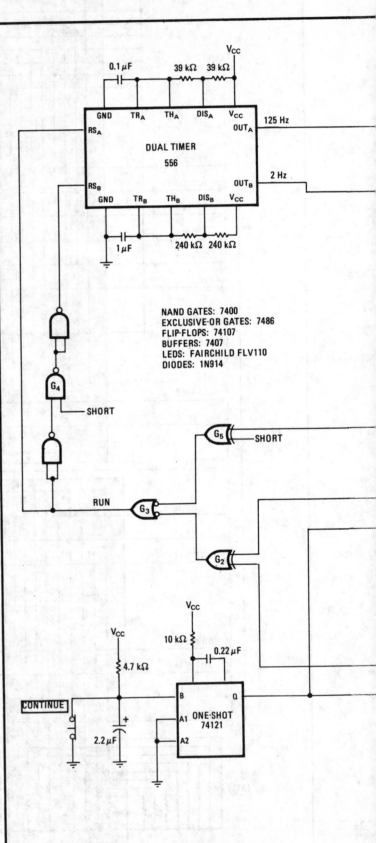

NAND GATES: 7400
EXCLUSIVE-OR GATES: 7486
FLIP-FLOPS: 74107
BUFFERS: 7407
LEDS: FAIRCHILD FLV110
DIODES: 1N914

The flow chart (Fig. 1) outlines the operation of the tester (Fig. 2). The left branch of the flow chart indicates that all circuits are tested for continuity, and all possible circuit combinations are checked for shorts. If the cable is faulty, the tester will stop and indicate an

2. The works. Cable tester indicates an open circuit by continuously lighting a single numbered LED. If a short is detected, two of the numbered LEDs are lighted, and testing is stopped. Testing can be resumed by pressing the CONTINUE push-button switch. A programed short is noted by two blinking numbered LEDs.

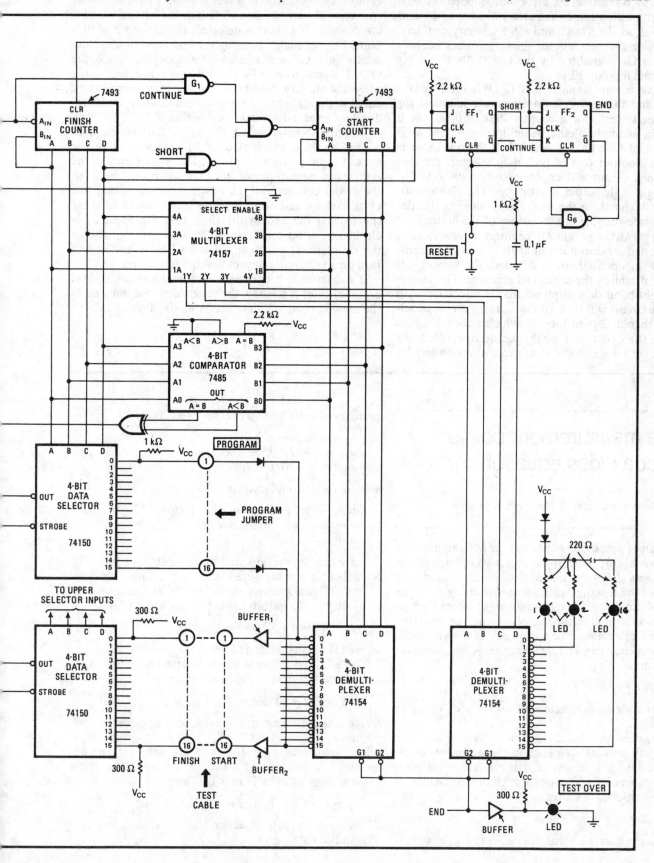

307

open circuit with a single numbered light-emitting diode, or a short circuit by lighting two numbered LEDs. The right branch of the flow chart shows this process.

Testing can be resumed by pushing the CONTINUE switch or by correcting the error that stopped the test. The RESET pushbutton switch clears flip-flops FF_1 and FF_2, as well as the START and FINISH binary counters. Both of these counters will log the same pulses because NAND gate G_1 is enabled by the CONTINUE signal ($\bar{Q}$ output) from flip-flop FF_1.

The input control signals (A, B, C, D) to the two data selectors and the two demultiplexers are identical for the continuity test. For a counter state of 0000, the 0 output pin of the left-hand demultiplexer is low, as is the output of $BUFFER_1$. If circuit 1 of the test cable is good, the 0 output pins of both data selectors are also low. A good circuit will enable exclusive-OR gate G_2, producing a high output at NOR gate G_3. This constitutes a RUN signal for the dual timer, allowing this device to be free-running at a frequency of 125 hertz.

As the START and FINISH counters advance, each cable is tested for continuity until all 16 checks are completed. If an open circuit is detected, the RUN signal goes low, disabling the timer and counters. The output of the right-hand demultiplexer that is associated with the faulty circuit will then go low, turning on its associated numbered LED to identify which circuit is open. Pressing the CONTINUE push-button overrides the tester's logic long enough to advance the counters by one bit, causing the testing to begin again.

When the tester completes all 16 continuity checks, it then goes on to look for all possible unwanted shorts. The 16th clock pulse from the timer returns both counters to their 0000 state and sets flip-flop FF_1. The START counter will now advance at 1/16th the rate of the FINISH counter. If a short is detected, the Q output of flip-flop FF_1 goes high, changing the test logic by enabling NAND gate G_4 and exclusive-OR gate G_5. Since the SHORT signal from FF_1 overrides the test logic only when the state of the START counter is greater than or equal to the state of the FINISH counter, there are no redundant error indications of cable shorts.

When a short is found, the lower half of the dual timer is enabled, which places a 2-Hz clock signal on the SELECT input of the multiplexer. The control lines of the right-hand demultiplexer are then alternated between the START counter and the FINISH counter so that two LEDs flash on and off to indicate which two circuits are shorted. At the end of the short test, flip-flop FF_2 is clocked to its set condition, and NAND gate G_0 inhibits the counters. The END signal from FF_2 is buffered to turn on a LED that indicates that the test is over.

If the tester is programed for a planned cable short and that short is missing, the tester identifies one end of the missing short at a time with a single blinking LED. □

Three measurement points give coax loss equation

by L.S. Gay
Standard Telephones and Cables Ltd., Basildon, Essex, England

The design of amplitude equalizers for both analog and digital coaxial-line systems requires a knowledge of the insertion loss (L) of the line in decibels, expressed as a function of the length (l) of the line, frequency (f) of the test signal, and perhaps temperature (T). Once this information is available in equation form, the insertion loss can be determined for any length of a given cable at any frequency and any temperature. A loss equation of the form

$$L = l(a + bf^{1/2} + cf)$$

usually provides a satisfactory fit over a wide range of frequencies.

The constants a, b, and c can be derived from three linear equations that are based on measurements of insertion losses in a length of cable at three different known frequencies. Carrying through this procedure, if the loss equation is rewritten as

$$\alpha = L/l = a + bf^{1/2} + cf$$

and α has measured values α_1, α_{10}, and α_{100} at frequencies of 1, 10, and 100, respectively, then

$$\alpha_1 = a + b + c$$
$$\alpha_{10} = a + 10^{1/2}b + 10c$$
$$\alpha_{100} = a + 10b + 100c$$

Solving for a, b, and c yields

$$b = (-10\alpha_1 + 11\alpha_{10} - \alpha_{100})/[11(10)^{1/2} - 20]$$
$$c = [\alpha_{10} - \alpha_1 - b(10^{1/2} - 1)]/9$$
$$a = \alpha_1 - b - c$$

For example, the loss in 1.85 kilometers of type 174 coaxial cable was measured at 20°C, yielding the values $\alpha_1 = 5.281$ dB/km, $\alpha_{10} = 16.584$ dB/km, and $\alpha_{100} = 52.61$ dB/km. Therefore, cable loss in dB at 20°C is

$$L = l(0.068 + 5.21f^{1/2} + 0.0045f)$$

where l is in kilometers and f is in megahertz.

The effect of different temperatures on the insertion loss can be included in the equation as follows:

$$L_T = l_0(1 + \gamma\Delta T)(a + bf^{1/2} + cf)$$

where l_0 is the length of the cable at the reference temperature T_0, and ΔT is $(T - T_0)$. Using a test signal with a fixed frequency, the value of the constant γ can be determined by measuring the insertion loss of a given cable at temperatures T_1 and T_2. Then

$$\gamma = (L_2 - L_1)/[L_1(\Delta T)_2 - L_2(\Delta T)_1]$$

where L_1 denotes the insertion loss at T_1, $(\Delta T)_1 = (T_1 - T_0)$, and so forth. □

Simple cable tester spots faults, identifies repairs

by Edward L. Raub, Jr.
Precision Tool Company of New London Inc., New London, Conn.

Automatic testing of small cable harnesses is all very well in production, but engineers are often confronted with smaller quantities of cables in differing configurations that still add up to a substantial total. In this situation, even as basic a tester as the one proposed in *Electronics*, August 22, p. 110, would be too specialized. But a vastly simpler scheme can be surprisingly effective.

This simple tester checks circuits as fast as an operator can push buttons, taking less than one second per circuit to verify faults and locate all pins involved in short and open circuits, transpositions, and misroutings. For example, a tester containing two 20-button jukebox switches easily checks a 40-conductor harness, including any jumpers, in 40 seconds. The unit does not require preprograming, and the principal component is a multi-button push switch with two poles per button, at least one of which is double-throw.

When the cable is initially connected to the tester, normally closed contacts of the push-buttons make all conductors electrically common at one end. As each button is pushed, one at a time, it separates a single conductor from the bundle, checks its continuity via the green lamp, and tests it for short circuits with other wires in the cable through the red lamp. The indicator lamps describe the condition of the cable as shown in the table.

If a fault is disclosed, a simple test procedure identifies both conductors of a mutually short-circuited pair, both members of an interchanged pair, both ends of an incorrectly routed wire, or both ends of a jumper. For example, if one button gives a green-and-red indication, it should be held down while each remaining button is pushed in turn. One of them will remove the red indication and leave green only, showing that the conductors associated with these two buttons are interchanged or shorted. This same procedure, applied to a red-only indication, identifies both ends of an incorrectly connected wire.

Where cables purposely are not wired straight through (pin 1 to pin 1, pin 2 to pin 2, etc.), a short adapter cable can be introduced between one end of the production cable and the tester. The adapter has the crossed connection reversed to emulate a single straight-through cable. The tester can accommodate cables with various connector types if appropriate matching connectors are added in parallel at the tester.

It's a good idea to keep a notebook with the tester which pictures each cable type and specifies the presence of jumpers and skipped pins. Otherwise, these would look like short and open circuits. But, with little practice, minimal reference is necessary to check out even cables with multiple jumpers. A series of these testers will pay for themselves many times over. □

INDICATION	CONTINUITY	TERMINATION
Green only	Good	Correct
Red only	Good	Incorrect
Green and red	Good	Correct with short circuit
None	Open	—

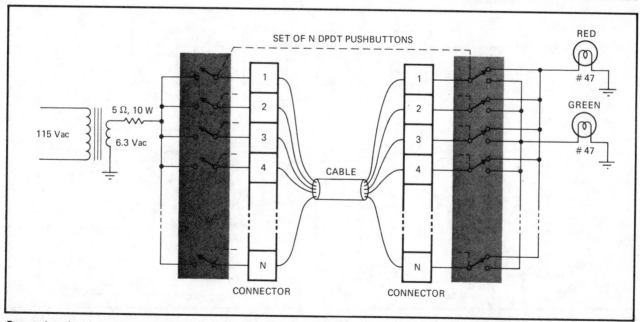

Comprehensive. Automatic cable tester can check circuits as fast as operator can push buttons, one circuit per second or faster. Red and green lamps indicate shorts, opens, transpositions, and misroutings of conductors in even the most complex cables.

Logic circuit tests wiring assemblies

by Steven Graham
Parsippany, N. J.

Before shipment or installation of wiring harnesses, the completed assemblies must be checked to verify that each pin of the connector at one end is wired to the corresponding pin of the connector at the other end. Open circuits, short circuits, and crossed wires can quickly be detected and identified by a testing circuit consisting of a pulse generator, a shift register, some gates, and light-emitting diodes. This circuit, shown in Fig. 1, provides an inexpensive and effective replacement for stepping switches, ohmmeters, and expensive analyzers.

To check a wiring assembly, the test-station operator plugs the two connectors into the test fixture, presses the CLEAR button if any of the LEDs is on initially, and then presses the START button. If the harness has been wired correctly, the LEDs turn on and off sequentially. Crossed wires are indicated when the LEDs come on out of sequence. A short circuit causes two LEDs to light simultaneously. An open circuit turns the LED on as soon as the harness is connected.

The circuit diagram shows that the 555 timer is connected as a free-running multivibrator with a frequency of a few hertz. The pulse train from the 555 clocks the flip-flops to shift the high starting pulse down the line, feeding a high input to each NAND gate sequentially.

If a wire in the harness is not connected, so that the input to a NAND gate is not connected to its flip-flop, that gate stays high all the time (even when the CLEAR button is pushed), and the LED stays on. If the wire bundle contains N wires, then N flip-flops and N LEDs are required. The 1-microfarad capacitor and the two resistors connected to the 555 may be changed to increase or decrease the test rate.

This circuit has been used for more than a year to check 12-wire jumper harnesses. It could be refined so that the LEDs turn on sequentially and stay on if the wiring is correct, and a latch could halt the sequential shift when a fault is located. The operator could do other things while the test proceeded; this improvement would be especially useful for many-wire harnesses. ☐

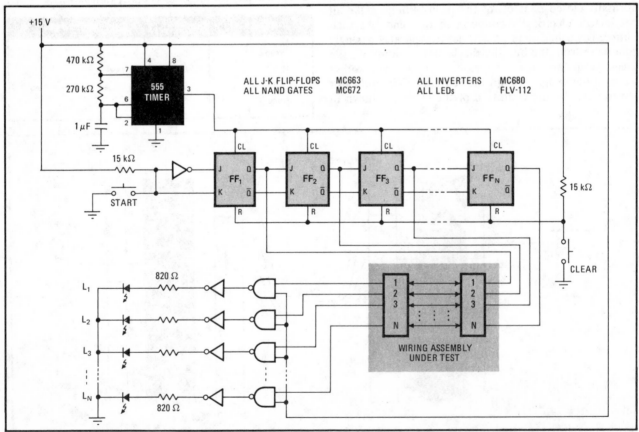

Flashing the word. Test arrangement checks feed-through wiring between two connectors on harness of N wires. Correct continuity is indicated by LEDs flashing on and off sequentially. Crossed wires cause LEDs to flash out of sequence, a short circuit makes two LEDs flash simultaneously, and an open causes a LED to glow continuously. Although high-threshold-logic elements are shown, TTL is satisfactory.

Timer ICs and LEDs form cable tester

by L.W. Herring
Showco Inc., Dallas, Texas

Recent developments in integrated circuits and light-emitting diodes make it possible to build a cable-fault indicator that is both inexpensive and compact. A tester of this sort is a convenient time-saving accessory to have on hand if you must periodically check a number of test and interconnection cables.

The circuit, which can fit into a small box, makes use of the versatile 555-type timer IC and single-package two-color LEDs. It can be designed to test from two-wire to 10-wire cables. It nicely indicates which lines are open, shorted, or OK on a simple readout panel. Since each line is tested and indicated individually, faulty cables are quickly located and, therefore, easy to repair.

The circuit's clock is constructed with several 555-type timer ICs, operating as a ring timer. As each timer turns on in sequence, a positive pulse is applied to each of the lines under test. For a maximum of four lines, therefore, at least four timer ICs will be needed to satisfy the clock requirements.

The other section of the tester contains the LED indicators. For each line under test, there is a differential transistor pair driving a two-color red/green LED. With the hookup shown, red indicates a short, and green indicates an open. (The newer red/yellow LEDs might be a little less confusing for the display than the red/green LEDs.)

Each differential pair looks for clock pulses at two places—obviously, each end of the cable. If the same pulse is at both ends of the same line, the differential pair remains balanced, and the LED for that line will not glow. But if the clock pulse appears only at the clock end of the line, the differential pair becomes unbalanced and forces current through the green (or yel-

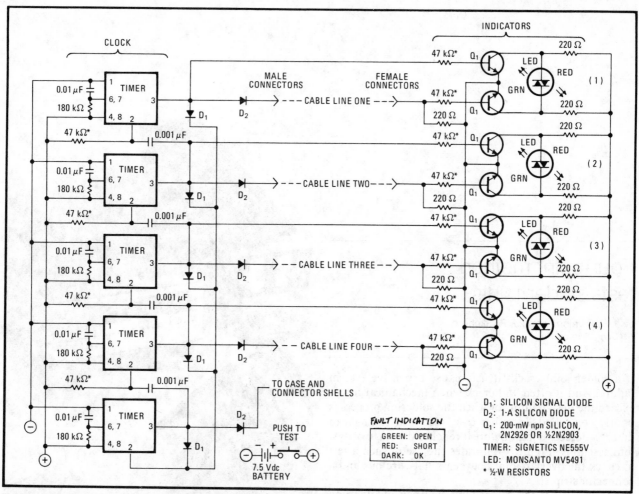

Finding cable faults. Compact tester checks cables for open-circuit or short-circuit conditions. A differential transistor pair at one end of each cable line remains balanced as long as the same clock pulse—generated by the timer ICs—appears at both ends of the line. A clock pulse just at the clock end of the line lights a green light-emitting diode, and a clock pulse only at the other end lights a red LED.

311

low) diode, indicating that the line is open.

Likewise, if a pulse appears only at the indicator end of the line, the differential pair tilts the other way, causing a reverse current and making the red diode light to show a short. When both LEDs remain dark, the cable line is OK.

The connectors on the cable lines introduce another possible fault—a short to the connector shell. This can be checked by adding another position to the clock and applying this additional clock pulse to the case of the tester. (The tester case cannot be tied to the positive supply as a solution, since the duty cycle of the LED is undesirably increased to 100%.) When there are more connector pins than there are lines to be tested in a given cable, the open indication on the unused pins can just be ignored.

The timing component values indicated for the timer

ICs set the clock pulse width at 2 milliseconds, which is fast enough to prevent lamp flicker, but not so fast as to cause capacitive coupling problems on long cables. (Cables as long as 500 feet can be tested.) The input to the differential pairs can be loaded to indicate a fault on high-resistance connections, but a lower value of resistance will then be needed to indicate a short.

The diodes in the clock section prevent a short from resetting the timers. The clock can also be implemented with an oscillator and a ring counter or, alternatively, with flip-flops and a one-of-10 or one-of-16 decoder.

Nickel-cadmium batteries are used to power the tester to avoid the problems of line-operated equipment. Over-all cost can be lowered by building the tester with discrete LEDs in place of the dual LEDs and by using penlight batteries. The tester becomes impractical for cables containing more than 10 wires. □

Four-point method tests solder joints

by J. R. Pivnichny and J. R. Skobern
IBM Corp., Endicott, N.Y.

If a solder joint cracks it may cause expensive system failure. And it often will crack when mechanical forces exceed the design limits or when the soldering process is poorly controlled. In either case, electrical testing can detect a defective joint before it reaches the stage of system assembly. Figure 1 illustrates the use of such a test to check the overlap joint between a flat-wire bus and a connector strip.

The quality of the solder joint between overlapping metal strips can be monitored with a four-point (or four-probe) resistance-measurement technique (Fig. 2). The output and return leads of a constant-current

1. Test arrangement. Measurement tests joint between bus and connector. Soldered assembly, in jig, is shown close up in Fig. 4.

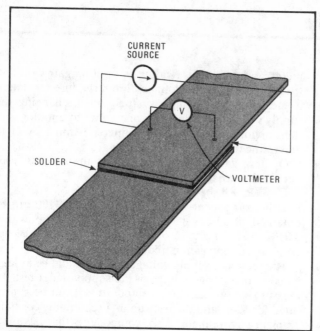

2. Solder joint. Four-point measurement monitors quality of connection between overlapped metal strips. Constant-current source drives current into and out of one strip; voltmeter measures drop between two points adjacent to current probes. Voltage indicates resistance to current spreading through solder to second strip.

3. Current flow. Section views through metal strips and solder joint show how quality of joint affects current spreading. (Scale of drawings is distorted, magnifying thickness of solder layer for clarity.) Good connection allows conduction through both metal strips, presenting low resistance to current flow and producing low voltage drop. Cracked joint restricts current flow and produces voltage drop that is typically three times as great as for good joint.

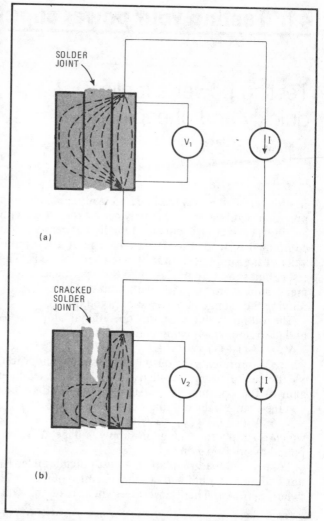

source are attached to one strip near the solder joint. The path for current flow includes the conductors on both sides of the joint and the solder interface between them. Voltage drop is measured between two points close to the current probes. This, divided by the known constant current, indicates the resistance between the two points.

A good solder joint allows current to flow through the solder and into the second metal strip (Fig. 3a). This spreading of the current produces a low resistance between the voltage-monitoring points. A cracked joint, however, interrupts the current path to the adjacent conductor (Fig. 3b). The constricted current path increases current density and hence the apparent resistance at the monitoring points.

A typical test arrangement uses a current of 100 milliamperes. The resistance values for good joints lie within 10% or 15% of an experimental average value, but a defective solder joint has a resistance that stands out as a 300% increase over the average level. Therefore, limits for go/no-go testing are readily established. Photographs of a working test arrangement are shown in Figs. 1 and 4.

4. Application. This flat-wire bus has been soldered to a beryllium-copper connector strip that has eight terminal points. The connector strip will be used to join the bus to a pc board, but first the quality of the solder joint is checked by using four of the terminal points as measurement probes. Current source is connected to the two outermost points; digital voltmeter is attached to the next two in.

Testing power supplies quickly and cheaply

by L. Tatapudi
Washington State University, Pullman, Wash.

In only a few minutes, the line and load regulation of a precision regulated power supply can be measured with an inexpensive test circuit. Usually, expensive test equipment is needed to detect a change of a few millivolts in the supply's output of a few tens of volts. The test circuit shown, (parts less than $30), permits accurate measurements to be made with a dc voltmeter by amplifying the change in power-supply voltage.

The output voltage of the operational amplifier is nulled to zero by adjusting potentionmeter R_P.

$$V_o = V_2(1+G) - V_1 G$$

where V_1 represents the output of the supply under test, V_2 the null reference voltage, and G the closed-loop gain of the op amp. If the supply's load and/or line voltage changes, the op-amp's output becomes:

$$V_o = V_2(1+G) - (V_1 - \Delta V_1)G = \Delta V_1 G$$

which is simply the change in supply voltage, ΔV_1, amplified by op-amp gain G.

To measure load regulation, adjust potentiometer R_P until a null is obtained at the circuit's output with switch S_1 open. Then close the switch, read the volt-meter, and divide this reading by op-amp gain G to find the change in supply voltage. Similarly, line regulation is measured by leaving switch S_1 open, changing the supply's ac line voltage fron one value to another, and then dividing the resulting voltmeter reading by G to determine the supply's output change.

Op-amp gain, of course, is simply the ratio of feedback resistance to input resistance:

$$G = (R_f + R_{fP})/R_1$$

For the component values noted, a gain of 100 can be obtained. The circuit equations are accurate within 0.01%, even for a gain of 1,000, provided that the op-amp's open-loop gain is about 100 decibels.

The reference supply voltage, V_{REF}, should be at least equal to the output voltage of the supply under test. To' measure supply stability, a standard cell can be substituted for V_{REF} and the test run in a reasonably constant ambient environment. Also, components that have low temperature drift should be chosen.

Measuring the supply's temperature coefficient is similar to the regulation measurement. The test circuit should be removed from the test power supply and kept at a reasonably constant ambient temperature.

If an op amp with a drift of 2 microvolts/°C is used, and if temperature varies by 50°C, then the circuit's offset voltage drifts by 10 μV. This change is considerably less than the output-voltage shift of most precision supplies over an eight-hour period or over a temperature range of 0°C to 70°C. The error introduced by the circuit, therefore, becomes practically negligible. □

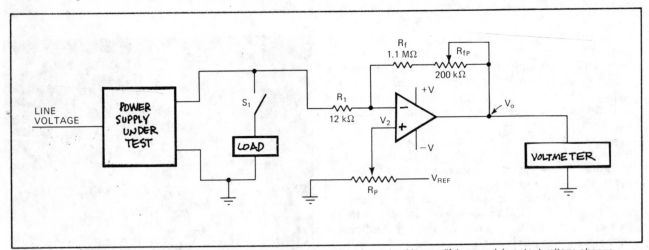

Regulation check. Power-supply line and load regulation can be accurately determined by amplifying supply's output voltage change.

Electronic load aids power-supply testing

by M.J. Salvati
Sony Corp. of America, Long Island City, N.Y.

An electronic load for testing the static and dynamic characteristics of small- to medium-sized power supplies can be assembled for a parts cost of about $12. The tests include voltage regulation (by either static or dynamic techniques), ripple vs current drain, transient response, and temperature vs current drain.

The device can provide a static (dc) load of 1–250 milliamperes or a dynamic (ac) load of up to 1 ampere

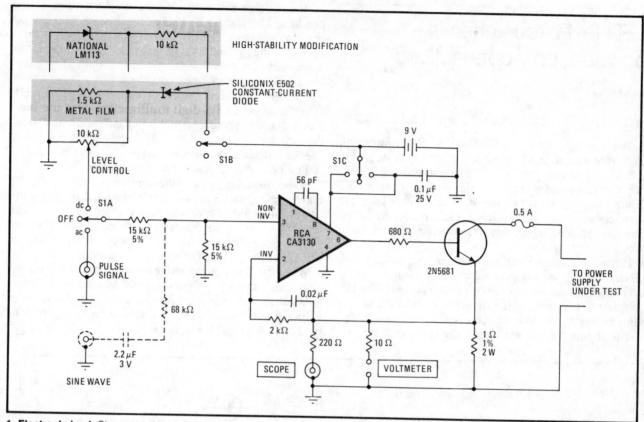

1. Electronic load. Characteristics of a power supply are tested with this circuit, which controls current delivered by the supply. Regulation, ripple, transient response, and temperature effects can be measured at currents up to 1 A peak or 0.25 A dc and voltages of 1.5 to 100 V.

peak current on power supplies with output voltages anywhere from 1.5 to 100 volts. The current drain in either mode is independent of output voltage of the power supply under test. The pulse-repetition rate in the ac mode can reach 30 kilohertz for a fast-rise pulse and 200 kHz for a sine wave. The average power dissipation is limited to 3 watts continuous and 5 W intermittent because of the small size of the switched transistor shown in the circuit diagram of Fig. 1. A higher-power transistor can be used if necessary, but switching speed may suffer.

As the diagram shows, the tester is essentially a variation of the classic current sink, one that can be modulated and in which the load current through the transistor is controlled by the CA3130 operational amplifier. The ability of the CA3130 to work from a single supply with ground-referenced input and its very low current drain allow the tester to be powered by a single 9-v transistor-radio battery. Because the device is self-powered, it can be used for testing very-low-voltage power supplies.

A switch at the input of the op amp selects either dc or pulsed operation of the supply. The dc mode uses an E502 constant-current diode in the reference-voltage source. It draws only 0.43 mA from the battery, and has a temperature coefficient close to zero. The voltage thus dropped across the level-adjustment potentiometer is very stable. If even greater stability is desired, the E502 and 1,500-ohm resistor can be replaced by the more expensive but superior LM113 voltage-reference diode and 10-kilohm resistor as shown in the diagram. The

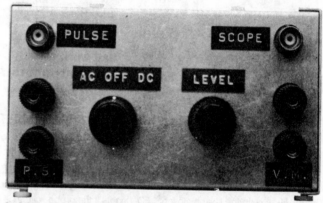

2. All packed up and ready to go. Complete electronic load circuit, including the 9-volt battery that powers it, is housed in a standard 3-by-2-by-5¼-inch aluminum box. Connectors can be seen.

modification shown in dashed lines allows superposition of sine-wave modulation on the dc bias for tests of output impedance vs frequency.

The current level is set by means of the level control in the dc mode and monitored by a dc voltmeter or a dc scope. The peak current level in the pulsed (ac) mode depends on the input-signal amplitude, and is monitored on a scope. The ratio of output current to input signal in this mode is 1 A/2 V peak. The conversion ratio at the scope and voltmeter terminals is 1 mV/mA in either mode. □

LED test circuit checks power-supply connections

by Harrel J. Tanner
Bellflower, Calif.

Before a circuit board is installed in new equipment, each pin should be checked to be sure that its power connections are in good order. Since this means checking the connections to both the supply voltage and ground lines, at least two measurements must be made for each pin. These continuity checks are uncomplicated but can become exceedingly time-consuming for a large system.

However, a simple test circuit based on light-emitting diodes lets you see whether voltage and ground connections exist after making only one measurement. The circuit, which is drawn in the diagram, operates from the same power supply as the circuit board it is monitoring.

The inputs for the test circuit are connected directly to the voltage-source and ground-return lines to be checked. The test probe is then touched to each pin on the circuit board. If only LED-1 glows, the pin is connected to the ground line. If only LED-2 glows, the pin is connected to the dc V_{CC} supply line. If both LEDs glow, an ac V_{CC} supply voltage exists at the pin.

There is a switch at the probe input to the test circuit. When this switch is open, the neon lamp lights if any line voltage is present. If the neon lamp remains dark, the switch can be closed and the circuit-board pin safely checked for dc power connections.

The power-supply input voltage to the test circuit is split so that only half the supply voltage ($V_{CC}/2$) reaches the LEDs. With the switch closed, if the pin voltage at the probe is zero (connected to ground), LED-1 is forward-biased as long as $V_{CC}/2$ is greater than the forward voltage of the LED. If supply voltage V_{CC} is present at the pin, LED-2 becomes forward-biased.

With the component values shown, this monitoring circuit checks for supply voltages of 28 v ac or dc and a line voltage of 115 v ac. Simply changing the resistor values permits other voltage levels to be monitored. A type 2N2107 transistor works well. □

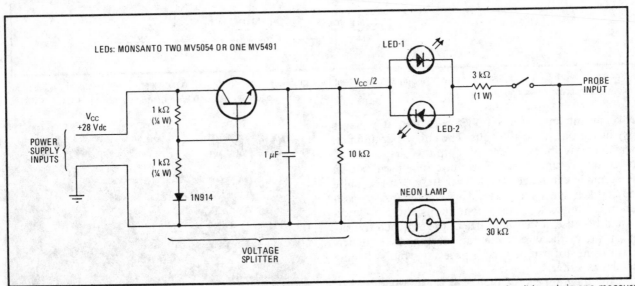

Power supply checker. Test circuit uses light-emitting diodes to check voltage and ground connections for circuit boards in one measurement. Here, with the switch closed, LED-1 lights if the probe voltage is at ground; LED-2 lights if the probe is at 28 V dc; and both LEDs light if the probe is at 28 V ac. With the switch open, the neon lamp lights if there is line voltage (115 V ac) present at the probe input.

Simple production testing of multioutput dc power supplies

by John Lawrence
IBM Corp., Kingston, N.Y.

Production testing of multioutput dc power supplies can be a time-consuming task. Typically, each output is tested separately, a digital voltmeter being used to monitor the voltage under various line and load conditions. There are usually only two operating conditions under which the output voltage must be measured to ensure that the power supply is operating properly—high line voltage with low load current and low line voltage with high load current—making it possible to design a simple inexpensive tester that requires a minimum of operator skill, and provides fast testing.

Basically, the tester consists of a pair of crowbar circuits and a pair of loads for each power-supply output (Fig. 1). Actually, one of the crowbar circuits is used in its standard configuration as an over-voltage detector (Fig. 2), while the other is modified for use as an under-voltage detector (Fig. 3). Each detector's output is fed to a panel indicator which provides an unambiguous "go" or "no-go" reading.

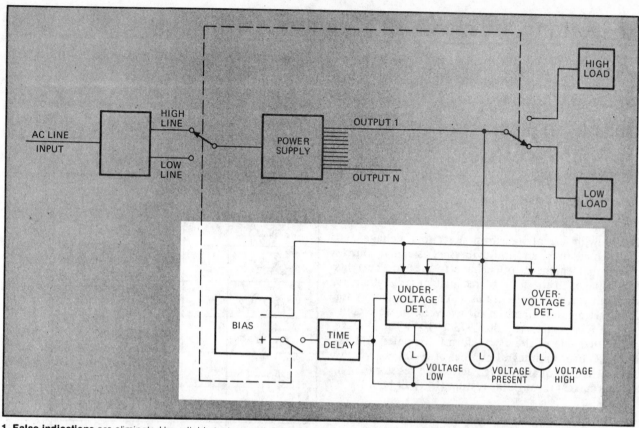

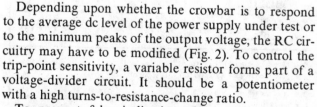

1. False indications are eliminated by reliable test setup that delays application of bias voltage until switching transients have settled.

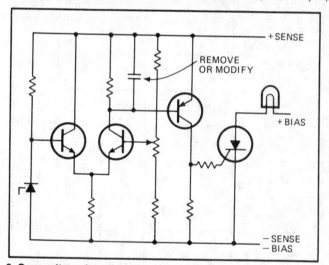

2. Over-voltage detector fires a lamp when sense input is too high.

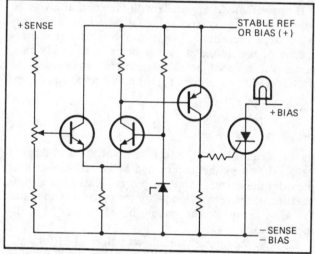

3. Under-voltage detector uses a modified over-voltage detector.

Depending upon whether the crowbar is to respond to the average dc level of the power supply under test or to the minimum peaks of the output voltage, the RC circuitry may have to be modified (Fig. 2). To control the trip-point sensitivity, a variable resistor forms part of a voltage-divider circuit. It should be a potentiometer with a high turns-to-resistance-change ratio.

To prevent false indications from line and load-switching transients, it is necessary to delay applying bias voltage to the monitoring circuits. The switching should be designed so that the bias is removed and reapplied each time the line and load are switched. This not only allows the monitoring circuits to ignore initial switching transients, but also turns off any SCRs that

have been previously fired.

If peak-to-peak ripple must also be monitored, a good approach is first to rectify the alternating current. The dc level is then amplified and fed to a level-detector which drives an appropriate indicator when the ripple exceeds some preselected value.

In addition to the fault indicators mentioned thus far, it is wise to include a voltage-present indicator as well. This will assure the operator that the equipment is in full working order. It is also a good idea to install test jacks so that the monitoring circuitry can be calibrated from time to time. □

Multiplying factors correct power for ac waveforms

by William D. Kraengel, Jr.
Valley Stream, N.Y.

The growing use of waveform generators, voltage-controlled oscillators, and multivibrators as signal sources means that engineers often have to measure currents and voltages in the form of rectangular, triangular, or sawtooth waves or pulse trains. (Conversion factors for voltmeter measurements on such waveforms were tabulated in *Electronics*, Aug. 30, 1973, p. 104.) The average power that one of these waveforms dissipates in a resistor (R) over an integral number of cycles is given by the root-mean-square voltage across the resistor (V_{rms}), the rms current through the resistor (I_{rms}), or both:

$$P = V_{rms}I_{rms}$$
$$= V_{rms}^2/R$$
$$= I_{rms}^2R$$

If measurements are made with meters that give true rms readings, the correct value for power can be calculated from the equations given above. But if the response of the ammeter or voltmeter is not truly rms, power values must be calculated from equations that contain a factor to correct for the meter response:

$$P = (V_m I_m) \times M$$
$$= (V_m^2/R) \times M$$
$$= (I_m^2R) \times M$$

In these equations, V_m and I_m are voltage and current values shown by the meters, and M is a multiplier that provides the correct value for power. Thus M is a combination of the conversion factor for meter response and the form factor for the waveform. Multiplier M is dimensionless.

The accompanying table shows values of M for various waveforms and various meters. For example, if a sawtooth voltage across a resistor is measured with a meter that responds to average voltage and is calibrated to rms for sine waves, then the power dissipated in the resistor is given by

$$P = (V_m^2/R) \times (32/3\pi^2)$$

For meters with a true rms response, M is always 1, so no column for true rms is included in the table.

If power is found from readings of both current and voltage meters, and the two meters have different responses, the power must be calculated from

$$P = V_m I_m (M_V M_I)^{1/2}$$

where M_V is the multiplier in the table that corresponds to the voltmeter response, and M_I is the multiplier that

MULTIPLIER (M) FOR POWER CALCULATION

Waveform	Ammeter or voltmeter response (see below)				
	I	II	III	IV	V
Sine:	1	1	$\pi^2/8$	1/2	1/8
Full-wave rectified sine:	1	1	$\pi^2/8$	1/2	1/2
Half-wave rectified sine:	2	1/2	$\pi^2/4$	1/4	1/4
Sine pulse:	T/t	t/T	$\pi^2 T/8t$	t/2T	t/2T
Segmental sine:	4E/C	E	$\pi^2 E/2C$	E/2	E/8
Full-wave rectified segmental sine:	4E/C	E	$\pi^2 E/2C$	E/2	E/2
Half-wave rectified segmental sine:	8E/C	E/2	$\pi^2 E/C$	E/4	E/4
Sine squared:	$12T/\pi^2 t$	3t/4T	3T/2t	3t/8T	3t/8T
Fractional sine pulse:	$4B/\pi A$	B/π	$\pi B/2A$	$B/2\pi$	$B/2\pi$
Triangle or sawtooth:	$32/3\pi^2$	2/3	4/3	1/3	1/12
Full-wave rectified triangle or sawtooth:	$32/3\pi^2$	2/3	4/3	1/3	1/3
Half-wave rectified triangle or sawtooth:	$64/3\pi^2$	1/3	8/3	1/6	1/6
Triangle or sawtooth pulse:	$32T/3\pi^2 t$	2t/3T	4T/3t	t/3T	t/3T
Square:	$8/\pi^2$	2	1	1	1/4
Dc and full-wave rectified square:	$8/\pi^2$	2	1	1	1
Half-wave rectified square:	$16/\pi^2$	1	2	1/2	1/2
Rectangular pulse:	$8T/\pi^2 t$	2t/T	T/t	t/T	t/T
Exponential pulse (critically damped):	$2T/\pi^2 e^2 t$	$e^2 t/2T$	$T/4e^2 t$	$e^2 t/4T$	$e^2 t/4T$

$A = [(\sin\alpha - \alpha\cos\alpha)/(1 - \cos\alpha)]^2$
$B = [2\alpha + \alpha\cos 2\alpha - (3/2)\sin 2\alpha]/(1 - \cos\alpha)^2$ $\alpha \equiv \pi t/T$ radians
$C = (1 - \cos\theta)^2$
$E = (\theta/180) - [(\sin 2\theta)/2\pi]$ θ = Conduction angle (degrees)
$e = 2.71828....$ $\pi = 3.14159....$

Ammeter or voltmeter response
I = Average-responding, calibrated rms for sines
II = Peak-responding, calibrated rms for sines
III = True average
IV = True peak
V = Peak-to-peak

corresponds to the ammeter used in the measurement.

The accuracy of some of these correction factors depends on how nearly the actual waveform approaches the ideal. Also, most ac meters do not give accurate readings for frequencies below 10 or 20 hertz, and they do not give any indication for dc. Thus the full-wave-rectified square wave may produce zero readings, depending upon the meter used. □

VOM with calibration circuit measures ignition dwell angle

by S.K. Wong
Torrance, Calif.

To extract the best gas mileage from an automobile engine equipped with the conventional Kettering ignition system, the distributor point gap or dwell angle must be set correctly from time to time. And, though the angle can be measured with a commercially available instrument known as a dwell meter, which has a scale calibrated in degrees, a cheap version may not be accurate, and an accurate one is expensive. The handy volt-ohm-milliammeter (VOM), however, can do the job just as well as the better dwell meters if a suitable calibration circuit is added to it.

A circuit for this function that costs about $5 in parts is diagrammed below. It includes a constant-current source and a voltage regulator so that the normal voltage variation of the car cannot affect the dwell-angle readings. Thus the accuracy of the VOM dwell meter is limited only by the accuracy of the VOM itself.

The circuit uses two of the four Norton operational amplifiers in a low-cost LM3900N integrated circuit. Since these amplifiers can operate from a single voltage supply anywhere in the range from 4 to 32 volts, they are well suited to this application where they tap their power from the low-voltage side of the ignition system.

Amplifier A_1 and transistor Q_1 constitute a constant-current source that provides a current of V_{D1}/R_4 (about 2 milliamperes) into the zener diode ZD_1 whenever a B+ supply voltage higher than the zener breakdown voltage is applied at points X and Y. This steady flow of current, in turn, maintains across the zener diode a constant reference voltage, V_{ref}, which is fed to the noninverting input of feedback amplifier A_2. Transistor Q_2 functions as a series pass regulator whose output (emitter) voltage, V_{cyl}, is controlled by A_2. The value of this voltage is

$$V_{cyl} = V_{ref}(R_9 + R_{10} + R_{11})/(R_9 + R_{10})$$

which cannot be higher than the B+ voltage. Hence if

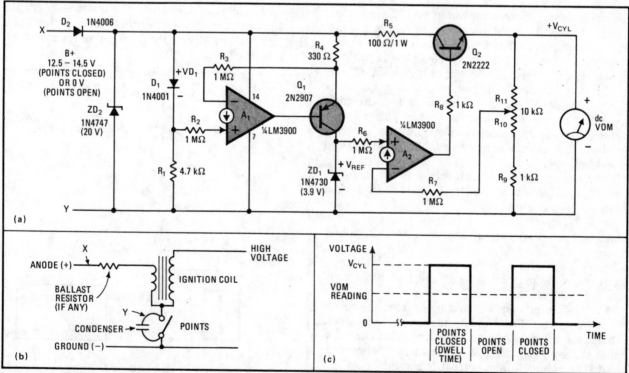

Dwell idea. Automobile distributor-point dwell angle can be measured with an ordinary VOM plus this circuit that costs about $5 to build (a). Peak voltage to meter is held constant by regulator; potentiometer is adjusted so that time-average voltage read on meter is easily converted to dwell angle in degrees. Circuit taps ignition system's primary voltage supply for power, so no other battery or power source is required. Protection against reversed connections and short circuits is built in. Calibration circuit is connected to ignition coil as in (b). For best gas mileage, dwell time is adjusted to give VOM reading that corresponds to the dwell angle prescribed by auto manufacturer (c).

the potentiometer (R_{10} and R_{11}) is adjusted to set V_{cyl} at a level substantially lower than the B+ voltage, variations of the latter have virtually no effect on the dwell-angle readings. Since the series pass voltage regulator (Q_2) has very low output impedance, operation is independent of the VOM input resistance.

For convenient and error-free dwell-angle readings on the VOM, a simple initial calibration is needed. This calibration is made by adjusting the potentiometer when the circuit is connected to the car at the X and Y points and the distributor points are closed. (An alternative method is to connect the X and Y leads of the circuit to the anode and cathode of the car battery, respectively, for calibration.) The voltage V_{cyl} is then set to the appropriate value shown in the table.

With the leads properly connected to the primary side of the ignition coil, the system is ready for making measurements. When the distributor points close and open repetitively while the engine is running, a train of rectangular voltage pulses with an amplitude of V_{cyl} is impressed upon the VOM. Because the VOM movement possesses mechanical inertia, the pointer cannot track

SETTING OF V_{CYL} FOR VARIOUS AUTOMOBILE ENGINES		
Number of cylinders in 4-stroke engine	Maximum dwell angle	V_{CYL}
8	45°	4.5 V
6	60°	6.0 V
4	90°	9.0 V

the pulses, so only an averaged voltage is indicated. This average voltage is effectively the dwell voltage. For example, a voltage of 2.7 v indicates a dwell angle of 27°. Rotating the point assembly then adjusts the dwell angle to the value suggested in the service manual for the particular model of automobile.

Diode D_2 and zener diode ZD_2 protect the circuit from accidental reversal of lead connections at X and Y and from high-voltage transients when the points open. Current-limiting resistors R_5 and R_8 protect transistor Q_2 and amplifier A_2 from overloading if the VOM leads are accidentally short-circuited.□

Converting a digital panel meter into a linear ohmmeter

by Jon L. Turino*
Xerox Corp., El Segundo, Calif.

For voltage and current measurements, digital panel meters are rapidly replacing analog meters in production test equipment. Resistance measurements, on the other hand, are still frequently being made with an analog meter, a resistance bridge, or a digital multimeter. But any standard voltage-type digital panel meter can be converted to a linear ohmmeter with the addition of a simple constant-current source. This not only eliminates many erroneous readings, but also makes a binary-coded-decimal output available for automated measurements.

The basic converter circuit is shown in the diagram. The value of the source resistor, R_S, for the field-effect transistor is computed from:

$$R_S = V_{GS}/I_D$$

where I_D is the drain current, and V_{GS} is the gate-source voltage:

$$V_{GS} = V_P[1 - (I_D/I_{DSS})^{1/2}]$$

where V_P is the pinchoff voltage, and I_{DSS} is the zero-gate-voltage drain current.

The V_{DD} power supply should be selected to provide 2 to 3 volts across the FET, plus the required gate-source voltage for constant-current operation, plus the maximum voltage needed across the resistance being measured. The value of drain current I_D should be set at 1 milliampere, or some multiple or submultiple of this, to minimize conversion mathematics.

If more than one resistance range is needed, a switch

to select different values of source resistance R_S can be added. A potentiometer that is twice the calculated value of R_S should be used instead of a fixed resistor. This permits the circuit to be calibrated and allows unit-to-unit variations in transistor parameters to be accommodated.

With the circuit shown, resistances from 10 ohms to 1,990 ohms can be measured with a 1-mA current source and a digital panel meter having a maximum full-scale reading of 1.99 volts. The test voltage for the resistors can never rise higher than 10 v, so that operator safety is assured and the front end of the meter will not be harmed. □

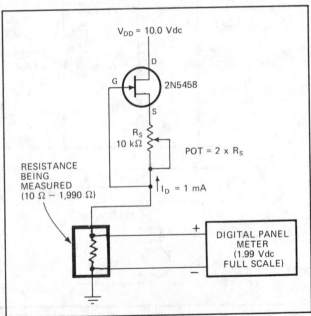

From voltage DPM to ohmmeter. FET constant-current source converts conventional voltage-measuring digital panel meter to linear ohmmeter. Resistance range, which can be made switch-selectable, is determined by value of source resistor R_S.

*Now with Tektronix Inc., Beaverton, Ore.

Dc differential voltmeter resolves 1 microvolt

by James Williams
Massachusetts Institute of Technology, Cambridge, Mass.

If you're dissatisfied with the choice of commercially available dc differential voltmeters, here's a high-performance unit that you can build yourself for about $800. Besides functioning as a high-resolution differential voltmeter, this instrument can serve as a picoammeter or an an adjustable voltage-reference source. It affords good stability, an absolute five-place accuracy of ±0.001%, and a resolution of 1 microvolt. It also provides an output for a ground-referenced stripchart recorder and overload protection for its nullmeter.

The voltmeter is intended for use with standard cells, temperature-compensated zener diodes, and other precision low-voltage sources. Its input voltage range is 0 to 10 v, and its operating temperature range is 20°C to 30°C.

In general, a high-resolution differential voltmeter makes a measurement in a classical potentiometric way. A stable voltage reference is placed across a variable voltage divider, whose output is applied to one input of a high-sensitivity voltmeter. The voltage to be measured is applied to the other input of the voltmeter. When the divider is adjusted to the same potential as the unknown voltage, the voltmeter will read zero. Since no current flows through the voltmeter during null, the unknown voltage sees an infinite impedance.

The block diagram of the voltmeter is given in Fig. 1. The instrument includes a high-stability solid-state voltage-reference source and a nullmeter having a full-scale resolution as fine as 5 μv. Since the input impedance of the nullmeter is known, the unit can also function as a highly accurate picoammeter for determining low-level offset and bias currents. If the meter goes off scale, there are indicators to show which way to bring the meter back on scale.

The output for the ground-referenced stripchart recorder is derived from the floating nullmeter without introducing leakage across either the voltage divider or the voltage to be measured. The buffer amplifier connected to the divider permits the voltmeter to be used as a variable voltage-reference source that can be set to within ±0.001%.

Briefly, here's how the instrument works. The ac line furnishes power to both the 125-v unregulated supply and the two ±15-v supplies, one of which is floating. The 125-v supply acts as a pseudo-current source while driving the voltage-reference source. The output of the reference, which is approximately 12.6 v, is resistively scaled to 10.000000 v (at 25°C) across the Kelvin-Varley voltage divider. The divider's output is buffered by an ultra-stable unity-gain amplifier that provides the REFERENCE OUTPUT terminal for the instrument. When the output from the divider equals the unknown voltage, the nullmeter will read zero so that the unknown is then equal to the divider setting.

For the ±15-v primary power supply (Fig. 2a), a monolithic tracking voltage regulator is wired in its standard configuration. The two 10-ohm resistors provide overload sensing, and the capacitors smooth out and prevent spurious oscillations. System ground is at

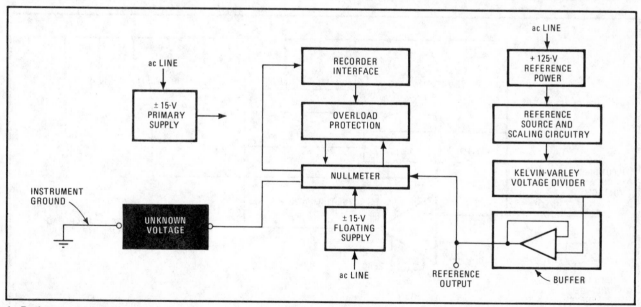

1. Performance plus trimmings. This high-resolution differential voltmeter takes advantage of modern solid-state technology to provide both accuracy and stability at reasonable cost. Its floating nullmeter, which is protected against overloads, assures a true differential measurement. The instrument also has a settable voltage-reference output, as well as a ground-referenced output for a stripchart recorder.

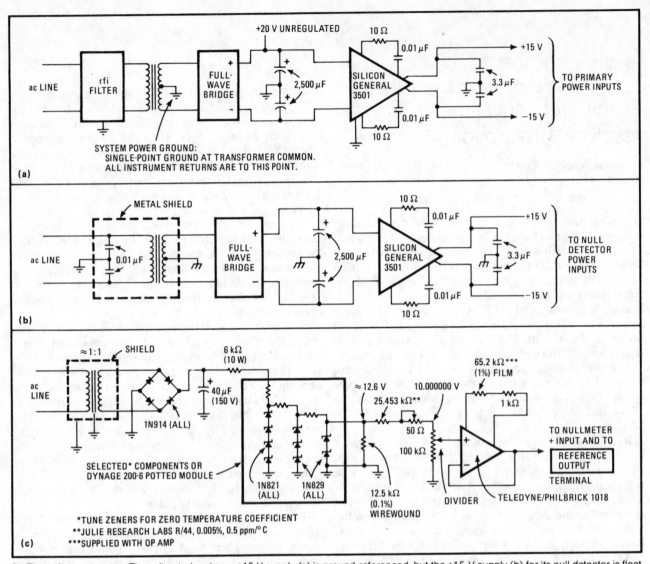

2. The voltage sources. The voltmeter's primary ±15-V supply (a) is ground-referenced, but the ±15-V supply (b) for its null detector is floating. The ultra-stable reference source (c), which is used to match the unknown voltage, contains an array of specially selected zeners.

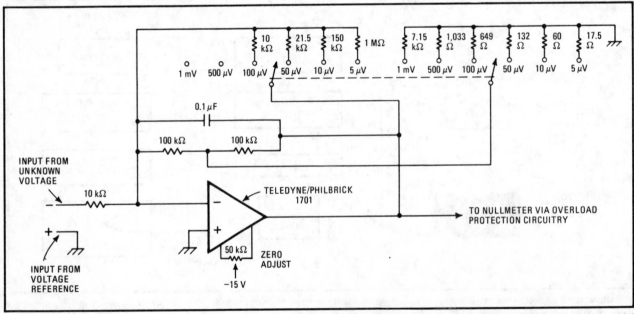

3. Precision null detector. A chopper-stabilized amplifier is at the heart of the instrument's null detector. A T-type feedback network, which is used to set amplifier gain, minimizes leakage problems and keeps the sizes of the feedback resistances at practical levels.

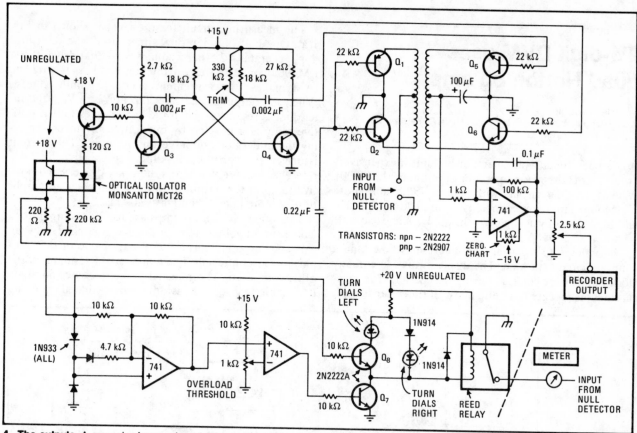

4. The outputs. A ground-referenced output for a stripchart recorder is developed from the null-detector's output by isolating the floating detector with an optical coupler. LED indicators show which way to null the meter. The reed relay disconnects the meter during overloads.

the transformer common, and all common power returns are brought to this point. There are no common power bus lines in the instrument—a precaution that must be taken to avoid corrupted grounds. Moreover, an rfi filter is used to block spikes from the ac line. A similar circuit, (Fig. 2b), but one with a floating ground, is used for supplying the instrument's null detector.

The voltage-reference source (Fig. 2c) is powered by the voltage derived from the transformer and its rectification components. The cascaded temperature-compensated zener diodes are specially selected for optimum matched parameters and are aged to produce stabilities greater than those of unsaturated standard cells. But a commercially available module can be used instead, if desired.

The reference output is scaled to 10 V across the divider. An ultra-stable, low-bias-current op amp buffers the output of the divider for the instrument's nullmeter input and its REFERENCE OUTPUT terminal. The output current for the voltage reference can range from 0 to 3.5 milliamperes. Its stability is ±1 ppm for a 10% shift in line voltage, ±2 ppm for a 1°C change in operating temperature, and ±5 μV maximum over a 24-hour period.

The instrument's null detector (Fig. 3) is designed around a chopper-stabilized amplifier. Since it is powered by a floating supply, this amplifier sees a true differential signal at its inputs. The power common line is used as one of the inputs, but the power and signal common returns are separated to minimize grounding loops and noise. A T-type feedback network sets amplifier

gain, helps to hold feedback resistances to practical levels, and avoids leakage problems.

Overload protection for the meter movement and the output for a stripchart recorder are provided by the circuit of Fig. 4. The ground-referenced recorder output preserves the integrity of the nullmeter's true floating ground and simplifies the interfacing of the recording device.

The input for this circuit, which is the output from the null detector, drives the pulse-amplitude modulator formed by the transformer and transistors Q_1 and Q_2. The signal is chopped at the frequency set by the multivibrator made up of transistors Q_3 and Q_4. The chopping drive signal must be fed through an optical isolator because the multivibrator, which is the source of the chopping signal, is instrument-grounded. The signal that appears at the transformer secondary is demodulated synchronously by transistors Q_5 and Q_6. The multivibrator's trim resistor is selected to give a symmetrical swing about zero at the demodulated output. This output is then amplified for the recorder hookup.

The input for the overload protection circuit is taken from the signal developed for the stripchart recorder. The first stage of this circuit takes the absolute value of the recorder output. When the meter is overloaded, transistor Q_7 conducts. If the base voltage of transistor Q_8 is high, the meter is off scale in its plus zone, and the TURN DIALS LEFT indicator will light. If Q_8's base is low, the meter is off scale in its minus zone, and the TURN DIALS RIGHT indicator will come on. In either case, the reed relay disconnects the meter during an overload. □

2½-digit DVM uses quad Norton op amp

by Erdal Musoglu
Medical Computing Center, Free University of Brussels, Belgium

A compact digital voltmeter can be built inexpensively around a quad Norton operational amplifier (LM3900). It has a 2½-digit display with polarity indication and a 1-megohm input impedance, is accurate to within 1%, and is powered by a single 5-volt supply. The basic scale is chosen as ±1.99 V.

The voltage to be measured determines how long a counting circuit stays on. The display shows how many clock pulses were counted during that period. The measurement is repeated two and one-half times per second.

The measuring circuit for the DVM is shown in Fig. 1(a). One half of a 556 dual timer, used as a reset flip-flop, generates a 2.5-hertz square wave that drives the ¼ LM3900 connected as an integrator. (This is why the DVM makes a measurement every 400 milliseconds.) When the output of the reset flip-flop is $+V_{CC}$, the integrator is reset. But when the output goes to 0, a positive ramp is generated by integration of current entering the integrator's noninverting terminal. This current is driven through the 150-kilohm resistor by the 2.4-v reference voltage V_{ref} across the zener diode. Each positive ramp at the output of the integrator has an amplitude of more than 4 V and lasts 200 ms.

Two other Norton op amps are used as comparators. The dc input voltage to be measured is applied between V_{ref} and the noninverting terminal of one of the comparators after filtering. The noninverting terminal of the other comparator is connected to the reference point via a variable resistor that is adjusted so that there is no

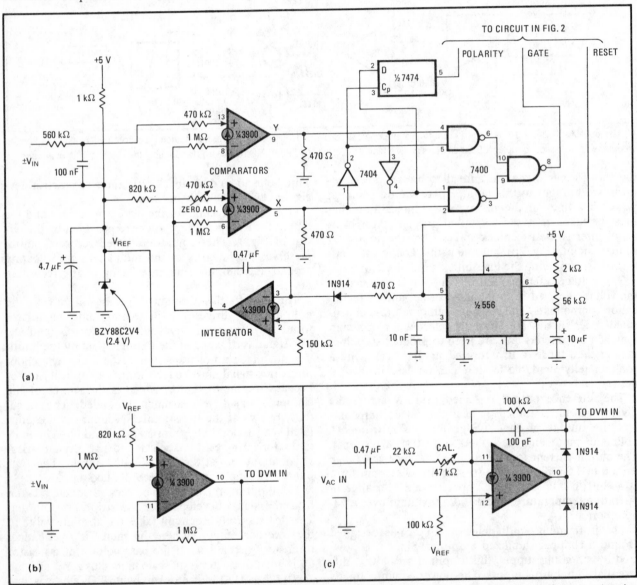

1. Measurement. Basic circuit for digital voltmeter (a) uses 2.5-Hz reset flip-flop to cycle integrator and comparators to generate gate pulse with duration proportional to voltage being measured. Gate pulse, polarity signal, and reset output are fed to counter and display portions of DVM in Fig. 2. If input voltage is referenced to ground, input stage (b) is used. For ac voltage measurement, converter (c) is added to circuit.

output gate pulse when $V_{in} = 0$. The inverting terminals of the comparators are driven by the integrator.

The outputs from the two comparators, X and Y, are applied to an exclusive-OR circuit. The XOR output is used to gate on the counter in the counting and display circuit, as shown in Fig. 2(a). The time that the gate is on is directly proportional to the amplitude of V_{in}. The XOR circuit is realized here using three NANDs and two inverters, for reasons of economy. Polarity information for the display circuit requires only one half of a 7474 dual D-type flip-flop.

The arrangement in Fig. 2(a) optimizes the package count for the counter, display, and clock of the complete DVM. Here the other half of the 556 timer is used as the clock generator. The nominal clock frequency is 2 kilohertz, and the meter can be calibrated with the 22-kΩ variable resistor that modifies this frequency.

Two one-shots, which have output pulses lasting 0.5 ms and 5 ms, respectively, are used for loading from and resetting the counters. The reset one-shot is activated by the leading edge of the reset flip-flop output that comes in from the circuit of Fig. 1(a), so the counters are reset immediately after the ramp ends. Because the reset time is quite long (5 ms), any spurious gate outputs that occur during the fall of the ramp are ignored by the counter circuits; the fall time of the integrator is less than 2 ms for the circuit of Fig. 1(a).

The total accuracy and stability of the DVM depend on the frequency stability of the clock generator and on the stability of the ramp's slope. If stable external components (e.g. polycarbonate capacitors and metal-film resistors) are used in these circuits, the least significant digit is in error by only ±1, so accuracy within 1% is obtained. Note that the frequency stability of the reset generator does not affect the accuracy or the stability of the DVM. To avoid error due to the bias current of the Norton amplifier, the source impedance must be less than 20 kΩ even though the input impedance of the DVM is 1 MΩ.

If ground-referenced signals are to be measured, the fourth Norton amplifier of the LM3900 package can be used as shown in Fig. 1(b). In this case, however, it is advisable to divide the input voltage by two—for example, by using a 2-MΩ resistor at the input of the circuit of Fig. 1(b) instead of 1 MΩ—and to have a nominal clock frequency of 4 kHz for better linearity.

The fourth amplifier of the package can also be connected as an ac-to-dc converter, as shown in Fig. 1(c), for measurement of ac voltages. □

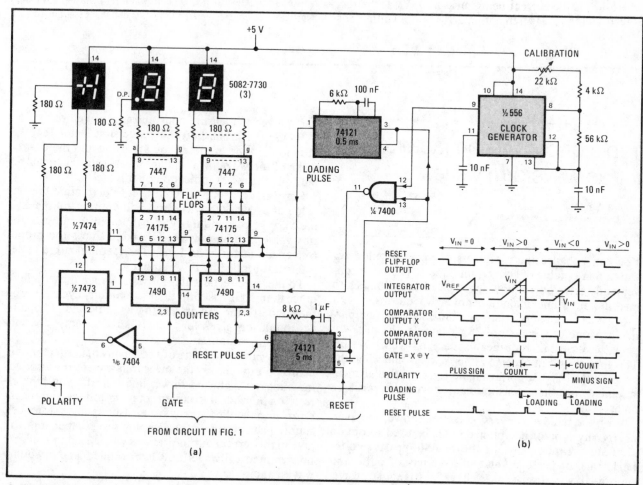

2. Display. In counter and display portion of digital-voltmeter circuit (a), clock pulses are counted by decade counters during gate pulse. After gate pulse, total count is loaded into D-type flip-flops that drive seven-segment displays via decoder-drivers. Counters are reset by 5-ms pulse from one-shot every 2.5 seconds for new measurement. Timing diagram (b) summarizes operation of DVM.

Measuring small currents with an ordinary voltmeter

by Robert J. Battes
Quantic Industries, San Carlos, Calif.

If it is necessary to measure extremely small currents only occasionally, the expense of a specialized instrument like an electrometer probably can't be justified economically. However, even semiconductor leakage currents and the input bias currents of FET-input operational amplifiers—on the order of nanoamperes and picoamperes—can be measured by a standard voltmeter, to within better than 5%. The meter should have a moderately high input impedance (approximately 10 megohms) and a reasonably good sensitivity rating (around 100 to 200 millivolts full scale).

The trick is to use the voltmeter's input attenuator as a calibrated current shunt, as shown in the figure. Then, only a single calculation is necessary to read nanoamperes or picoamperes directly from the voltmeter scale, since:

$$I_{test} = V_m/R_{in}$$

where I_{test} is the current being measured, V_m is the displayed voltage measurement, and R_{in} is the voltmeter's input resistance. The current is measured accurately, because voltmeter input attenuators are usually specified within ±5% of their nominal value.

As an example, assume the voltmeter being used is a standard economy-priced 3½-digit multimeter. The most sensitive multimeter current-measuring range usually found on such an instrument is 2.000 milliamperes full scale, providing a resolution of 0.001 mA, or 10^{-6} amperes. The voltmeter section of this type of multimeter usually has a sensitivity of 0.2000 volt full scale and an input impedance of 10 megohms. With the meter connected as shown, each 0.0001 v displayed on the meter will represent a current as small as 10 pA, or 10^{-11} A. When the meter is used this way, its current-measuring sensitivity is increased by five orders of magnitude. □

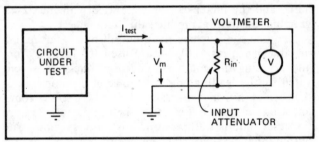

Applying Ohm's law. Nanoampere or picoampere currents can be measured accurately with a standard voltmeter by taking advantage of the tight tolerances of input attenuators of today's instruments.

Table of conversion factors for ac waveform values

by M.J. Salvati
Sony Corp. of America, Long Island City, N.Y.

You can enhance the usefulness of your ac voltmeter with a handy table of conversion factors. The table conveniently lets you employ any type of ac voltmeter to measure any value of a number of ac waveforms.

Most ac voltmeters accurately indicate only one particular value of a waveform, for example, the peak-to-peak, zero-to-peak, root-mean-square, or average value. This limitation can become rather bothersome when the proper meter is just not available for a particular measurement, or when nonsinusoidal waveforms must be measured.

With the table of conversion factors shown, however, nearly any type of ac voltmeter can be used to obtain accurate measurements of the peak-to-peak, zero-to-peak, rms, or average value of a variety of pulse and sinusoidal waveforms, as well as a triangular wave. Probably the most helpful are the factors given for the widely used average-responding rms-calibrated meter, since it causes the greatest confusion and error when it is employed to measure nonsinusoidal waveforms.

To use the table, find the conversion factor that applies to the type of meter you are using and the desired value of the waveform you are measuring. Then simply multiply the meter indication by this factor.

For instance, suppose you want to determine the rms value of a sawtooth waveform and your ac voltmeter is the average-responding type, calibrated to indicate the rms value of a sine wave. The table shows the proper conversion factor to be 1.038. The reading on the meter is then multiplied by this number.

To measure rectangular pulses having a duty cycle of other than 50%, first find their actual duty cycle (D) and then modify the meter reading as indicated. The conversion factors given for white (Gaussian) noise are only rough approximations.

The accuracy of some of these conversion factors depends on how closely the measured waveforms approximate ideal waveforms. Power-line distortion and the effects on non-ideal rectifiers may introduce significant errors into rectified sine-wave measurements. Moreover, simple peak rectifiers that employ series capacitors will give highly erroneous indications when used to measure nonsymmetrical waveforms like rectified sine or square waves, and pulses. □

WAVEFORM		VOLTMETER TYPE					
		Peak-to-Peak	True Peak	Peak-Responding, rms cal for sines	True rms	Average-Responding, rms cal for sines	True Average
SINE:	pk-pk	1.000	2.000	2.828	2.828	2.828	3.140
	0-pk	0.500	1.000	1.414	1.414	1.414	1.570
	rms	0.353	0.707	1.000	1.000	1.000	1.111
	avg	0.318	0.637	0.900	0.900	0.900	1.000
RECTIFIED SINE: (FULL WAVE)	pk-pk	1.000	1.000	1.414	1.414	1.414	1.570
	0-pk	1.000	1.000	1.414	1.414	1.414	1.570
	rms	0.707	0.707	1.000	1.000	1.000	1.111
	avg	0.637	0.637	0.900	0.900	0.900	1.000
RECTIFIED SINE: (HALF WAVE)	pk-pk	1.000	1.000	1.414	2.000	2.828	3.140
	0-pk	1.000	1.000	1.414	2.000	2.828	3.140
	rms	0.500	0.500	0.707	1.000	1.414	1.570
	avg	0.318	0.318	0.450	0.637	0.900	1.000
SQUARE:	pk-pk	1.000	2.000	2.828	2.000	1.800	2.000
	0-pk	0.500	1.000	1.414	1.000	0.900	1.000
	rms	0.500	1.000	1.414	1.000	0.900	1.000
	avg	0.500	1.000	1.414	1.000	0.900	1.000
RECTIFIED SQUARE: (HALF WAVE)	pk-pk	1.000	1.000	1.414	1.414	1.800	2.000
	0-pk	1.000	1.000	1.414	1.414	1.800	2.000
	rms	0.707	0.707	1.000	1.000	1.272	1.414
	avg	0.500	0.500	0.707	0.707	0.900	1.000
RECTANGULAR PULSE: ($D = X/Y$)	pk-pk	1.000	1.000	1.414	$1/D^{1/2}$	$0.9/D$	$1/D$
	0-pk	1.000	1.000	1.414	$1/D^{1/2}$	$0.9/D$	$1/D$
	rms	$D^{1/2}$	$D^{1/2}$	$1.414\, D^{1/2}$	1.000	$0.9/D^{1/2}$	$1/D^{1/2}$
	avg	D	D	$1.414\, D$	$D^{1/2}$	$0.9\, D$	1.000
TRIANGLE AND SAWTOOTH:	pk-pk	1.000	2.000	2.828	3.464	3.600	4.000
	0-pk	0.500	1.000	1.414	1.732	1.800	2.000
	rms	0.289	0.577	0.816	1.000	1.038	1.153
	avg	0.250	0.500	0.707	0.867	0.900	1.000
WHITE NOISE:	pk-pk	← See notes →					
	0-pk	← See notes →					
	rms	← See notes →			1.000	1.127	1.253
	avg	← See notes →			0.798	0.900	1.000

NOTES:
1. Apparent pk-pk noise (scope trace width) ≈ 6 rms units (for 99.5% probability of instantaneous noise peak exceeding this level)

2. Tangentially measured pk-pk noise ≈ 2 rms units

3. Apparent pk-pk noise ≈ 3 tangentially measured pk-pk units

Voltage-regulator IC
biases expanded scale meter

by Alan D. Wilcox
University of Virginia, Charlottesville, Va.

To monitor the state of charge of a standby storage-battery system, only voltages between 12 and 15 volts need to be read. A conventional test meter reading 0 to 15 v full scale will suffice, but readings can more easily be observed when the voltmeter has an expanded scale that reads from a minimum of 10 v to a maximum of 15 v.

One such expanded-scale circuit is shown in the figure. The battery provides a 10-v bias to the meter so that when a voltage source of 10 to 15 v is applied to the combination, the meter shows the difference of 0 to 5 v. But this arrangement is unsatisfactory, both because it must have a battery for operation and because its accuracy depends on the battery having a potential of exactly 10 v.

There is a better way. Since the voltage to be monitored will be above 12 v, a National Semiconductor LM723 voltage regulator can be used as shown in the figure to provide a stable 10-v bias. A 500-microampere meter and series resistor R_2 constitute the 0-to-5-v voltmeter. If the battery voltage should drop below about 11.7 v, regulation falls off, but this inaccuracy can be corrected by using a 1.5-v dry cell if readings below 12 v are necessary. The dry cell does not affect the accuracy of the meter calibration—it simply extends the reading range down to about 10.2 v.

The unit draws about 3 milliamperes and can be used continuously across the storage-battery system. The entire circuit can be constructed on a small circuit board and mounted on the terminal posts of the 500-μA meter.

The circuit is calibrated by applying 15 v to the input and adjusting R_1 for 10 v at the output of the 723. Then, R_2 is set for a full-scale reading on the meter. For the 500-μA meter, 200 μA corresponds to 12 v, 300 μA to 13 v, etc. Normal battery voltage reads near center scale, and small deviations can be seen at a glance. □

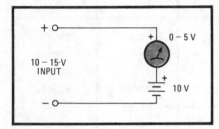

The right idea. This circuit displays very precise readings of 0 for 10-v input, 100 for 11-v input, and so on up to 500 for 15-v input. Adjustment of R_1 and R_2 calibrates it accurately. Circuit shown in inset also displays voltage in the 10–15-v range but requires a battery of exactly 10 v for accurate reading. Note that the 1.5-v dry cell used in the main circuit does not affect its calibration and is not necessary for readings above 11.7 v.

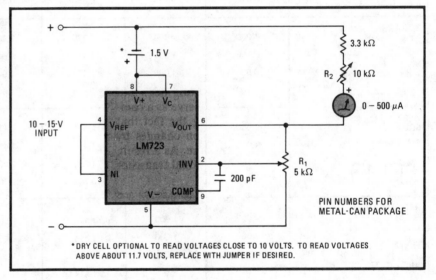

*DRY CELL OPTIONAL TO READ VOLTAGES CLOSE TO 10 VOLTS. TO READ VOLTAGES ABOVE ABOUT 11.7 VOLTS, REPLACE WITH JUMPER IF DESIRED.

Building your own digital voltmeter

by Don Aldridge
Motorola Semiconductor Products, Inc., Phoenix, Ariz.

Currently available low-cost digital-to-analog converters are making it possible to design digital voltmeters that are inexpensive and yet that are reasonably accurate. Here's a suggestion for building a 2-2/3-digit (0 to 255 counts) DVM for approximately $35.

The meter is a closed-loop system that uses a clocked binary counter feeding a digital-to-analog converter to produce a staircase ramp function. The output of the converter is compared to the unknown input signal, and the clock pulse is terminated when the input signal level and the staircase function level are equal.

Clock pulses are generated by two cross-coupled TTL NAND gates. The clock frequency is set for 330 kilohertz so that a maximum of 256 counts is provided in less than a millisecond. A high-speed clock like this allows the counting to be done without being detected in the display by the human eye. A fast clock also avoids the need to have latches store the previous total count while the system is sampling and counting. The clock pulses are applied to two sets of counters—a binary counter chain in the feedback loop that controls the converter, and a binary-coded-decimal counter chain that provides an easy interface with the seven-segment digital readouts.

The d-a converter generates an output sink current that is proportional to the value of the applied digital word. The maximum full-scale value of this current, which is typically 2.0 milliamperes is set by a reference voltage and a reference resistor. The converter's output current is compared with the current from an input buffer amplifier. This buffer amplifier provides the meter with a high input impedance while supplying an output current of up to 2.0 mA for comparison with the converter output.

A second amplifier acts as a high-gain comparator to stop the clock when the current ramp from the conver-

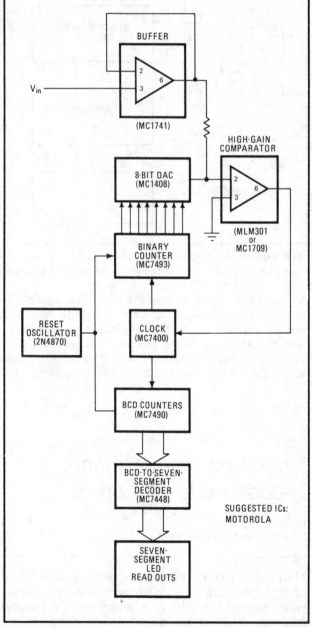

DVM outline. Economical but accurate 2-2/3 digit voltmeter takes advantage of today's low-cost digital-to-analog converters.

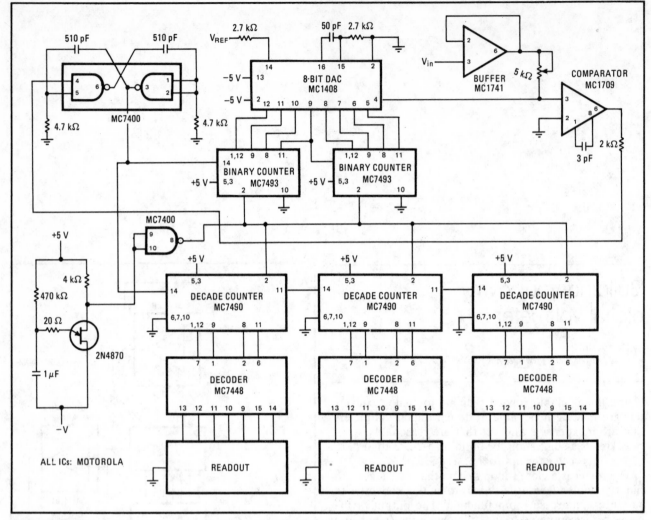

DVM details. Unknown input signal is compared to the output current from the digital-to-analog converter. When these two signals are equal, the clock is stopped. The same clock is used to drive the converter's binary counters and the display's BCD counters.

ter exceeds the current from the input buffer amplifier. A unijunction-transistor oscillator is used to reset both sets of counters so that the unknown voltage is re-sampled about every 0.5 seconds. And BCD-to-seven-segment decoders convert the outputs of the BCD counters to the proper format for the seven-segment light-emitting-diode displays.

For the components used here, the meter can measure up to 2.55 v (to within ±5 millivolts) in 10-mv steps. Different full-scale values can be obtained by using suitable input voltage dividers or by providing a fixed-gain, rather than a unity-gain, input buffer. □

Increasing voltmeter input impedance to 10¹² ohms

by J.R. Laughlin
San Jacinto College, Pasadena, Texas

Most commercial voltmeters, whether they have analog or digital readouts, provide relatively low input impedances, only on the order of 10 megohms, which makes accurate voltage measurements difficult for many circuits. But, by combining a couple of low-leakage field-effect transistors with an operational amplifier, you can raise the input resistance of your voltmeter to approximately 1,000,000 megohms.

Any dc voltage applied to the gate of the input FET will be reproduced at the circuit's output with sufficient amplitude to drive any type of voltmeter. If Motorola's type MC1436 op amp is used with a 35-volt supply, the circuit can handle input voltages as high as 30 v without an attenuator. If a wide frequency response is desired, Signetics' type 531 op amp can be used with a lower supply voltage. And, because of its low current drain, National's type LM308 op amp is best for battery-operated voltmeters.

A voltage divider to ground at the circuit's input permits higher voltage measurements to be made, but significantly lowers the circuit's input resistance. However,

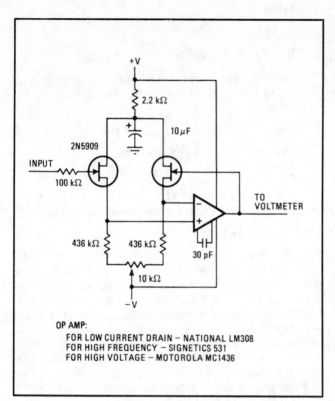

OP AMP:
FOR LOW CURRENT DRAIN – NATIONAL LM308
FOR HIGH FREQUENCY – SIGNETICS 531
FOR HIGH VOLTAGE – MOTOROLA MC1436

since FET gate-leakage current is in the low-picoampere range, the resistors used for the voltage divider can have values that are quite large without introducing significant errors. For example, a 1,000-megohm resistor to ground, along with another resistor having the appropriate value to obtain the desired ranging, will still provide an unusually high input resistance of several thousand megohms.

Great care must be taken to prevent extraneous leakage paths to ground. You will invariably degrade the circuit's input resistance considerably by using standard binding posts, or by providing a switching arrangement for the voltage divider, or by terminating the input FET's gate lead on a circuit board.

The circuit will handle ac voltages, although its input impedance will be reduced somewhat by stray capacitance. However, even this lowered input impedance will be much higher than what is usually available from commercial instruments.

The 10-kilohm potentiometer can be used to counteract op-amp offset and drift or to zero whatever offset voltage may result when very high resistance values are used for a voltage divider. □

High-impedance input. FET circuit lets you raise the input resistance of any voltmeter to 1,000,000 megohms, a factor of 10⁵.

Getting the most out of the digital multimeter

by Louis M. Xuster, Jr.
IBM Korp., Kingston, N.Y.

Your digital multimeter can be used in many more ways than the function switch on the front panel indicates. When it is set to measure resistance, the digital multimeter can be thought of as a precision current source plus a digital voltmeter, a combination that can be used for measurements other than determining resistance values.

To do these other jobs with your multimeter, you must first "calibrate" its ohms range settings. As an example, consider the Fluke model 8000A—its "calibration" table is:

Ohms range setting	Current	Full-scale voltage
200 Ω	5 mA	0.2 v
2 kΩ	5 mA	2 v
20 kΩ	0.1 mA	2 v
200 kΩ	1 µA	0.2 v
2 MΩ	1 µA	2 v
20 MΩ	0.1 µA	2 v

The meter's precision current source can now be used to check current meters or to bias a circuit. Also, the forward voltage through a pn junction can be measured at various currents. This is useful for determining whether a device is silicon or germanium, or to match the junc-

tion voltages of two or more transistors, or to match diodes, or to compute the effective series resistance of a junction from two readings.

You can even measure capacitance, including very large values. First connect the meter across the capacitor (observe polarity) and then short the capacitor with a jumper. When the meter reading goes to zero, remove the short and time the reading with a stopwatch. Stop the watch when the reading reaches 1,000. For the Fluke 8000A:

Ohms range setting	Each second is equal to:
200 Ω	10,000 µF
2 kΩ	1,000 µF
20 kΩ	100 µF
200 kΩ	10 µF
2 MΩ	1 µF
20 MΩ	0.1 µF

Additionally, you can use your multimeter to determine the internal resistance of a battery, one that supplies under 2 v, by computing the difference between two readings. Simply subtract the battery's no-load voltage from the voltage reading obtained on the 2-kilohm ohms range setting. This yields the battery resistance in kilohms. For instance, suppose the no-load voltage measures 1.533 v and the "2-kilohm" reading is 1.563:

1.563 – 1.553 = 0.010 kilohms = 10 ohms

Furthermore, you can take data for plotting a battery's charge/discharge curve. □

Op amp converts
DVM to fluxmeter

by Lawrence F. Marinaccio
Mine Safety Appliances, Evans City, Pa.

The flux and flux density in a magnet usually are measured with a search coil and either a ballistic galvanometer or a galvanometer especially designed for use as a fluxmeter. Such fluxmeters are delicate, require special provisions for mounting and leveling, and must be calibrated from a mutual-inductance standard or a standard magnet.

A direct-reading fluxmeter that does not use a galvanometer and does not require calibration can be made with two operational amplifiers and a digital voltmeter, as shown in the circuit diagram. When the search coil moves through the magnetic field, a voltage is induced across its terminals. This voltage is amplified in the first op amp, and integrated in the second op amp. The integrated output voltage is displayed on the digital voltmeter; the gain of the amplifier stage is adjusted so that the reading of the voltmeter directly represents the flux density in the magnetic field.

The voltage induced in an N-turn search coil cutting flux lines ϕ is given by Faraday's law:

$$e = N(d\phi/dt) \times 10^{-8} \text{ volts}$$

Therefore the number of flux lines cut in T seconds is

$$\phi = (10^8/N) \int_0^T e \, dt \text{ lines}$$

If the area of the loop is A square inches, the flux density B is ϕ/A lines per square inch. Flux density is commonly expressed in units of gauss (1 gauss = 6.44

lines/in.^{2}), so

$$B = (1.55 \times 10^7/NA) \int_0^T e \, dt \text{ gauss}$$

In the fluxmeter circuit, which has a voltage gain of (R_2/R_1) in the amplifier stage, the output from the integrator is

$$E_O = (R_2/R_1)(1/RC) \int_0^T e \, dt \text{ volts}$$

Therefore, the flux density is given by

$$B = (1.55 \times 10^7/NA)(R_1 RCE_O/R_2) \text{ gauss}$$

The value of R_1 is set at 3122 ohms to make the DVM read directly; therefore, for the circuit as shown,

$$B = 100 \, E_O \text{ gauss}$$

In the measuring circuit, the offset-null potentiometer R_N is adjusted to give a zero drift reading on the DVM. The search coil is then placed with its plane perpendicular to the flux in the magnetic field that is to be measured, and the reset switch is closed momentarily to ensure zero initial charge on capacitor C. Then the search coil is either rotated 90° or removed to a flux-free region. The resulting voltage pulse is amplified and integrated by the circuit to produce output voltage E_O that is displayed on the digital voltmeter. If the flux density is 1,000 gauss, the DVM reads 10 volts.

An unselected 741 op amp was used in this circuit, but if lower fields are to be measured and greater sensitivity is required, a low-drift op amp should be used. □

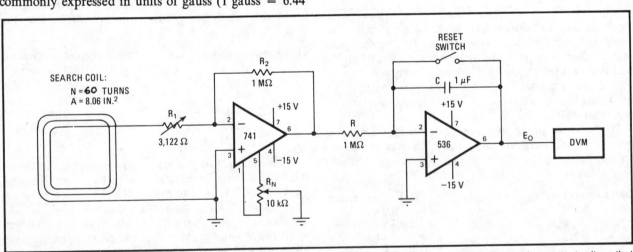

Fluxmeter. When search coil is flipped out of magnetic field, induced voltage pulse is amplified and integrated to produce output voltage that is displayed on digital voltmeter. Component values in circuit are chosen so that magnetic flux density in gauss is 100 times the DVM reading. This simple fluxmeter is more rugged than the galvanometers often used for magnetic field measurements, and it does not require calibration.

43. Pocket-calculator shortcuts

Using pocket calculators to square numbers directly

by Paul B. Wesling
Itel Corp. / ISS Division, Cupertino, Calif.

Calculation	Entry Operation	Display Register	K Register	K Operation
CALCULATOR OPERATIONS				
n^2	Enter number	n	Clear	—
	Hold K buttoh [X	n	n	Multiply
	+/=	n^2	Clear	—
n^3	Enter number	n	Clear	—
	Hold K button [X	n	n	Multiply
	+/=	n^2	n	Multiply
	+/=	n^3	Clear	—

The inexpensive four-function calculator with the constant register, which is now available for less than $100, can do addition, subtraction, multiplication, and division, as well as chain and mixed calculations. But, with a little know-how, it can be made to take reciprocals [*Electronics,* "Finding reciprocals easily with pocket calculators," Jan. 18, 1973, p. 186] and to square a number or raise a number to some integer power, without clearing or re-entering any of the data.

To square a number, especially a long one, the user usually writes it down, presses the multiply ($\times$) key, re-enters the number, and then presses the add/equal ($+/=$) key. An easier way is to load the number to be squared into the constant (K) register, then multiply the constant and display registers to get the answer. The steps are:

- Enter the number to be squared
- Press and hold down the K key
- Press and release the $\times$ key
- Release the K key
- Press and release the $+/=$

The square of the original number is now in the display register and can be used for additional computations.

To cube a number, hold the constant key down through both the multiply and add/equal operations, then release the constant key and press the add/equal once more. Again, the answer is in the display register. Any integer power of any number can be calculated by simply extending this method.

The table summarizes the operations required for squaring and cubing. □

Three-step shortcut for finding square roots

by James R. Whitmore
Whitmore Electronics Co., Miami, Fla.

Although a very useful tool, the popular four-function calculator is intended primarily for home use, and therefore, it cannot directly perform such sophisticated mathematical functions as finding square roots. However, here is a three-step technique that uses only the three functions of addition, subtraction, and division, which are always available on the home calculator, to determine square roots accurately.

Each step involves four mathematical operations, and the number of steps can be increased if greater accuracy is desired. With this technique, an initial approximate answer must be estimated—the closer this first approximation, the fewer steps are needed to compute a square root with at least four significant digits.

An example, in this case finding the square root of 624, will illustrate how to use the method. The approximate answer could be 20, 25, or 30. While the estimate of 30 is not too close to the correct answer, it is still within the range of this three-step technique. Here are the steps for obtaining the square root of 624 when the first approximation is 30:

Step 1:
- 624/30 = 20.8 (divide by 30)
- 20.8 − 30 = −9.2 (subtract 30)
- −9.2/2 = −4.6 (divide by 2)
- −4.6 + 30 = 25.4 (add 30)

Step 2:
- 624/25.4 = 24.566929
- 24.566929 − 25.4 = −0.833071
- −0.833071/2 = −0.4165355
- −0.4165355 + 25.4 = 24.983465

Step 3:
- 624/24.98 = 24.979983
- 24.979983 − 24.98 = −0.000017
- −0.000017/2 = −0.0000085
- −0.0000085 + 24.98 = 24.979992 (answer)

(If the estimate of 25 had been chosen as the first approximation, then only two steps would have been required to reach an accurate final answer.)

For an eight-digit calculator, the last step should contain at least four most significant digits in the divisor (24.98 in the example). If the calculator has a constant register, the answer can be easily verified without losing the data. □

Fast number conversion from any base to base-10

by Robert P. Harris
McDonnell Douglas Aircraft Co., St. Louis, Mo.

Changing numbers from a base-q (any base) system to a base-10 system need not be a long and tedious process. Moreover, if you are converting whole numbers, it's even possible to do the computation mentally.

The generalized polynomial for converting from any number to any base q is:

$$a_n q^n + a_{n-1} q^{n-1} + \ldots + a_1 q + a_0 q^0$$
$$+ a_{-1} q^{-1} + a_{-2} q^{-2} + \ldots + a_{-m} q^{-m}$$

Solving this polynomial can be a relatively lengthy process. Here's a simpler way to do the number conversion for whole numbers:

- Multiply the most significant digit by the base q.
- Add the next most significant digit.
- Multiply the result by the base q.
- Add the next most significant digit.
- Multiply the result by the base q.
- Continue through to the addition of the least significant digit.

Suppose the octal number $2,450_8$ is to be converted to a decimal number. The sequence of mathematical operations will be:

- $2 \times 8 = 16$
- $16 + 4 = 20$
- $20 \times 8 = 160$
- $160 + 5 = 165$
- $165 \times 8 = 1,320$
- $1,320 + 0 = 1,320_{10}$

This procedure is the inverse of the well-known technique for changing from a base-10 number to a base-q number. To make the conversion, you divide the base-10 number by the new base q and collect the remainders of each step of the division. □

Calendar computations: past, present, and future

by R. Wilson Rowland
Vitro Labs, Silver Spring, Md.

Once you master this technique, you will be able to name the day of the week for any given calendar date, besides being able to determine the number of days occurring between two given dates.

The technique is to compute the day number of a specific date by considering day 1 as Sunday, Dec. 29, in 1596 (and day 2 as Monday, Dec. 30, in 1596, etc.). The year of 1596 is used here for convenience—and it is close to 1582, the year in which our current calendar system was introduced.

When you divide this day number by 7, you will get a whole number and a fraction; this result represents the number of weeks since day 1. The fraction indicates what the day of the week is—1/7 is Sunday, 2/7 is Monday, . . ., and 0/7 is Saturday. If the day numbers are found for two different dates, the difference between these two numbers will yield the number of days between the two dates.

Correction terms, which are given in the tables, are used to account for the nonstandard lengths of months and centuries. When you read the month-correction table, be sure to remember that 1700, 1800, and 1900 were not leap years. (MC indicates a month correction, and CC indicates a century correction.)

Three equations are needed for a computation. A given date is expressed in terms of a YEAR, a MONTH, and a DAY. Using these numbers, first find:

$$day\ of\ year = (MONTH - 1) \times 30 + MC + DAY$$

Next, compute:

$$day\ number = [(YEAR - 1597) \times 365.25]_{truncated} + CC + day\ of\ year$$

To perform the truncation called for in this equation, simply subtract whatever fraction, if any, results from the multiplication by 365.25. And finally, find:

$$(day\ number)/7 = whole\ weeks + (day\ of\ week)/7$$

As an exercise, you can determine that the first Independence Day—July 4, 1776—occurred on a Thursday. Your computations should be: day of year = 186 and day number = 65,567 = 9,366 + (5/7). For accurate answers, your calculator must have eight digits. □

CENTURY CORRECTION				
Year	1597–1700	1701–1800	1801–1900	1901–2100
Correction	3	2	1	0

MONTH CORRECTION												
Month	January	February	March	April	May	June	July	August	September	October	November	December
Leap year correction	0	1	0	1	1	2	2	3	4	4	5	5
Other year correction	0	1	−1	0	0	1	1	2	3	3	4	4

Storing two constants instead of just one

by J. Snaper
U.S. Navy, Fleet Post Office, New York

Another capability of the HP-35 calculator is its ability to store and utilize two constants—a handy computational aid for performing calculations like dual conversions of long strings of numbers.

The calculator's operating manual describes how to make use of only a single constant in the store/recall register. As an example, the manual gives this method:

- Key-in conversion factor
- Push STORE
- Key-in numbers for conversion
- Recall conversion factor
- Operate arithmetic key for answer

For each additional number to be converted, the conversion factor must be recalled, making the operation a little unwieldy for large strings of numbers.

A simpler and more convenient method is to fill the calculator's memory stack with the conversion factor by pushing the ENTER key three times. This causes the factor to recirculate in the memory and become a constant, allowing the store/recall register in effect to store a second conversion factor.

The improved two-constant technique becomes:

- Key-in conversion factor
- Push ENTER key three times
- Enter number for conversion
- Operate arithmetic key for answer, push CLx key

The calculator is now programed with the conversion constant and additional conversions can be carried out indefinitely in a simple two-step operation:

- Key-in number for conversion
- Operate arithmetic key for answer

If desired, a second conversion factor can be entered in the STORE register and recalled after the first conversion is complete. In this way, the double conversion of a long string of numbers can be done very simply and efficiently:

- Key-in number for conversion
- Operate arithmetic key
- Recall second conversion factor
- Operate arithmetic key for answer

Of course, the HP-35 calculator greatly simplifies root computations, as many users probably already realize. The square-root function is a direct push-button operation, but there is no key for finding cube or nth roots directly. A short program does the job:

- Key-in root desired
- Operate $1/x$ key
- Key-in number for which root is desired
- Operate x^y key for answer □

Doing statistical analysis with a single data entry

by Walter V. Manka
American Precision Industries Inc., Delevan Div., East Aurora, N.Y.

Engineers frequently find it necessary to determine the mean, variance, and standard deviation of experimental data. Classically, this statistical information is computed separately so that the data must be entered more than once. With the HP-35 calculator, however, the mean, variance, and standard deviation can be found with a single entry of the data.

The table outlines a method for solving a convenient form of the equation for the standard deviation:

$$S.D. = [[\Sigma(D_i)^2/N] - [\Sigma D_i/N]^2]^{1/2}$$

where D represents the data value, N represents the number of data values, and i varies from 1 to N. With this equation, data values must be entered only once, and the mean, variance, and standard deviation can be read directly from the calculator's display. Furthermore, the need for writing down calculations is minimal. □

MEAN, VARIANCE, AND STANDARD DEVIATION			
Enter each data value with this key sequence		After the last data value is entered execute this key sequence	
KEY	DISPLAY	KEY	DISPLAY
(DATA)$_i$	D_i	N	N
ENTER ↑	D_i	÷	$\Sigma (D_i)^2/N$
ENTER ↑	D_i	RCL	ΣD_i
RCL	ΣD_{i-1}	N	N
+	ΣD_i	÷	MEAN
STO	ΣD_i	ENTER ↑	MEAN
R ↓	D_i	X	$(\Sigma D_i/N)^2$
ENTER ↑	D_i	−	VARIANCE
X	$(D_i)^2$	$\sqrt{}$	STANDARD DEVIATION
+	$\Sigma (D_i)^2$		

Calculator totals two sets of numbers simultaneously

by Jack Greenfeder
Public Service Electric and Gas Co., Newark, N.J.

Quantities representing two different categories of data must often be totaled when one entry for each category appears on various pages of a log or printout. For example, if you wanted to add kilowatt hours and peak kilowatt demand that are both recorded on several monthly bills, you could list the amounts in two separate columns and total them separately. However, these amounts can be totaled simultaneously on a moderately priced pocket calculator that has a combined memory entry and summation key (M+ on the Bowmar MX-90, TI-2550, or equivalent) and a clear/entry (CE) key.

To simultaneously add two columns, A and B, with values A_1, A_2, . . . and B_1, B_2, . . . , the trick is to sum all A values in the normal manner while entering the B values into memory. In entering the values, the basic sequence of keys is: A_1, +, B_1, M+, CE. Keys A_1 and + prepare the calculator to add to number A_1 any number that is followed by a function such as +, X, or =. Pressing B_1 and M+ performs no function except to display B_1 and store it in memory. Pressing CE clears B_1 as if a mistake had been made, leaving the display as it was before B_1 was pressed. Pressing A_2 and + adds A_2 to A_1 within the main register, and then pressing B_2, M+, and CE adds the number B_2 to B_1 in the memory without affecting the column A summation. The total that is in the memory can be displayed at any time by pressing the memory retrieval (MR) key. The display can then be returned to its previous condition by the CE key.

For example, the totals of the two columns in the box can be found by following this sequence:

A	B
A_1 = 2	B_1 = 1
A_2 = 4	B_2 = 3
A_3 = 6	B_3 = 5
A_4 = 8	B_4 = 7
A_5 = 10	B_5 = 9
A_6 = 12	B_6 = 11
A_7 = 14	B_7 = 13
ΣA = 56	ΣB = 49

STEP	QUANTITY	KEY	DISPLAY
1	A_1	2	2
2		+	2
3	B_1	1	1
4		M+	1
5		CE	2
6	A_2	4	4
7		+	6
8	B_2	3	3
9		M+	3
10		CE	6
11	A_3	6	6
12		+	12
13	B_3	5	5
14		M+	5
15		CE	12
16	A_4	8	8
17		+	20
18	B_4	7	7
19		M+	7
20		CE	20
21	A_5	10	10
22		+	30
23	B_5	9	9
24		M+	9
25		CE	30
26	A_6	12	12
27		+	42
28	B_6	11	11
29		M+	11
30		CE	42
31	A_7	14	14
32	ΣA	+	56
33	B_7	13	13
34		M+	13
35	ΣB	MR	49

Fast method converts numbers from base 10 to any other

by Hans Treichel
Siemens Corp., Cherry Hill, N.J.

Engineers, programers, and others who have undergone the drudgery of converting numbers from the decimal system to systems with other bases will welcome this quick and simple conversion method. If a pocket calculator is available, no manual calculation or recording is needed other than jotting down the answer.

A chart is provided as reference for conversion to hexadecimal, octal, and binary numbering systems. The first column provides equal fractional parts of the numbering system to be used; e.g., hexadecimal notation the column is divided into 16 fractional parts 0/16, 1/16, 2/16, 3/16, . . . 15/16. In the other columns, each fractional part is assigned a digit; the digits are assigned consecutively, starting with the smallest fractional part of the numbering system.

The first step in conversion is to divide the decimal number by the base of the numbering system to which you are converting. If the number following the decimal point is greater than or equal to a fractional number in the chart, record the equivalent number as the least significant digit (LSD) in the new numbering system. Next divide the base number into the result of the first step. Look at the chart again and record the equivalent number as the second LSD. Repeat this process until the division produces a number smaller than 1.

As an example, let's convert the decimal number 321 to its hexadecimal equivalent:

1. Divide 321_{10} by 16 to get 20.0625.
2. From the chart, 0.0625 corresponds to 1, so record 1 as LSD.
3. Divide 20.0625 by 16, getting 1.2539.
4. From the chart, 0.2539 is greater than 0.25 but less than 0.3125, so record 4 as the second LSD.
5. Divide 1.2539 by 16, getting 0.0784.
6. From the chart, 0.0784 is greater than 0.0625 but less than 0.125, so jot down 1 as third LSD.
7. Since the result in step 5 is less than 1, conversion is complete. Answer is 141_{16}.

As you can see, the answer 141_{16} was reached in only seven steps, and nothing had to be written down except the answer itself.

As another example, using the larger digits in hexadecimal notation, convert 687_{10} to base 16:

1. 687/16 = 42.9375.
2. From chart, 0.9375 corresponds to F as the LSD.
3. 42.9375/16 = 2.6836.
4. From chart, 0.6836 corresponds to A as second LSD.
5. 2.6836/16 = 0.1677.
6. From chart, 0.1677 corresponds to 2.
7. The result in step 5 is less than 1, so conversion is complete. Answer is $2AF_{16}$.

The chart provided shows equivalent numbers in the hexadecimal, octal, and binary numbering systems. However, what makes this method unique is that the table need only be expanded to enable conversion to any number system; simply divide the numbering system into equal fractional parts; (e.g., base 5 would be 0/5, 1/5, 2/5, 3/5, and 4/5) and assign the digits within the numbering system to each fractional part: 0/5 corresponds to 0; 1/5 to 1; 2/5 to 2; 3/5 to 3; and 4/5 to 4.

Thus, to convert 28_{10} to base 5, jot down this table:

CHART FOR CONVERTING DECIMAL NUMBERS TO HEXADECIMAL, OCTAL, OR BINARY NOTATIONS

Numbering System Fractional Parts	Equivalent Digits		
	Hexadecimal	Octal	Binary
0.9375 to 0.9999	F	7	1
0.8750	E	7	1
0.8125	D	6	1
0.75	C	6	1
0.6875	B	5	1
0.6250	A	5	1
0.5625	9	4	1
0.5	8	4	1
0.4375	7	3	0
0.375	6	3	0
0.3125	5	2	0
0.25	4	2	0
0.1875	3	1	0
0.125	2	1	0
0.0625	1	0	0
0.0	0	0	0

Decimal fraction	Base-5 digit
0.8	4
0.6	3
0.4	2
0.2	1
0	0

Then go through the conversion steps:
1. 28/5 = 5.6.
2. 0.6 corresponds to 3 as LSD.
3. 5.6/5 = 1.12.
4. 0.12 corresponds to 0 as second LSD.
5. 1.12/5 = 0.224.
6. 0.224 corresponds to 1.
7. Result in step 5 is less than 1, so conversion is complete. Answer is 103_5. □

Finding reciprocals easily with pocket calculators

by D.R. Wheeler
Raytheon Services Co., Burlington, Mass.

Since the advent of electronic calculators, many engineers now own and use them daily. These versatile tools can perform a variety of arithmitic functions to get answers quickly and easily, but obtaining the reciprocal of a number is quite cumbersome, since most inexpensive calculators don't have a "1/x" key. Many users write the number on paper, clear the machine, enter 1, press "divide," re-enter the number and then press the "add/equal" key.

Although this method is viable, many of the pocket calculators can solve the problem more directly by using the "constant" (K) register. If n is the number, then its reciprocal, 1/n, can be found directly, as shown in the table:

■ Depress and hold the "constant" key.
■ Press "divide" key.
■ Press "add/equal" key.
■ Release the "constant" key.
■ Press "add/equal" key. □

CALCULATOR OPERATIONS

Operation		Accumulator/display register	K register	K operation flip-flop
Hold K button	÷	n	clear	÷
	+/=	1 (n ÷ n)	n	÷
	+/=	1/n	clear	clear

Four-function calculators time chess matches

by Steven Sutphen
University of Alberta, Edmonton, Canada

Two 4-function calculators are the heart of a digital clock for chess matches. Really two decrementing clocks, this chess timer:

- Displays the time remaining from an initial two hours for each player.
- Allows the users to add extra time.
- Provides an accuracy to within 1/100 of a minute.

The clock is portable, runs on 9-volt rechargeable batteries, and costs less than $30 for parts. Almost any kind of 4-function calculator can be used; the only requirement is that pressing the = key must cause an operation to repeat.

The complete clock assembly includes two calculators, two extra 4½-digit displays so that the White player (playing the white pieces) can see the timing remaining on the Black player's calculator and vice versa, momentary-contact START WHITE and START BLACK switches, and a four-pole, double-throw RUN/STOP switch that also initially starts White's clock decrementing. An oscillator and some logic gates complete the hardware.

To set up the chess clock for a match, the RUN/STOP switch is placed in the STOP position. In this state, the two calculators operate normally, and each player makes the following keyboard entries: 120.01 - .01 =. This sets the initial time to two hours (120.00 minutes) for each player.

When the match is ready to begin, the RUN/STOP switch is placed in the RUN position, thus starting White's clock decrementing every 1/100 minute. After White has completed his move, he presses the START BLACK switch, which stops his own clock and starts Black's.

When additional time is to be added, the procedure involves simply STOPing the clock and ADDing in the additional time. For example, to add in one hour (60 minutes), the players enter: +60 = -.01. If mistakes are made, the normal calculator operations will correct them.

The calculators perform normally when the RUN/STOP switch is in the STOP position. With the switch in the RUN position and the clock powered up, capacitor C_1 takes a while to charge, thus allowing the R-S flip-flop formed by the two NAND gates to set. This action is the same as would have happened if Black had pressed the START WHITE switch.

The portion of the circuit consisting of four inverters, capacitor C_2, and the MC14040 divide-by-2^{12} integrated circuit form a (5/3)-hertz oscillator that generates a pulse every 0.01 minute. The output of this oscillator gates the D_3-digit drive-pulse from the calculator into the K_2 keyboard input of the calculator. This gating is done on whichever of the two calculators is currently turned on by the CD4013 D-type flip-flop. The effect of this gating is the same as pressing the = key one hundred times per minute, thereby causing the calculator to subtract .01 one hundred times per minute.

The D flip-flop synchronizes the clock and the enabling transitions. The FDZ37 light-emitting-diode displays are added, along with their 8864 drivers, so each player may see both his own and his opponent's time. It is assumed that the chess players will not depress the START buttons simultaneously; the rules of the game prohibit this.

For lower power consumption, liquid-crystal displays can be used instead of LEDs. The requirements of the display are 4½ signed digits. For a more accurate clock,

Digital chess timer. Less than $30 worth of parts, including two 4-function calculators and a duplicate LED display for each, make this portable timer with dual decrementing clocks. The assembly shown here uses APF Electronics Mark 40 calculators but, with minor modifications to the digit-drive/keyboard-input gating portion of the circuit, almost any type could serve.

a crystal oscillator should be used, with more stages of division. Including an audio alert to indicate negative times is an obvious refinement.

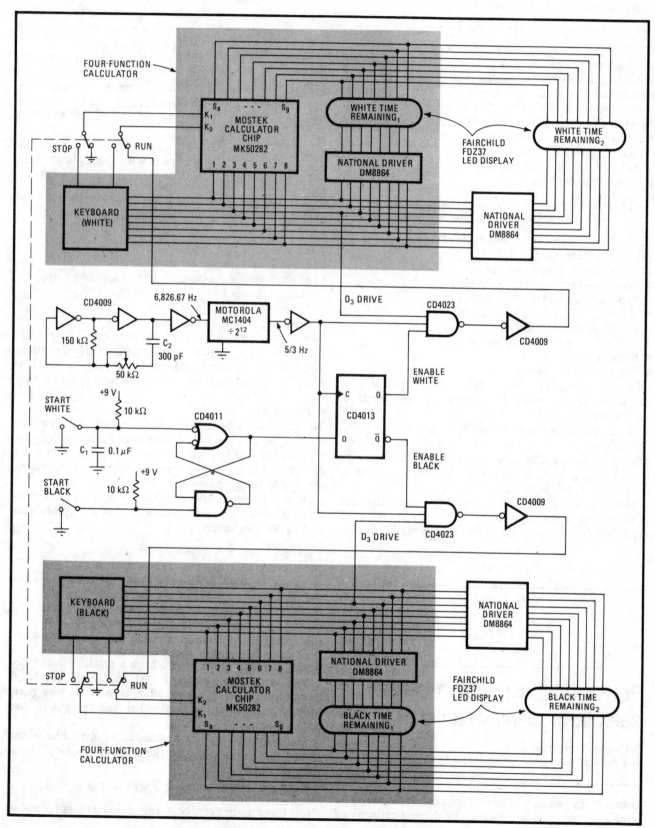

Evaluating polynomials and finding their roots

by Philip R. Geffe
Westinghouse Electric Corp., Baltimore, Md.

The HP-35 calculator has enough storage capacity to allow the user to evaluate any polynomial in a single continuous chain operation without writing down any intermediate calculations. Furthermore, this chain operation can be used to find the real roots of the polynomial with Newton's method. Again, no calculations need be written down, and the polynomial's roots can be obtained to 10 significant figures.

To evaluate the polynomial, P(x), first write it (or think of it) in the form:

$$P(x) = a_n x^n + a_{n-1} x^{n-1} + ... + a_1 x + a_0$$
$$= [(... (a_n x + a_{n-1}) x + a_{n-2}) x + ... + a_1] x + a_0$$

And a simple program allows P(x) to be evaluated for a given argument, x_0:

- Write x_0—Press STO and CLx
- Write a_n—Press ENTER, RCL, and ×
- Write a_{n-1}—Press +, RCL, and ×
- Write a_{n-2}—Press +, RCL, and ×
- Continue chain operation
- Write a_1—Press +, RCL, and ×
- Write a_0—Press +
- $P(x_0)$ is now displayed

Of course, if some of the coefficients are negative, you can write them as positive numbers, and then depress the − key instead of the + key.

A polynomial's real roots can be found by using the above program as a subroutine within an iterative procedure having a quadratic error function. The error in an iteration, then, is approximately the square of the error in the previous iteration.

Since the algorithm will not converge unless the first trial root is approximately correct, polynomial P(x) must first be evaluated for a few arguments until two are found that yield opposite signs. For example, suppose that P(a) is positive and P(b) is negative. A real root will then lie on the x-axis between a and b. Accordingly, this interval can be bisected to find the mean argument, c:

$$c = \frac{1}{2}(a+b)$$

P(c) will then be either positive or negative (if c is not a root). If P(c) is positive, then a root lies between b and c; if it is negative, the root is between a and c.

Proceed in this way until you have about two significant figures for the root. Now, switching to Newton's method will usually produce a solution that converges very rapidly because of the quadratic behavior of the error function—an error of, say, 10^{-4} is reduced to 10^{-8} in only one iteration.

Let P'(x) be the derivative of P(x), and let x_1 be the first approximation to the root. With this estimate held in the calculator's side storage register, the following program can be used:

- Calculate $P(x_1)$ [in x register]
- Press ENTER [$P(x_1)$ is now in y register]
- Calculate $P'(x_1)$ [in x register]
- Press ÷, CHS, RCL, and +

These steps complete one iteration. The calculator display now contains x_2, which is the improved approximation of the root.

The program continues:

- Press ENTER, ENTER, RCL, and ÷

The display now shows the ratio of x_k/x_{k-1}, where k is the index of the current approximation. Program iterations should be continued until this ratio is equal to unity. Whenever it is not unity, the next program step is:

- Press R, STO, and CLx

The calculator's side register now contains root approximation x_2, and the next iteration is started by looping back to the first step of the "root" program. When the ratio of x_k/x_{k-1} is unity, then the side register contains the root to 10 significant figures.

As can be seen, both programs are chain computations, allowing the calculator's display to replace pen and paper completely. □

Polynomial expansion beats calculator display limits

by Charles Lotterman
Northrop Corp., Electronics Div., Hawthorne, Calif.

Occasionally, when you're multiplying or dividing two large numbers, you will exceed the display capacity of your calculator—even if you have a machine as sophisticated as Hewlett-Packard's HP-45, which rounds off the answer. But, by taking advantage of the way polynomials are multiplied or divided, you can get around this problem.

Any number can be expanded as a polynomial whose base is 1,000. For example, the number 123,456,789 can be written as:

$$123 \times 1{,}000^2 + 456 \times 1{,}000^1 + 789 \times 1{,}000^0$$

Now this number can be manipulated as a polynomial,

with the three-digit significant figures of the number being treated as the coefficients of the polynomial.

To multiply two such polynomials:

- Multiply each three-digit group of one number by each three-digit group of the other number in an orderly manner. (Your calculator's constant storage capability will be convenient to use during this operation.) For each multiplication, the digits that fall to the left of the three least-significant digits are carried into the next higher-order term.
- Sum the three-digit terms that produce the corresponding power of 1,000, including all the carry factors from the lower-order terms.
- Arrange the results in ascending order of powers of 1,000 to obtain the answers.

As an illustration of this technique, let's multiply 123,456,789 by itself. The carry terms will be enclosed by parentheses. The problem is:

$$[123\ 456\ 789] \times [123\ 456\ 789]$$

First, each three-digit group of the multiplicand is multiplied by the least-significant three digits of the multiplier:

$$789 \times 789 = (622)\ 521$$
$$456 \times 789 = (359)\ 784$$
$$123 \times 789 = (097)\ 047$$

Then, each three-digit group of the multiplicand is multiplied by the next-most-significant three digits of the multiplier:

$$789 \times 456 = (359)\ 784$$
$$456 \times 456 = (207)\ 936$$
$$123 \times 456 = (056)\ 088$$

Finally, each three-digit group of the multiplicand is multiplied by the most-significant three digits of the multiplier:

$$789 \times 123 = (097)\ 047$$
$$456 \times 123 = (056)\ 088$$
$$123 \times 123 = (015)\ 129$$

The results of each of these multiplications are arranged so that the three-digit groups belonging to the same power of 1,000 can be added together:

		123	456	789		
×		123	456	789		
				(622)	521	
			(359)	784		
		(097)	047			
			(359)	784		
		(207)	936			
	(056)	088				
		(097)	047			
	(056)	088				
(015)	129					
			(1)	(2)		
15	241	578	750	190	521	

The answer, therefore, is: 15,241,578,750,190,521.

A similar technique can be used for division:

- Set up the numbers in the format used for long division.
- Perform a trial division using your calculator's divide function.
- Round the results to a three-digit integer and multiply by the divisor.
- Subtract the results of the multiplication from the dividend. The high-order term of the resulting polynomial must be zero.
- Continue this process—dividing, multiplying, and subtracting, as in long division—until you obtain the desired number of places for the quotient.
- Sum the results for the answer.

A numerical example will make the procedure clearer. We will divide 123,456,000 by 456,000. To keep the computations neat, let X = 1,000. The problem is:

$$\frac{123(X^2) + 456(X^1) + 000(X^0) + 000(X^{-1})}{456(X^1)}$$

The trial division produces:

$$\frac{123,456,000}{456,000} = 270\ (X^0)$$

Proceed now as in long division. Multiply:

$$270(X^0) \times 456(X^1) = 123(X^2) + 120(X^1)$$

Subtract:

$$\begin{array}{r} 123(X^2) + 456(X^1) + 000(X^0) \\ - \quad 123(X^2) + 120(X^1) \\ \hline 000(X^2) + 336(X^1) + 000(X^0) \end{array}$$

Divide:

$$\frac{336(X^1) + 000(X^0)}{456(X^1)} = 737(X^{-1})$$

Multiply:

$$737(X^{-1}) \times 456(X^1) = 336(X^1) + 072(X^0)$$

Subtract:

$$\begin{array}{r} 336(X^1) + 000(X^0) + 000(X^{-1}) \\ - \quad 336(X^1) + 072(X^0) \\ \hline 000(X^1) - 072(X^0) + 000(X^{-1}) \end{array}$$

Divide:

$$\frac{-072(X^0) + 000(X^{-1})}{456(X^1)} = -158(X^{-2})$$

Continue in this way until you obtain the accuracy desired. The complete long-division array looks like this:

$$\begin{array}{r} 270(X^0) + 737(X^{-1}) - 158(X^{-2}) \\ 456(X^1) \overline{\smash{\big)}\ 123(X^2) + 456(X^1) + 000(X^0) + 000(X^{-1}) + 000(X^{-2})} \\ 123(X^2) + 120(X^1) \\ \hline 336(X^1) + 000(X^0) \\ 336(X^1) + 072(X^0) \\ \hline -072(X^0) + 000(X^{-1}) \\ -072(X^0) - 048(X^{-1}) \\ \hline +048(X^{-1}) + 000(X^{-2}) \end{array}$$

The answer is found from the quotient:

$$(270 \times 1,000^0) + (737 \times 1,000^{-1}) - (158 \times 1,000^{-2}) + (106 \times 1,000^{-3})$$

or, 270.736 842 106, with a small negative remainder. □

Evaluating e^x
with constants

by Steve Larson
Maynard L. Larson Co., Yankton, S.D.

This straightforward procedure for computing e^x produces answers that are accurate to six or more decimal places. No paper is necessary—just a common pocket calculator having a constant register.

The method, in effect, constructs the product of e^A $\times$ (e$^{0.1}$)^B $\times$ (e$^{0.01}$)^C $\times$ (e$^{0.001}$)^D $\times$ . . . , where A, B, C, D, . . . are the digits of x—for example, the value of e$^{A.BCD}$. In practice, however, negative powers of e are used because of the way in which the calculator's constant register is loaded.

Four constants will usually be needed for a computation, and they should be memorized or written down, say, on the back of the calculator. These values are: e^{-1} = 0.3678794, e$^{-0.1}$ = 0.9048374, e$^{-0.01}$ = 0.9900498, and e$^{-0.001}$ = 0.9990005. Moreover, "free" significant digits are easily obtained for very small values of x since e^x = 1 + x (e.g., e$^{0.000306}$ = 1.000306).

As a sample problem, let's evaluate e$^{2.513306}$. For this function, A = 2, B = 5, C = 1, and D = 3:

$$e^{2.513306} = e^2(e^{0.1})^5(e^{0.01})(e^{0.001})^3 e^{0.000306}$$

The key strokes are:
- Enter 1.000306, which is equivalent to e$^{0.000306}$
- Press the divide key.

- Enter 0.9990005, which is e$^{-0.001}$.
- Press and hold the constant key.
- Press the add/equal key two times (one time less than the exponent of e$^{0.001}$).
- Release the constant key.
- Press the add/equal key. The display now contains e$^{0.003306}$.
- Press the divide key.
- Enter 0.9900498, which is e$^{-0.01}$.
- Press the add/equal key. The constant key is not used because division occurs only once. The display now contains e$^{0.013306}$.
- Press the divide key.
- Enter 0.9048374, which is e$^{-0.1}$.
- Press and hold the constant key.
- Press the add/equal key four times.
- Release the constant key.
- Press the add/equal key. The display contains e$^{0.513306}$.
- Press the divide key.
- Enter 0.3678794, which is e^{-B}.
- Press and hold the constant key.
- Press the add/equal key once.
- Release the constant key.
- Press the add/equal key to get the final answer.

The display register now contains the value of e$^{2.513306}$:

$$e^{2.513306} = 12.345677$$

The technique is fast, too—the total keying time for this example will be about half a minute.

The same procedure can be used even if x is negative—simply compute e^{-x} first and then find the reciprocal of the result.

Chain operation
for finding e^x

by Russell E. Price
Hughes Aircraft Co., Space and Communications Group, El Segundo, Calif.

It is possible to evaluate the exponential function to an accuracy of within 0.002% with the ordinary four-function calculator. And since the procedure is a chain operation, there's no need to write down any intermediate computations.

For values of x between 0 and 10, the equation is:

$$e^x = (...(((x \div N + 1)x \div (N - 1) + 1)x \div (N - 2) + 1)... \times \div (1) + 1$$

where N is the number of iterations required to achieve a specific accuracy for a given value of x. The graph shows how many iterations are needed to evaluate e^x to accuracies of within 0.05%, 0.01%, and 0.002%. For instance, to find the value of e^5 (where x = 5) to an accuracy of within 0.01%, you will need 15 iterations. The procedure is both fast and simple—you only need to remember the value of x and to be able to count N keystrokes.

For large values of x, you can even make do with fewer iterations than indicated on the graph without sacrificing accuracy. Suppose, for example, you want to find $e^{9.3}$ to within 0.05% accuracy. First find $e^{0.93}$ to within 0.005% accuracy and then multiply the result by itself 10 times (raise the result to the 10th power):

$$e^{9.3}\pm0.05\% = (e^{0.93}\pm0.005\%)^{10}$$

Instead of 22 iterations, you need only seven. □

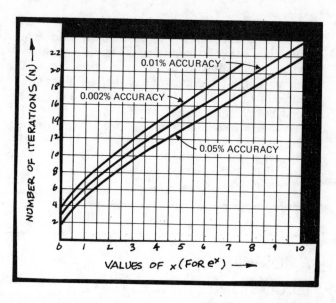

Counting keystrokes
to get results

by Frank Alexander
FMC Corp., Chemical Group, Marcus Hook, Pa.

If you're fond of counting keystrokes, here are three ideas that will put your counting to good use—for evaluating the exponential function, or for finding decibel equivalents or even music notes. The trick is to find a convenient integer power of the quantity you wish to evaluate.

For the exponential function, if you choose $e^{0.1}$ as this basic quantity, you can evaluate e^x to seven significant figures.
• Enter 1.1051709 (which is $e^{0.1}$) as a constant.
• Raise this constant to the power needed to obtain x.
To evaluate $e^{2.3}$, for instance, raise 1.1051709 to the 23rd power:

$$e^{2.3} = (e^{0.1})^{23}$$

With this procedure, three-digit values of x can be found by using $e^{0.01} = 1.0100502$ as your constant but, naturally, many more keystrokes must be counted.

The same sort of technique—counting the number of keystrokes—can be used to convert from decibels to a voltage gain by remembering that $10^{1/20} = 1.1220185$.
■ Enter 1.122085 as a constant.
■ Multiply it by itself as many times as there are decibels to be converted.
A quantity of 12 dB, for example, requires raising the constant to the 12th power:

$$(10^{1/20})^{12} = 3.9810729$$

Of course, other fractional ratios of powers of 10 can be treated in the same way.

Undoubtedly, Johann Sebastian Bach had the four-function pocket calculator in mind when he proposed that music notes be separated by the 12th root of 2. In this case, the constant becomes:

$$2^{1/12} = 1.0594632$$

Each time this constant is raised to the next integer power, the music frequency is increased by one note. In the tempered chromatic scale (ASA 1936), for instance, part of the note progression will be computed as:

A_3 = 220.00000 hertz
$A\#_3$ = 233.08190 Hz
B_3 = 246.94169 Hz
C_4 = 261.62563 Hz
$C\#_4$ = 277.18272 Hz

through to:

A_4 = 440.00045 Hz

(This last number for note A_4 includes a round-off error of 0.00045.) □

Evaluating logarithms
by counting keystrokes

by Louis R. Baerst
Rockwell International, Autonetics Division, Anaheim, Calif.

Counting keystrokes can also be applied to evaluating logarithms and antilogarithms. To do this, though, your calculator should have a constant register.

For example, to determine the value of a base-10 logarithm ($\log_{10}N$), choose a convenient power of 10—say, $10^{0.01} = 1.0233 = k$. Enter k in the constant register and multiply it by itself m times, until you see number N in the display register. The number of keystrokes

(m) divided by 100 is the value of log N.

The same procedure can be used for any positive base or number, either by modifying the initial k value or by dividing or multiplying by the appropriate factor. The accuracy of the procedure for base-10 logarithms can be doubled by letting k = 1.01158 = $10^{0.005}$ and then dividing m keystrokes by a factor of 200.

To find an antilogarithm, the method is reversed. First multiply the mantissa of the log by 100 (or whatever factor you are using) to get the value of m. Then raise k to the mth power to obtain the result.

A similar technique can be employed to raise a number to a fractional power without using logarithms. Suppose you want to find the value of $1.75^{2.3}$. First determine m by multiplying constant k by itself until number N is displayed. If k = $10^{0.005}$ = 1.01158, then m = 49 (1.01158^{49} = 1.758). Next multiply m by the exponent (49 × 2.3 = 112), and then raise k to this power to obtain the final result (1.01158^{112} = 3.631). The answer, therefore, is $1.75^{2.3}$ = 3.631.

Remember that the number of keystrokes can be reduced by making use of appropriate factors. □

Another way to compute e^x

by James C. Frauenthal
Harvard University, Cambridge, Mass.

Are you satisfied with the methods already suggested in these columns for evaluating e^x? If not, then try this one. It is fast, easy to remember, does not make use of any pre-computed constants, and does not require any numbers to be reentered or written down. You can even estimate the size of the error to be expected.

The algorithm, although not strictly convergent, does work:

$$e^x = \lim [1 + (x/m)]^m$$
as (x/m) approaches 0
and m approaches infinity

where m is an arbitrary number that you choose. Therefore, to evaluate e^x for any arbitrary value of x, you raise the quantity of $[1 + (x/m)]$ to the mth power. If you are using a pocket calculator, it is convenient to make m an integer power of 2 (like 2, 4, 8, 16, . . .).

Moreover, the value chosen for m determines the size of the error in the final answer. To see this, you can expand both e^x and $[1 + (x/m)]$ in their respective power series and take the difference between the two:

$$e^x - [1 + (x/m)]^m$$
approximately equals $(x^2/2m) + ...$

Clearly then, if the quantity of $(x^2/2m)$ is chosen to be small, the higher-order terms in the series on the right-hand side of this equation can be neglected. And the absolute error can be regarded as being on the order of $(x^2/2m)$.

To use the algorithm, first choose m so that the quantity of $(x^2/2m)$ is tolerably small. Then the keying sequence becomes:
- Enter the value of x.
- Divide x by m.
- Add 1 to the quotient of (x/m).
- Raise the factor of $[1 + (x/m)]$ to the mth power.

It should be noted that if m is chosen sufficiently large, the accuracy of the final answer can exceed eight significant digits. □

Computing sine and cosine with linear interpolation

by H.W. Crowley
Analog Devices, Inc., Norwood, Mass.

Simple linear interpolation is a good way to approximate both sine and cosine trigonometric functions to an accuracy of within better than 5%. It's not necessary to learn any new constants—you can make use of the ones that you never really forget:

sin 30° = 0.500
sin 45° = 0.707
sin 60° = 0.866
sin 90° = 1.00

Conveniently, angles remain in degrees, rather than having to be converted into radians. To find the cosine of an angle, it is a simple matter to first determine the sine of an equivalent angle, making use of the identity:

$$\cos \theta = \sin(90° - \theta)$$

The procedure is straightforward. For angles between 0° and 30°:
- Multiply the angle by 0.0166,
which is 0.500/30°.
For angles between 30° and 45°:
- Subtract 30° from the angle.
- Multiply this number by 0.0138,
which is (0.707 – 0.500)/(45° – 30°).
- Add 0.500.
For angles between 45° and 60°:
- Subtract 45° from the angle.
- Multiply this number by 0.0106,
which is (0.866 – 0.707)/(60° – 45°).
- Add 0.707.
For angles between 60° and 90°:
- Subtract 60° from the angle.

- Multiply this number by 0.00447, which is $(1.0 - 0.866)/(90° - 60°)$.
- Add 0.866.

As an example, evaluate $\sin 49°$. Since $\sin 45° = 0.707$ and the increment per degree is 0.0106, the interpolation is:

$$\sin 49° = \sin 45° + 4°(0.0106)$$
$$\sin 49° = 0.707 + 0.0424 = 0.7494$$

which is accurate to within 0.7% of the exact value (0.7547) of $\sin 49°$.

There is another sine approximation that is a bit slower than the linear-interpolation approach, but is far more accurate. It is valid for angles of less than 90° and provides an accuracy to within better than 0.01%. Let:

$$x = \theta(in\ degrees)/90°$$

Then:

$$\sin \theta = ax + bx^3 + cx^5$$

where:

$$a = 1.5706268$$
$$b = -0.6432292$$
$$c = 0.0727102$$

If you memorize the constants, even this method can be quite fast. □

BIBLIOGRAPHY
"Approximations for Digital Computers," C. Hastings, Princeton University Press, 1955.

Polynomial evaluations can be fast and accurate

by David Rowland
Electro Scientific Industries Inc., Portland, Ore.

Both trigonometric and logarithmic functions can be approximated accurately by evaluating polynomials with the four-function calculator. Very few keystrokes are required to find any one function, and each procedure is relatively easy to remember. The table shows the simple keying sequences needed for the sine, tangent, arcsine, and arctangent functions, as well as those for common and natural logarithms and the exponential function.

The worst relative error these approximations produce is about ±0.0005, which means that the answer is accurate to at least three significant digits. The relative error is the difference between the exact function value and the approximated function value divided by the exact function value:

relative error = (exact – approximated)/exact

The relative errors for the approximations given here are: ±0.00015 for the sine, ±0.0005 for the tangent, ±0.0005 for the arcsine, ±0.00022 for the arctangent, ±0.0005 for the base-10 logarithm, ±0.00003 for the base-e logarithm, and ±0.00025 for the exponential.

To get the most out of these approximations, you should keep a couple of basic equivalents in mind. For example, the cosine can be computed from:

$$cos(x) = sin(90° - x)$$

Similarly, the tangent of an angle lying between 45° and 90° can be found by making use of:

$$tan(x) = 1/tan(90° - x)$$

This relationship is also useful for evaluating the arctangent when x is greater than 1.

Solving for the arcsine can become troublesome, because as this function's argument approaches 1.0, its slope becomes infinite, and no polynomial can track an infinite slope. You can extend the range of the approximation given in the table by using the double-angle formulas, or you can compute $cos(x)$ as:

$$cos(x) = [1 - sin(x)^2]^{1/2}$$

and then divide the result into the known value of $sin(x)$. This permits the approximation for the arctangent to be used for the evaluation.

Unfortunately, there doesn't seem to be an easy way to compute the value of 10^x. One possible approximation for 10^x is:

$$(1 + 1.1499196x + 0.6774323x^2 + 0.2080030x^3 + 0.1268089x^4)^2$$

which does not reduce to a convenient format. □

BIBLIOGRAPHY
"Approximations for Digital Computers," C. Hastings, Princeton University Press, 1955.

CALCULATOR KEYING SEQUENCES

$\sin(x)$ $-90° \leqslant x \leqslant 90°$	$\tan(x)$ $-45° \leqslant x \leqslant 45°$	$\arcsin(x)$ $-0.7 \leqslant x \leqslant 0.7$	$\arctan(x)$ $-1 < x < 1$	$\log_{10}(x)$ $10^{-\frac{1}{2}} \leqslant x \leqslant 10^{\frac{1}{2}}$	$\log_e(x)$ $e^{-\frac{1}{2}} \leqslant x \leqslant e^{\frac{1}{2}}$	e^x $0 < x < 1$
Enter 0.01x	Enter 0.01x	Enter x	Enter x	$z = (x-1)/(x+1)$	$z = (x-1)/(x+1)$	Enter 8.469
X 0.5924	X 1.324	X 1.671	Square	Enter z	Enter z	− x
Square	Square	Square	+ 1.897	Square	Square	Take reciprocal
− 1.257	+ 0.4686	+ 1.561	Take reciprocal	X 0.36415	X 0.70225	X x
Square	Square	Square	X 67.44	+ 0.86304	+ 1.99938	X 2.122
+ 0.1645	+ 1.5275	+ 54.89	+ 21.73	X z	X z	+ 1
X 0.01x	X 0.01x	X x	X x			Square twice

Programing an SR-56 to serve as stopwatch

by Martin Tobias
Boulder, Colo.

A Texas Instruments SR-56 key-programable calculator can be made to count and display minutes and seconds accurately within a few seconds in several hours.

The program is shown in the accompanying table. After loading it, enter: Fix 2 GTO 5 0. The display then reads 0.00. The clock is started and stopped by pressing R/S and is reset by entering GTO 5 0. If the program is stopped while it is changing from one time reading to the next, it is necessary to press RCL 0 after pressing R/S. The time to be displayed is held in register 0 as mm.ss—that is, one or more digits for minutes, a decimal point, and two digits for seconds.

Program steps 00 to 07 and 17 to 25 make the calculator run in a loop, adding 0.01 each time and pausing to display the up-to-the-second count. Steps 08 to 16 are run through when the seconds count has reached 59, and the program then adds 0.41 to clock up one minute and reset the seconds to 00.

Loops 08-16 and 17-25 contain the same number of program steps, making the interval between displayed times visually the same, irrespective of which loop the program goes around.

Steps 21 to 24 are dummy instructions inserted to adjust the cycle time to 1 second. This particular sequence made the author's calculator run slightly fast. It gained 2 seconds in 10 minutes, or 9 s in one hour—about +0.3%. The cycle time can be trimmed by altering the dummy instructions: changing instruction 24 to NOP makes the program run slightly faster, changing instruction 23 to = slows it down. Or, one can delete or add a dummy instruction. The dummy function should not involve rounding-off, however, (e.g. $1/x$ $1/x$), because the round-off error would snarl up instruction 11.

The clock slows slightly as the count increases. Although it may run slightly fast at first, the accuracy will improve as the count proceeds. The attainable accuracy of a few seconds in several hours is adequate for such activities as timing dark-room operations, cuing records into a tape-recorder, or timing a boiled egg. □

SR-56 PROGRAM
Title: STOPWATCH

LOC	CODE	KEY	COMMENTS
00	94	=	
01	59	pause	} displays time
02	33	STO	
03	00	0	
04	12	INV	
05	37	x = t	
06	01	1	
07	07	7	
08	84	+	}
09	01	1	
10	94	=	
11	32	x ⩾ t	} loop 1
12	84	+	
13	92	.	
14	04	4	
15	01	1	
16	42	RST	}
17	84	+	}
18	92	.	
19	00	0	
20	01	1	} loop 2
21	46	NOP	
22	46	NOP	
23	46	NOP	
24	94	=	
25	42	RST	}
26			
27			
48			
49			
50	92	.	}
51	05	5	
52	09	9	} reset
53	32	x ⩾ t	sequence
54	15	CLR	
55	42	RST	}

REGISTERS

0	mm · ss

NOTES

Initialize with fix 2 GTO 50

Start with R/S

Stop with R/S RCL 0 *if* *neccessary*

Reset with GTO 50

HP-25 calculator
serves as clock

by Jack L. Aker
San Jose, Calif.

The HP-25 calculator can be programed to serve as a clock, displaying the time of day as HH.MMSS. One or more digits show the hour, followed by a decimal point, and then two digits indicate minutes, and two digits the seconds.

As shown by the accompanying program steps, the last displayed value of time is kept in register 1 in decimal-hours format. The execution time of the program sequence (3.2975146×10^{-4} hours, or about 1.2 seconds) is then added to that value. If the incremented value is less than 13, it is converted to the hr/min/sec representation and displayed for about ¾ second (the pause period).

If the incremented decimal-hours time is greater than 13, only the decimal portion is retained, and a 1 is added to it (so that the hour after 12 is 1, not 13). The incremented value in register 1 is then converted to the HH.MMSS format and displayed for ¾ second.

In either case, the program then recycles after the pause.

To operate the HP-25 as a clock, first enter the program. Then, in the run mode, initialize registers 4 and 7 by the following entries:

    3.2975146
    EEX
    CHS
    4
    STO 4
and:
    13.00
    STO 7

To run the clock program, enter the initial value of time in HH.MMSS format, and press:

    f FIX 4
    g → H
    STO 1
    f PRGM
    R/S

HP-25 CLOCK PROGRAM		
LOCATION	CODE	KEY ENTRY
01	24 01	RCL 1
02	24 04	RCL 4
03	51	+
04	23 01	STO 1
05	24 07	RCL 7
06	21	x ⇄ y
07	14 41	f x < y
08	13 13	GTO 13
09	15 01	g FRAC
10	01	1
11	51	+
12	23 01	STO 1
13	14 00	f →H.MS
14	14 74	f PAUSE
15	13 01	GTO 01

REGISTER	CONTENTS
1	decimal time
4	3.2975146×10^{-4}
7	13.00

If 24-hour timekeeping is preferred, 24.00 is stored in register 7 instead of 13.00, and a 0 is entered at location 10 in the program instead of a 1.

The accuracy of the HP-25 as a clock depends on its internal clock oscillator for the correctness of the value for program execution time that is stored in register 4. This number can be changed, if necessary, to give accuracy within a few seconds during several hours. To adjust the timing, compare the timing accuracy with an electric clock over several hours. Divide the difference in seconds by the number of seconds of running time, and multiply this quotient by the value in register 4 to find the fractional correction that must be added to or subtracted from the value in register 4. □

Program provides card storage
of SR-52 data-memory contents

by David T. Phillips
Glendan Co., Goleta, Calif.

Data tables and computation results can be stored on the magnetic cards normally used by the Texas Instruments SR-52 calculator for program storage. The stored data has the full 13-place accuracy used internally by the calculator, rather than the 10-place accuracy of the light-emitting-diode display.

The SR-52 card-programable calculator stores its program in the 28 registers R70 – R97. Each register holds eight program steps. The contents of registers R70 – R83 can be stored or read from side 1 of a program card, and the other 14 registers are read in or out from side 2 of the card.

The SR-52 stores computational data and results in registers R00 – R19. There is no direct provision for card storage of the data that is in these 20 data-memory registers. However, the short program shown below exchanges the contents of registers R00−R19 with the contents of registers R70−R89, thus allowing storage of the data-register contents on a program card and also reloading of the data from the card.

The contents of up to 14 of these registers can be stored on half of the card, and the remaining six data registers share the second half of the card with the SWAP program. The program takes about 15 seconds to exchange the contents of two sets of 20 registers.

Under the program shown in the table, buttons are pushed in the following order: in the calculate mode, 19 STO 90 GTO 168 LRN; then in the learn mode, LBL A (RCL 90 STO 98 + 70) STO 99 IND RCL 98 IND EXC 99 IND STO 98 .1 +/− SUM 99 SUM 98 RCL 98 IFPOS 184 LBL B RCL 90 HLT LBL C STO 90 HLT.

The instruction IFPOS 184, which the coding form shows at program-storage locations 207−210, loops the program back to IND RCL 98 at location 184. Program A exchanges the register contents, B shows the highest register exchanged, and C allows the user to alter the number of registers to be exchanged.

To store data, first enter or compute data in registers R00−R19. Next load the SWAP program from side 2 of the card. Then swap the register contents, by pressing key A. Finally, write the new card by pressing INV 2nd READ once for each side of the card. To see the number of the highest register to be swapped, press key B. To change the highest register, enter the number of the new highest register and then press key C.

To recall data, first read in both sides of the SWAP card, by pressing 2nd READ. Then move the data to registers R00−R19 by pressing key A. After that, proceed with computations, loading of program, and the like. □

SR-52 Coding Form — Program Title: SWAP

LOC	CODE	KEY	COMMENTS	LOC	CODE	KEY	COMMENTS	LOC	CODE	KEY	COMMENTS
000					85	+		200	09	9	indices
			Program storage locations		07	7			44	SUM	
			000 − 159 are registers		00	0			09	9	
			R70 − R89 used for data	180	54	)			08	8	
			storage.		42	STO	Set		43	RCL	
159					09	9	upper	205	09	9	
160	10		Register 90		09	9	index		08	8	Test low
	00			184	36	IND	Start loop	207	80	IFPOS	index
	00			185	43	RCL	fetch lower		01	1	(0 is positive)
	00		"19 STO 90"		09	9	register		08	8	close loop
	00		Highest		08	8	contents	210	04	4	
165	00		register		36	IND	Store lower		46	LBL	
	00		to be		48	EXC	in upper and		12	B	Display
	19		exchanged	190	09	9	fetch upper		43	RCL	highest
168	46	LBL	Main		09	9	contents		09	9	register
	11	A	program		36	IND	Store	215	00	0	from 90
170	53	(			42	STO	upper		81	HLT	
	43	RCL			09	9	contents		46	LBL	
	09	9		195	08	8	in lower		13	C	Enter
	00	0			01	1			42	STO	new
	42	STO	Set		94	+/−		220	09	9	highest
175	09	9	lower		44	SUM			00	0	register
	08	8	index		09	9	Decrement		81	HLT	in 90

LABELS	
A	SWAP
B	Last register
C	Ent last register

REGISTERS	
00	←→ 70
01	←→ 71
02	←→ 72
03	⋮
18	←→ 88
19	←→ 89
90	Highest reg. − normally 19
98	Index 00 − 19
99	Index 70 − 89

46. Curve-fitting programs

Curve-fitting program matches measured data

by Glen Miranker
Yale University, New Haven, Conn.

A Fortran computer program called FIT can do your curve fitting for you. The program, which utilizes a least-squares method of approximation, takes a set of n data points and fits a polynomial (up to degree n − 1) to these points.

FIT determines the coefficients of the polynomial by solving a system of normal equations, which are derived by considering some quantity, y, as a polynomial function of another quantity, x. Then, for the ith data point:

$$\Delta + y_i = a_0x_i^0 + a_1x_i^1 + a_2x_i^2 + ... + a_nx_i^n$$

where Δ is the difference between the "correct" data value and the observed or measured data value. If the coefficients provide a good fit, Δ can be neglected. Summing over the data points yields:

$$\Sigma(a_0x_i^0 + a_1x_i^1 + a_2x_i^2 + ... + a_nx_i^n \nu\, y_i)^2 = \Delta^2$$

which is the form of a least-squares fitted curve. FIT computes the coefficients to minimize Δ.

To find the best-fitting curve for a given set of data, all FIT needs to know is the values of the observed data points and the desired degree of the polynomial approximation. The first part of the program (statement numbers greater than 999) accepts the data, stores it, and organizes it for use in the rest of the program.

At this point in FIT's program list, a subroutine (like the one called FUNCTION at the end of FIT's program list) can be used to redefine the x variable so that approximations can be made to curves that are not strictly polynomials in x. For example, if $y = \sin^2(x)$, a polynomial fit can be made by letting $F = \sin(x)$ since y is a polynomial in $\sin(x)$.

The second part of the program, statement numbers from 99 to 999, set up the normal equations. Statements 20 through 90 then solve this normal equation system, avoiding cumulative errors through judicious use of single- and double-precision variables. In the final part of the program (statement numbers less than 20), the residuals (differences between the fitted and the measured

Getting a good fit. Fortran instruction list for curve-fitting program named FIT generates a polynomial, of up to degree n − 1, to fit a set of n measured data points. By writing a subroutine, like the one called FUNCTION at the bottom of this list, approximations can be made to curves that are not strictly polynomials. The program makes use of a least-squares approximation method to do the curve fitting.

```
*    THIS IS THE FIRST LINE OF FIT
        DOUBLE PRECISION D(51,52)
        REAL X(100),Y(100),W(0/100),Z(0/100),A(51),B(51,52),C(51,52)
        TYPE 1001
1001    FORMAT(' ARE YOU USING STORED DATA? ',$)
        ACCEPT 1002,COMMEN
1002    FORMAT(A1)
        IF(COMMEN.EQ.'Y')GO TO 6000
        TYPE 1000
1000    FORMAT(' PLEASE ENTER THE NUMBER OF SAMPLES - MAXIMUM 100',/)
        ACCEPT 2000,NP
        WRITE(10,2000)NP
2000    FORMAT(I2)
        TYPE 3000
3000    FORMAT(' ENTER THE DATA TABBING ONCE AFTER ENTERING',
       *  ' THE X DATA')

        TYPE 4000
4000    FORMAT(' TYPE IN THE DATA POINTS.',/,/,' SAMPLE NUMBER
       *  XDATA        YDATA',/)
        DO 5001 I=1,NP
        TYPE 4500,I
4500    FORMAT(1H+,T7,I12,T21,$)
        ACCEPT 5000,X(I),Y(I)
5000    FORMAT(2G)
        WRITE (10,5000)X(I),Y(I)
5001    CONTINUE
        END FILE 10
        REWIND 10
6000    READ (10,2000)NP
        DO 100 I=1,NP
        READ (10,5000)X(I),Y(I)
        X(I)=F(X(I))
100     CONTINUE
        TYPE 200
200     FORMAT(' ENTER THE ORDER OF THE DESIRED POLYNOMIAL',/,
       *  ' (MAXIMUM = THE NUMBER OF POINTS-1)',/)
        ACCEPT 300,M
300     FORMAT(I2)
        W(0)=NP
        DO 401 I=1,NP
        DO 400 J=1,2*M
        W(J)=W(J)+X(I)**J
        Z(J)=Z(J)+Y(I)*X(I)**J
400     CONTINUE
        Z(0)=Z(0)+Y(I)
401     CONTINUE
        DO 500 I=1,M+1
        DO 500 J=1,M+1
        B(I,J)=W(J-2+I)
        B(I,M+2)=Z(I-1)
500     CONTINUE
*
*       THE FOLLOWING SERIES OF NESTED DO LOOPS DO THE FOLLOWING.
*       THE FIRST STEPS THE DO SYSTEM SOLVING FOR EACH COEFFICIENT
*       SUCCESIVELY.
*       THE SECOND CLOCKS THE DO LOOP SYSTEM DECREASING THE MATRIX
*       SIZE BY ONE ROW AND ONE COLUMN EACH ITERATION.

*       THE THIRD AND THE FOURTH TAKE THE ITH ROW AND DIVIDE IT BY
*       ITS NTH COEFFICIENT. THEN MULTIPLIES THE ITH ROW BY THE NTH
*       COEFFICIENT OF THE (I+1)TH ROW. FINALLY IT SUBTRACTS THE
*       I+1TH ROW FROM THE ITH.
*       THE LAST TWO DO LOOPS RESTRUCTURE MATRIX D SO THAT IT
*       CONTAINS THE C MATRIX MINUS THE NTH COLUMN AND THE LAST ROW.
*
        DO 50 N=1,M+1
        DO 20 I1=1,M+1
        DO 20 J1=1,M+2
20      D(I1,J1)=B(I1,J1)
        DO 40 K=1,M
        IF(N-K)25,25,23
23      L=1
        GO TO 27
25      L=2
27      DO 30 I=1,M+1-K
        DO 30 J=1,M+3-K
        C(I,J)=(D(I,J)/D(I,L))*D(I+1,L)-D(I+1,J)
30      CONTINUE
        DO 40 I=1,M+1-K
        DO 40 J=1,M+2-K
        IF(J.GE.L)GOTO 35
        D(I,J)=C(I,J)
        GO TO 40
35      D(I,J)=C(I,J+1)
40      CONTINUE
        A(N)=D(1,2)/D(1,1)
50      CONTINUE
        DO 90 I=1,M+1
        TYPE 70,I,A(I)
70      FORMAT(' COEFFICIENT NUMBER',I3,'= ',1PE15.5)
        WRITE (11,70)I,A(I)
90      CONTINUE
        TYPE 10
10      FORMAT(' DO YOU WANT A LIST OF RESIDUALS?',$)
        ACCEPT 1002,ANS
        IF(ANS.NE.'Y')GO TO 1
        DO 5 K=1,NP
        THEORY=0.
        DO 7 I=1,M+1
7       THEORY=A(I)*X(K)**(I-1)+THEORY
        RESID=Y(K)-THEORY
        TYPE 3,K,RESID
5       WRITE(12,3)K,RESID
3       FORMAT(' DATA POINT',I3,'  ',1PE15.5)
1       STOP
        END
***********************************************************************
******   THIS FUNCTION ALLOWS APPROXIMATIONS TO BE MADE TO CURVES THAT  *****
******     ARE NOT STRICTLY POLYNOMIALS BY REDEFINING THE "X" VARIABLE.  *****
***********************************************************************
        FUNCTION F(X)
        F=1./X**2
        RETURN
        END
```

curves) are calculated, providing some indication of how good the fit is and allowing convenient comparison of fits of different degree for a given data set.

The sample program list shown for FIT, with the FUNCTION subroutine, could be used to check the pass characteristics of a nonlinear amplifier, which should have a pass characteristic of $1/x^2$. The size of the residuals computed by FIT could indicate how much of the amplifier's distortion can be analyzed as a second-order effect. □

Weighted averaging simplifies curve fitting

by Richard E. Blake
Vast Inc., Waldoboro, Maine

A program called Focus considerably eases the job of curve fitting, especially if you are working with data that does not approximate a recognizable function. As long as you have sufficient data, Focus will work—without being modified—on a variety of data patterns. It will quickly fit data without having either convergence or accuracy problems.

Focus takes the wrinkles out of otherwise erratic data by using a weighted average. The weights used are $W_1 = 1$, $W_2 = 2$, and $W_3 = 1$. Each point n, which is represented by P(n), is averaged with its neighbors:

$$P(n) = \frac{W_1 P(n-1) + W_2 P(n) + W_3 P(n+1)}{W_1 + W_2 + W_3}$$

Since end points lack enough neighbors, they require special attention. For the first point, W_1 is set equal to 0; and for the last point, W_3 is also set to equal 0.

The averaging is repeated for each point a specified number of times, which should suit your specific appli-

cation. But don't forget that the data begins to lose significance as the averaging continues. Ultimately, you'll get a straight line for an absolute average.

When using Focus, you are faced only with basic decisions. First, establish which axis should be used to order the points. This decision determines the neighbors that are the heart of the method. Next determine if the data from the remaining axis can be used as a reference, or should the data from both axes be averaged?

After you determine these answers, you can then decide how many times the averaging should take place. It is easy enough to change this number, and perhaps the best solution is to try a few different numbers. And finally, you have the option to remove data through some desired criteria and to do a possible refit.

Two Fortran routines, labeled Focus and FIT2 in the figure, make up the program—subroutine FIT2 is used to control subroutine Focus. They are simple listings that should work on almost any machine. Before FIT2 is called, the independent axis (AB) and the dependent axis (ER) are stored, the coordinate pairs are ordered in increasing values of AB, and obviously bad values of ER are removed.

Focus follows these steps:
■ Data to be averaged is stored in ORIG to determine residuals.
■ Data points are averaged NFOC times.
■ The average residual is calculated.

```
      SUBROUTINE FIT2(AVE1,AVE,DELT1,DELT2)
C AVE1  IS THE AVERAGE RESIDUAL FROM THE FIRST PASS AT FOCUS
C AVE   IS THE AVERAGE RESIDUAL FROM THE SECOND PASS AT FOCUS
C DELT1 IS THE WORST RESIDUAL FROM THE FIRST PASS
C DELT2 IS THE WORST RESIDUAL FROM THE SECOND PASS
C NOTE THAT .1 APPEARS OFTEN ON PRINTED VARIABLES, SINCE THEY
C   WERE 10 TIMES REAL SCALE
      DIMENSION ORIG(1000)
      COMMON AB(1000),ER(1000),NTPS
      IY=10
      CALL FOCUS(NTPS,ER,IY,AVE1,ORIG,DELT1)
      AVE=AVE1*2.5
C 2.5 TIMES THE AVERAGE RESIDUAL WILL NOW BE USED TO ELIMINATE DATA
      WRITE(6,1410)
 1410 FORMAT(/////"  DATA REMOVED BETWEEN PASS ONE AND TWO",///,
     *"  BEARING      DATA      FIT DIFFERENCE (10X REAL VALUES)")
      DO 42 I=1,NTPS
      DIF=ABS(ORIG(I)-ER(I))
      IF(DIF-AVE)42,42,41
   41 CONTINUE
      WRITE(6,411) AB(I),ORIG(I),ER(I),DIF
  411 FORMAT(4F10.3)
      DO 415 J=I,NTPS
      AB(J)=AB(J+1)
      ORIG(J)=ORIG(J+1)
  415 ER(J)=ER(J+1)
      NTPS=NTPS-1
      I=I-1
   42 CONTINUE
C NOTICE THAT THE CALLING SEQUENCE HAS BEEN CHANGED!
C THE NEXT FOCUS WILL BE ON THE ORIGINAL DATA STORED IN ORIG NOW.
      CALL FOCUS(NTPS,ORIG,IY,AVE,ER,DELT2)
C THE FOLLOWING CODE PLOTS THE FITTED DATA ON A H.P.7210A
      CONX=100.
      CONY=320.
      IPC=0
      DO 55 I=1,NTPS
C 2.63 AND 20. ARE SCALE FACTORS FOR THE PLOTTER
      IX=(AB(I)+CONX)*2.63
      IY=(ORIG(I)+CONY)*20.
      WRITE(6) IPC,1,IX,IY
   55 IPC=1
C THE FOLLOWING CODE PRINTS ANGLES AND ERRORS FOR FURTHER PROCESSING
      WRITE(6,156)
  156 FORMAT("1  ANGLE   ERROR")
      DO 56 I=1,74
      ANG=(I-1)*50
      DO 57 J=1,NTPS
      IF(ANG-AB(J)) 58,57,57
   57 CONTINUE
   58 ANG=ANG*.1
      ERROR=ORIG(J)*.1+.05
      WRITE(6,157) ANG,ERROR
   56 CONTINUE
  157 FORMAT(F7.0,F7.1)
      RETURN
      END
```

```
      SUBROUTINE FOCUS(NDATA,DATA,NFOC,AVE,ORIG,DELT1)
C NDATA IS THE NUMBER OF DATA POINTS TO BE FIT
C DATA  IS THE DATA ARRAY
C NFOC  IS THE NUMBER OF TIMES THE DATA IS TO BE AVERAGED
C AVE   IS THE AVERAGE RESIDUAL ( DIFFERENCE BETWEEN ORIGINAL & FIT)
C ORIG  IS THE ORIGINAL DATA (STORED TO CALCULATE RESIDUALS)
C DELT1 IS THE WORST RESIDUAL
      DIMENSION DATA(1),ORIG(1)
      DO 20 I=1,NDATA
   20 ORIG(I)=DATA(I)
C THE FOLLOWING CODE (TO STATEMENT 30) IS THE ACTUAL FOCUSING
      DO 30 I=1,NFOC
      D1=DATA(1)
      DATA(1)=(D1*2.+DATA(2))*.33333
      NUM1=NDATA-1
      DO 25 J=2,NUM1
      D2=D1
      D1=DATA(J)
   25 DATA(J)=(D2+DATA(J)*2.+DATA(J+1))*.25
   30 DATA(NDATA)=(D2+DATA(NDATA)*2.)*.33333
      AVE=0.
      DELT1=0.
C CALCULATE RUNNING ERROR FOR AVERAGE ERROR
      DO 250 I=1,NDATA
      DIF=ABS(DATA(I)-ORIG(I))
      AVE=AVE+DIF
      IF(DIF-DELT1) 250,250,245
  245 DELT1=DIF
  250 CONTINUE
      X=NDATA
      AVE=AVE/X
      RETURN
      END
```

Getting an accurate fit. These two Fortran listings make up a curve-fitting program called Focus. (The subroutine FIT2 controls the subroutine Focus.) The program, which fits data by using a weighted average, is fast, as well as accurate. The solid line in Graph 1 shows how accurately Focus can generate a function to fit the data points (dots). If the averaging is repeated too many times, the fitted curve (dashed line) loses accuracy. Graph 2 shows the best fit that can be obtained for the same data points with a least-squares technique.

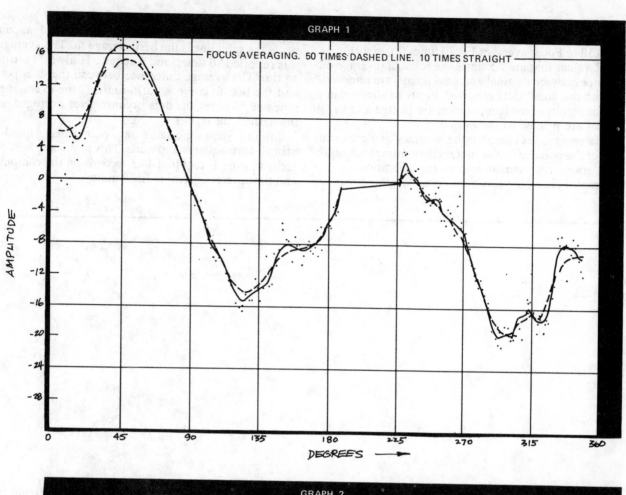

GRAPH 1

FOCUS AVERAGING. 50 TIMES DASHED LINE. 10 TIMES STRAIGHT

AMPLITUDE

DEGREES ⟶

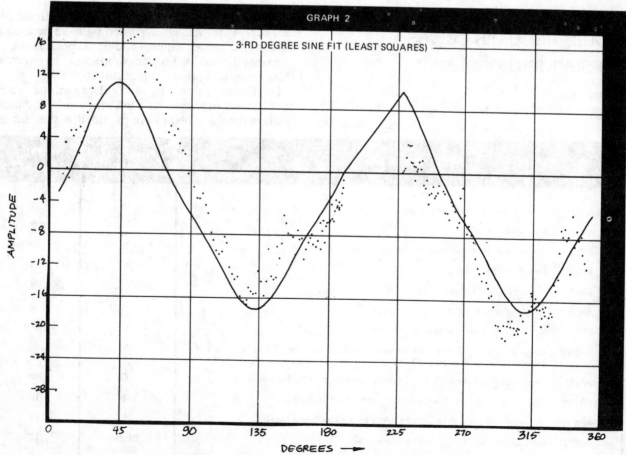

GRAPH 2

3-RD DEGREE SINE FIT (LEAST SQUARES)

AMPLITUDE

DEGREES ⟶

FIT2 follows these steps:
- A call to Focus averages ER 10 times (IY = 10).
- ER values that are 2.5 times the residual (average difference between original and final points) are removed.
- With this "bad" data removed, Focus is called again.
- The results of the computation are plotted and key fit values are printed as the output.

The two graphs compare the accuracy of Focus with that of the popular least-squares curve-fitting technique. Both graphs represent an instrument calibration.

Graph 1 shows the results of Focus' weighted-average approach. The data points are represented as dots, while the solid line is the best average fit. The averaging was repeated 10 times, and it required only 5.34 seconds to run. The average difference between the data points and the best-fit curve is 1.076 units. If the averaging is repeated 50 times, the data becomes over-averaged, and the dashed line results.

Graph 2 shows the same data points being fitted by using a least-squares approach. This plot is the best of a series of runs. It required 49.3 seconds on the computer, and the difference error is 3.568 units.   □

Computer plots curves on standard printer

by David Klein
Automation Industries Inc., Vitro Labs Division, Silver Spring, Md.

Although most computer facilities contain digital plotters, curves are frequently plotted by hand because using a digital plotter requires additional programing and turnaround time. A Fortran subroutine, however, enables a standard printer to plot curves directly.

The Fortran subroutine of Fig. 1 can print any number of curves simultaneously, although only 12 different symbols (one is a blank) are provided in this instance.

ARGUMENT DEFINITIONS		PRINTOUT SYMBOL	INTEGER DESIGNATION
ARG1:	Name of array under which curve data is stored	0	1
ARG2:	M dimension of array	*	2
ARG3:	Number of curves to be plotted (N dimension of array)	X	3
ARG4:	Starting point of X axis	+	4
ARG5:	Amount X should be incremented	.	5
ARG6:	Final value of X (end of X axis)	A	6
ARG7:	Name of array in which symbol data is stored	D	7
ARG8:	Integer indicator — logic 0 tells subroutine to generate its own linear X axis, logic 1 tells subroutine that user is generating X axis	4	8
ARG9:	Name of array in which user's X axis is stored (Use logic 0 if ARG8 is logic 0)	Q	9
ARG10:	Value to which ARG9 is dimensioned (Use logic 1 if ARG8 is logic 0)	#	10
ARG11:	Number of data points to be plotted if ARG8 is logic 1, otherwise logic 0	$	11
ARG12:	Increment in which X-axis values are to be printed	Blank	12

```
FORTRAN IV G LEVEL 20          PLOT           DATE = 72349      09/48/47

0001          SUBROUTINE PLOT(DATA,NS,KURVS,XSTART,XSTEP,XMAX,ISYM,MAN,XDATA,HV
             1,NPTS,INCRMT)
0002          DIMENSION ALINE(101),BLINE(101),DATA(KURVS,NS),SYMBL(12),ISYM(12),
             1IY(12),XDATA(MV)
0003          DATA BLANK/' '/,DOT/'/'/,SYMBL/'C','*','X','+','.','A','0',
             1'+','Q','#','$',' '/,ABAK/'I'/
0004          DATA CENTR1/1.5/,CENTR2/51.5/,BLINE/101*'-'/
0005          AMAX=0.0
0006          AMIN=0.0
0007          XVAL=XSTART
0008          NO=1
0009          INC=N.RMT+1
0010          DO 6 N=1,INC
0011        6 IY(N)=0
0012          BLINE(1)=ABAK
0013          BLINE(26)=ABAK
0014          BLINE(51)=ABAK
0015          BLINE(76)=ABAK
0016          BLINE(101)=ABAK
0017          DO 10 I=1,101
0018       10 ALINE(I)=BLANK
0019          NSTEPS=1.0+((AMAX-XSTART)/XSTEP)
0020          IF(NPTS.LT.NSTEPS) NSTEPS=NPTS
0021          DO 20 K=1,NSTEPS
0022          IF(DATA(1,K).GT.AMAX) AMAX=DATA(1,K)
0023          IF(DATA(1,K).LT.AMIN) AMIN=DATA(1,K)
0024       20 CONTINUE
0025          IF(AMIN.LT.0.0) GO TO 30
0026          SCALE=100/AMAX
0027          CENTR=CENTR1
0028          T1=AMAX
0029          T2=0.75*AMAX
0030          T3=0.5*AMAX
0031          T4=0.25*AMAX
0032          T5=0.C
0033          GO TO 60
0034       30 AIMIN=-AMIN
0035          IF(AMAX.GT.AIMIN) GO TO 40
0036          IF(AMAX.EQ.0.0) GO TO 35
0037          SCALE=50/AIMIN
0038          T1=AIMIN
0039          T2=0.5*AIMIN
0040          T3=J.0
0041          T4=0.5*AMIN
0042          T5=AMIN
0043          GO TO 50
0044       35 SCALE=100/AIMIN
0045          CENTR=101.5
0046          T1=J.0
0047          T2=0.25*AMIN
0048          T3=0.5*AMIN
0049          T4=0.75*AMIN
0050          T5=AMIN
0051          GO TO 60
0052       40 SCALE=50/AMAX
0053          T1=AMAX
0054          T2=0.5*AMAX
0055          T3=J.0
0056          T4=0.5*(-AMAX)
0057          T5=-AMAX
0058       50 CENTR=CENTR2
0059       60 VARX=XSTART
0060          ICNTR=CENTR
0061          DO 110 J=1,NSTEPS
0062          IF(MAN.EW.1) VARX=XDATA(J)
0063          ALINE(ICNTR)=DOT
0064          Y=J*XSTEP
0065          IF((VARX.GT.(XSTEP*0.25)).OR.(VARX.LT.(Y*0.25))) GO TO 80
0066          WRITE(6,5)T5,T4,T3,T2,T1
0067        5 FORMAT(1H ,T4,F10.2,T29,F10.2,T54,F10.2,T7v,F10.2,T104,F10.2)
0068          DO 70 M=1,102
0069       70 ALINE(M)=BLINE(M)
0070       80 DO 81 L=1,KURVS
0071          IY(L)=(DATA(L,J)*SCALE)+CENTR
0072          ALINE(IY(L))=SYMBL(ISYM(L))
0073       81 CONTINUE
0074          DO 83 M=1,KURVS
0075          DO 82 N=1,KURVS
0076       82 IF(((IY(M).EQ.IY(N)).AND.(M.NE.N)).AND.(.NOT.((ISYM(N).EQ.12)
             1.OR.(ISYM(M).EQ.12)))) ALINE(IY(M))=SYMBL(11)
0077       83 CONTINUE
0078          IF(NO.NE.1) GO TO 95
0079       85 WRITE(6,4)ALINE
0080        4 FORMAT(1H ,1UIA1,T16,F15.4)
0081       95 IF(MAN.EQ.1) XVAL=XUATA(J)
0082          IF(MAN.NE.1) VARX=VARX+XSTEP
0083          IF(NO.NE.1) GO TO 105
0084          WRITE(6,4)ALINE,XVAL
0085      105 NO=NO+1
0086          IF(NO.LE.IN) NO=1
0087          IF(MAN.NE.1) XVAL=XVAL+XSTEP
0088          DO 90 M=1,101
0089       90 ALINE(M)=BLANK
0090      110 CONTINUE
0091      120 WRITE(6,9)
0092        9 FORMAT('1')
0093      130 RETURN
0094          END
```

1. Software plotter. Subroutine written in Fortran permits computer printer to plot directly up to 12 curves at the same time. Since one of the printout symbols is a blank, one of the curves can be made invisible. The X axis can be scaled in a number of ways, even with a special function, such as a logarithmic curve. Points of intersection between two curves are noted by the $ printout symbol.

The X axis can be started or stopped at any value and incremented by any amount. In addition, the user can specify at what increment the X-axis values are to be printed out.

Also, an option is included that allows the user to select any function he wishes to scale the X axis—for example, a logarithmic function. When this option is used, the fifth argument of the call statement positions the Y axis within a window around zero that is within 25% of the X increment. The other argument definitions and the 12 printout symbols are listed in the table.

X-axis scaling is determined by the maximum and minimum data values of the first curve to be plotted. When these data points are all positive or all negative,

the program will position the X axis at the top or bottom of the printout page. When the data values are both positive and negative, the X axis is printed in the center of the printer field allocated for the graph.

The user can scale the Y axis to a value larger than the maximum value of the desired function by filling the plotting-data array for the first curve with a function that will be scaled by the program according to the desired maximum and minimum values. Since this function is not the desired curve, it can be printed with the blank printout symbol so that it will be invisible. But whenever it crosses either the X or Y axis, it will blank out the printout symbol for that axis.

If the X and Y values of any two curves are the same, the $ symbol is printed, unless one of the curves is invisible. The invisible curve, then, can also be used to blank selected portions of a function.

The user's main program must include:

- A call statement, for example, CALL PLOT (ARG1, ARG2, ..., ARG12).
- An INTEGER array dimensioned to 12.
- A REAL*4 array dimensioned N, M, where N is the number of curves to be plotted, and M is greater than or equal to the number of data points.

A symbol to plot each curve is designated by an integer stored in array ARG7. The table shows each printout symbol and its associated integer callout. If the array is called NSYM and two curves are to be plotted with NYSM(1) = 12 and NYSM(2) = 3, then the first curve will be invisible, and the second will be indicated by X.

Figure 2 contains a sample of a main program calling in subroutine PLOT to graph four curves simultaneously. The resulting printout of three cosine functions (printout symbols 0, X, and +) and a single sine function (printout symbol *) is also shown. When any of the curves intersect, the $ symbol is printed.

It is best to retrieve the data generated for subroutine PLOT on a high-speed printer that has a 132-character

```
       DIMENSION  A(4,200),NSYM(12),R(2,100),XRAY(100)
       SAX=6.28
       START=-6.28
       DO 200 M=1,130
       A(1,M)=COS(START)*2.0
       A(2,M)=SIN(START)
       A(3,M)=COS(START*0.3)
       A(4,M)=COS(START*3.07)*2.0
       START=START+0.1
200    CONTINUE
       DO 250 N=1,4
250    NSYM(N)=N
       CALL PLOT(A,200,4-6.28,0.1,SAX,NSYM,0,0,1,0,10)
       X=1.0
       HRADR=50.0
       SQRH=SQRT(HRADR)
       DO 300 N=1,100
       XRAY(N)=10.0**X
       R(1,N)=300.0
       R(2,N)=1.23*(SQRH+SQRT(XRAY(N)))
       X=X+0.05
300    CONTINUE
       NSYM(1)=12
       NSYM(2)=7
       CALL PLOT(R,100,2,0.0,40.0,100000.0,NSYM,1,XRAY,100,76,2)
       STOP
       END
```

2. Calling in the subroutine. Sample program shows how subroutine PLOT can be used to obtain graph of four curves simultaneously. There are three cosine functions (represented by symbols 0, X, and +) and a sine function (represented by the * symbol).

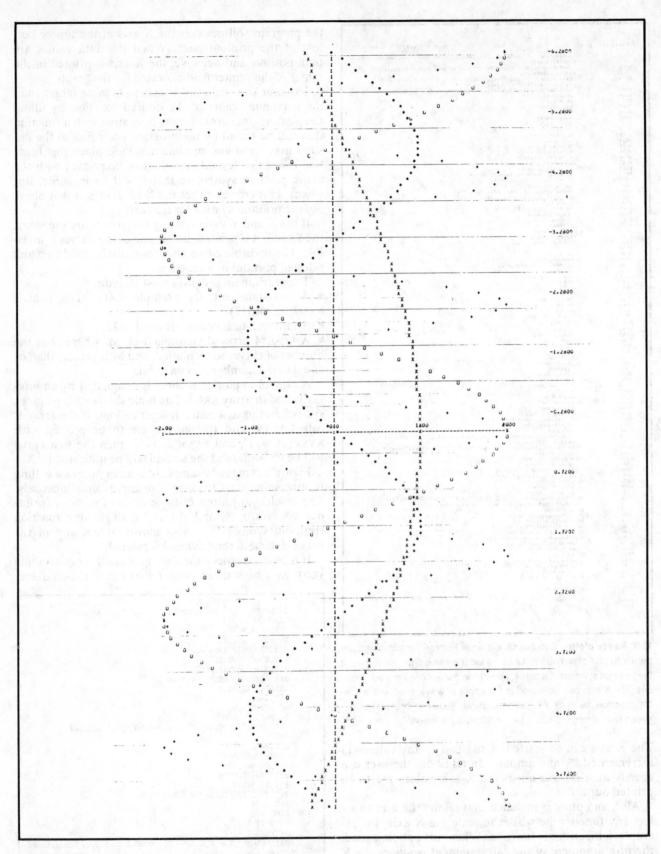

field. If the field is smaller, the format statements can be appropriately modified. A teleprinter terminal can be used for data retrieval, but the subroutine uses a carriage typeover control to which this type of terminal does not respond. As a result, a teleprinter leaves a one-space break in the plot where the Y-axis values are printed out. If the plot begins with the Y axis (the first curve being plotted has an initial X value of zero), then this limitation does not apply. □

47. A variety of power supplies

Doubling the frequency of switching regulators

by Leo Lehner
Motorola Semiconductor Products Inc., Phoenix, Ariz.

A new breed of switching power transistors is making possible smaller and lighter designs that cost less and are more efficient. In some cases, one of these transistors can replace a pair of older transistors and yet provide better efficiency. Moreover, the frequency of switching-regulator power supplies can now be raised from the audible 10-kilohertz region to the quiet 20-kHz region. The devices even can handle kilowatt loads at this higher frequency.

There are three of these triple-diffused 125-watt silicon transistors from which to choose—types 2N6306, 2N6307, and 2N6308. They have a collector current rating as high as 8 amperes and a breakdown voltage rating (BV_{CBO}) of up to 700 volts. Their switching rise time is 0.6 microsecond, and their switching fall time is 0.4 μs. Hundred-unit pricing is $3 to $5.

It is well known that operating on a signal at a high frequency permits the size of inductors and capacitors to be minimized. The benefits of this technique are particularly noticeable when the switching-regulator type of power supply is compared with the dissipative series-pass-regulator type of power supply.

The switched supply is significantly lighter and less bulky. It can use a small high-frequency transformer instead of the large and heavy power transformer needed to make voltage transformations at the 60-hertz line fre-

quency. Filter chokes and filter capacitors can also be smaller. And, because its efficiency is better, not as much heat must be dissipated, allowing literally pounds of heat sink to be trimmed from a power-supply package, as illustrated by the photos (Fig. 1) of two 500-watt supplies.

An example of a power supply that operates at 20 kHz is shown in Fig. 2, both as a block diagram and as a detailed schematic. Of course, the heart of this inverter circuit is the switching power transistors—two type 2N6308 devices. Since they can switch 220-v rectified ac directly, there is no need for a bulky and power-consuming 60-hertz input power transformer. Additionally, switching losses are reduced to a minimum because of their submicrosecond switching speed.

The operating frequency of the circuit is determined by the clock control circuitry, which consists of a temperature-compensated unijunction transistor and a J-K flip-flop that acts as a phase splitter. This phase splitter is driven by an RC oscillator and produces the push-pull control signal for the switching transistors.

A pair of three-input NAND gates passes the complementary square-wave control signals from the flip-flop to the Darlington drivers of the switching power transistors. These NAND gates process the complementary control signals, the pulse delay signal, and the crossover sense signal for proper firing of the inverter.

A quad two-input NAND gate package controls the on-time pulse width duration of the high-voltage switches. Variable-duty-cycle regulation is accomplished in the feedback loop by introducing the proper delay for the leading edge of the pulse delay signal, which is applied to the three-input NAND gates along with the other control signals.

Highly efficient low-voltage Schottky-barrier diodes

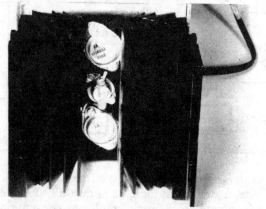

DISSIPATIVE SUPPLY

SWITCHED SUPPLY

1. Before and after. Because of its greater efficiency and higher operating frequency, a switching-regulator power supply is smaller and weighs less than a conventional dissipative line-frequency (60-hertz) supply. Here, a new generation of fast-switching power transistors eliminates pounds of heat sinking for a 500-watt supply. The 125-W devices switch up to 8 A at submicrosecond speeds.

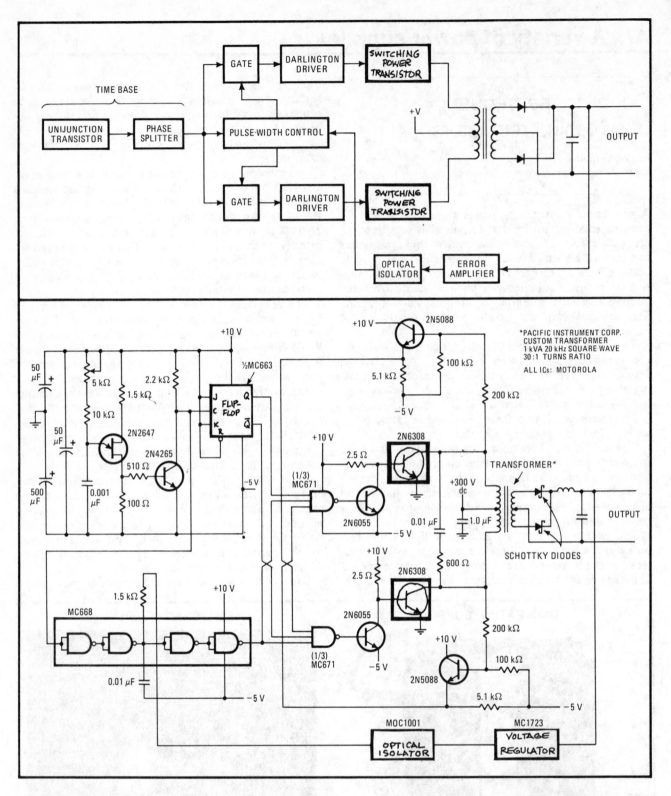

2. Switched supply. New type of switching power transistors can operate at twice the speed of older types, raising inverter switching frequency from an audible 10 kilohertz to a quiet 20 kHz. This higher frequency means better efficiency and a smaller transformer. The 20-kHz inverter shown (in both the block diagram and the schematic) makes use of an optical isolator in its feedback loop.

are used to rectify the 20-kHz signal coming from the transformer's secondary. For low-voltage (around 5 v) power-supply applications, the small forward voltage drop (approximately 0.4 v) of the Schottky diodes provides a significant increase in over-all supply efficiency, as compared to a supply employing conventional silicon rectifiers.

A feedback loop containing a voltage regulator and an optically coupled isolator supplies the regulation information needed for pulse-width control. The optical isolator, which has a phototransistor output, also provides ground isolation between the output dc voltage and the input control circuitry. □

Public-address amplifier serves as variable ac-power source

by William D. Kraengel Jr.
Valley Stream, N.Y.

Alternating voltages at moderate power, low distortion, and variable amplitude and frequency are obtainable over an extended range by a technique similar to one previously proposed [*Electronics*, Dec. 20, 1973, p. 121], but with simpler and more readily obtainable equipment—namely, an ordinary monophonic or public-address amplifier—but with less power output.

In the earlier proposal, a stereo amplifier was differentially coupled to the output of an audio oscillator to provide low audio frequencies at voltages of 0 to 130 volts. However, the frequency range can easily be extended to low ultrasonic frequencies with even higher voltages. Naturally, the higher the quality of the amplifier and transformer, the greater the frequency range available for any given distortion level. The voltage obtainable is limited by the amplifier's available output power and by the breakdown voltage of the external output transformer.

Using a PA amplifier in place of the more expensive stereo amplifier eliminates the requirement for any input transformer. It has a further advantage in that most models have 4-, 8- and 16-ohm and 25- and 70-volt outputs, so that the proper impedance or voltage tap is easily selected for the desired output conditions. On the debit side, the output power is only half that of a comparatively rated stereo amplifier, and its distortion may be somewhat greater, especially at frequency extremes.

The output voltage is:

$$E_{\mathrm{amp}} = (P_{\mathrm{amp}}R_{\mathrm{tap}})^{1/2}$$

E_{amp} is the amplifier's output voltage developed across the chosen output tap, which matches load (R_{tap}) at the power level (P_{amp}) required for the final output voltage, E_{out}—which is N times the amplifier output voltage (N is the transformer's turns ratio).

Ordinary filament transformers (used backward) are available with a large selection of input and output voltages to match input impedance and output voltage for almost any amplifier power level. For example, a recent application required a 100-v, 0.1-A supply over the range of 100 to 1,000 hertz. At a typical amplifier's maximum output, 20 watts, the formula given previously shows that an 8-ohm load calls for an output of 12.65 v, at which the load draws 1.58 A. A 12.6/115-v filament transformer steps this up by a factor of about 10, slightly higher than the application requires, but slightly turning down the amplifier's volume control provides the proper level. Thus, the inexpensive amplifier and transformer provide an almost perfect impedance match and an acceptable distortion level over the entire frequency range. □

Power source. An ordinary public-address amplifier can provide alternating voltages over a wide band of audio frequencies. The exact voltage and current levels are controlled by the unit's gain.

Power supply's VC product sets interrupt capability

by C.A Watson Jr.
E-Systems Inc., Greenville, Texas

It's easy to calculate how long a power supply can continue to provide its regulated output voltage during interruption of the primary power source. The voltages and the storage capacitance in the supply determine this. Interrupt capability (also called holdover, holdup, or carryover time) is important for preserving data in volatile memories during momentary power interruptions or while standby power goes on line during an outage.

The holdup time is estimated and tradeoffs in its optimization are evaluated by the expressions given here for the capacitive-storage supply shown in the figure. The capacitor may be only large enough to reduce ripple to within the range of the voltage regulator, or it may be larger.

The input voltage must be equal to or greater than the sum of the desired regulated load voltage plus the minimum drop in the regulator, and the input current to the regulator is the sum of the regulator current plus the

357

load current. For most efficient regulators and normal loads, the current drawn off by the regulator is small compared to the current to the load, so I_{in} is nearly equal to I_{load}.

To estimate the interrupt capability of a typical 5-volt, 1-ampere supply in which the minimum dropout voltage of the regulator is also 5 V, let

$I_{in} = I_{load} = 1$ A
$V_{load} = 5$ V
V_{reg} = minimum drop across regulator = 5 V
$V_{in} = 15$ V
$C = 1,000$ microfarads

If the primary power source fails, the capacitor discharges through the regulator into the load until its voltage drops to $(V_{reg} + V_{load})$. The load current remains constant, and therefore I_{in} remains constant, so the discharge is linear with time. The interrupt capability in seconds is therefore given by

$$t = [(V_{in} - V_{reg} - V_{load})C]/I_{in}$$

where the units are volts, amperes, and farads. For this example,

$t = (15 - 5 - 5) \times (1 \times 10^{-3})/1$
$= 5 \times 10^{-3} = 5$ milliseconds

In other words, the storage capacitor is drained at a rate of 1 V/ms until the minimum voltage for the regulator-load combination is reached and normal voltage across the load can no longer be maintained.

The price paid in input power for this 5-ms capability is the product of the load current and the excess voltage, V_{ex}, above the minimum required for the regulator and load. In this case, $V_{ex} = 15 - 10 = 5$ V, so the extra power required for the 5-ms capability is 5 V × 1 A, or 5 watts.

The energy stored in the capacitor is

$E_C = \frac{1}{2} V_{in}^2 C = (15^2 \times 1 \times 10^{-3})/2$
$= 0.1125$ joule

If it is necessary to have 50 ms of interrupt capability, rather than 5 ms, the $V_{ex}C$ product must be multiplied by 10 (if the load current and voltage-regulator requirements are not changed). The two extreme solutions are to multiply V_{ex} by 10, so that V_{in} is 60 V, or to increase C to 10,000 μF.

If V_{in} is raised to 60 V, the energy stored in the capacitor is

$E_C = (60^2 \times 1 \times 10^{-3})/2 = 1.8$ J

The power price of the 50-ms capability is $V_{ex}I_{in} = 50$ V × 1 A = 50 W.

If the voltage is unchanged, but capacitance is multiplied by 10,

$E_C = (15^2 \times 1 \times 10^{-2})/2 = 1.125$ J

and the power price = 5 V × 1 A = 5 W, which is the same as for 5 ms with 1,000 μF.

Thus the tradeoffs are clearly defined: increased power cost and stress versus increased size and bulk. Of course, intermediate solutions in which both V_{in} and C increase are also possible. □

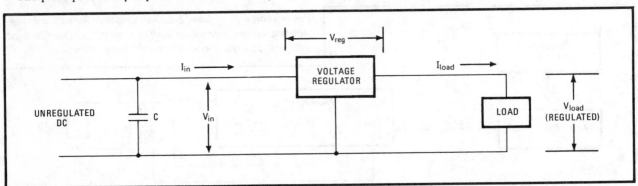

Sustaining the output. In the case of failure of the unregulated dc power to this power supply, the regulated output voltage and load current are maintained as long as the capacitor voltage is greater than the load voltage plus the minimum drop across the regulator. The capacitor discharges at a fixed rate, so the duration of interrupt capability depends linearly on capacitance and excess voltage.

Monolithic IC simplifies
dc-to-dc converter design

by D.H. Treleaven and A.D. Moore
Microsystems International Ltd., Ottawa, Canada

Battery-powered calculators and digital voltmeters use low-power dc-to-dc converters to obtain from the fewest possible batteries the voltages their logic circuits need. With the converter described here, a single battery of 5 to 10 volts can be made to yield an MOS-compatible output of 18 volts at currents up to 40 milliamperes.

Designed around a monolithic integrated circuit that consists of a zener diode voltage reference, a compara-

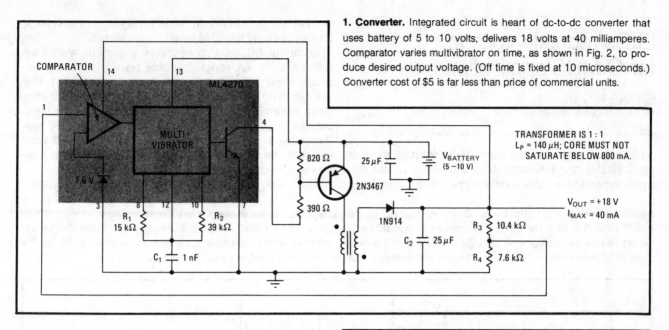

1. **Converter.** Integrated circuit is heart of dc-to-dc converter that uses battery of 5 to 10 volts, delivers 18 volts at 40 milliamperes. Comparator varies multivibrator on time, as shown in Fig. 2, to produce desired output voltage. (Off time is fixed at 10 microseconds.) Converter cost of $5 is far less than price of commercial units.

tor, a multivibrator, and an output current switching transistor, the cost of the entire converter is about $5. Equivalent commercial units now cost about $30.

The circuit diagram (Fig. 1) shows that the battery is the supply for both the IC and the 2N3467 external power-booster transistor. The on-chip transistor and the booster transistor are switched on and off by the multivibrator. When the transistors are on, the 1N914 switching diode is reverse-biased so that primary current and therefore energy are built up in the transformer. When the multivibrator turns off, the collector of the booster transistor flies low. The anode of the switching diode therefore flies high, causing the diode to conduct; and the energy stored in the transformer is transferred to output filter capacitor C_2, which in turn supplies the load.

The scope-trace photographs in Fig. 2 show voltage waveforms at the anode of the 1N914 switching diode. While the multivabrator is on, the anode is reverse-biased. When the multivibrator turns off, the anode voltage first flies high, and energy is transferred from the transformer to the output capacitor. Then the open-circuited primary and secondary of the transformer start ringing with stray capacitance, producing damped oscillations in the anode voltage.

The multivibrator is off for a period of 0.7 R_1C_1 (which is 10 microseconds here), independent of the battery voltage. It is on for a period of time controlled by the comparator, up to a maximum value of 0.7 R_2C_1. The two inputs to the comparator are the 7.6-volt zener reference voltage, and the voltage-divider voltage $V_{out}R_4/(R_3+R_4)$. The comparator varies the multivibrator mark/space ratio to equalize these two voltages, so that

$$V_{out}R_4/(R_3+R_4) = V_{ref} = 7.6 \; volts$$
or
$$V_{out} = 7.6(R_3+R_4)/R_4 \; volts$$

The output voltage has a minimum value of 7.6 v, and its maximum value is limited only by the usual power considerations—the available load current is inversely

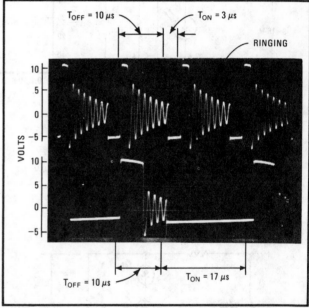

2. **Waveforms.** Scope photographs show voltage at anode of 1N914 switching diode as multivibrator turns transistors on and off. Top trace: 10-volt battery, 3-milliampere load current, short on-time. Bottom trace: 5-volt battery, 40-mA load current, long on-time.

proportional to output voltage. For the circuit shown in Fig. 1, for example, if R_3 were changed to 1.4 kilohms, the output would be 9 v with a maximum load current of 80 mA.

The converter shown in Fig. 1 has an efficiency of 65%, a load regulation of 10 mv/mA, and a line regulation (i.e., a change of output voltage with battery voltage) of 90 mv/v.

The on-chip output transistor can drive the transformer directly for circuit output powers of up to about 150 mw, and in many applications a simple inductor can be used in place of the pulse transformer. □

LEDs regulate voltage for C-MOS applications

by Calvin R. Graf
Kelly Air Force Base, San Antonio, Texas

As a voltage regulator, the useful light-emitting diode is particularly suited to complementary-MOS circuit designs, especially in automotive applications. The large current surges caused by widely varying input-voltage levels are easily handled by a LED regulator.

In circuit (a), an LED operates in parallel with load resistance R_L. (A series-dropping resistor is placed between these two devices and the power supply.) The voltage drop across the LED (V_{LED}) remains rather constant, ranging from about 1.6 to 1.7 volts, over a large current (I_{LED}) variation from approximately 5 to 50 milliamperes. It is this characteristic constant forward voltage that can be used for regulating the voltage in low-power, low-current circuits.

The voltage across the LED also remains fairly con-

Regulating voltage with LEDs. Single-LED voltage regulator (a) maintains output voltage level at 1.6 to 1.7 volts, in spite of an input voltage variation from 3 to 15 V. The graph in (b) shows that regulation is "lost" only when the load resistance drops below 37.5 ohms. To increase the regulated output-voltage level, the LEDs are connected in series (c); to increase the output current, the LEDs are wired in parallel (d). The graph in (e) illustrates how LED current changes with a varying input-voltage level, but output current remains fairly constant.

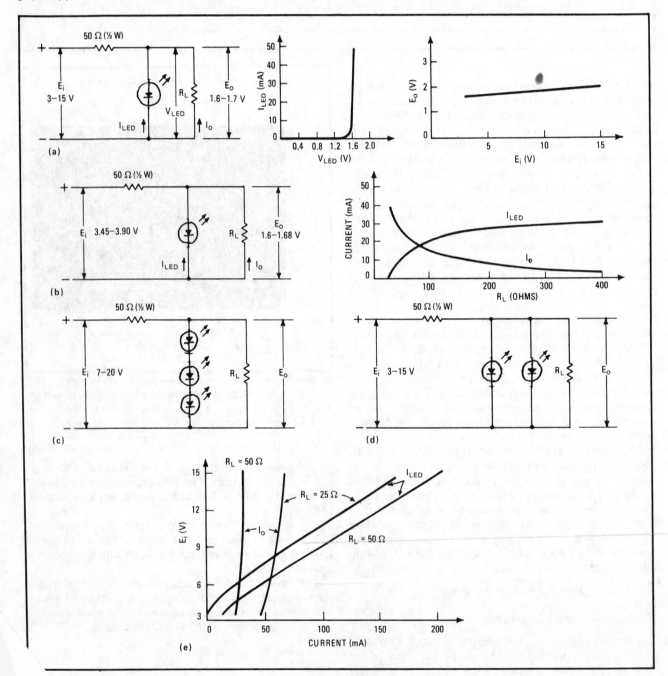

stant for a large swing in input voltage, as illustrated by the graph of E_o versus E_i in (a). LED voltage increases by only approximately 0.4 v as the input voltage goes from 3.5 to 15 v.

In (b), the influence of the load resistance on both the current drawn by the LED and the output current is plotted for an input voltage variation of 3.45 to 3.90 v. When the load resistance drops below approximately 37.5 ohms (and the series resistor is 50 ohms), LED voltage decreases to less than 1.6 v, and the output-voltage level is determined entirely by the load resistance, and not the LED.

To increase the level of the regulated output voltage, several LEDs can be connected in series, as is done in (c). This configuration produces a regulated output voltage as long as the input voltage to the LEDs does not drop below 1.6 v times the number of LEDs being used. Higher load currents can be achieved by connecting a number of LEDs in parallel, as is done in (d). Or, to raise the output voltage, as well as the current level, the LEDs can be connected in a series/parallel manner to get the desired results.

The value of the series-dropping resistor determines the input voltage level at which the LED starts to control the output voltage. The higher the value of this resistor (above 50 ohms nominal), the higher the input voltage must be to make the LED conduct.

How brightly the LED glows depends on the input-voltage level. The LED gets brighter as input voltage increases (for a fixed value of load resistance), but the load current remains almost constant, as illustrated by the graph in (e).

Usually, the luminous intensity of a LED is established at a given current level, which generally ranges from 5 to 30 mA, and at a nominal LED voltage of 1.6 to 1.7 v. Although a LED can still operate properly at continuous current levels as high as 50 mA, continuous current levels of 200 mA or so should be avoided. They cause the LED to exceed its safe operating temperature, reducing its average 20-year half-life.

Additionally, since a LED is a visual current-indicating device, it makes a handy front-panel circuit monitor. For example, it can indicate when circuit power is on, (LED lit), when the circuit input voltage is too high (LED bright), when the load current is too heavy (LED dim), and when the circuit is turned off (LED dark). ☐

General-purpose op amp forms active voltage divider

by Peter Church
Parsec Laboratory, St. Thomas, U.S. Virgin Islands

The everyday 741-type operational amplifier easily transforms a single-ended power supply into a dual supply.

For less than $1, the active voltage divider of (a) can be built. It is useful for powering circuits that require a balanced supply with a ground, but draw only a little current through the ground line. The output-voltage ratio, V_1/V_2, is determined by resistors R_1 and R_2:

$$V_1/V_2 = R_1/R_2$$

This ratio can be kept fixed or made adjustable by using potentiometers as resistors R_1 and R_2. More current, up to 1 ampere, can be handled by the active divider by adding a heat-sinked pass transistor, as shown in (b).

For breadboarding, either divider configuration (a) or (b) simply may be included as part of the circuit being laid out. The 0.1-microfarad capacitors in divider (a) can be removed if no fast transients will be encountered in the circuit to be powered, provided that the op amp's level of internal noise can be tolerated.

The 741-type op amp is well-suited for this application because of its high gain over a wide power-supply voltage range and its excellent internal protection circuitry. The single-ended supply voltage should not exceed the op-amp's 36-volt input supply range. ☐

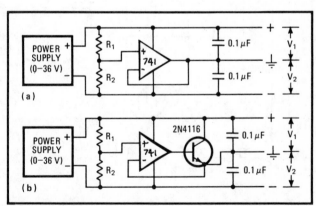

Active divider. Ordinary op amp (a) changes single-voltage supply to dual-voltage supply. Resistance ratio (R_1/R_2) determines output-voltage ratio (V_1/V_2). Additional output current is made available by following the op amp with a pass transistor, as shown in (b).

Power supply transients kept under control

by Ralph Tenny,
Texas Instruments, Dallas, Texas

Two specifications of power supply performance can easily be overlooked, since most manufacturers never mention them. These are turn-on/turn-off spikes and voltage rate-of-rise at turn-on. Most integrated circuits can be damaged or destroyed by power supply spikes which momentarily exceed the device voltage rating. Fortunately, not many commercial supplies do this. However, it is important that in-house designs be checked for spiking during design debugging. In addition, some digital systems with multiple power-supply requirements may lock up if the power supplies come on in a particular order, so it is important to know the voltage rate-of-rise of each supply.

The circuit shown in Fig. 1 will energize ac-powered individual dc supplies or power-supply systems connected to a controlled outlet, P_1. And it will furnish a scope sync signal to allow detailed examination of the power supply output during turn-on. Turn-on can be at line zero crossing or at an adjustable point near line peak to reliably check for worst-case turn-on conditions.

The circuit is based on two triacs which control the ac power to the power supply under test; Q_1 is resistively triggered from the line and turns on and off at zero crossing. Q_1 is controlled by Q_2; when Q_2 is turned on, it diverts gate drive from Q_1. However, if Q_2 turns on in midcycle, Q_1 does not turn off until the next zero crossing. Q_2 is turned on by dc drive from Z_{2A} via Q_3. Z_2 is controlled by a line-derived trigger from Z_1. A line voltage sample (A) is used to generate a phase-variable trigger. This is accomplished by a resistive attenuator and a TTL Schmitt Trigger (Z_{1A}). Adjustment range is sufficient to generate a trigger 90° after zero crossing. After inversion in Z_{1B}, this trigger is applied continuously to a two-bit shift register (Z_2). Z_2 is cleared by a latch or allowed to run at 60 Hertz. At the first trigger after Z_2 is released, Z_{2B} switches and produces a sync signal. On the next trigger, Z_{2A} switches and applies gate drive to Q_2, which turns on. At the next zero crossing, Q_1, which was conducting, turns off (mode 1 operation).

Mode switch SW_2 has three positions to allow these checks: turn-on at zero crossing or at line peak, and turn-off to allow checking for turn-off spikes. In position 1, the power supply is switched by Q_1 at zero crossing.

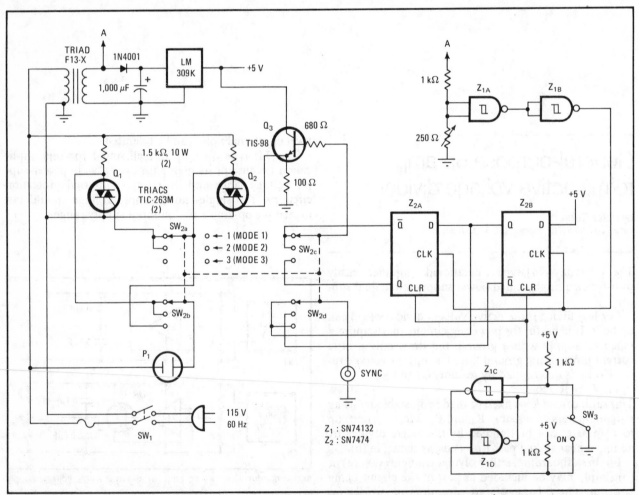

Transient testing. This power-supply transient-response tester, in conjunction with an oscilloscope, can measure turn-on time at zero crossing (mode 1) or line peak (mode 2) and turn-off time (mode 3).

362

With SW_3 off, Q_2 is conducting to hold Q_1 off until SW_3 is turned on. Sync is generated a minimum of 16 milliseconds before Q_1 turns on. In mode 2, everything is the same, except that sync is generated just before Q_1 turns off. In mode 3, Q_1 is not triggered and Q_2 switches the power supply on command, 16 milliseconds after sync.

A safety note: SW_1 opens both sides of the line; this is the minimum acceptable arrangement. At best, the entire circuit should be operated on an isolation transformer. When adjusting the trigger for proper phase angle turn-on of Q_2, be sure to use a filament transformer if an isolation transformer is not available. ☐

Regular stereo amplifier can be variable ac source

by M.J. Salvati
Sony Corp. of America, Long Island City, N.Y.

Here's how to turn an ordinary hi-fi stereo amplifier into the power supply for a variable-frequency power source. The setup produces a regulated ac output voltage that typically contains less than 0.2% distortion and that is adjustable from 0 to 130 volts root-mean-square at any frequency between 50 and 400 hertz.

The two channels of the stereo amplifier are driven 180° out of phase with each other so that the load can be connected differentially across the amplifier's "hot" output terminals. This technique avoids the inherent danger of paralleling the outputs of a transistorized power amplifier.

The output power available depends primarily on the particular power amplifier used. (About 220 watts can be obtained from an amplifier like the Sony TA-3200F.) Naturally, the amplifier's power bandwidth characteristics must satisfy the application. Usually, any oscillator that has an rms output of 5 v with less than 0.05% distortion will be adequate. If the precise operating frequency matters, then the oscillator's frequency accuracy and stability also are important. In some applications, a frequency counter might be a useful addition.

Variable-frequency power sources are available commercially as single-package systems costing from $700 to $1,100 for a 250-w unit. But all the equipment required for the setup shown in the diagram can be purchased new for less than $600. And even greater saving can normally be realized, since a suitable oscillator is generally available in most laboratories. If a suitable hi-fi amplifier can also be "found," the cost of the complete setup can be pared to a mere $35.

Transformer T_1 provides two equal-amplitude but opposite-phase drive signals for the power amplifier. Since most hi-fi power amplifiers have an input impedance of around 50 kilohms, impedance matching need not be considered. Transformer T_1 must have a good low-frequency response and a turns ratio that provides the proper drive level for the power amplifier. Generally, a turns ratio (from primary to each half of the secondary) of 1:1 or 2:1 is suitable for most oscillator/amplifier combinations.

A good frequency response from 50 to 400 Hz is also essential for transformer T_2. The turns ratio required for T_2 depends on the power-output rating and load characteristics of the power amplifier. To determine T_2's turns ratio, it's necessary to compute the amplifier output voltage (per channel) appearing across the specified load impedance (which is usually 8 ohms) at the maximum rated power output:

$$E = \sqrt{P_{out}R_{load}}$$

Since transformer T_2 is operated "backwards," select a 120-v power transformer with a secondary voltage rating that is twice this calculated amplifier voltage. ☐

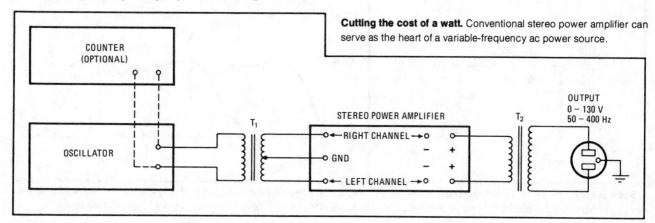

Cutting the cost of a watt. Conventional stereo power amplifier can serve as the heart of a variable-frequency ac power source.

Power supply design made fast and simple

by Onis J. Cogburn
Texas A&M University, College Station, Texas

A straightforward design technique lets you engineer a simple power supply quickly and easily and then check out the final circuit with only an oscilloscope. Since the design equations are based on the scope test display, there is no need for intermediate calculations. Checkout is further speeded because the percent ripple is determined directly from the peak value of the dc output voltage and the peak-to-peak value of the supply's output ripple voltage.

Figure 1 shows the schematic of a simple power supply along with a graph of its output voltage, which, in this case, is also the capacitor voltage. The percent ripple (% ripple) and ripple factor (f_r) can be found from the scope display of output voltage:

$$(\% \text{ ripple}) = (E_r/E_{o(pk)}) \times (100\%)$$
$$f_r = (\% \text{ ripple})/(100\%) = E_r/E_{o(pk)}$$

Also, since the voltage between time t_A and time t_B depends on the time constant set up by load resistor R_L and capacitor C, the output voltage at time t_B can be written as:

$$e_B = E_{o(pk)} \exp(-t_{(A-B)}/R_L C) = E_{o(pk)} - E_r \qquad (1)$$

Dividing this equation by $E_{o(pk)}$ yields:

$$(E_{o(pk)} - E_r)/E_{o(pk)} = \exp(-t_{(A-B)}/R_L C)$$

or:

$$(E_{o(pk)}/E_{o(pk)}) - (E_r/E_{o(pk)}) = \exp(-t_{(A-B)}/R_L C)$$

which can be rewritten as:

$$1 - f_r = \exp(-t_{(A-B)}/R_L C)$$

Inverting this equation and taking the natural logarithm of both sides of the inverted equation gives:

$$\ln[1/(1 - f_r)] = t_{(A-B)}/R_L C$$

The value of capacitor C can now be computed:

$$C = t_{(A-B)}/R_L \ln[1/(1 - f_r)] \qquad (2)$$

It is also possible to compute capacitance in terms of known (desired) quantities like output voltage, load current, and ripple. From the time period between point A and point C, ripple frequency F can be found:

$$t_{(A-C)} = 1/F$$

and:

$$t_{(A-D)} = 1/2F$$

Since the leading edge of the ripple voltage follows the dashed sine wave, angle θ becomes:

$$\theta = \arcsin[(E_{o(pk)} - E_r)/E_{o(pk)}] = \arcsin(1 - f_r)$$

The time between points D and B is:

$$t_{(D-B)} = t_{(D-C)}(\theta/90°)$$

and:

$$t_{(A-B)} = t_{(A-D)} + t_{(D-B)}$$
$$t_{(A-B)} = (1/2F) + (1/2F)[\arcsin(1 - f_r)/90°]$$
$$t_{(A-B)} = (1/2F)[1 + \arcsin(1 - f_r)/90°] \qquad (3)$$

Combining Eqs. 2 and 3 permits capacitor C to be computed from given quantities:

$$C = (1/2F)[1 + \arcsin(1 - f_r)/90°]/$$
$$(E_{o(pk)}/I_L) \ln[1/(1 - f_r)] \qquad (4a)$$

where:

$$E_{o(pk)}/I_L = R_L$$

For half-wave rectification, capacitor C can be expressed as:

$$C = (1/4F)[3 + \arcsin(1 - f_r)/90°]/$$
$$(E_{o(pk)}/I_L) \ln[1/(1 - f_r)] \qquad (4b)$$

With these equations, the values of additional capacitors, such as those required by pi filters, can be determined by using only capacitive reactances, series resistances, and a voltage-divider type of computation.

A typical shunt-regulated supply is drawn in Fig. 2; it employs a zener diode for regulation. The graph depicts a scope display of capacitor voltage, E_C. The guard voltage established by series resistor R_S and the zener assures that the ripple will not cause capacitor voltage to drop below the output voltage. An acceptable approximation for this guard voltage is $V_Z/0.8$, where V_Z is the

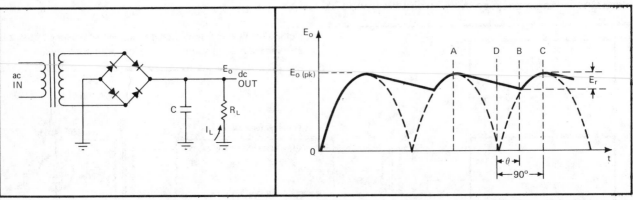

1. Basic supply. This simple power supply circuit can be checked out by observing a scope display of only the output voltage. The speedy design technique used to build the supply permits the value of capacitor C to be found easily from the desired supply specifications.

zener voltage. The peak capacitor voltage can then be written as:

$$E_{C(pk)} = E_r + V_Z/0.8 \qquad (5)$$

The output ripple voltage is:

$$E_{r(out)} = E_r r_Z/(r_Z + R_S) \qquad (6)$$

where r_Z is the ac resistance of the zener. Series resistor R_S can be computed from this relationship:

$$R_S = (E_{C(pk)} - V_Z)/(I_L + I_{Z(min)}) \qquad (7)$$

where $I_{Z(min)}$ is the minimum current required to operate the supply above the knee in the zener's character-istic curve; an acceptable value is $0.2I_{Z(rated)}$. From the minimum value of zener current, $0.2I_{Z(rated)}$, and the maximum value, $0.8I_{Z(rated)}$, an appropriate guideline for zener power rating can be established:

$$P_Z \text{ must be greater than or equal to } V_Z I_L/0.6 \qquad (8)$$

Equations 1 through 8 make possible the rapid design of a fairly efficient power supply, one that can be quickly and easily checked out with a standard oscillo-scope. Naturally, conventional design practices apply to the selection of all diodes and transformers. More complex supplies can also be designed this way. □

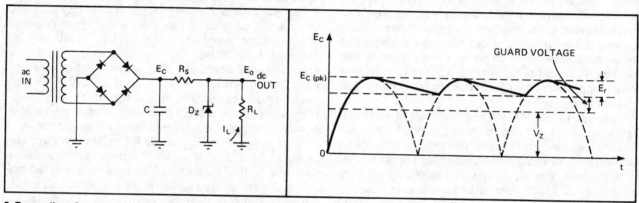

2. Precaution. Guard voltage of shunt-regulated supply prevents ripple voltage from dropping capacitor voltage below output voltage.

Voltage-regulated power supply delivers constant current

by Thomas E. Skopal
Acopian Corp., Easton, Pa.

Obtaining a power supply that has constant-current operation or is susceptible to adjustable current-limiting can often be a problem because such power supplies are not as readily available as constant-voltage supplies. However, if a voltage-regulated supply has provision for remote sensing and a voltage-adjustment range equal to the required compliance, it can provide a constant current. Most power-supply engineers know how to do this, but judging from the number of calls we receive from power-supply users, many of them are not familiar with the technique.

Normally, the remote-sensing terminals of a voltage-regulated supply are connected to the load separately from the output-current leads. The regulator senses the load voltage and varies the output voltage of the supply. By this means, it compensates for the voltage drops in the load lines, which vary with output current; thus, it maintains a constant voltage across the load. If the sensed load has a constant impedance, the supply's output current remains constant, even when compensation for impedance variations outside the sensing loop causes the supply's output voltage to vary.

Therefore, a constant current can be maintained through a circuit by sensing the voltage across a resistor and connecting the circuit requiring the constant current in series with the resistor, but outside the sensing loop. The current may be set to any desired amplitude within the rating of the supply by adjusting the supply's output voltage setting.

The power supply must have range of output-voltage adjustment at least as great as the required voltage-compliance range (the range of voltages needed to sustain a given value of constant current over a range of load resistances). In addition, the voltage across the resistor must be set no greater than the difference between the supply's maximum output voltage rating minus the compliance range. For example, a 1-ampere constant current with a compliance range of 1 to 5 volts may be obtained from a 0-to-7-v supply and a resistor no greater than 2 ohms. A "slot" adjust supply—one not adjustable down to 0 V—may also be used if its slot range equals or exceeds the necessary voltage compliance, and if the voltage maintained across the resistor equals or exceeds the minimum limit of the slot range.

Most power supplies provide for external voltage adjustment by means of a potentiometer wired in series with one of the sense lines. The load is connected between this sense line and its respective output terminal. On some supplies, the other set of output/sense terminals has a smaller compliance. □

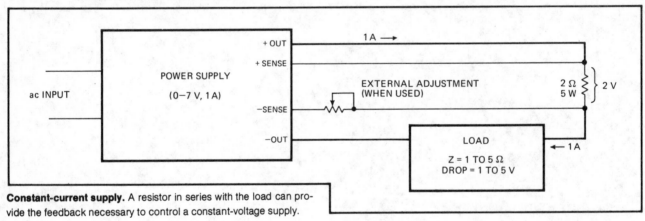

Constant-current supply. A resistor in series with the load can provide the feedback necessary to control a constant-voltage supply.

48. Glossaries of electronics terminology

An abbreviated guide to electronics abbreviations

by John C. McKechnie
Maitland, Fla.

The use of abbreviations and acronyms in electronics literature enhances the reading, the writing, and the comprehensibility of information exchange. However, the pervasiveness of such terms has made understanding more difficult for many readers who are not familiar with specialized aspects of the technology under discussion. This alphabetized list of more than 150 terms has been compiled during recent months from a large group of technical periodicals. Since new abbreviations are constantly being generated, readers can add new definitions as they are encountered.

a-d	analog to digital
ADS	address data strobe
AIM	avalanche-induced migration
ALU	arithmetic/logic unit
ANSI	American National Standards Institute
AOI	AND/OR invert
ASCII	American Standard Code for Information Interchange
ATE	automatic test equipment
ATS	automatic test system
BBD	bucket-brigade device
BCD	binary-coded decimal
Boram	block-oriented random-access memory
b/s	bits per second
CAD	computer-aided design
CAM	content-addressable memory
CATT	controlled avalanche transit time
CCD	charge-coupled device
CML	current-mode logic
C-MOS	complementary-metal-oxide semiconductor
CMRR	common-mode rejection ratio
CPU	central processing unit
CROM	control read-only memory
CRT	cathode-ray tube
CRC	cyclic redundancy check
CVD	chemical-vapor deposition
CVT	constant-voltage transformer
d-a	digital to analog
DAS	data-acquisition system
DFA	digital fault analysis
DI	dielectric isolation
DIP	dual in-line package
DMA	direct memory access
DMAC	direct-memory-access control
DMM	digital multimeter
D-MOS	double-diffused metal-oxide semiconductor
DMS	dynamic mapping system
DMUX	demultiplexer

DPM	digital panel meter
DTL	diode-transistor logic
DVM	digital voltmeter
Earom	electrically alterable read-only memory
EBCDIC	extended binary-coded-decimal interchange code
ECL	emitter-coupled logic
EDP	electronic data processing (or processor)
EFL	emitter-follower logic
EFTS	electronic funds-transfer system
EOC	end of conversion
EPROM	erasable programable read-only memory
EROM	erasable read-only memory
ESS	electronic switching system
Extnd	extended data transfer
FDM	frequency-division multiplex
FET	field-effect transistor
FFT	fast Fourier transform
FIFO	first in, first out
FPLA	field-programable logic array
F-PROM	field-programable read-only memory
GDS	graphic data system
HiNIL	high-noise-immunity logic
HTL	high-threshold logic
IC	integrated circuit
ICE	in-circuit emulator
IDS	input-data strobe
IEC	infused emitter coupling
I^2L	integrated injection logic
I/O	input/output
J-FET	junction field-effect transistor
JI	junction isolation
Laput	light-activated programable unijunction transistor
LASCR	light-activated silicon controlled rectifier
LCD	liquid-crystal display
LED	light-emitting diode
LIC	linear integrated circuit
LIFO	last in, first out
LNA	low-noise amplifier
LPTTL	low-power transistor-transistor logic
LRU	least recently used
LSB	least significant bit
LSI	large-scale integration
MDS	microprocessor-development system
MESFET	metalized semiconductor field-effect transistor
MHL	microprocessor host loader
MIS	metal insulator silicon
MLA	microprocessor language assembler
MLB	multilayer board
MLE	microprocessor language editor
MNCS	multipoint network control system
MNOS	metal-nitride-oxide semiconductor
Modem	modulator/demodulator
MOS	metal-oxide semiconductor
MOSFET	metal-oxide-semiconductor field-effect transistor
μP	microprocessor

MPU	microprocessor unit
MSB	most significant bit
MSI	medium-scale integration
MTBF	mean time before failure
MTD	mass tape duplicator/verifier
MTTF	mean time to failure
MUX	multiplexer
NAND	inverted AND gate
NDRO	nondestructive readout
n-MOS	n-channel metal-oxide semiconductor
NOR	inverted OR gate
NRZ	non-return to zero
NRZI	non-return to zero inverted
OCR	optical character recognition
ODS	output data strobe
OEM	original-equipment manufacturer
OPAL	operational performance-analysis language
PAR	program-aid routine
pc	printed circuit
pcb	printed-circuit board
PDP	plasma display panel
PIA	peripheral interface adapter
PLA	programable logic array
PLL	phase-locked loop
PM	phase modulation
PMG	permanent-magnet generator
p-MOS	p-channel metal-oxide semiconductor
POS	point of sale
PPI	plan-position indicator
	also, programable peripheral interface
PRACL	page-replacement algorithm and control logic
PROM	programable read-only memory
PTH	plated-through holes
PUT	programable unijunction transistor
RALU	register and arithmetic/logic unit
RAM	random-access memory
RIM	read-in mode
RMM	read-mostly mode
ROM	read-only memory
RTL	resistor-transistor logic
R/W	read/write
SBS	silicon bilateral switch
SC	semiconductor
SCA	subchannel adapter
SCR	silicon controlled rectifier
SDLC	synchronous data-link control
S/H	sample and hold
SIP	single in-line package
SOS	silicon-on-sapphire
SSI	small-scale integration
SUS	silicon unilateral switch
TBMT	transmitter buffer empty
TTL	transistor-transistor logic
T^2L	transistor-transistor logic
TTY	teletypewriter
TWT	traveling-wave tube
UART	universal asynchronous receiver/transmitter
URCLK	universal receiver clock
Usart	universal synchronous/asynchronous receiver/transmitter
USRT	universal synchronous receiver/transmitter
UTCLK	universal transmitter clock
UUT	unit under test

VCO	voltage-controlled oscillator
VIL	vertical injection logic
VTR	video-tape recorder
XOR	exclusive-OR gate

□

Digital-testing glossary reflects industry usage

Robert E. Anderson
Omnicomp Inc., Phoenix, Ariz.

Digital testing of integrated circuits and printed-circuit boards applies a wide range of programing, testing, and troubleshooting techniques. A lot of new terminology has evolved to describe many of these techniques. The definitions given in the following glossary are consistent with typical use of this terminology in industry.

Types of testing

Functional: verifies correct logical operation.

Parametric: verifies analog parameters within specified tolerances.

Static: test rate is slow, relative to the operating frequency.

Dynamic: test rate (or timing resolution) is comparable to the operating frequency (or period).

Truth-table: static functional testing.

Clock-rate: dynamic functional testing.

Dc: static parametric testing.

Ac: dynamic parametric testing.

Testing terminology and techniques

Algorithmic pattern generation: real-time generation of input test patterns during test execution according to specified procedures, formulas, or algorithms. Also refers to procedures or algorithms used in automatic-test-generation software for specific fault sets.

Automatic test generation (ATG), automatic-test-pattern generation (ATPG): calculation of a specific set of input test patterns with a computer program providing algorithmic and heuristic routines.

Bidirectional I/O pins: pins that function for both input and output.

Comparison testing: real-time comparison between the actual output responses of the device under test and those of a known-good reference device when the same input stimulus patterns are applied to both devices in parallel.

Comprehensiveness: the percentage of the faults in a specific fault set that can be detected by means of a fault program.

Control points or pins: input pins provided for testing or fault-isolation purposes that can control the state of internal memory elements.

Device model, circuit model: a set of data that logically describes the correct operation of a device or circuit.

Digital IC (SSI, MSI, LSI): digital integrated circuit, a monolithic group of logic elements. May be small-scale integration (e.g., gates, flip-flops, latches); medium-scale integration (e.g., decoders, adders, counters); large-scale integration (e.g., memories, microprocessors).

Digital signature: a numerical representation of a set of logic states, typically used to describe the logic-state history at one DUT output pin during the complete test program.

DUT, UUT, MUT: device, unit, or module under test.

Emulation: the use of hardware or software to generate in real-time the expected correct output responses for comparison to the DUT.

Equivalent faults: two or more faults that cause the same output responses and that cannot be isolated from the board output pins and internal nodes being monitored by the tester.

Fault defect: an anomaly that prevents the correct operation of the device. "Defect" and "fault" are often used interchangeably, although "fault" is the theoretical or practical result of a physical "defect."

Fault dictionary: a set of fault signatures, each of which indicates the probable faults that could cause the error message matching the signature.

Fault isolation: determining the cause of a test failure, typically by identifying a defective component or process failure on a board.

Fault-isolation resolution: the average number of components to which a fault can be isolated.

Fault model: a set of data that logically describes the operation of a device or circuit containing one or more faults.

Fault set: a group of all faults of specific types.

Fault signature: a particular output response or set of responses generated when a test program is executed on a device containing a fault. A typical fault signature consists of the incorrect output-pin numbers and the test step number at which a test program first detects a fault.

Forward-trace, Reverse-trace: particular algorithms used by automatic-test-generation software.

Functional board tester: a tester that verifies the correct logical operation of a logic board by applying test patterns at the board-edge connector. The output responses usually are monitored at the connector, although some test points may be used.

Gray-code test patterns: A sequence of input patterns in which only one input pin changes state at each test step.

Guided probe, guided clip: a fault-isolation technique in which the test system automatically displays the next mode or IC that the operator should probe or clip. The system leads the operator along a path back from a faulty output pin to the location of the fault. A software algorithm uses stored interconnection information and expected responses at each node to determine the next node to be probed.

In-circuit tester, bed-of-nails tester, in-situ tester: a tester that checks the individual components on a board using a fixture that provides access to each node of each component. Used to test for short and open circuits on bare boards, correct values of analog components (using a guarding technique), and correct functions of individual ICs (using a pulsing technique).

Indeterminate (X) state: the unknown logic state of a memory element caused by critical races or oscillations, or existing after power is applied and before initialization. Some simulators can model indeterminate states and typically assign an X to indicate an indeterminate state.

Initialization: applying input patterns to a logic circuit so that all internal memory elements achieve a known logic state.

Input pins: the terminals of the device to which input logic signals may be applied.

Input/output pins, I/O pins: the set of input pins and output pins on the device.

Input-stimulus pattern, input pattern, input-test vector: the set of logic states applied to the DUT input pins during a particular time period.

Interface adaptor, device adaptor: a unit that provides a mechanical and electrical interconnection between the tester and the device under test may include special stimulus, measurement, load, and switching circuitry unique to a device or family of devices, but is not provided in the tester.

Internal node: a junction between internal logic elements within an IC.

Known-good device, known-good board: a reference device or board that is presumed to function correctly.

Logic circuit, logic board, logic-circuit board: an assembly containing a group of interconnected digital ICs.

Logic element: a unit that performs a basic logical function (e.g., a single OR gate).

Logic states, logic signals: the binary (1 or 0) values at the nodes of logic elements and ICs at a particular time.

Manual analysis, manual test programing: the generation of input and output test patterns by a test engineer or technicians who studies the function or structure of a logic circuit.

Node: a junction between interconnected ICs on a logic board.

Output pins: the terminals of the device at which its output logic signals may be obtained.

Output response pattern, output pattern, output test vector: the set of logic states produced at the output pins of the device under test during a particular time period.

Pseudorandom patterns: a repeatable sequence of input test patterns that appears statistically random.

Signature-testing: comparison of the actual output digital signatures, such as transition counts, with the expected correct signatures recorded from a known-good device.

Simulation, digital simulation: modeling of the operation of a logic circuit by a computer program containing device models and topology information about their interconnections.

Skew: the time difference between the logic-state changes on different input pins within a particular test pattern.

Stuck-at-1, stuck-at-0: a particular fault model in which a faulty node remains at a logical 1 or 0 state, regardless of the inputs applied.

Stored-response testing: comparison of the actual output responses of the DUT with the expected correct output responses stored within the tester. The expected correct responses can be recorded from a known-good device or determined by manual analysis or software simulation. Stored-response testing of-ten implies storage of the actual logic states, although such digital signatures as transition counts could be the stored responses.

Test pattern, test step, test vector: the input and output patterns valid during a particular time period.

Test points or pins: output pins provided for testing or fault-isolation purposes that can monitor the nodal responses.

Test program: a particular group of test sequences or test patterns.

Test sequence: a group of test steps or test patterns.

Transition counts: a particular digital signature used in logic-board testing. □